Graduates of Foreign Nursing Schools

25TH ANNIVERSARY 1977 - 2002

maggie 2012 (7).

Official Study Guide *for the*

CGFNS

Qualifying Exam

maggie

5TH Edition

Readers of the CGFNS Official Study Guide are expressly warned to consider and adopt all safety precautions that might be indicated as a result of the activities described herein, and to avoid all potential hazards. By following the instructions and information contained in this Official Study Guide, readers willingly assume all risks in connection with such instructions.

The Commission on Graduates of Foreign Nursing Schools, hereafter CGFNS, shall not be liable for any special, consequential or exemplary damages resulting, in whole or in part, from readers' use of, or reliance upon, the material and information contained in this Official Study Guide.

CGFNS has designed the information in this Official Study Guide to test nursing knowledge and to provide the opportunity to gain English language proficiency. This information is not designed to form the basis of the reader's nursing practice or patient care recommendations.

The CGFNS Official Study Guide is not a substitute for basic education or an in-depth review of nursing textbooks. It does not guarantee success on the CGFNS Qualifying Exam or the National Council Licensure Exam for Registered Nurses (NCLEX–RN® examination).

Publisher: Commission on Graduates of Foreign Nursing Schools
Content Editor: Catherine R. Davis, PhD, RN
Content Assistant: Monique M. Rawls, RT (R)(T)
Contributors: Linda Burnes, MSN, RN, Professor, Delaware County Community College School of Nursing, Media, Pennsylvania; Carol Carofigilio, MSN, RN, Nursing Faculty, Helen Fuld School of Nursing at Camden County, Blackwood, New Jersey; Susan Burrows-Clark, MSN, RN, CNS, C, Nursing Faculty, Helen Fuld School of Nursing at Camden County, Blackwood, New Jersey; Normajean Colby, MSN, RN, CPN, Professor, Widener University School of Nursing, Chester, Pennsylvania; Barbara Ferris, RN, BSN, C, Administrative Shift Coordinator, Underwood Memorial Hospital, Woodbury, New Jersey; Carol Hanna, DNSc, RN, Assistant Professor, Delaware County Community College, Media, Pennsylvania; Nancy Sharts-Hopko, PhD, RN, FAAN, Nursing Faculty, College of Nursing at Villanova University, Villanova, Pennsylvania; Rochell Kuhn, MS, CRNP, Instructor, Episcopal Hospital, Philadelphia, Pennsylvania; Susan M. Landon, MSN, RN, Instructor, Episcopal Hospital, Philadelphia, Pennsylvania; Karen Montalto, DNSc, RN, Nursing Faculty, Helen Fuld School of Nursing at Camden County, Blackwood, New Jersey; Kathleen Mulcahey, MSN, RN, CNAA, Adjunct Faculty, Helen Fuld School of Nursing at Camden County, Blackwood, New Jersey; Elizabeth W. O'Brien, MSN, RN, Helen Fuld School of Nursing at Camden County, Blackwood, New Jersey; Sandra Opfer, MSN, RN, Coordinator of Patient Care Services/Mental Health, Underwood Memorial Hospital, Woodbury, New Jersey; Patricia Price, MSN, RN, Nursing Faculty, Helen Fuld School of Nursing at Camden County, Blackwood, New Jersey; Catherine Staines, MSN, RN, C, Nursing Faculty, Helen Fuld School of Nursing at Camden County, Blackwood, New Jersey; Doris Vallone, PhD, RN, Assistant Professor, Widener University School of Nursing, Chester, Pennsylvania
Reference to Chapter 6: TOEFL, 2001-2002 Bulletin of Information for TOEFL, TWE, TSE. United States Edition Princeton: Educational Testing Service

For further information, contact: Marketing and Communications Department, CGFNS, 3600 Market Street, Suite 400, Philadelphia, PA 19104–2651 USA. Internet: www.cgfns.org

Copyright © 2003 by the Commission on Graduates of Foreign Nursing Schools (CGFNS)

All rights reserved. Certain portions of this work © 1986, 1990, 1995, 2000 and 2003. No part of this work covered by the copyright hereon may be reproduced or used in any form or by any means—graphic, electronic or mechanical, including photocopying, recording, taping or information storage and retrieval systems—without written permission from the publisher.

Commission on Graduates of Foreign Nursing Schools, CGFNS, the CGFNS logo and the CGFNS Qualifying Exam are registered trademarks of the Commission on Graduates of Foreign Nursing Schools.

Library of Congress Catalogue Card Number # 95-067493   ISBN # 0-9630592-2-X

1st Edition printed in the United States of America, 1986. 2nd Printing, 1987. 3rd Printing, 1989.
2nd Edition printed in the United States of America, 1990. 2nd Printing, 1991. 3rd Printing, 1993.
3rd Edition printed in the United States of America, 1995. 2nd Printing, 1998. 3rd Printing, 1998. 4th Printing, 1999.
4th Edition printed in the United States of America, 2000. 2nd Printing, 2001. 3rd Printing, 2002.
5th Edition printed in the United States of America, 2003. 2nd Printing 2004. 3rd Printing 2005

Order forms for additional copies of this Official Study Guide may be obtained by writing to: CGFNS StoreFront, 3600 Market Street, Suite 400, Philadelphia, PA 19104–2651 USA, or can be purchased on-line at www.cgfns.org

Earning Your CGFNS Certificate

As a graduate of a nursing school located outside the United States, you may be required to earn a certificate from the Commission on Graduates of Foreign Nursing Schools (CGFNS) in order to practice as a registered nurse in the United States. CGFNS has prepared this Official Study Guide to help you earn your CGFNS certificate.

Earning a CGFNS certificate is a three-part process. First, you submit your academic records and licensure/registration materials to CGFNS for a credentials review. If you meet the requirements of the credentials review, you then take the CGFNS Qualifying Exam and a CGFNS approved English language proficiency exam. When you pass both the CGFNS Qualifying Exam and the English language proficiency exam, you will be awarded a CGFNS certificate.

The CGFNS Qualifying Exam

The CGFNS Qualifying Exam is a one-day examination that tests your knowledge and understanding of nursing as it is taught and practiced in the United States today.

The CGFNS Qualifying Exam uses objective, multiple-choice questions and is designed by testing experts to help you predict your likelihood of passing the U.S. registered nurse licensure examination, which is called the National Council Licensure Examination for Registered Nurses, or NCLEX-RN® examination. CGFNS conducts annual validity studies to determine how accurately the Certification Program predicts success on the NCLEX-RN examination. These studies show that the majority of nurses who earn a CGFNS certificate on their first try also pass the NCLEX-RN examination on their first try. Therefore, if you pass the CGFNS Qualifying Exam and the English language proficiency exam the first time you take them, you can be reasonably sure that you will also pass the NCLEX-RN examination. It is important, however, to take the NCLEX-RN examination as soon as possible after earning a CGFNS certificate. Your chances of passing the NCLEX-RN examination will begin to decline if you wait too long.

How the CGFNS Official Study Guide Can Help You Earn Your CGFNS Certificate

This Official Study Guide can help you to earn your CGFNS certificate in several ways. First, the Official Study Guide provides important information about the steps you must take to apply for the CGFNS Certification Program. In Chapter 2, you will find a description of the application process, along with details about the educational and licensure/registration requirements you must meet to be eligible to take the CGFNS Qualifying Exam.

In addition to showing you how to apply for the CGFNS Certification Program, the main objective of this Official Study Guide is to provide you with information to help you prepare to take the CGFNS Qualifying Exam. Chapter 3 provides an overview of the CGFNS Qualifying Exam, including information about how the exam is organized. Chapter 3 also describes the NCLEX-RN examination. Chapters 5 through 7 provide detailed descriptions of the content of the exam. These chapters also contain sample questions like the ones in an actual CGFNS Qualifying Exam. Following the sample questions, you will find the correct answers, along with explanations describing why the right answers are correct and the wrong answers, incorrect.

Chapters 10 through 13 contain four complete practice tests. These practice tests are like the CGFNS Qualifying Exam you will take as part of the CGFNS Certification Program. The practice tests include questions that are similar to the questions in the actual CGFNS Qualifying Exam. However, none of the questions in this Official Study Guide have appeared or will appear on the CGFNS Qualifying Exam.

In addition, the Official Study Guide also provides valuable background information to help you do your best on the CGFNS Qualifying Exam. Chapter 4 tells you how to read, understand and answer objective, multiple-choice test questions. Chapter 5, in addition to describing the design of the CGFNS Qualifying Exam, also describes the registered nurse's role in the healthcare delivery system in the United States.

In Appendix A, you will find a glossary of terms that you can refer to if you read a term in the Official Study Guide that is not familiar to you. The guide also includes suggested lists of reading materials in Chapters 6 and 8 to help you prepare for both the CGFNS Qualifying Exam and the English language proficiency exam. To become familiar with the answer sheets used for the CGFNS Qualifying Exam, use the samples provided in Appendix B when taking the practice tests.

For More Help Preparing for the Qualifying Examination

CGFNS cannot promise that every nurse who uses this Official Study Guide will pass the CGFNS Qualifying Exam. How well you do on the exam will depend on your knowledge of nursing as practiced in the United States.

Using this Official Study Guide should, however, help you learn how to answer the type of objective, multiple-choice questions found in the CGFNS Qualifying Exam. It should also teach you about the format and structure of the exam. The English language practice tests should help you identify the strengths and weaknesses in your understanding of the English language. This Official Study Guide can also identify areas in the nursing process and client needs categories in which you require further study before taking the CGFNS Qualifying Exam.

If you want more help getting ready for the English language proficiency exam, use the enclosed form to order one or more volumes of the CGFNS Practice English Series. Each volume in the Practice English Series includes a practice English audio tape and an accompanying booklet. You may obtain any tape and booklet in the Practice English Series to begin preparing for the English language proficiency exam, and add other tapes and booklets if you want to practice with additional questions. Official TOEFL and TOEIC study materials designed by the Educational Testing Service (ETS) may be purchased directly from ETS. Official study material designed by IELTS may bepurchased directly from IELTS, Inc. See page 28 for contact information.

CGFNS wishes you success on the CGFNS Qualifying Exam and the English language proficiency exam, and a successful and productive career as a registered nurse.

CGFNS Origins and Current Activities

Establishment of CGFNS

The Commission on Graduates of Foreign Nursing Schools (CGFNS) is a nonprofit organization based in Philadelphia, Pennsylvania, in the United States of America. CGFNS was founded through the efforts of a number of organizations. Among these founders were several U.S. government agencies and private, nonprofit associations, including two prominent U.S. nursing organizations: the American Nurses Association (ANA) and the National League for Nursing (NLN).

Though it was established in 1977, CGFNS' origins predate its founding. During the late 1960s and early 1970s, changes in immigration laws and regulations resulted in a steady increase in the numbers of nurses entering the United States as immigrants with preferred status because they had skills that were in short supply in the United States. Additional numbers were admitted as persons of "distinguished merit and ability" on non-immigrant visas who were eligible for indefinite extension.

In order to practice as registered nurses in America, nurses educated outside the United States first had to be licensed in the United States. Then, as now, each U.S. state and territory administered the licensing process through its own board of nursing. While individual state licensure requirements varied, nearly all states required registered nurses to pass a national registered nurse licensure exam in order to earn a license.

Many of the internationally educated nurses who came to the United States and took the registered nurse licensure examination did not pass the exam. Without an RN license, they could not work as a registered nurse in the United States.

Many of the nurses who failed to become licensed as RNs had entered the United States on temporary work visas that limited the length of their stay. These unlicensed nurses frequently were unable to earn a living and had to leave the United States when their visas expired.

Some internationally educated nurses remained in the United States. Many of these nurses found other work. Some worked as nurses aides or nursing assistants. In these positions, their salaries were not as high as those of registered nurses.

Institutions that needed registered nurses often could not find enough RNs to fill vacant job positions. Some internationally educated nurses who had not been able to earn RN licenses in the United States found themselves being asked to perform the duties of registered nurses in these institutions, despite the fact that it placed patients at great risk and required these nurses to break the law.

The founders of CGFNS believed that it was important for nurses educated outside the United States to know before they left their home country whether or not they could expect to pass the U.S. registered nurse licensure examination. This, in turn, would help curb abuses such as those described above. And so, in 1977, CGFNS was established, in part, to help internationally educated nurses determine their likelihood of passing the licensure exam.

CGFNS' Mission

Now, as in the 1970s, thousands of nurses from a wide range of countries continue to seek work as registered nurses in the United States each year. Some of these nurses have completed nursing programs that are quite similar to U.S. nursing programs. They may be comfortable speaking English as it is spoken in the United States. Their educational credentials and professional qualifications may be comparable to those of U.S. nurses. These nurses may not have much difficulty meeting state licensure requirements for internationally educated nurses, which still generally include passing the U.S. registered nurse licensure exam, now called the National Council Licensure Exam for Registered Nurses (NCLEX-RN examination). These nurses also may not have much difficulty finding work as registered nurses in the United States.

Other internationally educated nurses may not have studied all of the subjects U.S.-educated nurses must study. Their education may not be comparable to the education U.S. nurses receive. These nurses may not know how to perform all the duties U.S. nurses perform. They may not speak and understand English well enough to communicate with their patients and colleagues. It may therefore be difficult for these nurses to pass the registered nurse licensure exam and become licensed in the United States. Nurses who do not pass the NCLEX-RN examination, are not permitted to work as registered nurses in the United States.

Today, as when it was established in 1977, CGFNS remains dedicated to its original mission, which includes helping you and other internationally educated nurses determine your chances of successfully becoming licensed as a registered nurse in the United States.

CGFNS' Certification Program

CGFNS works to fulfill this part of its mission through the three-part CGFNS Certification Program. As previously noted, this program includes a credentials review, a Qualifying Exam of nursing knowledge, and a test of English language proficiency.

The CGFNS Qualifying Exam and the English language proficiency exams are offered both in the United States and at many locations throughout the world. Studies show that most nurses who earn a CGFNS certificate on their first attempt also pass the NCLEX-RN examination the first time. Because the CGFNS Qualifying Exam and the English language proficiency exams are offered internationally in so many different locations, you can assess your chances of successfully becoming licensed in the United States without having to travel to the United States.

Most U.S. states require a nurse who graduated from a nursing school outside the United States to hold a CGFNS certificate before she/he can take the NCLEX-RN examination. This requirement usually applies to both U.S. citizens and non-citizens who are graduates of nursing schools located outside the United States. As a graduate of a nursing school located outside the United States, you should contact the board of nursing in the state where you plan to work before applying for licensure as a registered nurse. Ask what requirements you must meet to get your license to work as a registered nurse in that state.

It is important to understand that each state in the United States sets its own requirements for licensure. Although all states give the same NCLEX-RN examination, the license that you will receive is a state license. It allows you to practice in that state only. If you move to another state, you will have to apply for licensure in the new state. The United States, at this time, does not have a national licensure system, per se. However, several U.S. states are participating in what is called multi-state licensure. If you pass the NCLEX-RN examination in one of these states, the license that you receive will permit you to practice in any other state that is a member of this group. To be certain you have the correct contact and licensure information, CGFNS will send you a complete, up-to-date listing of state boards of nursing after you earn your CGFNS certificate.

Other CGFNS Activities

In addition to the Certification Program for registered nurses, CGFNS also offers other services and programs for nurses and other healthcare professionals.

Credentials Evaluation Service

The Credentials Evaluation Service issues a report based on an evaluation of a healthcare professional's educational and professional licensure/registration credentials by CGFNS. A CGFNS credentials evaluation report presents an applicant's credentials in terms of U.S. comparability. A central difference between this service and the CGFNS Certification Program is that there is no examination component in the Credentials Evaluation Service.

As with the CGFNS Certification Program, the CGFNS Credentials Evaluation Service is a prerequisite for state licensure in certain U.S. states and territories. However, unlike the Certification Program, which is used to gauge your chances of passing the NCLEX-RN examination and becoming licensed as a registered nurse in the United States, the Credentials Evaluation Service can be used to evaluate your eligibility for licensure as either a registered nurse or a practical (vocational) nurse in the United States. The Credentials Evaluation Service also is used by U.S. nursing schools to determine academic placement of international students.

VisaScreen™: Visa Credentials Assessment

The VisaScreen: Visa Credentials Assessment program was created in response to legislation that now requires foreign healthcare professionals to complete a screening program in order to qualify for certain occupational visas. The International Commission on Healthcare Professions (ICHP), a division of CGFNS, administers VisaScreen, which enables foreign healthcare professionals to meet the screening requirements by verifying and evaluating their credentials to ensure that they meet the government's minimum eligibility standards.

Applicants who successfully complete the program, composed of an educational analysis, licensure validation, English language proficiency assessment and, in the case of nurses, an exam of nursing knowledge, receive a VisaScreen Certificate, which can be presented to a consular office or, in the case of adjustment of status, the attorney general as part of a visa application.

Credentials Verification Service for New York State

CGFNS created a customized service, the Credentials Verification Service for New York State, to independently verify credentials of foreign-educated healthcare professionals who are seeking licensure in New York State. The New York State Education Department now requires that foreign-educated registered nurses, licensed practical nurses, physical therapists, physical therapist assistants, occupational therapists and occupational therapy assistants obtain independent verification of the authenticity of their credentials from a State Education Department-approved credentials verification service. CGFNS has been authorized by the New York State Education Department to provide such a service.

The program independently collects and verifies the authenticity of an applicant's educational and registration/licensure credentials. Once verified, the credentials are forwarded to the New York State Education Department to be evaluated as part of the applicant's licensure application.

CGFNS maintains one of the world's largest and most comprehensive information collections on international nursing education and licensure. CGFNS also takes an active part in policy discussions about international nursing education, licensure and practice.

General Information About CGFNS

CGFNS supports the United Nations Declaration of Human Rights. This document states that individuals have the right to migrate from one country to another. However, CGFNS is an immigration-neutral organization. CGFNS does not encourage people to migrate to the United States, nor does it discourage them from doing so.

CGFNS is not an employment agency or a recruiting service, nor is it affiliated with any employment agency or recruiting service.

Although CGFNS can help you evaluate your potential to become licensed as a nurse in the United States, CGFNS cannot help you find work as a registered nurse. Nor can CGFNS act on your behalf in gaining admission to a college or university in the United States. Similarly, CGFNS cannot help you with visa or immigration problems.

CGFNS

Applying to Take the CGFNS Qualifying Exam

How CGFNS Determines Your Eligibility for the Exam

As previously noted, the CGFNS Certification Program is a three-part process. In the first part of the Certification Program, the credentials review, CGFNS examines your educational background and registration/licensure credentials. The credentials review is designed to verify that you are a first-level general nurse. If CGFNS finds through the review that you are a first-level general nurse, you will be eligible to take the CGFNS Qualifying Exam. If you do not meet these requirements, you will not be scheduled for the CGFNS Qualifying Exam.

In reviewing your credentials, CGFNS examines the documentation you submit with your application to determine the answers to three questions:

1. Are you a first-level, general nurse?

2. Do you meet the educational requirements?

3. Do you have appropriate licensure/registration documents?

The guidelines CGFNS observes in determining the answers to these questions are explained below.

Are You a First-Level, General Nurse?

To be eligible to take the CGFNS Qualifying Exam, you must be educated and licensed as both a first-level and a general nurse as defined historically by the International Council of Nurses. The International Council of Nurses' historical definition of a first-level nurse is as follows:

A nurse is a person who has completed a program of basic nursing education and is qualified and authorized in his/her country to practice nursing. Basic nursing education is a formally-recognized program of study which provides a broad and sound foundation for the practice of nursing and for post-basic education which develops specific competency.

At the first level, the educational program prepares the nurse, through study of behavioral, life and nursing sciences and clinical experience, for effective practice and the direction of nursing care, and for the leadership role. The first-level nurse is responsible for planning, providing and evaluating nursing care in all settings for the promotion of health, prevention of illness, care of the sick, and rehabilitation; and functions as a member of the health team. (International Council of Nurses, ICN Constitution, 1983)

In most countries, including the United States, a first-level nurse is called a registered nurse or a professional nurse.

If you are a second-level nurse in your native country, you cannot sit for the CGFNS Qualifying Exam or be licensed as a registered nurse in the United States. In most countries, second-level nurses are called enrolled nurses, vocational nurses, practical nurses or nursing assistants.

To be eligible for the CGFNS Qualifying Exam, you must also be educated and licensed as a general nurse in the country where you received your nursing education. What is a general nurse? A general nurse has studied theory and has had clinical practice in a broad spectrum of nursing areas. Persons educated and licensed as maternity nurses or midwives, children's nurses, psychiatric nurses and other specialized nurses are not eligible to take the CGFNS Qualifying Exam unless they have also received education as a general nurse. Physicians and other healthcare or allied health professionals are not permitted to take the exam.

In the United States, first-level or registered nurses are licensed to practice as general nurses. Thus, all basic U.S. nursing education programs prepare generalists. A nurse who wishes to specialize in the United States must first complete a basic education program that prepares her/him to work as a general nurse.

Do You Meet the Educational Requirements?

In addition to being a first-level, general nurse, you must meet specific educational requirements to be eligible to take the CGFNS Qualifying Exam. These requirements include:

1. Successful completion of a senior secondary education that is distinct from your nursing education. If you have not completed a full upper secondary school education, you may meet this CGFNS requirement by obtaining a "General Education Development (GED) Diploma." This secondary school equivalency diploma is recognized in the United States. You can obtain more information about earning a GED Diploma by contacting:

   > GED Testing Service
   > American Council of Education
   > One Dupont Circle NW, Suite 250
   > Washington, DC 20036
   > USA
   > Telephone: (202) 939-9490

2. Graduation from a general nursing program. This program must be given by a government-approved or recognized nursing school. It must be at least two years in length.

3. Both theory and clinical education (taken together) in nursing care of the adult (including medical and surgical nursing), nursing care of children, maternal/infant nursing and psychiatric/mental health nursing.

You may have graduated from a government-approved, general nursing program without

completing theory and clinical practice in the four areas listed above. In that case, you may be able to meet the CGFNS requirement by taking and passing a nursing course in the missing area. The completion course must be offered by a government-approved school of nursing and must include both theory and clinical practice in the same course. Non-academic work experience and/or in-service education do not meet the CGFNS education requirements.

Do You Have Appropriate Registration Documents?

CGFNS also reviews your nursing registration/ licensure documents to verify that you have the following:

- an initial registration/license as a first-level, general nurse in the country in which you completed your nursing education;

- a current, first-level, general nurse registration/license.

The nursing registration or license you hold outside the United States indicates that you can legally practice nursing in that country.

Application Procedures

You cannot take the CGFNS Qualifying Exam until CGFNS has received all the necessary application materials and determined your eligibility by reviewing your credentials.

The application process, and all of the materials you will need to apply for the CGFNS Certification Program, are outlined in a booklet entitled, Path to CGFNS Certification: Applicant Handbook. To obtain a copy of the handbook, contact your national nurses' association, the U.S. embassy or consulate in your country, or the CGFNS Customer Service Department at:

> CGFNS
> Attn.: Path Handbook Request
> 3600 Market Street, Suite 400
> Philadelphia, PA 19104-2651 USA
> Telephone: (215) 349-8767
> Facsimile: (215) 349-0026
> E-mail: support@cgfns.org
> Website: www.cgfns.org

You can also contact the CGFNS Customer Service Department if you have further questions or concerns after you apply for, or as you move through, the Certification Program. Whenever you write, fax or e-mail to CGFNS, always be sure to include your CGFNS identification number, your full name and your birth date.

Potential employers and others may request application materials for you or ask questions about CGFNS policies and procedures. However, except in special circumstances, other information will be released only to you, as the applicant for the CGFNS Certification Program.

The CGFNS Qualifying Exam

As previously discussed, the CGFNS Certification Program was developed to help you and other internationally educated nurses determine if you are likely to pass the U.S. registered nurse licensure examination and become a registered nurse in the United States. Chapter 3 describes both the NCLEX-RN examination and the CGFNS Qualifying Exam. It also provides an overview of the format and structure of the CGFNS Qualifying Exam.

RN Licensure in the United States and the NCLEX-RN Examination

In the United States, many regulatory responsibilities are divided between the federal government and the state governments of each of the U.S. states and territories. For example, the federal government is responsible for issuing federal visas to persons from other countries who wish to enter the United States. However, state governments are responsible for licensing individuals to practice in many professions, including nursing.

No single license allows a nurse to practice in every state in the United States. Each state government issues its own license. State licenses are based on state laws. Generally speaking, the nursing law that governs the practice of nursing in a state is called the Nurse Practice Act. This law regulates nursing practice only in that individual state. In each state, a state board of nursing, or similar regulatory body, is appointed to carry out the particular requirements of the state's Nurse Practice Act.

Although each state develops its own procedures for licensure, there are some common requirements. Currently, every U.S. state and territory requires that registered nurses not licensed in another U.S. state take and pass the NCLEX-RN examination before they can be licensed. The NCLEX-RN examination is, therefore, a nationwide licensure exam for registered nurses in the United States. Both United States-educated and internationally educated nurses must pass the NCLEX-RN examination. In addition, as previously discussed, internationally educated nurses are also required to hold a CGFNS certificate in most states and territories.

Computerized Adaptive Testing Format of the NCLEX-RN Examination

The NCLEX-RN examination is a multiple-choice test. Prior to 1994, the examination was administered in what is referred to as a "paper-and-pencil format," meaning that test-takers used a pencil to mark the answers on a paper answer sheet. In April 1994, the National Council of State Boards of Nursing (NCSBN), the organization that develops the NCLEX-RN examination, introduced a new exam format. This format is called Computerized Adaptive Testing (CAT).

With CAT, the NCLEX-RN examination is administered to test-takers by means of a computer, instead of paper and pencil. Each question is presented individually on the computer screen. The test-taker "keys in" her/his response using only two computer keys. Therefore, test-takers do not need any special computer skills to take the NCLEX-RN examination using the computer adaptive format. If the test-taker answers a question correctly, the next question the computer presents will be slightly more difficult. If the test-taker answers a question incorrectly, the computer will present a question that is slightly less difficult. In this way, a computerized adaptive test tailors itself to each individual test-taker.

Despite the change in the way the NCLEX-RN examination is administered, the format of the exam remains the same. The NCLEX-RN examination is still a multiple-choice test, just like the CGFNS Qualifying Exam. Similar to the CGFNS Qualifying Exam, each question in the NCLEX-RN examination addresses a single client need.

When you take the NCLEX-RN examination on a computer, you must think carefully before choosing an answer. In a CAT test, once you have answered a question, you must go on to the next question. You cannot go back to a previous question, nor can you change any of your answers.

With CAT, nurses and nursing students schedule their own NCLEX-RN examination dates and times. When you are accepted for NCLEX-RN testing, the board of nursing in the U.S. state or territory in which you want to practice will tell you where the nearest NCLEX-RN testing sites are located. You must schedule your examination within 30 days of your acceptance. Your test results should be available within two to three weeks after you take the NCLEX-RN examination.

The Paper-and-Pencil Format of the CGFNS Qualifying Exam

The CGFNS Qualifying Exam is still administered in a paper-and-pencil format. This gives the CGFNS Qualifying Exam several distinct features that differentiate it from the NCLEX-RN examination but do not affect the exam's ability to predict your likelihood of passing the NCLEX-RN examination. For example, when you take the CGFNS Qualifying Exam, you can go back and review your answers in the section being administered at that time. You can change any answers you think are incorrect. You can answer any questions you may have skipped.

Why CGFNS Uses An Objective, Multiple-Choice Exam Format

Many internationally educated nurses are unfamiliar with taking an objective, multiple-choice exam. For this reason, many inquire as to why CGFNS uses an objective, multiple-choice format for the CGFNS Qualifying Exam.

There are several reasons why CGFNS uses this type of exam. Multiple-choice examinations measure your knowledge more objectively and, therefore, more accurately than essay tests, especially when large numbers of people are being tested. That is because many different reviewers would be needed to grade a large number of essay exams, and each reviewer might have a different grading methodology.

A multiple-choice test can offer some distinct advantages for test-takers. For example, the response choices in multiple-choice tests can often help test-takers recall information. If a test-taker cannot remember the correct answer, the suggested responses can sometimes help him or her decide what it is. Objective, multiple-choice tests may also be less difficult than essay tests for nurses whose first language is not English.

A multiple-choice test can generally be completed more quickly than an essay test. Thousands of nurses take the CGFNS Qualifying Exam each year. The multiple-choice format allows the CGFNS test vendor to score your responses more accurately and report test results more quickly.

Objective, multiple-choice tests are generally considered to be more fair than any other type of test. All of the questions on the CGFNS Qualifying Exam are written and reviewed by experts. CGFNS eliminates any questions that are confusing, biased or hard to understand.

In the United States, objective or multiple-choice testing is used to certify and license nurses as well as other professionals. Colleges and universities also rely heavily on objective entrance examinations.

If you are not familiar with objective, multiple-choice testing, refer to Chapter 4 of this Official Study Guide, which provides a brief overview of how to read, understand and answer objective, multiple-choice questions. CGFNS also publishes the book, *How to Take Tests: Strategies for the CGFNS Qualifying Exam and the NCLEX-RN® examination.* This study aide emphasizes how to prepare to take the CGFNS Qualifying Exam, how to analyze multiple-choice questions, how to develop and maintain a positive attitude when taking a multiple-choice test and how to control test anxiety. CGFNS also publishes, *How to Study: Preparing for the CGFNS Qualifying Exam and the NCLEX-RN® examination*, which recommends study techniques and practices for the exams. Both books are available by calling the Customer Service Department at (215) 349-8767 or by visiting the CGFNS website at www.cgfns.org.

Validity of the CGFNS Examination

Every examination has a purpose. Some examinations are designed to measure how much a person has learned about a particular subject. This kind of examination is called an achievement test. You have probably taken many achievement tests during the course of your education.

Some examinations are designed to determine a person's ability to undertake a specific course of study. You may have taken an examination like this when you applied to nursing school.

As noted above, the CGFNS Qualifying Exam, in combination with the English language proficiency exam, is designed to help you and other internationally educated nurses measure your likelihood of passing the NCLEX-RN examination. Special statistical analyses, called validity studies, are used to determine whether or not an examination is achieving its objectives. If a validity study shows that an examination is doing what it is meant to do, the examination is said to be a valid predictor.

The annual CGFNS validity studies have indicated an important parallel between the CGFNS Certification Program and the NCLEX-RN examination. Approximately 85 percent to 90 percent of the internationally educated nurses who earn a CGFNS certificate on their first testing also pass the NCLEX-RN examination the first time, as well. Internationally educated nurses who require multiple testing before they earn the CGFNS certificate usually have to take the NCLEX-RN examination more than once.

Overview of the Content of the CGFNS Qualifying Exam

The CGFNS Qualifying Exam measures your knowledge of nursing and is based on what nurses must know and do in the United States. This may be different from what nurses in other countries must know and be able to do. The foundations of the CGFNS Qualifying Exam are client (patient) needs. These are described in detail in Chapter 5, Design of the CGFNS Qualifying Exam. This is the same kind of information you will be tested on if you take the NCLEX-RN examination.

English is the language of the United States. Most of your patients will speak English, and the people with whom you will work will speak English. Patient records also will be written in English. Therefore, to practice nursing in the United States, you must be able to communicate in English as it is spoken in the United States.

For these reasons, the NCLEX-RN examination is written and administered only in English, as are all the questions in the CGFNS Qualifying Exam. On both examinations, the nursing questions are written in English at a reading level that a graduate of a U.S. nursing school would understand. The English language proficiency exam is designed solely to test your English language skills.

Examination Structure

The CGFNS Qualifying Exam is composed of 260 questions, divided into two different exam booklets. These exam booklets are called Nursing Part 1 and Nursing Part 2.

Nursing Part 1 includes 150 questions. This part of the exam is given in the morning. You will have two hours and 30 minutes to complete this portion. You will then have a lunch break. After lunch, you will take Nursing Part 2. There are 110 questions in Part 2 of the nursing exam. You will have one hour and 50 minutes to answer these questions.

To complete both Nursing Part 1 and Nursing Part 2 within the allotted time, you must read and answer each question in one minute. You will probably be able to read and answer some questions in less than a minute. That will allow you more time to spend on the questions you find more difficult. Do not spend too much time on any one question.

You must complete as much of the CGFNS Qualifying Exam as you can in the time allotted. You will not be given any additional time, and you will not be permitted to answer any questions after the proctor has told you to stop. Your exam booklet will not be returned to you after the proctor has collected it.

Examination Scoring

The CGFNS Qualifying Exam scoring is done by the CGFNS test vendor. Credit is given for each correct answer. If you do not answer a question or if you mark more than one response to a question, you will not receive any credit for that question. All answers must be marked on the answer sheet, not in the exam booklet.

When taking the CGFNS Qualifying Exam, if you are not sure which answer is correct, mark the answer that seems most correct. Your score is based on the number of questions you answer correctly. However, there is no penalty for guessing. When in doubt, it is best to guess rather than leave an answer blank.

To determine your score, the total number of correct responses is calculated and then converted to a scale. The CGFNS scale ranges from 1 to 800, with 400 required for passing.

CGFNS provides you with your scaled score as well as the passing score for the exam. In addition to the score report, CGFNS also provides a graphic diagnostic profile of how well you performed in each area of client needs. Client need categories are described in Chapter 5.

Examination Results

Approximately five weeks after your examination, the CGFNS test vendor forwards your test scores to CGFNS. Between five and six weeks following your examination, CGFNS will send you a letter telling you if you passed or failed the CGFNS Qualifying Exam. Your English language proficiency exam results will be sent directly to you from the testing service.

You may access your pass/fail test status through the CGFNS website at www.cgfns.org approximately five weeks after completing your CGFNS Qualifying Exam.

If you pass both the CGFNS Qualifying Exam and the English language proficiency exam, you will receive a CGFNS certificate. The following chart outlines the steps to be taken if you fail either the CGFNS Qualifying Exam or the English language proficiency exam, or both.

[If You...]	[You Must...]
Fail both the CGFNS Qualifying Exam _and_ English language proficiency exam	_Retake and pass both_ the CGFNS Qualifying Exam and English language proficiency exam
Pass English language proficiency exam, _but fail_ the CGFNS Qualifying Exam	_Retake and pass_ the CGFNS Qualifying Exam _within two years_ of passing the English language proficiency exam
Pass the CGFNS Qualifying Exam, _but fail_ the English language proficiency exam	_Retake_ the English language proficiency exam _within two years_ of passing the CGFNS Qualifying Exam
Do not pass the English language proficiency exam _within two years_ of passing the CGFNS Qualifying Exam	_Retake and pass both_ the CGFNS Qualifying Exam and the English language proficiency exam

You will need to provide proof of CGFNS certification when you apply for a registered nurse license in many U.S. states. Some organizations will accept notarized photocopies of your CGFNS certificate as proof; others will require that CGFNS inform them directly that you have earned a CGFNS certificate. CGFNS will send a letter verifying your status as a certificate holder. This notification letter is called a "Verification of Certificate Status." This service must be requested in writing. There is no fee for this service.

CGFNS does not issue or make duplicate certificates. However, CGFNS can send you an official letter verifying the date of your certification. You may also want to photocopy your CGFNS certificate and keep copies for future use.

Examination Schedule

The CGFNS Qualifying Exam is given four times a year. Each exam is given on the same day all over the world and takes an entire day. Each time the CGFNS Qualifying Exam is given, new test questions are used.

Once you are scheduled (rostered) to take the CGFNS Qualifying Exam, your date and exam location will be posted on the CGFNS website, www.cgfns.org. You must check your schedule and eligibility information on our website. Your exam schedule will be displayed. You should print this page for your record.

For current information on applying to the CGFNS Certification Program, as well as upcoming CGFNS Qualifying Exam dates and locations, contact the CGFNS Customer Service Department for a copy of the free publication entitled, _Path to CGFNS Certification: Applicant Handbook_ or visit the CGFNS website at www.cgfns.org.

How to Read, Understand and Answer Objective Exam Questions

This chapter shows you how to read, understand and answer the objective, multiple-choice questions used in the CGFNS Qualifying Exam.

General Description of the Exam Questions

In an examination that uses objective questions, you are given all of the information you need to answer the question. You then identify the answer you believe is correct. You do not have to write your own explanation, as you would for an essay question, or fill in any blank spaces. The questions are called "objective" because there can be no interpretation of the answer when it is scored. The answer is either correct or incorrect.

In an exam that uses multiple-choice questions, you are given a number of possible answers from which to choose. In the CGFNS Qualifying Exam, you are given four possible answers from which to select the one answer you believe best answers the question. Even if you believe another answer that is not given would be better, you may choose only from those choices given to you. An example of this type of question is given in the box below.

After you decide which answer is correct, you must record that answer. In the CGFNS Qualify Exam, a separate answer sheet is provided for this purpose.

You will find sample answer sheets for use with this Official Study Guide in Appendix B.

The answer sheet has numbers on it corresponding to each question on the exam. Beside each of the numbers on the answer sheet, you will find four circles. Each of the circles has a letter (A, B, C or D) above it. Fill in and darken completely the circle on the answer sheet below the letter that corresponds to the letter beside the answer you wish to choose. For example, the correct answer to the question below is "D." You would fill in the circle beneath the letter "D" corresponding to the appropriate question on the answer sheet—in this case, number one. You must fill in each circle completely. A check mark or "X" in the circle cannot be read by the computer that scores your exam and will be recorded as an incorrect response.

QUESTION

1. A woman who has type 2 diabetes is to receive an oral hypoglycemic agent. Which of these measures should the nurse instruct the woman to include in her daily care?

POSSIBLE ANSWERS
   A. Eating most meals at home
   B. Eliminating desserts except fruit
   C. Being aware of the availability of special diabetic foods
   D. Maintaining a regular meal schedule

ANSWER SHEET

	A	B	C	D
1.	○	○	○	●
2.	○	○	○	○
3.	○	○	○	○

Suggestions on How to Answer Exam Questions

First, read the question carefully and completely. Then, think about the patient in the question and decide what is being asked. Relate the question to the information about the patient. Use only the information you have been given in the description corresponding to that question.

Read each possible answer thoroughly. Eliminate any obviously wrong answers. If possible, avoid choosing an answer that includes the words never, all, always, ever and none. Answers with these words are usually wrong. Sometimes, all of the answers given seem correct. If this is the case, after you have read all of the answers, go back and read the question again. Perhaps, the question asks you to choose what you would do first. Remember that, although all of the answers may be right, only one should be done first. This is why it is so important for you to understand the information given to you in the description and to know exactly what is being asked in the question.

Remember that you have a set amount of time to take each portion of the exam. Nursing, Part 1, has 150 questions. You have two hours and 30 minutes to answer all of these questions. This means you have an average of one minute to answer each question. It does not mean that you must take a full minute to answer each question, if you can figure out the right answer in less time. However, if you take more than an average of one minute for each question, you will not finish that portion of the exam.

It may take you less than one minute to answer some questions and more than one minute to answer others. These times usually balance each other out over the entire exam. Go on to the next question if you read and think about a question for a few moments but cannot decide which answer is correct. Answer the easiest questions first. Because you are graded on the number of correct answers, it is important for you to answer as many questions as you can.

If you read through all of the questions in the exam and still have some time left, go back to the questions you did not answer. If you are still not certain, guess at the answer. There is no penalty for guessing. However, only correct answers count toward your score.

When you mark your answers on the answer sheet, remember that each question has a corresponding number. Be sure that you mark your answer beside the same number on the answer sheet. Fill in and darken the circle completely. Be sure that the circle you darken is under the same letter as the one beside the answer you have chosen. Do not get confused and darken the circle above the letter that you wish to choose. If you skip a question, be sure to skip that same number on the answer sheet.

If you make a mistake, erase your mistake completely and cleanly. If you do not, the computer scoring your test will not be able to read your answer sheet correctly and may record your response incorrectly. Do not make extra marks on the answer sheet; these could also confuse the computer. If you need to make any calculations or notes, write them in your exam booklet, not on the answer sheet.

There is only one right answer for each question. If you mark more than one answer, you will not get credit for any of the answers. If it is not clear which answer you have chosen, the answer will be marked wrong. Be very careful! Stray marks on the answer sheet or incomplete erasures must be avoided because the actual exam is computer-scored.

Alternate Item Types

In 2004, CGFNS introduced several different types of questions into its exam. These are called alternate item types and include such things as charts, graphs, and multiple correct answer and short answer questions. You may see one or two of these questions on the examination. For more information on alternate item types, go to the CGFNS website at www.cgfns.org.

Design of the CGFNS Qualifying Exam

Introduction

This chapter explains the purpose and structure of the CGFNS Qualifying Exam. To help you understand the way the CGFNS Qualifying Exam is designed, the context for nursing within the American healthcare delivery system is described. Then, the actual structure of the test plan for the exam is discussed, including the exam's emphasis on client needs.

Factors Influencing the Registered Nurse's Role in the American Healthcare System

The American healthcare system is undergoing enormous change. Much of this change reflects concern within government, the health professions, hospitals, the insurance industry, employers who provide health insurance to workers and families with the rapid rise over the last 30 years in the cost of healthcare. The United States spends more money per capita on healthcare than any other developed nation. Yet there is concern that many people are excluded from access to healthcare and that much of the money is wasted.

Shortened Stays

Among the ways that hospitals reduce the cost of the care they provide is the shortened stay. Clients (patients) may spend little time in the hospital, even if they are quite ill. Most surgery in the United States is now performed on an outpatient or same-day basis. New mothers are discharged within 24 hours of a vaginal delivery. People undergo much diagnostic testing as outpatients. They recuperate in their homes or in long-term care facilities. Terminally ill people often die at home with hospice support for their families.

In general, this means clients who are hospitalized are more ill, have more complex needs, and need more nursing care than was true a few years ago. Treatments and procedures that occurred in intensive care units in the past are managed in regular medical or surgical units today. In addition, clients and their families need careful teaching to safely manage care after clients leave the hospital.

Efficiency in Staffing

In hospital settings, administrators are reorganizing their nursing staffs to be as cost-effective as possible. Nurses are often grouped into patient care teams with other types of healthcare workers or nursing assistants. Because hospitalized clients have more nursing needs than was true in the past, and because hospitals cannot afford to overstaff, nurses find that their work loads have increased over the last several years.

Advanced Practice Nurses

Another way that healthcare agencies are reducing costs is to make greater use of advanced practice nurses, such as nurse practitioners, nurse midwives or nurse anesthetists. These specially trained nurses most often have additional education beyond their basic registered nurse education. They independently assess and manage routine health maintenance and minor or chronic illnesses.

Expanded Home Health and Community Services

In addition to these changes within hospitals to make healthcare less costly, more nurses are working in homecare and community settings. Even in those settings, it is routine for nurses to administer, or teach family members to administer, treatments and medications that were used only in critical care units a decade ago. For example, clients may go home with a central venous infusion or on a ventilator, and require nurse visits once or more per day. Most hospitals now have homecare departments to organize nursing care for clients after they are discharged. Staff nurses work closely with the homecare nurses to plan clients' discharge.

Because hospitalized clients are so ill, and because nurses in homecare and community settings manage such complex health needs, a nurse's ability to assess clients' health status and to monitor change has never been so important. In addition, nurses increasingly coordinate care provided to clients' by numerous departments or providers, fulfilling the role of case manager. Because many different organizations or government agencies provide health insurance for most Americans, nurses must increasingly consider clients' individual insurance coverage in coordinating their care.

5

Advanced Technology

Another important stimulus for change in the American healthcare delivery system is the common use of advanced technology for diagnosis, treatment, rehabilitation and maintenance of clients who just a few years ago might not have survived. One example of this is the routine use by diabetic clients of electronic serum glucose level testing devices. Other examples include the growing network of renal dialysis centers across the country, the increased use of home dialysis and the expanding numbers of individuals who have undergone kidney transplants.

With increased technology has come more specialization in the provision of healthcare. Healthcare systems have become more complex associations of many departments or agencies. Clients sometimes feel that their care is fragmented and impersonal.

Human Rights

Since the civil rights movement of the 1960s and 1970s, American society has become more keenly attuned to the autonomy and individual rights of all members of society, regardless of race, ethnicity, religious beliefs, gender, sexual orientation or physical ability. Laws in the area of civil rights have shaped the way institutions deal with their employees as well as their clients.

The Patient Bill of Rights, adopted by the American Hospital Association and organizations that regulate healthcare, must be made available to clients in hospitals and nursing homes. The rights of clients to be fully informed of all treatments, to refuse treatments and to know the identity of all personnel involved in their care are assured.

Malpractice

The American healthcare system has increasingly embraced a philosophy of self-care, or collaboration in care with clients and their families. Clients increasingly question their care if they believe their care is inadequate or inappropriate. They have also become more likely to use the legal system to address their grievances. In part, this may reflect the increasing lack of healthcare personnel's direct contact with patients and the increased use of technology.

Healthcare providers have turned to the strategies of quality control and risk management in addressing concerns related to the complexity and fragmentation of care and to legal risk. Nurses play a central role in quality assurance and risk management.

To Summarize

- The American healthcare system is undergoing rapid change.
- The needs of hospitalized clients are more complex than in the past, yet hospitals are trying to staff more efficiently.
- Increasingly, nurses must consider costs and clients' insurance coverage in coordinating their care.
- More healthcare services are decentralized.
- Nurses must facilitate clients' rapid discharge from hospitals and coordinate their care in home and community settings.
- The ability to accurately assess complex health needs and to work in a collaborative relationship with clients and their families to manage those needs is crucial.
- Increased sensitivity to individual rights and to employees' and clients' use of the legal system to resolve grievances influences policies and procedures throughout the healthcare system.

The Foundation of the CGFNS Qualifying Exam

The CGFNS Qualifying Exam tests your nursing knowledge. The nursing knowledge assessment is based on what nurses must know and do when they practice nursing in the United States. The traditional clinical areas of nursing practice—medical, surgical, maternity, pediatric, psychiatric and community health nursing—are covered, but the questions are not grouped by clinical areas. The exam demonstrates an integrated approach to nursing. This approach will be described below.

The CGFNS Qualifying Exam ensures that you have the same level of understanding of nursing, with various client groups and in various settings, as beginning graduates of American schools of nursing.

Nursing is an art and a science that incorporates concepts from the biological, psychological and social sciences. The focus of nursing practice is to assist people to achieve and maintain the highest level of health and function possible for them. Nursing of individuals and families is a personal, planned activity.

Nurses diagnose human responses to health or illness situations, and they respond to assessed needs of clients across the life span. When nurses refer to "clients," they mean individuals, families or groups of people. Clients live in a social context. They have varying capacities to fulfill roles and make choices about their lifestyles.

The Structure of the CGFNS Qualifying Examination

The CGFNS Qualifying Exam tests your understanding of client needs. The framework of client needs was selected for the NCLEX-RN examination and the CGFNS Qualifying Exam because it provides a universal structure for defining nursing actions and competencies across all settings for all clients. Four major categories of client needs organize the content of the examination. The percentage of questions reflecting each client need area is indicated below (Table 1) and a detailed discussion of client needs follows.

Table 1. Percentage of questions on the CGFNS Qualifying Exam relating to each area of Client Needs

---

Client Needs

Safe, Effective Care Environment (21–33%)

Health Promotion and Maintenance (6–12%)

Psychosocial Integrity (6–12%)

Physiological Integrity (43–67%)

Other concepts and processes fundamental to the practice of nursing are integrated throughout the four major categories of client needs. These include nursing process, caring, communication/documentation, and teaching/learning. A description of the five phases of the nursing process is included in this chapter.

A few questions on the exam will test factual knowledge or its interpretation. Most of the questions will test your ability to use knowledge in clinical situations. It is important to remember that the NCLEX-RN examination tests your understanding of client needs as well.

Client Needs

The CGFNS Qualifying Exam measures your understanding of client needs. Basic human needs have been identified by various nursing groups, and the labels applied to them vary. They are areas in which disruption reduces the client's level of health. Developmental processes, such as puberty, childbirth or menopause, as well as illnesses or injury can cause these disruptions. The client may have alterations in one or more of these areas at the same time. None of these basic human needs can be considered separately. Alterations in one area can affect the extent to which the client's other basic human needs are being met.

The CGFNS Qualifying Exam and the NCLEX-RN examination both employ the same underlying conceptual model of client needs. In this model, as described in the National Council of State Boards of Nursing publication, *Test Plan for the National Council Licensure Examination for Registered Nurses* (Chicago: National Council of State Boards of Nursing, Inc., 2004), client needs are grouped into the following four major categories:

1. Safe, Effective Care Environment

2. Health Promotion and Maintenance

3. Psychosocial Integrity

4. Physiological Integrity

Diseases that affect just one body system can tax the individual and his or her family in several, or even all, of these areas at the same time. Each of these four client need categories are discussed below (See also Table 2). All content categories reflect client needs across the life span in a variety of settings.

Table 2. Client Needs model on which the CGFNS Qualifying Exam and the NCLEX-RN® examination are based.

Needs Categories

I. Safe, Effective Care Environment
  - Management of care
  - Safety and infection control

II. Health Promotion and Maintenance

III. Psychosocial Integrity

IV. Physiological Integrity
  - Basic care and comfort
  - Reduction of risk potential
  - Pharmacological and parenteral therapies
  - Physiological adaptation

Client Need Category One: Safe, Effective Care Environment

The need for a safe, effective care environment refers to the patient's degree of freedom from harm, iatrogenic illness or injury during care, and the client's need for care that is coordinated and of high quality. The client should be prepared for treatments and procedures, and the treatments and procedures should be carried out safely and effectively. It is expected that practice is continually revised to reflect newly established biomedical and nursing knowledge.

The first client need in this category is **Management of Care**. This takes into account all of the client's needs, because the nurse works with all other healthcare team members. Management of care is outcome-oriented and entails providing integrated, cost-effective care to clients by coordinating, supervising and/or collaborating with members of the multi-disciplinary healthcare team.

The nurse's database in relation to the need for management of care will include such considerations as:

- advance directives;
- advocacy;
- case management;
- client rights;
- concepts of management;
- confidentiality;
- continuity of care;
- Continuous Quality Improvement;
- delegation;
- ethical practice;
- incident/irregular occurrence/variance reports;
- informed consent;
- legal responsibilities;
- organ donation;
- consultation and referrals;
- resource management; and
- supervision.

The second client need in this category is **Safety and Infection Control.** The need for environmental safety refers to protecting clients and healthcare personnel from environmental hazards.

The nurse's database related to the client's need for environmental safety includes:

- accident prevention;
- disaster planning;
- error prevention;
- handling of hazardous and infectious materials;
- medical and surgical asepsis;
- standard (universal) and other precautions; and
- use of restraints.

Client Need Category Two: Health Promotion And Maintenance

This category refers to the client's need for continued growth and development throughout the life span, self-care and support systems, and prevention and early treatment of disease.

Nursing care related to this client need category includes assessment of expectant parents' knowledge and expectations of birth and infant care, assessment of maternal and fetal status during labor, assessment of new parents and newborn infants, and parent education about the needs of their children in anticipation of every stage of development.

Nursing care also includes assessment of children's physical growth and development and of their parents' understanding of normal growth and development. Nursing care includes provision of anticipatory guidance for developmental transitions, such as puberty or marriage. It includes assessment of clients' attitudes toward sexuality and reproduction, the provision of sex education, and helping clients make decisions about birth control measures. In addition, nurses assist clients in preparing for retirement and in planning for self-care during their later years.

The nurse's database in relation to the client's need for continued growth and development throughout the life span includes:

- reproductive and sexual history;
- risk factors;
- nutritional status;
- maternal physical status during pregnancy and postpartum;
- support systems available during pregnancy;
- parental perceptions of pregnancy;
- parental coping during pregnancy;
- results of maternal and fetal diagnostic tests;
- maternal progress and stress in pregnancy and labor;
- fetal assessment;
- presence of complications during pregnancy and labor;
- neonatal assessment;
- adjustment to parenthood;
- infant's or child's physical status including height, weight, head circumference, vital signs, dentition, gross and fine motor abilities, vision, sexual development, general changes of aging, cognitive functioning (including conceptualization, rational thinking, problem-solving and decision-making), socialization, verbal abilities, toileting, self-care, self-dressing and self-feeding;
- peer relationships;
- morality;
- presence of stressors;
- marital status;

- presence of anxiety;
- depression or social isolation;
- nutritional status;
- recreational activities;
- career;
- sexuality;
- concerns about retirement;
- client's and family's knowledge of developmental changes and tasks; and
- resources available to the client and family.

To meet this need, nurses use knowledge, skills and abilities that include:

- aging process;
- developmental stages and transitions;
- expected body image changes;
- family planning;
- family systems;
- genetic counseling;
- human sexuality;
- labor and delivery;
- newborn care;
- parenting;
- prenatal care;
- reproduction; and
- well-child care.

This client need category also addresses prevention and early detection of disease. Nursing care related to prevention and early detection of disease includes administration of vaccines and immunizing agents, the conduct of health and illness screening and the interpretation of screening tests.

The nurse's database in relation to the client's need for prevention and early detection of disease includes:

- age, sex, height and weight;
- physical assessment;
- health history;
- psychosocial history;
- identification of health risks;
- presence of allergies; and
- resources available to the client and family.

To meet this need, nurses use knowledge, skills and abilities that include:

- community resources;
- concept of wellness;
- disease prevention;
- healthcare screening;
- lifestyle choices;
- principles of immunity; and
- techniques of physical assessment.

Client Need Category Three: Psychosocial Integrity

The nurse meets the client's and significant other's need for psychosocial integrity in stress and crises-related situations throughout the life span by providing and directing nursing care.

Nursing care related to the client's need for psychosocial integrity includes assessment of the client's sources of emotional support, the client's adjustment to a physical or emotional impairment and the client's need for increased or decreased sensory stimulation. The nurse plans interventions to improve the client's coping, encourages the client to talk about his or her fears, helps the client deal with negative attitudes related to illness, encourages the client to persist with psychotherapy, plans interventions to deal with anxiety related to pain or changed body functioning and teaches the client to communicate more effectively. The nurse also involves the client's significant other in the plan of care.

Nursing care related to the need for psychosocial integrity also includes assessment of the client's home environment, the client's and family's understanding of the causes of illness, the family's emotional response to a client's chronic disorder and the family's pattern of interaction. Nurses teach home caregivers about the client's therapy and assess them for signs of burnout. The nurse assesses the quality of homecare and arranges for spiritual support during life transitions or crises. The nurse supports terminally ill clients and their families. The nurse provides counseling to families of handicapped patients. The nurse responds to family members' needs when the client is hospitalized, for example, adjusting visiting hours for them.

The nurse's database in relation to the need for psychosocial integrity includes:

- health history;
- physical and emotional symptoms;
- social factors related to coping;
- coping behaviors;
- resources available to the client;
- accountability;
- behavior norms;
- communication skills;
- principles of teaching and learning;

- cultural, religious and spiritual influences on health; and
- psychodynamics of behavior.

Knowledge, skills and abilities required to address the need for coping/adaptation include:

- anxiety;
- coping mechanisms;
- diversional activities;
- environmental stressors;
- family interactions;
- mental health concepts;
- religious and spiritual influences on health;
- sensory/perceptual alterations;
- situational role changes;
- stress management; and
- unexpected body image changes.

Another area addressed under the client need category, Psychosocial Integrity, is managing and providing care for clients with acute and chronic psychiatric disorders. Nursing care related to this need includes psychosocial assessment of the client's orientation to reality, alcohol or drug withdrawal, potential for suicide, effectiveness of interventions and risk of violence toward others.

Nurses help clients to understand their behavior. They provide client teaching and counseling for drug and alcohol abuse, physical or emotional abuse by others, management of disruptive behavior and management of depression. Nurses teach family members how to manage the client's behavior. Nurses develop strategies for clients with low self-esteem, and they implement behavioral modification programs.

The nurse's database in relation to caring for clients with acute and chronic psychiatric disorders includes:

- community resources;
- family systems;
- mental health concepts;
- psychopathology; and
- treatment modalities.

Knowledge, skills and abilities of the nurse that are related to the need for psychosocial adaptation include:

- behavior modification;
- chemical dependency;
- child abuse;
- counseling;
- crisis intervention;
- domestic violence;
- elder abuse;
- post-traumatic stress syndrome;
- psychopathology;
- reality orientation;
- therapeutic communication; and
- therapeutic environment.

Client Need Category Four: Physiological Integrity

This category of client need refers to adequate functioning of the body systems, including the respiratory, circulatory, urinary, gastrointestinal, neurological, immune, endocrine, reproductive, integumentary and musculoskeletal systems. Most illnesses, acute and chronic, and many treatments and medications affect multiple systems. The nurse promotes physiological adaptation and reduces the potential risk of complications or adverse effects of treatments.

The first client need in the category of physiological integrity is **Basic Care and Comfort**. Nursing care related to this need involves assisting in the performance of activities of daily living, modified because of health alterations, and providing comfort. Basic care and comfort includes such tasks as measurement of vital signs, performing urine tests, giving an enema and dressing a wound. It also includes assessment and care related to nutritional and fluid intake and elimination.

Nurses assess the client's nutritional status and factors that affect it, such as income level and culturally based dietary practices, adapt a diet to the client's special requirements, teach about normal nutrition, and counsel clients trying to gain or lose weight.

Nursing care includes assessment of the client's ability to perform self-care and activities of daily living. It includes planning for adjustments in self-care and activities of daily living that are necessitated by physical impairments. Nurses help clients with impaired mobility or sensory deficits install equipment in their homes to enhance their ability to perform activities of daily living. They help clients deal with anxiety due to changed physical functioning and teach clients about personal hygiene, the avoidance of infection and exercise. Nurses plan urinary and bowel retraining programs with clients when needed. They can assist clients in choosing recreational activities that fit their age and condition. Finally, nurses evaluate clients' perceptions of their condition and their compliance with prescribed therapy.

The nurse's database in relation to the client's need for basic care and comfort includes:

- age, sex, cultural and personal preferences, knowledge of hygiene and socioeconomic status;
- integrity of the skin, nails, hair, oral cavity and perineum as well as risk factors for problems in these areas;
- presence of special devices that need care, such as contact lenses or dentures;
- vital signs, including the quality of the pulse and respirations;
- factors that may affect the vital signs;
- characteristics of urine, feces and other body fluids being eliminated;
- tissue integrity at the site of body fluid elimination;
- patency and placement of drainage and decompression tubes;
- wound sites;
- results of diagnostic tests;
- fluid intake and diet history;
- activity level;
- psychological factors affecting nutritional intake;
- drug and alcohol use;
- physical status;
- client's and family's knowledge; and
- resources available.

Knowledge, skills and abilities of the nurse that are related to the need for basic care and comfort include the following areas:

- disease prevention;
- health and wellness;
- health promotion programs;
- health screening;
- immunizations;
- lifestyle choices; and
- techniques of physical assessment.

The second client need in this category is **Pharmacological and Parenteral Therapies**. Nursing care related to this need involves managing and providing care related to the administration of medications to clients in varied healthcare settings. Nurses administer blood, chemotherapy and intravenous solutions and make adjustments based on the client's response.

The nurse's database in relation to the need for pharmacological and parenteral therapies includes:

- administration of blood and blood products;
- calculation for medication administration;
- central venous access devices;
- chemotherapy;
- expected effects;
- intravenous therapy;
- parenteral fluids;
- pharmacological actions;
- side effects;
- total parenteral nutrition; and
- untoward effects.

The third client need in the category of physiological integrity is **Reduction of Risk Potential**. Nursing care related to this need includes reducing the likelihood that clients with an existing condition or undergoing a treatment or procedure will develop complications and/or health problems. It also includes proper positioning of immobile patients. Nurses assess their clients' tolerance for physical activity, and they intervene to promote sleep. Nurses act to prevent complications of care. They assess wound healing, provide cast care and prepare clients for procedures. Nursing care also includes modification of the care plan on the basis of diagnostic tests.

The nurse's database in relation to the need for reduction of risk potential includes:

- blood glucose monitoring;
- caring for clients after procedures/surgery;
- cast care;
- diagnostic tests;
- insertion of nasogastric tubes;
- managing immobility;
- monitoring clients during procedures/surgery;
- preparing clients for procedures/surgery;
- pulse oximetry;
- range of motion exercises; and
- specimen collection.

The fourth client need in the category of physiological integrity is promoting **Physiological Adaptation**, which involves managing and providing care to clients during the acute and chronic phases of existing healthcare conditions. Nursing care related to this need includes assessment of all body systems. Nurses assess and manage an emergency until a physician arrives, including the provision of cardiopulmonary resuscitation. Nurses suction clients' respiratory tracts and provide tracheostomy care. They also modify care based on the client's response to therapies.

The nurse's database regarding the client's need for physiological adaptation includes:

- cardiovascular alterations;
- endocrine/metabolic alterations;
- fluids and electrolytes;
- gastrointestinal alterations;
- hemodynamics;
- immune system alterations;
- infectious processes;
- integumentary/musculoskeletal alterations;
- medical emergencies;
- neurosensory alterations;
- renal/urinary alterations;
- reproductive therapy;
- radiation therapy;
- respiratory alterations;
- respiratory care;
- unexpected response to therapies; and
- vital signs.

Summary of Client Needs

Nurses in the United States assess and meet client needs through the use of the nursing process. Once these needs are identified, the nurse plans ways to help the client meet them. The goal of nursing care is to help clients maintain or return to functional patterns of health in each of the client need areas described in this section. It is important to remember that client needs will be the focus of the CGFNS Qualifying Exam and the NCLEX-RN examination.

Integrated Content Areas

The following concepts are integrated throughout the CGFNS and NCLEX-RN examinations. The majority of questions on the examination will test at least one of these concepts:

Nursing Process: a step-by-step problem-solving approach to meeting client needs that is used by nurses in the United States. It includes five steps: assessment, analysis, planning, implementation and evaluation. A complete description of the nursing process immediately follows this section.

Caring: the interaction of the nurse and client in an atmosphere of mutual respect and trust. The nurse provides hope, support and compassion to help achieve desired outcomes.

Communication: verbal and nonverbal interactions between nurse and client, client families and members of the healthcare team.

Documentation: validation of client care through a written record, usually the client's chart.

Teaching/Learning: helping patients and families acquire the knowledge, skills and attitudes necessary for behavioral changes.

The Five Phases of the Nursing Process

The nursing process is integrated throughout the CGFNS Qualifying Exam and the NCLEX-RN examination. Nurses in the United States are taught a step-by-step, problem-solving approach to determining and meeting their clients' needs. This problem-solving approach is called the nursing process. Nursing books may differ slightly in how they describe the nursing process, but all agree that there are five basic steps to this problem-solving approach. They are:

1. Assessment
2. Analysis
3. Planning
4. Implementation
5. Evaluation

Nursing students are taught to use the nursing process in thinking about clients. It is expected that in their work nurses will plan and document their nursing care to reflect this approach.

Step One: Assessment

Assessment refers to the establishment of an information base. It includes gathering subjective and objective information, confirming data and communicating findings.

In the assessment phase, the nurse gathers the information about the client that is needed to plan appropriate nursing care. Ideally, an initial nursing assessment is comprehensive. In reality, the urgency of the client's needs at the time of the initial assessment determines how much time can be taken. The nurse's assessment of the client's status is important because all other steps in the nursing process are based on this information.

In preparing to assess a specific client, the nurse may have access to information from other healthcare professionals, such as the physician, the social worker or other nurses. The nurse may also have access to a patient record containing information about past healthcare or the assessment and treatment provided by other health professionals. The nurse may have an opportunity to talk with family members about why this client has come for healthcare now. There may be witnesses to a sudden illness or injury who can provide background information. It is important for the nurse to use as much information as can be found from these sources so that time with the client can be used most efficiently.

Two broad types of information are gathered in a nursing assessment: subjective information and objective information.

Subjective information refers to what the client, family members or witnesses say about his or her condition. It is what they think, feel, remember or believe. The nurse cannot directly observe this type of information. This is how the nurse learns the history of the development of a specific problem, what the client tried to do about the problem before seeking healthcare and his or her understanding, beliefs, and feelings about the health problem. These pieces of information are part of the nursing history.

The nursing history also includes general background information about the client's past health and the health of family members. The nurse will ask the patient questions reviewing the body systems, such as the respiratory or circulatory systems. The nurse will assess the client's usual activities of daily living and how they may have been altered by a current illness. The nurse will also assess the client's growth and development, history of coping with crises in the past and sources of support. The way the nurse, the staff or significant others react to the client may be significant in addressing the client's health needs.

The nurse's concerns are whether or not the client, the client's family and the healthcare team are able to meet the client's health needs in the client's environment, and how the illness or injury alters the client's ability to function.

The subjective assessment must be communicated to other members of the healthcare team to be most useful to the client, and this is usually done by means of the client's chart. Most institutions have developed standardized forms used to record the nursing assessment. The information must be recorded clearly and accurately. Direct quotes by the client should be marked as such and used whenever possible. The information should be both complete and brief. This is not the stage in the nursing process for the nurse to convey what he or she thinks about the client's situation.

Objective information is the information gathered through use of the five senses: sight, hearing, touch, smell and (rarely, if ever, in nursing practice) taste. Laboratory and diagnostic test results and assessments by other members of the healthcare team are included as objective information, even though the nurse usually does not gather this information directly. Nurses extend the use of their hands and senses with various diagnostic equipment, such as the thermometer, the scale and the stethoscope. What makes this information objective is that it can be confirmed by other people using the same equipment or the same procedures.

Nurses in the United States are taught physical assessment skills, and it is expected that they will assess each client thoroughly upon or near the time of admission and then as often as needed, depending upon change in the client's condition. These repeated assessments are usually much briefer than the initial assessment.

Initially the nurse will thoroughly assess the client's status in relation to the problem that made him or her seek healthcare. In addition, if the client's urgency of need does not preclude it, the nurse will assess each body system. As the nurse performs the assessment, the nurse will note how the client's status conforms to the norm for his or her developmental stage.

As with the subjective assessment, the objective assessment must be recorded in the client's record promptly. Many institutions have forms or checklists for this purpose.

Step Two: Analysis

Analysis refers to the nurse's identification of actual or potential healthcare needs or problems, based on the nursing assessment. Analysis includes the interpretation of data, the formulation of nursing diagnoses and the communication of the nurse's analysis.

Once the nurse has completed the initial subjective and objective client assessment, the nurse will begin to develop the plan of nursing care. At this point, the nurse must reflect upon all of the information gathered about the client. The analysis step of the nursing process is the point at which the nurse organizes information and makes initial conclusions about the client's status. These conclusions are the nursing diagnoses.

To identify the nursing diagnoses, the nurse will note particularly those observations deviating from what is normal for a person of the client's developmental status or reflecting developmental change. Based on these data and what the client has said about their responses to current illness, injury or developmental transitions, the nurse will consider how well the client's needs are being met and how the client's ability to function has been altered.

Unlike the medical diagnosis of a disease and the pathological changes it causes, nursing diagnoses focus on the client's coping with, and adaptation to, his or her developmental status, illness or injury. The nursing diagnoses will include the category label for the patient's response, and it will state whether the response is actual or potential. It will briefly state the observation that led the nurse to a particular conclusion, and will identify the physical or psychosocial process to which the response is related.

 *Chapter 5*

Many institutions have adopted the North American Nursing Diagnosis Association (NANDA) classification of human responses to illnesses and developmental or situational crises. An example of a nursing diagnosis using the NANDA terminology is: Alteration in comfort (pain) related to fourth degree perineal tear during delivery as evidenced by client's verbalizations and tearful expression.

The client's nursing diagnoses reflect the client's current health status. They may vary frequently during the course of an illness. This is different from the medical diagnosis, which remains the same until the individual recovers or dies.

To be useful to the client, the nursing assessment must be documented, and nursing diagnoses must be reported to the healthcare team.

Step Three: Planning
The planning phase refers to prioritizing the nursing diagnoses, setting goals for meeting client needs and designing strategies for achieving those goals. The nurse addresses these three questions:

1. What is to be done about the nursing diagnoses?
2. How is it to be done?
3. When is it to be done?

The answers to these questions comprise the nursing care plan.

The nursing care plan is a written document initiated by one nurse so that other nursing staff on the unit know what nursing care the client needs and when. Each nurse who cares for the client may modify the care plan as the client's status changes or as ways to make care more effective are discovered. In addition to care indicated by the nursing diagnoses, nursing care related to the physician's diagnosis and treatment is included on the care plan. There are several things that the nurse must do in the planning step of the nursing process. These planning activities, usually done simultaneously, include:

• setting priorities;
• establishing long-term and short-term goals and objectives;
• determining outcome criteria;
• developing the plan of care and modifying it as needed;
• collaborating with healthcare team members in planning care; and
• communicating the nursing care plan.

Setting priorities means deciding the relative urgency of attending to each nursing diagnosis. In deciding the order in which the nursing diagnoses should be addressed, the nurse will consider the client's physiological needs, client and family preferences and feelings of urgency about a given problem, the overall treatment plan for the client, the demands of the total case load, and hospital or healthcare agency policies.

Establishment of Long-Term and Short-Term Goals and Objectives
Goals refer to outcomes of care. Objectives are the steps that must be accomplished for the goal to be achieved. The objectives may change frequently as the client progresses toward achievement of the goals of care.

Many acute care facilities, such as hospitals, now plan care using a critical pathway model. This means for a specific illness or injury, the client is expected to have a certain length of admission. During each day, the client is expected to meet specific objectives to accomplish established short-term goals reflecting the client's medical status, day of admission and preparation for discharge. The client's goals, objectives and status are reviewed daily to assure that the client is progressing as expected or to determine if the client has additional health needs or problems. This approach to planning care increases the efficiency of hospitals and reduces wasted in-patient days.

Long-term goals refer to outcomes that are expected upon follow-up or a regular check-up, or at a later developmental stage. Short-term goals refer to outcomes expected when an acute illness is resolved. For example, "The client will attain height and weight at or above the 50th percentile by age by the second birthday" is an appropriate long-term goal for a low birth-weight baby. A short-term goal might be, "The client will attain a weight of 2.5 kilograms by the fourth week." The goals of care should be client-focused. They are outcomes the nurse is assisting the client to achieve. The goals, particularly the long-term goals, will guide discharge planning. Client teaching to prepare for discharge will address the goals.

Objectives, which are steps the client will take in achieving the goal, are also written from the client's perspective. For example, "The client will give a return demonstration of a baby bath before discharge from the postpartum unit." The goals and objectives must be realistic, acceptable to the client and family and in agreement with the overall treatment plan for the client.

Determining Outcome Criteria

As the goals and objectives of care are established, concrete ways to evaluate whether or not they are met are identified for each. This includes the establishment of deadlines by which goals and objectives are met. Criteria and deadlines reflect both the client's health needs or problems and the length-of-stay guidelines for a particular client's condition.

There are several reasons for anticipating to what degree and by when the client will achieve goals and objectives. One reason is to ensure that the client will progress toward discharge in a timely manner. Another is to motivate the client and the nurse to keep progressing toward these aims. But criteria and deadlines must be realistic. Failure to meet an objective at the expected time can be discouraging. If the client does not achieve objectives or goals, they must be reviewed. It may be that the client's health needs or problems were more complex than the nurse realized; that deadlines, goals or objectives were not reasonable; or that referral to additional supportive services is required. The nurse will be guided by experience and by the client assessments in determining outcome criteria and deadlines.

Developing the Plan of Care and Modifying it as Needed

Once the goals and objectives have been established with outcome criteria, the nurse identifies appropriate nursing care activities (interventions) and selects those that will be most effective in helping the client meet the objectives in the anticipated time.

The plan of care will be more effective if the client and family, as well as other healthcare team members, are involved in its development. It needs to reflect consideration of the client's developmental status, gender, culture and religious values. Moreover, clients are unique, and what works best for one person may not be the preferred strategy with another. The plan of care incorporates concern for the client's safety, comfort and optimal functioning.

The nursing care plan will reflect various types of nursing care activities: monitoring client status, nursing treatments, client and family teaching and the referral of the client or family to other sources of assistance. The nurse may have to identify alternate interventions if the ones initially selected do not result in the client meeting the objectives of care within the allotted time.

The Nursing Care Plan Includes Nursing Orders

Nursing orders describe the nursing care activities to be done for or with the client to meet each objective, including how the activities should be carried out, at what time and for how long. Nursing orders must be compatible with orders written by the physician and others because they must fit into the overall treatment plan. Examples of nursing orders include:

1. Offer 300 ml of fluid at least q 2 h while client is awake, for a total intake of 2400 ml every 24 hours.

2. Have client perform return demonstration of fundal massage during postpartum admission assessment.

3. Perform range-of-motion exercises while bathing client.

Collaboration with Healthcare Team Members in Planning Care

Development of the nursing care plan includes identification of health or social service resources available to the client and family. In addition, the nurse plans nursing team assignments to most suitably match team members with clients according to their needs. Finally, the nurse coordinates care provided to clients by members of the healthcare team.

Communicating the Nursing Care Plan

The nursing care plan helps the client only if it is communicated. Careful documentation of the plan of care requires that nursing goals and objectives be identified for each nursing diagnosis with the deadlines by which they are to be achieved. For each objective, nursing orders are listed with the times they are to be carried out. Nursing activities that must be performed based upon medical orders are also listed and scheduled.

In addition, the plan of care is reported to the healthcare team and because it is developed in collaboration with the client and family, the plan should be reviewed periodically with them.

Step Four: Implementation

During this step in the nursing process, the nurse actually initiates and completes the actions necessary to accomplish the short-term and long-term goals. The nurse gives the planned nursing care to the client. This includes organizing and managing the client's care, counseling and teaching the client and family, providing care to achieve established goals, supervising and coordinating the care provided by nursing personnel and communicating nursing interventions.

The nurse may give nursing care personally or may delegate aspects of the nursing care to other nursing staff members. If the nurse assigns tasks to others, the nurse is still responsible for making sure that the nursing care is given according to the nursing orders on the nursing care plan. Client care conferences may be arranged to provide more consistent, focused care.

Nursing care is focused on assisting clients and families to maintain optimal functioning. Nursing care includes encouraging clients and families to adhere to the treatment regimen. The nurse may facilitate client relationships with family as well as with healthcare team members. Clients and their families need to be informed as to the client's health status, and they require teaching as to correct principles, procedures and techniques for health maintenance and health promotion. Care is modified in accord with clients' preferences, needs or problems. Also, clients and their families are referred to appropriate resources when necessary.

Nurses strive to provide an environment conducive to the client's attainment of the goals of care. Clients need anticipatory guidance prior to surgery, childbirth or other procedures, particularly those that are invasive. Nursing interventions must be communicated to ensure safe, coordinated care for the client. Nursing interventions and the client's responses to them are recorded, and staff are provided with complete, accurate reports on the status of their assigned clients.

Step Five: Evaluation
Evaluation is the last step in the nursing process. It is an ongoing activity throughout the period in which nursing care is given and after. The nurse will continually ask whether or not the goals of nursing care have been met. Over time, the nurse will assess the reasonableness of the short-term and long-term goals, the objectives and the client's progress in meeting them. The nurse will examine client responses to care, including both those that are expected and those that are unexpected. The nurse will assess the overall effect of therapeutic interventions on the client and family, including whether the client is experiencing any new problems as a result of the nursing care.

The nurse will evaluate whether or not the client and family understand the information they receive. In addition, the nurse continually assesses the client's and family's ability to monitor the client's status and carry out procedures. The client's and family's self-care ability is an important factor in health maintenance and health promotion, recuperation and death with dignity.

The nurse will also evaluate whether the nursing care is keeping the client as safe and as comfortable as possible. The nurse will need to evaluate the client's use of time, energy, supplies and equipment in carrying out the nursing care. The discovery of new information about the client may require that the nurse revise the plan of care.

Each nurse who provides nursing care to the client, following the nursing care plan, will consider these questions and make or suggest appropriate modifications in the nursing care plan. Evaluation may be the most important part of the nursing process because it answers the question, "Is the nursing care helping the client achieve the objectives and goals of care?" This allows nurses to use their time as efficiently as possible, because care that does not facilitate a client's progress is not continued.

Evaluation must be communicated for it to be useful to the client. Client responses to therapy, care and teaching are documented and reported to relevant members of the healthcare team. In addition, caregivers' and staff members' responses are communicated when they suggest modification of the plan of care.

Summary of the Nursing Process
The steps in the nursing process are described here as though they follow one after the other in sequence. In reality, nurses do not think this way. In many instances, several steps are carried out at the same time. Both assessment and evaluation are ongoing. Whenever the nurse provides nursing care, he/she will ask whether it is effective. If it is not, then the objectives, plan and nursing activities need to be changed. All of the steps in the nursing process overlap and cannot be considered separate and distinct.

The ideal situation is one in which the client can participate throughout the nursing process. If the client is too ill, too upset, comatose or confused, this will not be possible. It may be possible to include family members in the process of planning, giving and evaluating care, but there will be times when the nurse must decide what the goals, objectives and plan of care should be.

The CGFNS Qualifying Exam Reflects Nursing Education in the United States

Most nursing education programs in the United States are located in two- or four-year colleges. Over the last 50 years, it has been clearly recognized that to provide high-quality nursing care, nurses need an educational foundation in the biological and physical sciences (such as anatomy, physiology, microbiology, physics and chemistry), in the social sciences (such as psychology, sociology and anthropology) and in the liberal arts (such as English composition, literature and ethics). The principles learned in these foundational subjects contribute to the nurse's ability to solve problems for the well-being of clients and to communicate clearly to patients and other health professionals. Even students in hospital diploma schools of nursing typically take their required foundation courses at nearby colleges.

Clinical nursing courses include hands-on client care experiences in a variety of settings. Students in one nursing program often have the opportunity to work with patients in several hospitals as well as schools, places of employment, senior citizens' centers, health centers and in clients' homes. Students are taught that nurses can help people meet their health-related needs in all settings.

Nurses practice as thinking, questioning professionals who are responsible and accountable for their own nursing actions. Assertiveness has become not only valued, but also essential to the practice of nursing. Each person caring for a client is responsible for his/her own actions on behalf of that person. Nurses must communicate promptly with their nursing colleagues, subordinates and superiors, as well as other healthcare professionals, about changes in the client's status and the client's response to care. Nurses are expected to serve as advocates for their clients. This often requires that nurses question the actions of other health professionals, including physicians. Although politeness is valued in the United States, as in all cultures, communication patterns in the United States are often said to be more direct than in many other parts of the world.

One unique feature of nursing is the comprehensive view nurses have of clients and their families. Nurses have developed systematic approaches to assessing people's nursing needs and systematically addressing these needs. The nursing process previously described evolved in this way. It is important to note that the focus in providing nursing care in the United States has shifted from the client's illness and medical diagnosis to the client as a total human being.

For this reason, nursing education in the United States takes an integrated approach to nursing content. Clients are not categorized according to the traditional clinical areas of medical, surgical, maternity, pediatric, psychiatric/mental health or community health nursing. Instead, clients and their families are recognized as often having nursing needs that simultaneously draw on the knowledge used in several of those areas. The integrated approach reflects a view of clients as bio-psycho-socio-cultural and spiritual beings.

Because nurses in the United States are taught an integrated approach to addressing clients' needs, the CGFNS Qualifying Exam and the NCLEX-RN examination also take an integrated approach. Both of these examinations test nurses' understanding of the four categories of client needs.

Nurses are still required to be knowledgeable about illnesses. However, nursing care is based upon assessing the patient's status, determining real or potential deficiencies in the patient's needs and planning appropriate nursing care to help the patient meet those needs.

Nursing education programs increasingly emphasize the nurse's role in illness prevention and health promotion. As the United States has become increasingly concerned about the high cost of healthcare, recognition has grown that it is far less expensive to teach people healthy ways of living than to treat illnesses resulting from poor health habits.

Conclusions

This chapter provides an overview of the way nursing is practiced in the United States and explains how the design of the CGFNS Qualifying Exam reflects U.S. nursing practice. It also discusses the integrated approach to nursing and the nursing process.

Chapters 6 and 8 contain a list of suggested readings and resources. These readings will help you study for the CGFNS Qualifying Exam and the NCLEX-RN examination. The suggested readings and resources deal specifically with the nursing process, physical assessment, client needs, nursing diagnoses and English language proficiency. These chapters should help you determine what you need to know to pass the CFFNS Qualifying Exam and the NCLEX-RN examination.

Reference
Test Plan for NCLEX-RN Examination, National Council of State Boards of Nursing, Inc. 2004.

5

Suggested Resources for English Language Study Materials

If you are interested in additional practice with your English language skills, you may wish to consult any textbook of English language principles. You may also wish to contact publishers and distributors for information regarding their English as a Second Language (ESL) books and materials. A list of publishing companies and distributors that carry ESL books and materials follows:

Alta Book Center
14 Adrian Court
Burlingame, CA 94010 USA
Telephone:
(800) ALTA-ESL or (650) 692-1285
Facsimile:(800) ALTA-FAX or (650) 692-4654
Website: www.altaesl.com
E-Mail: info@altaesl.com

Ballard and Tighe Publishers
480 Atlas Street
Brea, CA 92821-3117 USA
Telephone: (800) 321-4332
Facsimile:(714) 255-9828
Website: www.ballard-tighe.com
E-Mail: info@ballard-tighe.com

Booklink
465 Broad Avenue
Leonia, NJ 07605 USA
Telephone: (201) 947-3471
Facsimile:(201) 947-6321
Website: www.intac.com/~booklink
E-Mail: booklink@intac.com

Cambridge University Press
40 West 20th Street
New York, NY 10011-4211 USA
Telephone: (212) 924-3900
Facsimile:(212) 691-3239
Website: www.cup.org
E-Mail: orders@cup.org

Harcourt College Publishers
310 Commerce Street, Suite 3700
Fort Worth, TX 76102 USA
Telephone: (800) 447-9479 or (817) 334-7500
Facsimile:(817) 334-8060
Website: www.harcourt.com
E-Mail: customer_service@harcourtbrace.com

Heinle and Heinle Publishers
20 Park Avenue
Boston, MA 02116 USA
Telephone: (800) 237-0053 or (617) 451-1940
Facsimile:(617) 426-4379
Website: www.heinle.com
E-Mail: reply@heinle.com

Houghton Mifflin Company
222 Berkeley Street
Boston, MA 02116 USA
Telephone: (800) 733-1717 or (617) 351-5000
Website: www.hmco.com
E-Mail: webmaster@hmco.com

Lado Institute Bookstore
2233 Wisconsin Avenue, N.W.
Washington, DC 20007 USA
Telephone: (800) 229-5236 or (202) 223-0023
Facsimile:(202) 337-1118
Website: www.lado.com
E-Mail: georgetown@ladoent.com or
           bookstore@ladoent.com

McGraw-Hill Companies
P.O. Box 182604
Columbus, OH 43272 USA
Telephone: (800) 262-4729
Facsimile:(614) 759-3644
Website: www.mhhe.com
E-Mail: customer.service@mcgraw-hill.com

Miller Educational Materials, Inc.
7300 Artesia Boulevard
Buena Park, CA 90621 USA
Telephone: (800) 636-4375
Facsimile:(888) 462-0042 or (714) 562-0237
Website: www.millereducational.com

Oxford University Press
198 Madison Avenue
New York, NY 10016 USA
Telephone: (800) 441-5445 or (212) 726-6000
Facsimile:(212) 726-6455
Website: www.oup-usa.org
E-Mail: esl@oup-usa.org

Prentice Hall Regents International
200 Old Tappen Road
Old Tappen, NJ 07675 USA
Telephone: (800) 223-1360
Facsimile:(800) 445-6991
Website: www.phregents.com
E-Mail: phr_web@prenhall.com

NOTE: Many of these publishers and distributors will be able to provide information on international representatives in locations around the world.

English Language Proficiency Examinations

Introduction

Because you must have a good command of the English language to fulfill your responsibilities as a registered nurse in the United States, the CGFNS Certification Program (CP) includes an English language proficiency examination. The English language proficiency examination is designed to distinguish those who do have adequate English language skills from those who do not. Taking the English language proficiency examination can help test-takers at all levels identify their particular strengths and weaknesses.

For an applicant to be exempt from the English proficiency requirement for the CP program, he/she must meet ALL of the following criteria:

1. Native language is English
2. Country of nursing education was Australia, Canada (except Quebec), Ireland, New Zealand, Trinidad and Tobago, or the United Kingdom
3. Language of instruction was English
4. Language of texts was English

Applicants must meet ALL of these criteria to be exempted from the English language proficiency examination requirement.

You have the option of taking any one of the following to meet the English language assessment requirement for the CGFNS Certification Program:

* Test of English as a Foreign Language (TOEFL) administered by the Educational Testing Service (ETS)

* Test of English for International Communication (TOEIC) administered by ETS

* International English Language Testing System (IELTS), Academic Module, administered by IELTS, Inc.

How to Prepare for English Language Proficiency Testing

Read This Book

Taking an exam can be a stressful experience. That is especially true if you are not familiar with the structure of the exam and the type of questions that will be asked. Reading the materials in this book will help familiarize you with this information. Knowing what to expect will make you more relaxed on the day of English language proficiency examination.

Study the Sample Questions and Explanations

The sample questions in this Study Guide are similar to questions that will appear on the English language proficiency examination. You should read the explanations of the sample questions. Review any questions that you answered incorrectly. This will allow you to pinpoint areas in which you might want to do additional studying. Take the English language practice test that is included in Chapter 7.

Study Additional Materials

As noted in the introduction for this guide, if you want more help getting ready for the English language proficiency examination, use the enclosed form to order one or both volumes of the CGFNS Practice English Series. Each volume in the Practice English Series includes a practice English audio tape and an accompanying booklet.

In addition to the materials provided by CGFNS, you may purchase official TOEFL and TOEIC study aides from the Educational Testing Service (ETS) or official IELTS study aids from IELTS, Inc. You should contact ETS or IELTS, Inc. directly for these materials at:

TOEFL
Educational Testing Service (ETS)
P.O. Box 6151
Princeton, NJ 08541-6151 USA
Telephone: (609) 771-7100
Website: www.ets.org

TOEIC
Educational Testing Service (ETS)
Rosedale Road, MS 10-P
Princeton, NJ 08541 USA
Telephone: (609) 734-1540
Facsimile: (609) 734-1560
Email: toeic@ets.org
Website: www.toeic.com

IELTS
IELTS, Inc.
100 East Corson Street, Suite 200
Pasadena, CA 91103 USA
Telephone: (626) 564-2954
Email: ielts@ceii.org
Website: www.ielts.org

Study for the English Language Proficiency Examinations

Study the English language proficiency section of this guide and other preparation materials well before the exam, and then briefly review the material the day before the test. Long hours of study the day before the exam will probably not improve your performance. It may even cause you to feel overwhelmed and anxious. It is important to try to relax and to get plenty of rest prior to taking any examination.

Description of the English Language Proficiency Examinations

How TOEFL is Structured

TOEFL has three sections: listening comprehension, structure and written expression, and reading comprehension. Each section measures your knowledge of an English language skill you will need in order to use English as it is spoken in the United States. The three sections of TOEFL are designed to complement one another. Together, they provide a complete picture of how well you understand English.

In July 1998, ETS introduced computerized testing for TOEFL examinees in the United States, Canada, Latin America, Europe, the Middle East, Africa, Australia and selected countries in Asia. Additional countries will be phased in until the current paper-and-pencil test is completely replaced with the computerized test in the near future.

The computerized version of TOEFL, like the paper test, includes the three sections identified above. While some questions are similar to those on the paper test, others are quite different. For example, the listening comprehension and reading comprehension sections include new question types designed specifically for the computer. The test also includes an essay that can be handwritten or typed on the computer. The essay measures and examines your ability to generate and organize ideas and support those ideas using the conventions of standard written English.

The TOEFL program has taken steps to assure that your test performance will not be influenced by a lack of computer experience. A computerized tutorial, designed for non-native speakers of English, has been developed to teach the skills needed to take the TOEFL on computer. The computerized tutorial, administered at the beginning of a test session, provides instruction and practice in the following areas: how to use the mouse; how to scroll; how to answer listening, structure and reading questions; and how to type the essay. In the tutorial, examinees can practice answering the types of questions for each section of the test. For more

information on the computerized test, you can access the ETS website on the Internet at www.toefl.org.

Listening Comprehension Section

The questions in this section test your ability to understand English as it is commonly spoken in the United States. When you take this section of TOEFL, you will hear short and medium-length conversations between two or more people. After each conversation, you will hear some questions. After you hear a question, read the four possible options and choose the best answer.

Reading Comprehension Section

This section assesses your ability to read and understand short passages similar in topic and style to those that students are likely to encounter in North American universities and colleges. This section contains reading passages and questions about the passages.

Writing/Essay Section

In this section you will have the opportunity to demonstrate your ability to write in English. You will be required to generate and organize ideas, to support these ideas with examples and to compose in standard written English.

An essay topic will be assigned to you on the day of the TOEFL examination and you will have 30 minutes in which to write your essay. A free TOEFL Information Bulletin that provides a list of potential writing topics may be obtained directly from the ETS.

Vocabulary/Structure Section

This section is designed to measure your ability to recognize language that is appropriate for standard written English. This section evaluates your knowledge of what English words mean and how they are used. In this section, you will demonstrate your knowledge of how nouns, verbs, adjectives, and adverbs relate to other words in a sentence. This part of the exam also measures your understanding of how the relationship between words in a sentence affects the meaning of the sentence.

How TOEIC is Structured

The TOEIC test is a paper-and-pencil test that consists of 200 multiple-choice questions divided into two separately timed sections. Although the actual testing time is approximately two hours, examinees must complete the biographical questions on the answer sheet and respond to a brief questionnaire about their educational and work history. Therefore, you should allow approximately 2.5 hours to take the test.

The Test of English for International Communication (TOEIC) measures the everyday English skills of people working in an international environment. The test is divided into two main sections:

Listening Comprehension Section

Test takers will hear a variety of recorded statements, questions, short conversations, and short talks in English, and answer 100 questions based on what they hear. there are four parts:

Part 1: Photographs (20 questions)

Part 2: Question-Response (30 questions)

Part 3: Short Conversations (30 questions)

Part 4: Short Talks (20 questions)

This section will take about 45 minutes to complete.

Reading Section

Test takers will read a variety of materials and respond at their own pace to 100 questions based on what they have read. there are three parts:

Part 5: Incomplete Sentences (40 questions)

Part 6: Error Recognition (20 questions)

Part 7: Reading Comprehension (40 questions)

This section will take about 75 minutes to complete.

How IELTS is Structured

The International English Language Testing System (IELTS) is an English proficiency exam designed to assess language skills of those for whom English is not the primary language. It is used by those who plan to study or work in countries where English is the language of communication.

IELTS is administered in more than 270 centers in over 100 countries. It covers four language skills: listening, reading, writing and speaking. Tests are administered regularly and by local demand. Results are available within two weeks. Applicants cannot repeat the test within 90 days.

IELTS is available in two modules – Academic and General Training. Academic reading and writing modules assess whether the applicant is ready to study or train in English at an undergraduate or postgraduate level. The Academic module is required for the CGFNS Certification Program.

IELTS test takers are tested in listening, reading, writing and speaking. Although the speaking component is not required for the CGFNS Certification Program, IELTS, Inc. requires the applicant to take all the components of the IELTS exam. Listening, reading and writing are completed in one day. Speaking can be done 7 days before or after the other tests. Computerized versions are available at certain centers but applicants can choose between the computerized and paper-based versions. The listening module takes 30 minutes, reading – 60 minutes, writing – 60 minutes and speaking – 11-14 minutes in a face-to-face interview. Applicants with advance notice may receive accommodations for visual or hearing difficulties.

Conclusion

The overview of English language proficiency examinations should give you a good idea of how well you understand English. To complete your understanding of the English language, study the sample questions and answers in Chapter 7.

English Language Exam Options	Passing Scores
TOEFL *Test of English as a Foreign Language*	540 (207)*
TOEIC *Test of English for International Communication*	725
IELTS	6.5 *(Academic Module)*

* score written in parenthesis refers to minimum passing score for the computerized version of the TOEFL examinination

Sample English Language Proficiency Questions

The first half of this chapter contains 100 sample questions on English language usage. The best way to use these materials in preparing for the actual English language proficiency examination is to make your own recording of the sample questions, or have someone read the script to you for Section I on pages 31-33. You should ask native English speakers to record or read aloud the male and female voices, using typical conversational intonation and speed. You should ask the readers to include a pause of 12 seconds between questions. This will allow you to better imitate the actual exam situation.

The sample questions begin on page 31 of this Official Study Guide. At the end of the sample questions, on page 39, you will find the correct answer for each question. The answers are followed by brief explanations. These explanations will help you understand what each question is designed to test. The explanations will also help you understand why the answers are correct.

The script for Section I: Listening Comprehension begins on page 31. The answer choices begin on page 33. You may use one of the extra answer sheets in Appendix B for the English language proficiency questions.

If you want more help getting ready, use the enclosed form to order one or more volumes of the CGFNS Qualifying Exam: Practice English Series. Each volume in the Practice English Series includes a practice English audio tape and an accompanying booklet. The tape and booklet are very effective in improving English language proficiency skills. Remember that the sample questions in this chapter do not include a cassette recording. Applicants can either make their own recordings of the scripts provided in this section or purchase one or more volumes of the CGFNS Qualifying Exam: Practice English Series for more help in preparing for English language proficiency questions on the English language exam.

Section I:
Listening Comprehension Script
Questions 1–10 should be read to you. You must choose the answer to each question from the four possible answer choices given on pages 33-35.

Example:
"Did you listen to the weather report this morning?"

    A. Not usually.
    B. It was raining.
    C. I didn't have time.
    D. Sometime soon.

The correct answer is (C). The speaker wants to know if someone listened to a report about the weather, probably on the radio or television. The question is in the past tense. Answer C responds to the question by suggesting that the person did not listen because he or she did not have enough time.

Questions 1–10
1. Was the new library built next to the convention center or in back of it?
2. Do you mind if I ask you a question?
3. When did Ann start working for the airline?
4. What do you plan to do about getting your computer repaired?
5. Don't you think she should've asked for permission to go?
6. Isn't he going to attend the workshop this afternoon?
7. Where do you plan to meet up with Mark later?
8. What excuse did he give you for not inviting her to his party?
9. How many people did they say they were expecting here tonight?
10. He returned from Los Angeles last week, didn't he?

In questions 11–25 you will hear statements. For each question, you must choose the response that expresses the same idea as the one you heard. Responses begin on page 33.

Example:
"The report was prepared for me by my secretary."

A. I had someone else do the report.
B. My secretary had trouble with the report.
C. The report wasn't ready in time.
D. My secretary reported a problem to me.

The correct answer is (A). The expression "to have X do something for Y," as in answer (A), gives the idea that X requests Y to do something. The meaning of the speaker's sentence is similar: The secretary prepared the report because the speaker requested it.

Questions 11–25
11. I couldn't believe he lost the books I lent him.
12. We'd better order the supplies today, or we'll have to wait another week.
13. A discussion regarding the revised work schedule is to be held in three weeks.

14. Pete was about to go to bed when he heard the phone ring.

15. I'm not sure I understand what the problem is.

16. Sarah enjoyed horseback riding as a girl, but she's since given it up.

17. The cause of the fire we saw last night was just reported on the radio.

18. Larry pretended to be surprised by the news even though he'd heard about it earlier.

19. Claire couldn't locate the documents she needed for the meeting.

20. Louise sent the photographs to us on January second, but they didn't get here until the end of the month.

21. The movie hadn't begun yet even though we arrived at the theater late.

22. The deadline for deciding about the trip is the day after tomorrow.

23. Bill's a lot older than he looks.

24. The airport hotel isn't at all expensive.

25. I wish I'd brought my address book with me.

In questions 26–45 you will hear short conversations between two speakers. After each conversation you will hear a question about it. The short conversations use three speakers: a man (M), a woman (W), and a narrator (N). Responses begin on page 33.

Example:

(M) "I got my sister this vase for her birthday. Now I have to mail it to California."

(W) "You'd better have it insured—just in case."

(N) "What does the woman imply?"

   A. The man forgot his sister's birthday.
   B. The vase might get broken.
   C. The man should call his sister first.
   D. She'd like to keep the vase.

The correct answer is (B). The woman suggests that the man should buy insurance for the package. This suggests that something might happen to the vase in the mail; for example, it might break.

Questions 26-45

26. **(M)** I'm glad you talked me into asking for a raise.

   (W) I can't believe you waited three years to do it.

   (N) What does the woman mean?

27. **(M)** Mackey's department store is having a great shoe sale this weekend.

   (W) Oh. [disappointed] I just bought a new pair at Simpson's last Saturday—and paid way too much.

   (N) What does the woman imply?

28. **(W)** Can I write a check here?

   (M) You'll have to get it approved at the manager's office first.

   (N) What does the man imply?

29. **(W)** Mary said you were interested in running for the school board next year.

   (M) [hesitant] Well…uh…actually, I told her I'd get back to her on that in a week or so.

   (N) What does the man imply?

30. **(M)** I just reminded Bob about our meeting this afternoon and he nearly bit my head off.

   (W) I know what you mean. He hasn't been himself lately.

   (N) What can be inferred about Bob?

31. **(W)** Do you have the new mystery by Sally Spears in hardback? I can't find it in the S's.

   (M) The new releases are all up front near the cash registers.

   (N) Where does this conversation take place?

32. **(M)** I'm really exhausted. Mr. Bradley's just going to have to wait until tomorrow for this report.

   (W) I'd think twice about that if I were you.

   (N) What does the woman imply the man should do?

33. **(W)** That new video we need for the training program costs $125.

   (M) Oh, no! [concerned] There's only $75 in the budget.

   (N) What does the man imply?

34. **(M)** I thought you'd be here earlier. Did you have any trouble finding my house?

   (W) Not at all. But just as I was leaving, I had a call from Patty.

   (N) What does the woman mean?

35. **(M)** What have Steve and Marty been arguing about all day?

   (W) I'm not sure. Maybe they just need a vacation. They've been putting in a lot of overtime lately.

   (N) What does the woman imply about Steve and Marty?

36. (W) I can't believe no one has taken our order yet. We've been sitting here at least 15 minutes.

(M) Oh, it's barely been five…and anyway, I warned you about the lunch crowd.

(N) What does the man imply?

37. (W) It's so foggy that I can barely see the road.

(M) Maybe we should get off here and wait it out.

(N) What does the man mean?

38. (W) This is really interesting! Have you read today's editorial?

(M) I haven't finished the sports section yet.

(N) What can be inferred about the man?

39. (M) Everyone's counting on our team winning the game on Sunday.

(W) You'll have to play better than you did last week.

(N) What does the woman mean?

40. (W) Well! I'm glad to see that you made it back from your ski trip without any injuries.

(M) Yeah…but I'm afraid my brother wasn't quite so lucky.

(N) What does the man imply?

41. (M) I think it's great that a lot of old houses near the university campus are finally being renovated.

(W) I do, too. But I'll bet students won't be able to afford to rent them anymore.

(N) What does the woman imply?

42. (M) Why are Carol and Dan having such a hard time finishing their research project?

(W) I heard their funds ran out about a month ago. They're trying to get a six-month extension.

(N) What does the woman say about Carol and Dan?

43. (M) Nancy, how would you like to play golf this weekend? We're looking for a fourth.

(W) Thanks. Ordinarily I'd love to, but I can't handle the additional expenses this month.

(N) What does the woman mean?

44. (W) I still have room for two more in my car. Will everybody else fit in yours?

(M) Sure. Then the other three can go with me.

(N) What does the man imply?

45. (M) I was sure the museum was on this block—next to a parking lot.

(W) This happens every time we come downtown. These one-way streets are so confusing.

(N) What can be inferred about the man and the woman?

Section I: Listening Comprehension Answer Choices

Questions 1-10

1. A. Yes, it is.
   B. Because it was the best location.
   C. It's going to be.
   D. Behind it.

2. A. I'd be happy to.
   B. None.
   C. I can't.
   D. Go ahead.

3. A. No, first she worked for her father.
   B. Right after she finished school.
   C. She enjoys traveling very much.
   D. As soon as she graduates.

4. A. At least $300.
   B. Only a few blocks from here.
   C. It's in the shop now.
   D. I haven't finished yet.

5. A. No, she doesn't.
   B. I told her it was OK.
   C. Yes, it was convenient.
   D. She didn't give me an answer.

6. A. Yes, he was busy all day.
   B. No, he's going home instead.
   C. He never pays attention.
   D. Not until it's over.

7. A. At six o'clock.
   B. If possible.
   C. In front of the restaurant.
   D. To finish our project.

8. A. He didn't tell me.
   B. She didn't come.
   C. She invited him yesterday.
   D. He hasn't heard about it.

9. A. Quite a few.
   B. Probably not.
   C. A little later.
   D. Mostly teachers.

10. A. He had a good time.
    B. He was there for a month.
    C. Yes, a week ago today.
    D. Yes, mainly in the city.

Questions 11-25

11. A. His behavior surprised me.
    B. I reported that the books were stolen.
    C. He didn't tell me the truth.
    D. I lost the books.

12. A. Let's order the supplies next week.
    B. The supplies will arrive next week.
    C. One week isn't long to wait.
    D. We should order the supplies right away.

13. A. Discussion of the work continued for three weeks.
    B. The schedule will be discussed three weeks from now.
    C. There will be three meetings about the schedule.
    D. The work schedule was revised three times.

14. A. Pete went to bed early.
    B. The phone was near the bed.
    C. The phone rang just before Pete got into bed.
    D. Pete was asleep when the phone rang.

15. A. I don't have a problem.
    B. Your problem is not a concern of mine.
    C. I'm sure you understand what to do.
    D. It's not clear to me what's wrong.

16. A. Sarah doesn't ride horses anymore.
    B. Sarah took the girl horseback riding.
    C. Sarah was afraid of horses when she was a girl.
    D. Sarah enjoys giving horseback riding lessons.

17. A. We now know how the fire was started.
    B. We just heard there was a fire.
    C. We didn't understand the radio report.
    D. We listened to the report on the radio last night.

18. A. The news was surprising to Larry at first.
    B. Larry pretended to be listening to the news.
    C. The news didn't surprise Larry.
    D. Larry pretended that he had heard the news.

19. A. Claire forgot to bring the documents with her.
    B. Claire didn't know where the meeting was held.
    C. Claire took notes at the meeting.
    D. Claire misplaced some important papers.

20. A. Louise finished taking the photographs at the end of January.
    B. Louise planned to send the photographs earlier.
    C. It took almost a month for the photographs to arrive.
    D. Developing the photographs took a long time.

21. A. We were able to see the beginning of the movie.
    B. We missed the first part of the movie.
    C. The movie started sooner than we expected.
    D. The theater isn't showing that movie anymore.

22. A. You should set the deadline soon.
    B. It's too late to think about the trip.
    C. The decision about the trip must be made by tomorrow.
    D. You have two days to make up your mind.

23. A. Bill's age is beginning to show.
    B. Bill looks younger than his age.
    C. Bill should take better care of himself.
    D. Bill isn't very old but looks it.

24. A. The tall building at the airport is a hotel.
    B. The prices at that hotel are quite reasonable.
    C. There isn't a good hotel in that town.
    D. Airport hotels are always expensive.

25. A. I haven't bought another address book yet.
    B. I didn't know which book had your address in it.
    C. I don't have my address book right now.
    D. I need to get another address book.

Questions 26–45

26. A. The man should've asked sooner.
    B. The man should wait three years.
    C. Three years have passed quickly.
    D. She's surprised the man asked her.

27. A. She went to the sale on Saturday.
    B. The department store doesn't have very good sales.
    C. She exchanged the shoes on Saturday.
    D. She's sorry she didn't know about the sale.

28. A. Checks are kept in the manager's office.
    B. The manager isn't in the office.
    C. The woman can't write a check.
    D. The store accepts some checks.

29. A. He promised to help Mary.
    B. He has an appointment next week.
    C. He hasn't made a decision yet.
    D. He's not ready to go back to school.

30. A. He canceled the meeting.
    B. No one has seen him lately.
    C. He's upset about something.
    D. He's usually on time for meetings.

31. A. In a library.
    B. In a record shop.
    C. In a bank.
    D. In a bookstore.

32. A. Read the report again.
    B. Finish the report today.
    C. Give her the report.
    D. Talk to Mr. Bradley about the report tomorrow.

33. A. He doesn't think they need the video.
    B. They can't afford the video.
    C. He knows where they can buy a cheaper video.
    D. They've already ordered 75 videos.

34. A. She was delayed by a phone call.
    B. She couldn't find the man's house.
    C. She forgot to ask Patty for directions.
    D. She went to Patty's house first.

35. A. They usually don't work together.
    B. They've been working too hard recently.
    C. They've never gotten along.
    D. They just got back from vacation.

36. A. The woman shouldn't be so impatient.
    B. He'd rather go to another restaurant.
    C. The restaurant's food isn't very good.
    D. He isn't ready to order.

37. A. The road won't be closed for long.
    B. They shouldn't drive in this weather.
    C. The road needs to be repaired.
    D. They should take a different route.

38. A. He's still reading the editorial section.
    B. He didn't find the editorial very interesting.
    C. He hasn't read the editorial.
    D. He read the editorial first.

39. A. The man's team should've won last week.
    B. Last week's game was very exciting.
    C. Her team is better than the man's.
    D. The man's team needs to improve.

40. A. His brother had a skiing accident.
    B. His brother couldn't go on the trip.
    C. He's lucky his brother was with him.
    D. He was afraid to go skiing with his brother.

41. A. The university owns the houses.
    B. The rent will increase after the houses are fixed up.
    C. The university has decided not to rent the houses to students.
    D. Students prefer to live on campus.

42. A. They need more money to finish the project.
    B. They haven't enjoyed working on the project.
    C. They finished their project last month.
    D. They are working on a six-month project.

43. A. She's busy every weekend this month.
    B. She doesn't think she's a good golfer.
    C. She doesn't usually enjoy playing golf.
    D. She can't afford to play golf.

44. A. They'll take two cars.
    B. The woman can ride in his car.
    C. Everyone will ride in his car.
    D. He'd rather go with the woman.

45. A. They don't know when they'll get downtown.
    B. They were given the wrong directions.
    C. They can't find the museum.
    D. They're unable to find a parking space.

Section II: Vocabulary

Questions 46–55 contain sentences from which words or phrases have been omitted. For each question, choose the one answer that best fits into the sentence.

Example:
The climate in San Francisco is greatly _____ by the ocean.
    A. evaporated
    B. combined
    C. influenced
    D. covered

The correct answer is (C). To say that the climate is "influenced" by the ocean means that the ocean affects the weather conditions in San Francisco. For example, the climate near the ocean is often milder than it is farther inland.

Questions 46–55

46. **The children were _____ for making so much noise.**
    A. drenched
    B. subverted
    C. reprimanded
    D. clamored

47. **Life in the frontier was often _____ for struggling pioneer families in the 1800s.**
    A. arable
    B. grueling
    C. compliant
    D. diffident

48. **Because they have agreed to compromise, both sides will have to make some _____.**
    A. mistakes
    B. discoveries
    C. concessions
    D. distinctions

49. **The committee finally _____ the results of last month's survey in a formal report.**
    A. diverged
    B. detracted
    C. deplored
    D. divulged

50. The audience was delighted with the violinist and gave her many _____ of applause.
    A. exhibitions
    B. cravings
    C. realms
    D. rounds

51. The purpose of the assignment is to _____ the students with the methods of scholarly research.
    A. acquaint
    B. inhibit
    C. apprehend
    D. devise

52. The mountains formed a _____ against the cold wind off the ocean.
    A. vanguard
    B. perimeter
    C. venture
    D. barrier

53. What a client tells a lawyer is _____ and should not be revealed.
    A. confidential
    B. lenient
    C. adamant
    D. excessive

54. Rice is a _____ food throughout much of the world.
    A. persistent
    B. staple
    C. paltry
    D. negligent

55. I fell asleep right away because the plot of the book I was reading was so _____ .
    A. monotonous
    B. notorious
    C. continuous
    D. instantaneous

In questions 56–70 you will read words or short phrases followed by four possible answer choices. You must choose the word or phrase that is closest in meaning to the word or phrase given.

Example:
incidence
    A. consequence
    B. occurrence
    C. testimony
    D. misfortune

The correct answer is (B). "Incidence" refers to the rate of occurrence of an event or situation. For example, one might refer to the "high incidence of crime."

Questions 56–70

56. utterly
    A. practically
    B. completely
    C. vaguely
    D. frequently

57. gorgeous
    A. graceful
    B. credible
    C. appreciative
    D. splendid

58. to meddle
    A. interfere
    B. oppose
    C. omit
    D. insult

59. to protect from damage
    A. conserve
    B. disclose
    C. gauge
    D. sway

60. hastily
    A. wastefully
    B. hurriedly
    C. horribly
    D. wondrously

61. varied
    A. integral
    B. consecutive
    C. diverse
    D. fanciful

62. ungainly
    A. awkward
    B. sterile
    C. unreasonable
    D. skillful

63. means of support
    A. durability
    B. livelihood
    C. standard
    D. endeavor

64. intentionally
    A. with force
    B. on purpose
    C. ardently
    D. habitually

65. hardly ever
    A. never
    B. rarely
    C. sometimes
    D. often

66. intrepid
- A. excited
- B. constant
- C. offensive
- D. brave

67. overtly
- A. willingly
- B. thoroughly
- C. openly
- D. precisely

68. meager
- A. apparent
- B. enough
- C. sparse
- D. raw

69. to grasp an idea
- A. memorize
- B. alter
- C. reveal
- D. comprehend

70. integrity
- A. complexity
- B. necessity
- C. honesty
- D. security

Section III: English Structure

In questions 71–100 you will read two-sentence dialogues. A small part of the second sentence is omitted. Choose from among the four possible answers provided the word or phrase that fits grammatically into the sentence.

Example:
"I've got to get this book back to the library!"
"I'm on my way there now _____ I might as well return it for you."
- A. or
- B. but
- C. for
- D. so

The correct answer is (D). The second person explains that because he or she is going to the library now, he or she will return the book. The meaning of "so" is similar to "because." "So" is a conjunction and is placed between the two clauses, and "because" is placed in front of the dependent clause.

Questions 71–100

71. "You don't have to go yet, do you? Your flight doesn't leave for two hours."
"My travel agent suggested _____ early."
- A. I check in
- B. that checking in
- C. me to check in
- D. for checking in

72. "Why don't you go to bed and finish that in the morning?"
"_____ I keep typing, I'll never get it done."
- A. However
- B. Even
- C. Unless
- D. Nevertheless

73. "Aren't you exhausted?"
"Yes. I'm not used to _____ this much."
- A. exercise
- B. exercising
- C. have exercised
- D. be exercising

74. "Is Professor Johnson still in the Physics Department?"
"No. She left the university _____ ."
- A. before two years
- B. quite a long time
- C. since two years
- D. the year before last

75. "I don't know whether to take algebra or geometry."
"Don't worry. Your adviser will tell you _____ you need."
- A. how much of
- B. which one
- C. about that
- D. that one

76. "How do you take your coffee?"
"With _____ sugar."
- A. little bit
- B. some of
- C. very few
- D. a little

77. "We'll never get home if this weather keeps up."
"I really wish the snow _____ ."
- A. stops
- B. will stop
- C. would stop
- D. to be stopping

78. "Is it a long trip from your house to work?"
"Oh no. It's only _____ ride."
- A. a 10-minute
- B. 10-minute
- C. 10-minutes
- D. the 10-minute

79. "Did you go to the concert with Susan last night?"
"No. _____ , but I didn't have a ticket."
A. I would have gone
B. I haven't gone
C. I wouldn't go
D. I would go

80. "I hope that report arrives in time for the meeting."
"It should since it is _____ right after lunch."
A. sent
B. been sent
C. being sent
D. sending

81. "Marcia is coming here during her vacation."
"That's great! I'm looking forward _____ her again."
A. to see
B. seeing
C. to seeing
D. be seeing

82. "I've decided to quit my job and start looking for one in advertising."
"If I were you, I _____ reconsider that decision."
A. may
B. would
C. will
D. had better

83. "Sam asked you about that earlier, but you didn't answer him."
"I _____ heard him."
A. must not have
B. must not
C. may not have to
D. did not

84. "Has Tom decided what he's going to serve at his dinner party?"
"He's considering _____ a chicken and rice dish."
A. he will make
B. going to make
C. to make
D. making

85. "I heard Joe just had his first book published."
"He's a great writer, _____?"
A. wasn't he
B. hasn't he been
C. won't he be
D. isn't he

86. "Does Holly really go to bed so early?"
"Yes, but she _____ stay up much later."
A. use to
B. used to
C. is used to
D. was used to

87. "Will you be able to give me a hand with the preparations?"
"Sure. We can do _____ you would like us to."
A. which
B. anything what
C. whatever
D. any which

88. "I just returned from a trip to New York."
"_____ the Statue of Liberty when you were there?"
A. Have you visited
B. Had you visited
C. Were you visiting
D. Did you visit

89. "Why don't we all go to the aquarium this weekend?"
"That's a good idea. Roger's never been there and _____."
A. neither have I
B. I don't either
C. I do too
D. so have I

90. "That was a terrible storm last night."
"I know. And the ocean is _____ rough that I don't think we should swim today."
A. so
B. very
C. too
D. enough

91. "We'll never get this done with only two of us."
"I still don't understand why Emily refused _____ us."
A. help
B. for help
C. to help
D. helped

92. "What did Kathy wear to the dance?"
"She wore a _____ dress."
A. blue, evening, long, beautiful
B. long, blue evening beautiful
C. blue, beautiful, evening, long
D. beautiful, long blue evening

93. "I've been looking for Harry, but he's not around."
"He _____ home. He had a headache."
A. may have gone
B. would go
C. could go
D. may go

94. "What was the weather report for today?"
"_____ supposed to rain all afternoon."
A. There will be
B. It will be
C. It is
D. There are

95. "I wish I could play the piano as well as you do."
"_____ regularly is the trick. That's all."
A. Practiced
B. Be practicing
C. Practicing
D. Practice

96. "You don't have to come to every meeting."
"I know, but _____ members do."
A. most
B. the most
C. most of
D. the most of

97. "Do you want to put that box in the closet?"
"Yes. I think it's _____ to fit."
A. small
B. small enough
C. enough small
D. so small

98. "Can you give me a ride home tonight?"
"Sorry. I didn't drive today, but I wish I _____."
A. were
B. had
C. would
D. can

99. "Aren't you finished yet?"
"I'm working _____ as I can."
A. fast
B. faster
C. so fast
D. as fast

100. "How is school going?"
"The courses I'm taking this semester are less difficult than _____ I took last semester."
A. of that
B. the ones
C. of those
D. which

Answers and Explanations to the Sample English Language Proficiency Questions

In this half of Chapter 7, you will find the correct answer to each sample question followed by a brief explanation about why the answer is correct. Compare these answers with the ones you marked on your answer sheet. The letter (A, B, C, D) after the number is the correct answer. If you chose the wrong answer, read the explanation to learn why the right answer was correct. Even if you chose the correct answer, you should read the explanation. It should help you more fully understand how the English language is used in the United States.

Section I: Listening Comprehension
1. D
The speaker is asking where the library was built. The question has two possible answers: "next to" or "in back of" the convention center. Answer (D), "behind it," has the same meaning as "in back of it."

2. D
The speaker is requesting permission to ask someone a question. "Go ahead," answer (D), is an informal expression used to tell someone to begin or continue doing something.

3. B
The question asks about a specific time ("when") in the past that Ann began to work for the airline. Only answer (B) refers to a specific time in the past.

4. C
The speaker wants to know if and how the listener will get the computer fixed. Answer (C) suggests that the listener has already taken the computer to be fixed.

5. B
The question suggests that the speaker believes the woman did not ask for permission, but she should have done so. Answer (B) implies that the speaker is mistaken and states that the woman was given permission to go.

6. B
The speaker asks the question in the negative ("Isn't he going to"). To show agreement, the response will also be in the negative. Answer (B) shows agreement with the speaker and provides further explanation about the man's activities.

7. C
The speaker is asking for the location ("where") of the meeting with Mark. Answer (C) is the only response that includes a location.

8. A
The speaker wants to know why the man didn't invite the woman to his party. Answer (A) suggests that the listener doesn't know because the man didn't say.

9. A
The speaker asks about the number of people expected to attend. Only answer (A) directly responds to the question "how many."

10. C
The speaker believes that the man returned last week and asks for confirmation of this information with the tag question, "didn't he?" Answer (C) confirms that "last week" is correct. "A week ago today" means "exactly one week ago."

11. A
When the speaker says "I couldn't believe," it suggests that he or she is surprised or shocked that the man lost the books. In answer (A) "His behavior" refers to losing the books.

12. D
The expression "had better" has the same meaning as "should" or "ought to." The speaker believes they should order supplies today, or right away, as in answer (D).

13. B
The statement suggests that the work schedule will be discussed in three weeks. The expression "in three weeks" has the same meaning as "three weeks from now," as in answer (B).

14. C
The statement says that Pete was "about to go to bed," which means that he was not yet in bed when the phone rang. In other words, the phone rang before Pete went to bed, as in answer (C).

15. D
The speaker suggests that he or she does not understand what the problem is or what is wrong. Only answer (D) expresses uncertainty about the problem.

16. A
The statement concerns what Sarah did in the past but does not do anymore. "Used to" refers to past habitual actions that no longer occur. To "give something up" means to stop doing it. Only answer (A) states that Sarah no longer rides horses.

17. A
The main idea of the sentence is that some people saw a fire last night and just now found out its cause, or how it was started, by listening to the radio. Only answer (A) suggests that the people recently learned how the fire was started.

18. C
The statement suggests that Larry acted like he was surprised, but he wasn't really surprised because he had already heard the news. Only answer (C) states that Larry wasn't surprised by the news.

19. D
To say that Claire couldn't locate the documents means that she was unable to find them. In answer (D), "misplace" means to lose. This suggests that she was unable to find the papers.

20. C
The statement says that Louise mailed the photographs on the first day of January. However, they didn't arrive until the end of January. In other words, it took almost one month, answer (C).

21. A
The speaker suggests that the movie did not begin before they arrived. In other words, it started after they arrived, which suggests that they were able to see the beginning of the movie, answer (A).

22. D
The expression "the day after tomorrow" means two days from now. The speaker suggests that a decision must be made then. To make a decision about something is to make up one's mind about it. Only answer (D) carries this meaning.

23. B
The statement suggests that Bill looks younger than he is. Therefore, (B) is the correct answer.

24. B
The speaker suggests that the hotel is not expensive. The expression "at all" is used to emphasize the point that the hotel's prices are not high. Answer (B) states that the prices are reasonable, which suggests they are not high.

25. C
The expression "to wish one had done something" suggests that the action was not completed. Therefore, the meaning of the statement is that the person did not bring the address book, answer (C).

26. A
The woman says she is surprised that the man waited such a long time to ask for a raise. In other words, she thinks he should have asked for it sooner, so (A) is the correct answer.

27. D
The woman's statement suggests that she is disappointed that she bought expensive new shoes at Simpson's when she could have paid less at a sale at another store. This implies that the woman did not know about the sale before she bought the new shoes, answer (D).

28. D
The man tells the woman that she can write a check but that the manager has to approve it before the store can accept it. So the correct choice is (D), because the store accepts only some checks, namely those that have been approved by the manager.

29. C
The woman heard the man wanted to run for the school board, but the man implies that he isn't sure he wants to. He says that he told Mary he would decide in about a week. Only answer (C) mentions that the man hasn't made his decision.

30. C
The man suggests that Bob got angry with him for no reason. The woman says that Bob "hasn't been himself," meaning that he has not been behaving as he usually does. The speakers imply that the reason for Bob's strange behavior is that he is upset about something, answer (C).

31. D
The woman mentions "mystery" and "hardback," both of which refer to books. So we know she wants a book, and since the man mentions cash registers, we understand that the conversation takes place where money is exchanged. Only answer (D) refers to a place where people buy books.

32. B
When someone suggests that another person should "think twice" about an idea, it implies that the speaker does not approve of the idea. The woman does not agree that the man should wait until tomorrow. Therefore, she implies that he should finish the report today, answer (B).

33. B
The woman says that the video costs $125, and the man, in a worried tone, says that there is only $75 in the budget. The man's worried tone suggests that they need the video, but don't have enough money to buy it, answer (B).

34. A
The man suggests that the woman is late and wonders why. She explains that she is late because she got a telephone call from Patty just before she left for the man's house. Only answer (A) explains the reason for her delay.

35. B
When the man asks what Steve and Marty have been arguing about, the woman tells him that they have been working a lot of overtime lately and are probably just tired from all the extra work. Only answer (B) refers to how much they've been working lately.

36. A
The woman is impatient because no one has taken their order in the restaurant. The man tells her that they have only been waiting a short time, and he reminds her that he had already warned her that the restaurant might be crowded at lunch. The man is implying that the woman should be more patient, so the correct choice is (A).

37. B
The woman is having difficulty seeing the road because of the heavy fog. The man replies they should probably stop somewhere and wait for the weather to improve. So the correct answer is (B), they should not be driving in such bad weather.

38. C
When the woman asks the man if he has read the editorial, he answers that he hasn't finished reading the sports. We understand from his reply that he hasn't had a chance to read the editorial yet, so the correct choice is (C).

39. D
The woman says that the man's team will have to play better, or improve, in order to win the game. Only answer (D) suggests this idea.

40. A
The woman is happy that the man didn't injure himself while skiing. The man replies that his brother wasn't as lucky as he was, which means that his brother did injure himself on the ski trip, answer (A).

41. B
The woman says that after the houses are renovated, or fixed up, students will no longer be able to afford them. She implies that the rent will increase, answer (B).

42. A
When the man asks why Carol and Dan are unable to finish their research project, the woman explains that they ran out of money. She says they are trying to get enough money to continue working for six more months. In other words, they need more money, answer (A).

43. D
The woman explains that she can't play golf because she has too many expenses this month. In other words, she can't afford to play, answer (D).

44. A
Because the man agrees that the woman can take two more people in her car and he can take the others, he implies they will drive two cars, answer (A).

45. C
When the man says he "was sure the museum was on this block," the use of the past tense implies that, in fact, it is not on that block. The woman suggests they are confused about the location because of the one-way streets. Both speakers imply that they have been unable to locate the museum, answer (C).

Section II: Vocabulary

46. C
Reprimanded means that the children were "scolded" because they were making too much noise.

47. B
Grueling, which means very difficult and tiring, is the only word that describes frontier life.

48. C
When you make concessions, you agree to let someone do or have something, especially to end an argument or disagreement. In this case, by agreeing to compromise both sides had to make concessions or give up something.

49. D
If you divulge information, you tell or reveal it to someone. In this case the information is revealed in the form of a written report.

50. D
In this sentence rounds are series, or sets, of applause. This is one of many meanings of "round."

51. A
To acquaint means to get to know or become familiar with something that was not previously known. In this sentence it is "the methods of scholarly research" that are not familiar to the students.

52. D
A barrier is something that acts like a fence or a wall to prevent something from moving from one area to another. In this sentence, the mountains act as the barrier that restricts the movement of the cold wind.

53. A
This sentence states that the information a client tells a lawyer is secret and private and may not be revealed to anyone. Confidential means secret and private.

54. B
A staple food is one that forms a regular, basic part of a person's everyday diet.

55. A
Something that is monotonous has a dull and regular pattern that never changes and is boring.

56. B
Utterly means completely, absolutely, or totally. If you have utterly misunderstood what someone said, you have misunderstood it completely.

57. D
A gorgeous person, place, or thing is splendid or magnificent. None of the other options give this meaning. The closest would be (A), graceful, but it means pleasing or attractive in line or movement; it has a weaker meaning than gorgeous.

58. A
To meddle means to interest oneself in what is not one's concern. In other words, to interfere (A) in another person's business is to meddle.

59. A
Conserve, the correct answer, means to keep something safe, to protect it from loss or damage. To conserve the Earth's natural resources means to protect them from overdevelopment or overuse.

60. B
Hastily means hurriedly. A job done hastily is usually done too quickly.

61. C
Varied means diverse, that is, having variety. Variety means different forms or types. A person with varied interests likes doing a number of different activities.

62. A
Ungainly means clumsy or awkward, that is, lacking in grace or smoothness. None of the other options comes close to this meaning, so (A) is the answer.

63. B
A livelihood, (B), is a means of support. It refers to the source or means of subsistence or how one obtains the necessities of life. What you earn at a job in order to support yourself is your livelihood.

64. B
To do something with intent is to do it on purpose, so intentionally means on purpose. A person who does something in this way is completely aware of doing it and often has an aim in, or a reason for, doing it.

65. B
Hardly ever means almost never or rarely. In the frequency scale it would appear as follows: always, often, usually, sometimes, seldom, hardly ever (rarely), never.

66. D
An intrepid person is a brave or fearless person, someone with courage.

67. C
If something is overt, it is open to view; therefore, overtly means openly. When someone shows anger overtly, this means that the person does not try to hide the anger.

68. C
Meager means lacking in quality or quantity, such as a meager diet. "Sparse," (C), has a similar meaning of very little in quality or quantity.

69. D
Someone who grasps an idea understands or comprehends it. A person with a firm grasp of an idea or subject understands it very well.

70. C
Integrity means a firm adherence to a code of values. A person who has this quality would not go against such a code by lying or stealing. So (C) is the correct answer. An honest person is trustworthy and has integrity.

Section III: English Structure
71. A
The verb "suggest" is often followed by a noun clause introduced by "that." The verb in the noun clause is in the subjunctive, the simple form of the verb. (A) is correct because "that" may be omitted. The phrase is understood to be: (that) I check in.

72. C
The second person means: I won't finish "If I don't" keep typing. The adverbial clause that expresses the condition "if not" is introduced by (C), "Unless."

73. B
"To be used to" is an idiom that means "to be accustomed to." It is followed by a gerund. (B) is the correct response because the gerund "exercising" is the object of the preposition "to."

74. D
The second response refers to a past action ("She left the university") and requires an expression that states a specific time. (D) means she left the university two years ago. It is the only completion that refers to a specific time in the past.

75. B
The first sentence sets up a choice between two courses. The second sentence needs a pronoun to take the place of one of the courses. "One" serves this function, and the determiner "which" indicates that a choice is to be made from a limited selection—algebra or geometry.

76. D
The second speaker wants to specify the amount of sugar to put in the coffee. Sugar is a non-countable noun, so it needs the non-countable quantifier "little" or "some," not the countable "few."

77. C
The verb "wish," when combined with "would stop," expresses an unreal (contrary-to-fact) condition in the present or future tense. In this situation, it is snowing at the moment and the second speaker wants it to stop.

78. A
In English, adjectives are not made plural to agree with the nouns they modify. In this structure, "minute" is part of a compound adjective used to modify the noun "ride." The indefinite article "a" is necessary with the singular noun "ride." Therefore, (A) is the correct answer.

79. A
The second speaker's statement includes an implied condition (if I had had a ticket), so the result clause requires a conditional verb. Because the action was completed in the past, a modal auxiliary (would) plus the present perfect (have gone) is required in the result clause. It means: "If I had had a ticket [implied], I would have gone, but I didn't have a ticket, so I didn't go."

80. C
The dependent clause in the second sentence is presented in the passive voice (since the person who is sending the report is not known). A passive verb is a verb phrase consisting of a form of the verb "be" followed by a past participle.

81. C
The idiom "I'm looking forward to" requires a gerund as the object of the preposition "to," so the correct answer is (C).

82. B
The expression "If I were you" suggests an unreal (contrary-to-fact) condition in the present. To complete the condition, the result clause should employ "would" followed by the simple verb form ("reconsider"), which conveys an unreal condition in the present tense.

83. A
The expression "must have" followed by the past participle is a past form that suggests probability. To say "I must not have heard" means "I probably did not hear."

84. D
The verb "consider" is one of several verbs that are followed by a gerund. In this case, the gerund (making) completes the object phrase. Therefore, (D) is the correct answer.

85. D
The tag question maintains the same tense as the verb in the statement it refers back to.

86. B

"Used to" refers to an habitual action in the past that no longer happens. It requires the simple form of the verb. (C), "Is used to," is in the present tense and means that someone is accustomed to doing or experiencing something. It is followed by the "-ing" verb form.

87. C

"Whatever" is an indefinite relative pronoun. It has the same meaning as "anything that."

88. D

The simple past tense, (D), is used to describe an action completed (at a specific time) in the past. The use of the simple past in both the main clause and the "when" clause suggests the actions took place at the same time.

89. A

The intended meaning of the second speaker is "Roger has never been there. I have never been there." When the two ideas are combined in a compound sentence, it is not necessary to repeat the main verb; only the auxiliary, which has the same tense as the main verb, is used. Because the sentence is in the negative, the compound is formed in one of two ways: AND + Subj. + aux. + NOT + EITHER (and I haven't either) or AND + NEITHER + aux. + Subj. (and neither have I) as in answer (C).

90. A

"So" is the only choice that can be used with "that." "SO + adjective + THAT + clause" expresses a cause (SO + adj.) -and- effect (THAT + clause) relationship.

91. C

"Refuse" is one of several verbs that are followed by an infinitive. The infinitive (to help) functions as the object of the verb.

92. D

When multiple adjectives are used, the general order of adjectives is as follows: general quality, shape, color, noun-as-adjective.

93. A

The modal "may" followed by the present perfect is used to express uncertainty about a past action.

94. C

The expression "supposed to" is used to introduce an expected action. "Supposed to" is preceded by the expletive "It is" to indicate present or future time.

95. C

A gerund ("practicing") can be used as the subject of a sentence.

96. A

"Most" is used here as an adjective modifying "members."

97. B

"Enough" is an adverb modifying the adjective "small." It is placed after the adjective, unlike most adverbs, which usually come before.

98. B

In conditional sentences with "wish," the past perfect form "had" is used to express an unreal condition in the past. Here "I had" means "I had driven."

99. D

The expression "AS + adverb + AS" is a form of comparison. Its use suggests that the two parts of the comparison are equal.

100. B

The completion requires a pronoun that refers to "the courses." "Those" is possible, but the preposition "of" in (C) is out of place. Only (B) provides the plural pronoun "the ones."

Suggested Study Resources

Study Resources for Nursing as Practiced in the United States

The following list of resources is included to help you study for the CGFNS Qualifying Exam. This list is not exhaustive. However, it does include publications commonly used in the instruction of nursing students in the United States.

In writing this Official Study Guide, CGFNS has made every effort not to quote material directly from any of the resources used. CGFNS has tried to broadly describe common concepts such as nursing diagnosis, the nursing process, and basic human needs. These concepts are nearly universal in the study of nursing in the United States.

Adult Health Nursing

Allender, J. A., & Spradley, B. W. (2001). *Community Health Nursing: Concepts and Practice* (5th ed.). Philadelphia: Lippincott, Williams & Wilkins.

Beare, P. G., & Myers, J. L. (1998). *Adult Health Nursing* (3rd ed.). St. Louis: Mosby.

Black, J. M., Hawks, J. H., & Keene, A. M. (2001). *Medical-Surgical Nursing: Clinical Management for Positive Outcomes*. Philadelphia: W. B. Saunders.

Black, J. M., & Matassarin-Jacobs, E. (1997). *Luckmann & Sorenson's Medical-Surgical Nursing: A Psychophysiological Approach*. Philadelphia: W. B. Saunders.

Burkhardt, M. A., & Nathaniel, A. K. (2002). *Ethics and Issues in Contemporary Nursing* (2nd ed.). Albany, NY: Delmar-Thomson Learning.

Burrell, L. O. (1997). *Adult Nursing: Hospital & Community Care of the Adult with Medical Surgical Problems*. East Norwalk, CT: Appleton & Lange.

Cherry, B., & Jacob, S. (2002). *Contemporary Nursing: Issues, Trends and Management*. St. Louis: Mosby.

Christensen, B. L., & Kockrow, E. D. (1999). *Adult Health Nursing* (3rd ed.). St. Louis: Mosby.

Clark. M. J. (1999). *Nursing in the Community* (3rd ed.). Stamford, CT: Appleton & Lange.

Davis, A. J. (1997). *Ethical Dilemmas and Nursing Practice* (4th ed.). Upper Saddle River, NJ: Prentice Hall.

Deglin, J., & Vallerand, A. (2002). *Davis' Drug Guide for Nurses*. Philadelphia: F. A. Davis.

Dossey, B. M., Keegan, L., & Guzetta C. E. (2000). *Holistic Nursing: A Handbook for Practice* (3rd ed.). Gaithersburg, MD: Aspen.

Ebersole, P., & Hess, P. (1998). *Toward Healthy Aging: Human Needs and Nursing Response*. St. Louis: Mosby.

Eliopoulos, C. (1997). *Gerontological Nursing*. Philadelphia: Lippincott, Williams & Wilkins.

Eliopoulos, C. (1999). *Manual of Gerontologic Nursing* (2nd ed.). St. Louis: Mosby.

Geissler, E. M. (1998). *Mosby's Pocket Guide Series: Cultural Assessment* (2nd ed.). St Louis: Mosby.

George-Cay, B., & Chernecky, C. C. (2002). *Clinical Medical-Surgical Nursing: A Decision Making Reference*. Philadelphia: W. B. Saunders.

Green, C. (2000). *Critical Thinking in Nursing*. Upper Saddle River, NJ: Prentice Hall.

Haber, D. (1999). *Health Promotion and Aging: Implications for the Health Professions* (2nd ed.). New York: Springer Publishing.

Humphrey, C. J. (1998). *Home Care Nursing Handbook* (3rd ed.). Gaithersburg, MD: Aspen.

Hunt, R., & Zurch, E. (1997). *Introduction to Community-Based Nursing*. Philadelphia: Lippincott, Williams & Wilkins.

Ignatavicius, D. D., Workman, L. M., & Mishler, M. A. (1999). *Medical-Surgical Nursing Across the Health Care Continuum* (3rd ed.). Philadelphia: W. B. Saunders.

Kennedy, E., & Ignatavicius, D. (1999). *Critical Thinking Study Guide for Ignatavicius Workman and Mishler Medical-Surgical Nursing Across the Health Care Continuum* (3rd ed.). Philadelphia: W. B. Saunders.

Kozier, B., Erb, G., Blais, K., Johnson, J. Y., & Temple, J. S. (1993). *Techniques in Clinical Nursing* (4th ed.). Redwood City, CA: Addison-Wesley.

Lemone, P., & Burke, K. M. (2000). *Medical-Surgical nursing: Critical Thinking in Client Care* (2nd ed.). Upper Saddle River, NJ: Prentice Hall.

Lewis, S. M., Heitkemper, M. M., & Dirksen, S. R. (2000). *Medical-Surgical Nursing: Assessment and Management of Clinical Problems*. St. Louis: Mosby.

McGann, J. A. (2002). *Handbook of Medical-Surgical Nursing* (3rd ed.). Springhouse, PA: Springhouse.

O'Toole, M. (1997). *Miller-Keane Encyclopedia and Dictionary of Medicine, Nursing and Allied Health*. Philadelphia: W. B. Saunders.

Pender, N. J., Murdaugh, C. L., & Parsons, M. A. (2002). *Health Promotion in Nursing Practice*. Upper Saddle River, NJ: Prentice Hall.

Perrin, K. O., & McGhee, J. (2001). *Nursing Concepts: Ethics and Conflict*. Thorofare, NJ: Slack Incorporated.

Pestonjee, S. F. (2000). *Nurse's Handbook of Patient Education*. Springhouse, PA: Springhouse Corporation.

Phipps, W. J., Sands, J. K., & Marek, J. F. (1999). *Medical-Surgical Nursing: Concepts and Clinical Practice* (6th ed.). St. Louis: Mosby.

Poirrier, G. P., & Oberleitner, M. G. (1999). *Clinical Pathways in Nursing: A Guide to Managing Care from Hospital to Home*. Springhouse, PA: Springhouse Corporation.

Ponech, T. S. (2000). *Nursing Management* . St. Louis: Mosby.

Rankin, S. H., & Stallings, K. D. (2001). *Patient Education: Principles & Practice* (4th ed.). Philadelphia: Lippincott, Williams & Wilkins.

Rundle, A., Carvalho, M., & Robinson, M. (1999). *Cultural Competence in Health Care: A Practical Guide*. San Francisco: Jossey-Bass.

Smeltzer, S., & Bare, B. (2000). *Brunner and Suddarth's Textbook of Medical-Surgical Nursing* (9th ed.). Philadelphia: Lippincott, Williams & Wilkins.

Sullivan, E. J. (1999). *Creating Nursing's Future*. St. Louis: Mosby.

Sullivan, E. J., & Decker, P. J. (2001). *Effective Leadership and Management in Nursing*. Upper Saddle River, NJ: Prentice Hall.

Swanson, E. A., Tripp-Reimer, T., & Buckwalter, K. (2001). *Health Promotion and Disease Prevention in the Older Adult: Interventions and Recommendations*. New York: Springer Publishing.

Vanetzian, E. V. (2001). *Critical Thinking: An Interactive Tool for Learning Medical-Surgical Nursing*. Philadelphia: F. A. Davis.

Community Health Nursing

Booth, K., & Luker, K. A. (1999). *A Practical Handbook for Community Health Nurses*. Malden, MA: Blackwell Science.

Clemen-Stone, S. A., Eigsti, D. G., & McGuire, S. L. (1997). *Comprehensive Family & Community Health Nursing*. St. Louis: Mosby.

Helman, C. G. (2001). *Culture, Health and Illness* (4th ed.). New York: Arnold.

Leininger, M., & McFarland, M. R. (2002). *Transcultural Nursing: Concepts, Theories, Research and Practice*. New York: McGraw Hill.

Luckmann, J. (1999). *Transcultural Communication in Nursing*. Albany, NY: Delmar.

Murray, R. B., & Zentner, J. P. (1997). *Nursing Assessment and Health Promotion: Strategies Through the Life Span*. E. Norwalk, CT: Appleton and Lange.

Spector, R. E. (2000). *Cultural Care: A Guide to Heritage Assessment and Health Traditions* (2nd ed.). Upper Saddle River, NJ: Prentice Hall.

Spector, R. E. (2000). *Cultural Diversity in Health and Illness* (5th ed.). Upper Saddle River, NJ: Prentice Hall.

Swanson, J. L., & Albrecht, M. (1997). *Community Health Nursing: Promoting the Health of Aggregates*. Philadelphia: W. B. Saunders.

Fundamentals of Nursing, Nursing Diagnosis and Nursing Process

Alfaro, R. (1998). *Applying Nursing Diagnosis and Nursing Process: A Step-by-Step Guide* (4th ed.). Philadelphia: Lippincott, Williams & Wilkins.

Anderson, K. N. (1997). *Mosby's Medical, Nursing, and Allied Health Dictionary*. St. Louis: Mosby.

Bickley, L. S. (1999). *Bates' Guide to Physical Examination and History Taking* (7th ed.). Philadelphia: Lippincott, Williams & Wilkins.

Bond M., & Holland S., (1998). *Skills of Clinical Supervision for Nurses*. Bristol, PA: Open University Press.

Carpenito, L. (2002). *Handbook of Nursing Diagnoses*. Philadelphia: Lippincott, Williams & Wilkins.

Chernecky, C. C., & Berger, B. J. (1997). *Laboratory Tests and Diagnostic Procedures* (2nd ed.). Philadelphia: W. B. Saunders.

Corbett, J. V. (2000). *Laboratory Tests and Diagnostic Procedures with Nursing Diagnoses* (5th ed.). Upper Saddle River, NJ: Prentice Hall.

Cox, H. C., Hinz, M. D., Lubno, M., Tilley, D. S., Newfield, S. A., Slater, M. M. & Sridaromont, K. L. (2002). *Clinical Applications of Nursing Diagnosis: Adult, Child, Women's, Psychiatric, Gerontic and Home Health Considerations.* Philadelphia: F. A. Davis.

DeLaune, S. C., & Ladner, P. K. (1998). *Fundamentals of Nursing: Standards and Practice.* Albany, NY: Delmar.

Ellis, J. R., & Hartley, C. L. (2000). *Managing and Coordinating Nursing Care* (3rd ed.). Philadelphia: Lippincott, Williams & Wilkins.

Fuller, J., & Ayers, J. (2000). *Health Assessment: A Nursing Approach.* Philadelphia: Lippincott, Williams & Wilkins.

Giger, J. N., & Davidhizar, R. E. (1999). *Transcultural Nursing: Assessment and Intervention* (3rd ed.). St. Louis: Mosby.

Groenwald, S. L., Frogge, M. H., Goodman, M., & Yarbo, C. (1997). *Cancer Nursing: Principals and Practice.* Boston: Jones & Bartlett.

Holmes, H. N. (1999). *Handbook of Diagnostic Tests* (2nd ed.). Springhouse, PA: Springhouse Corporation.

Ignatavicius, D., & Hausman, K. A. (1999). *Pocket Companion for Medical-Surgical Nursing Across the Healthcare Continuum.* Philadelphia: W. B. Saunders.

Ignatavicius, D., & Workman, M. (2002). *Medical-Surgical Nursing.* Philadelphia: W. B. Saunders.

Kee, J. L. (1999). *Laboratory and Diagnostic Tests with Nursing Implications* (5th ed.). Stamford, CT: Appleton & Lange.

Kosko, D. A., & Nettina, S. M. (2000). *Primary Care Practice.* Philadelphia: Lippincott, Williams & Wilkins.

Kozier, B., Erb, G., Berman, A. J., & Burke, K. (1998). *Fundamentals of Nursing: Concepts, Process, and Practice.* Redwood City, CA: Addison-Wesley.

Lubkin, I. M. (1998). Chronic illness: *Impact and Interventions* (4th ed.). Sudbury, MA: Jones & Bartlett.

Luckmann, J., Sweeney, K., Workman, L. M. (1997). *Saunders' Manual of Nursing Care.* Philadelphia: W. B. Saunders.

Marquis, B. L., & Huston, C. J. (2000). *Leadership Roles and Management Functions in Nursing: Theory and Applications* (3rd ed.). Philadelphia: Lippincott, Williams & Wilkins.

McCaffery, M., & Pasero, C. (1999). *Pain: Clinical Manual.* St. Louis: Mosby.

McCann, J. A. (2001). *Diagnostics: An A to Z Nursing Guide to Laboratory Tests and Diagnostic Procedures.* Springhouse, PA: Springhouse Corporation.

Metheny, N. M. (2000). *Fluid and Electrolyte Balance* (4th ed.). Philadelphia: Lippincott, Williams & Wilkins.

O'Toole, M. (1997). *Miller-Keane Encyclopedia & Dictionary of Medicine, Nursing & Allied Health* (6th ed.). Philadelphia: W. B. Saunders.

Pagana, K., & Pagana, T. (1999). *Mosby's Diagnostic and Laboratory Test Reference.* (4th ed.). St. Louis: Mosby.

Peterson, V. R. (1999). *Just the Facts: A Pocket Guide to Basic Nursing* (2nd ed.). St. Louis: Mosby.

Potter, P. A., & Perry, A. G. (1999). *Basic Nursing: A Critical Thinking Approach.* St. Louis: Mosby.

Potter, P. A., & Perry, A. G. (2001). *Fundamentals of Nursing* (5th ed.). St. Louis: Mosby.

Sparks, S. M., & Taylor, C. M. (2000). *Nursing Diagnosis Reference Manual* (5th ed.). Springhouse, PA: Springhouse Corporation.

Sullivan, E., & Decker, P. (2001). *Effective Leadership and Management in Nursing.* Upper Saddle River, NJ: Prentice-Hall.

Taylor, C., Lillis, C., & LeMone, P. (2001). *Fundamentals of Nursing: The Art and Science of Nursing Care.* Philadelphia: Lippincott, Williams & Wilkins.

Venes, D., Thomas, C. L. & Taber, C. W. (2001). *Taber's Cyclopedic Medical Dictionary* (19th ed.). Philadelphia: F. A. Davis.

Weber, J. R. (2001). *Nurses' Handbook of Health Assessment.* Philadelphia: Lippincott, Williams & Wilkins.

Nutrition and Diet Therapy

Dudek, S. (2001). *Nutrition Essentials for Nursing Practice* (4th ed.). Lippincott, Williams & Wilkins.

Grodner, M., Anderson, S. L., & DeYoung, S. (2000). *Foundations and Clinical Applications of Nutrition: A Nursing Approach* (2nd ed.). St. Louis: Mosby.

Jaffe, M. (1998). *Geriatric Nutrition and Diet Therapy* (3rd ed.). Englewood, CO: Skidmore-Roth.

Lutz, C., & Przytulski, K. (2001). *Nutrition and Diet Therapy* (3rd ed.). Philadelphia: F. A. Davis.

Mahan L. K., & Escott-Stump, S. (2000). *Krause's Food, Nutrition & Diet Therapy.* Philadelphia: W. B. Saunders.

Martin, J., & Conklin, M. T. (1999). *Managing Child Nutrition Programs: Leadership for Excellence.* Gaithersburg, MD: Aspen.

Peckenpaugh, N., & Poleman, C. (1999). *Nutrition Essentials and Diet Therapy* (8th ed.). Philadelphia: W. B. Saunders.

Pennington, J. (1989). *Food Values of Portions Commonly Used.* Philadelphia: Lippincott, Williams & Wilkins.

Phillips, L. D. (2001). *Manual of IV Therapeutics.* Philadelphia: F. A. Davis.

Williams, S. R. (1999). *Essentials of Nutrition and Diet Therapy.* St. Louis: Mosby.

Maternity Nursing

Dickason, E. J., Silverman, R. L., & Kaplan, J. A. (1998). *Maternal-Infant Nursing Care* (3rd ed.). St. Louis: Mosby.

Gilbert, E., & Harmon, J. (1999). *Manual of High Risk Pregnancy and Delivery.* St. Louis: Mosby.

Gorrie, T. M., McKinney, E. S., & Murray, S. S. (1998). *Foundations of Maternal-Newborn Nursing* (2nd ed.). Philadelphia: W. B. Saunders.

Ladewig, P. W., London, M. L., Moberly, S., & Olds, S. B. (2002). *Contemporary Maternal-Newborn Nursing Care.* Upper Saddle River, NJ: Prentice Hall.

Mattson, S., & Smith, J. E. (2000). *Core Curriculum for Maternal-Newborn Nursing* (2nd ed.). Philadelphia: W. B. Saunders.

McKinney, E. S., Ashwill, J. W., Murray, S. S., James, S. R., Gorrie, T. M., & Droske, S. C. (2000). *Maternal-Child Nursing.* Philadelphia: W. B. Saunders.

Novak, J. C., & Broom, B. L. (1999). *Ingalls & Salerno's Maternal and Child Health Nursing* (9th ed.). St. Louis: Mosby-Yearbook, Incorporated.

Olds, S. B., London, M. L., & Ladewig, P. A. (2000). *Maternal Newborn Nursing* (6th ed.). Upper Saddle River, NJ: Prentice Hall.

Pilliteri, A. (1999). *Maternal and Child Health Nursing* (3rd ed.). Philadelphia: J. B. Lippincott.

Reeder, S. J., Martin, L. L., & Koniak, D. (1997). *Maternity Nursing: Family, Newborn, and Women's Health Care.* Philadelphia: Lippincott, Williams & Wilkins.

Sherwen, L. N., Scoloveno, M., & Weingarten, C. T. (1999). *Maternity Nursing: Care of the Childbearing Family* (3rd ed.). Stamford, CT: Appleton & Lange.

Sherwen, L. N., Scoloveno, M., & Weingarten, C. T. (1999). *Clinical Companion for Maternity Nursing* (3rd ed.). Stamford, CT: Appleton and Lange.

Wong, D. L., Perry, S. E., & Hockenberry, M. (1998). *Maternal Child Nursing Care.* St. Louis: Mosby.

Pediatric Nursing

Ball, J. W., & Bindler, R. M. (1999). *Pediatric Nursing: Caring for Children* (2nd ed.). Upper Saddle River, NJ: Prentice Hall.

Betz, C. L., & Sowden, L. A. (2000). *Mosby's Pediatric Nursing Reference* (4th ed.). St Louis: Mosby.

Craft-Rosenberg, M., & Denehy, J. (2001). *Nursing Interventions for Infants, Children and Families.* Thousand Oaks, CA: Sage Publications.

Curley, M. A., & Moloney-Harmon, P. A. (2001). *Critical Care Nursing of Infants and Children* (2nd ed.). Philadelphia: W. B. Saunders.

Engel, J. (2002). *Mosby's Pocket Guide Series: Pediatric Assessment* (4th ed.). St. Louis: Mosby.

Friedman, M. (1998). *Family Nursing: Research, Theory and Practice* (4th ed.). Stamford, CT: Appleton & Lange.

Opperman, C. S. (1998). *Contemporary Pediatric Nursing.* St. Louis: Mosby.

Potts, N. L., & Mandleco, B. L. (2002). *Pediatric Nursing: Caring for Children and Their Families.* Clifton Park, NY: Delmar-Thomson Learning.

Schulte, E., Price, D., & Gwin, J. (2001). *Thompson's Pediatric Nursing: An Introductory Text* (8th ed.). Philadelphia: W. B. Saunders.

Wong, D. L. (1999). *Whaley & Wong's Nursing Care of Infants and Children.* St. Louis: Mosby.

Pharmacology

Abrams, A. (2001). *Clinical Drug Therapy.* Philadelphia: Lippincott, Williams & Wilkins.

Aschenbrenner, D. S., Cleveland, L. W., & Venable, S. J. (2002). *Drug Therapy in Nursing.* Philadelphia: Lippincott, Williams & Wilkins

Carpenter, D. O. (2001). *Nursing IV Drug Handbook* (7th ed.). Springhouse, PA: Springhouse Corporation.

Cleveland, L. W., Aschenbrenner, D. S., Venable, S. J., & Yensen, J. A. (1999). *Nursing Management in Drug Therapy.* Philadelphia: Lippincott, Williams & Wilkins.

Deglin, V. (2001). *Davis' Drug Guide for Nurses.* Philadelphia: F. A. Davis.

Eisenhauer, L. A., Nichols, L. W., Spencer, R. T., & Bergan, F. W. (1997). *Clinical Pharmacology and Nursing Management*. Philadelphia: Lippincott, Williams & Wilkins.

Fernandez, M., & Giannini, R. (2002). *Modell's Drugs in Current Use and New Drugs, 2002* (48th ed.). New York: Springer Publishing.

Hodgson, B., & Kizior R. (2002). *Saunders' Nursing Drug Handbook*. Philadelphia: W. B. Saunders.

Karch, A. M. (2001). *Lippincott's Nursing Drug Guide*. Philadelphia: Lippincott, Williams & Wilkins.

Kee, J. L., & Hayes, E. R. (1997). *Pharmacology: A Nursing Process Approach*. Philadelphia: W. B. Saunders.

Keltner, N. L., & Folks, D. G. (2001). *Psychotropic Drugs* (3rd ed.). St. Louis: Mosby.

Kuhn, M. (1997). *Pharmacotherapeutics: A Nursing Process Approach*. Philadelphia: F. A. Davis.

Lehene, R. (1995). *Pharmacology for Nursing*. Philadelphia: W. B. Saunders.

Lilley, L. L., & Aucker, R. S. (1999). *Pharmacology and the Nursing Process* (2nd ed.). St. Louis: Mosby.

Rice, J., & Skelley, E. G. (1997). *Medications and Mathematics for the Nurse*. Albany, NY: Delmar.

Roth, L. S. (1998). *Mosby's Nursing and Drug Reference*. St. Louis: Mosby.

Spratto, G. R., & Woods, A. L. (2002). *PDR Nurses' Drug Handbook*. Albany, NY: Delmar.

Williams, B. R., & Baer, C. L. (1998). *Essentials of Clinical Pharmacology in Nursing* (3rd ed.). Springhouse, PA: Springhouse Corporation.

Wong, D. L., & Eaton, M. (2001). *Wong's Essentials of Pediatric Nursing* (6th ed.). St. Louis: Mosby.

Psychiatric Nursing

Bailey, D. S., & Bailey, D. R. (1997). *Therapeutic Approaches to the care of the mentally ill*. Philadelphia: F. A. Davis.

Barry, P. D. (1997). *Mental Health and Mental Illness*. Philadelphia: Lippincott, Williams & Wilkins.

Burgess, A. W. (1998). *Advanced Practice Psychiatric Nursing*. Stamford, CT: Appleton & Lange.

Dreher, B. B. (2001). *Communication Skills for Working with Elders* (2nd ed.). New York: Springer Publishing.

Fontaine, K. L., & Fletcher, J. S. (1999). *Mental Health Nursing* (4th ed.). Menlo Park, CA: Addison-Wesley.

Fortinash, K. M., & Holoday-Worret, P. A. (1999). *Psychiatric Nursing Care Plans* (3rd ed.). St. Louis: Mosby.

Frisch, N. C., & Frisch, L. E. (1998). *Psychiatric Mental Health Nursing*. Albany, NY: Delmar.

Haber, J., Krainovich-Miller, B., Leach-McMahon, A., & Price-Hoskins, P. (1997). *Comprehensive Psychiatric Nursing*. St. Louis: Mosby.

Keltner, N. L., Schwecke, L. H., & Bostrom, C. E. (1998). *Psychiatric Nursing* (3rd ed.). St Louis: Mosby.

Shives, L. R. (1997). *Basic Concepts of Psychiatric Mental Health Nursing*. Philadelphia: Lippincott, Williams & Wilkins.

Sommers, M. S., & Johnson, S. A. (2002). *Diseases and Disorders: A Nursing Therapeutics Manual*. Philadelphia: F. A. Davis.

Townsend, M. (2000). *Psychiatric Mental Health Nursing: Concepts of Care*. Philadelphia: F. A. Davis.

Varcarolis, E. M. (2002). *Foundations of Psychiatric Mental Health Nursing: A Clinical Approach* (4th ed.). Philadelphia: W. B. Saunders.

Videbeck, S. L. (2001). *Psychiatric Mental Health Nursing*. Philadelphia: Lippincott, Williams & Wilkins.

CGFNS Practice Test Instructions

Preliminary Instructions for Taking the Practice Tests

The following chapters of the Official Study Guide are organized exactly like the CGFNS Qualifying Exam that you will take on examination day. These chapters demonstrate what it will be like to take the actual CGFNS Qualifying Exam. The instructions for each part of the complete practice tests are like the instructions that will be read to you when you take the CGFNS Qualifying Exam at the examination center.

Some of the instructions that you will receive at the examination center are not contained in this Official Study Guide. Those instructions address such topics as introducing the examination day staff and describing the examination materials.

The instructions in this chapter of the Official Study Guide are written for you so that you can familiarize yourself with them prior to the actual examination. It is important that you follow the instructions exactly as they are given so that you will know exactly what to do when you take the CGFNS Qualifying Exam at the examination center.

The CGFNS Qualifying Exam is given over a one-day period. The examination takes four hours and 20 minutes, plus additional time for registration and other miscellaneous items. You should try to complete each of the following practice tests in the allotted amount of time. During the examination, the time will be divided according to the following schedule:

Time Schedule for the CGFNS Qualifying Exam

MORNING SESSION
NURSING, Part 1
Two hours and 30 minutes
150 Questions

LUNCH BREAK .... one hour

AFTERNOON SESSION
NURSING, Part 2
One hour and 50 minutes
110 Questions

If you cannot devote four hours and 20 minutes to taking an entire practice test in one sitting, you should set aside at least enough time to take one complete part of a practice test. Do this until you have taken an entire practice test. It is important to try to take each part in a single sitting, even if you must take different parts of the tests on different days.

Do not read the questions in a practice test until you are ready to take that test for the first time. After you have finished a practice test, you may use the questions again as a review. This will give you more practice in answering questions of this type. It also will help you learn more about how the English language is used and how nursing is practiced in the United States.

To prepare to take a practice test, sit in a comfortable chair at a table or some other hard writing surface. Be sure that there is enough light for you to see clearly and that you have at least two sharpened pencils with good erasers. If your pencils do not have good erasers, you will need an extra eraser so that you can completely erase any answer or other mark you want to remove from your answer sheet. You will also need this Official Study Guide.

When you take the CGFNS Qualifying Exam, you will be allowed to have only pencils, your exam booklet and an answer sheet on the table. You may not use scratch paper, notes, calculators or books. If you want to work out dosage problems or make other notes, do so in the margins of your exam booklet. Remember, however, not to make any stray marks on your answer sheet.

When you take a practice test, you may want to ask someone to read the instructions to you. The instructions will be read to you when you take the actual exam at the examination center. The person who reads the instructions will tell you when to begin the exam and will also time each part of the exam. When the time allotted for each portion has expired, this person will tell you to stop.

When you take a practice test, even if you are not able to answer all the questions, you should be able to see how many questions you can answer correctly in the allotted amount of time.

Tear out an answer sheet for the part of the practice test you are taking. You will find the answer sheets in Appendix B of this Official Study Guide. Use a separate answer sheet for each part of the practice tests.

Mark your answers on your answer sheet rather than in the Official Study Guide. When you take the CGFNS Qualifying Exam, you will not have time to transfer your answers from the exam booklet to your answer sheet, nor will you get any credit for answers that are not marked on your answer sheet.

Before you begin timing your practice test, fill in all of the identifying information for items 1–13 of the answer sheet. You will find these spaces at the top of each answer sheet.

You should practice filling in the information requested for these 13 items even though you will not be sending your practice test answer sheets to CGFNS. It is important that you practice filling in this information so that you learn how to do this accurately. These 13 items provide important information that makes it possible for CGFNS to match the right person with the right score.

If you are going to time yourself while taking the practice tests, look at a clock when you are ready to begin answering the questions. Make a note of the time. You may wish to use an alarm clock or timer. Set the clock or timer so that the alarm will ring when it is time for you to stop.

Do not spend too much time on any one question. If you do not know the answer, skip that question. Go on to the next question, or choose the answer that seems to be most correct. If you finish before your time has expired, you may go back to any questions you have skipped.

If you skip a question during one of the practice tests, circle the number of the question. If you have time to go back to that question, the circle will make it easier to find. Do not circle the number on your answer sheet. If you make extra marks on the answer sheet during the actual CGFNS Qualifying Exam, your answers could be scored incorrectly. Remember: If you skip a question, be sure to skip the same number on your answer sheet.

After you have finished taking a practice test, compare your answers with the correct answers that immediately follow each test. When you compare your answers with the correct answers, you will be able to see what your strengths and areas for improvement are. Included with the correct answer are the rationales for the right answer as well as for the incorrect options. These rationales should help you with your test-taking skills and should help you identify areas of further study.

Practice Test
Nursing, Part 1

Instructions For Timing
Nursing, Part 1
Questions 1–150

You will be given two hours and 30 minutes to complete the first part of each practice test. If you finish this part of the practice test before it is time to stop, you may use this time to check your answers. You may also go back to answer any questions you have skipped.

When you are ready to start Nursing, Part 1, check to see what time it is. Note the time on the inside cover of your Official Study Guide. Or, set an alarm clock to let you know when to stop answering questions.

If someone is timing your test, ask her/him to tell you when you have only 10 minutes left. You may want to use the remaining 10 minutes to check your answers. You may also want to use this time to return to any questions you have skipped.

When the time allotted for this part of the practice test has expired, you must stop answering questions. Even if you have not answered all the questions, you must stop when the allotted time expires. If you stop at this point, you will see how many questions you will probably be able to answer correctly on the actual CGFNS Qualifying Exam. After you complete Nursing, Part 1, take a break before beginning the next part of the practice test.

General Instructions for Answering
Nursing, Part 1
Questions 1–150

Each question in the test has four possible answers. You are to select only one answer for each question. Read each question through carefully before you decide which one of the suggested answers is correct. Your answers must be marked on the separate answer sheet, not in the test book. You must use a soft lead pencil to mark your answers.

There is one type of question in the test – multiple choice. Here are two examples that include information regarding the use of the answer sheet.

1. This test is designed to measure
   A. reading speed.
   B. cultural background.
   C. general knowledge.
   D. specific nursing knowledge.

2. Which of these procedures should you follow in taking this test?
   A. Select one answer for each question.
   B. Use a pen for marking answers.
   C. Choose an answer before you have read the whole question.
   D. Scribble in your test book.

The correct answer to question one is (D). The correct answer to question two is (A).

When marking the answer sheet, blacken only one circle for each question. Blacken the circle completely. Do not use X's or check marks. If you decide to change your answer, erase your original answer thoroughly. If you do not, your new answer may be scored incorrectly. You must use a soft lead pencil to mark your answers.

Be sure you understand these directions before beginning the test:

1. Read each question carefully.

2. From among the suggested answers provided, select the one answer that best answers the question—even if you think that some other answer, not listed, would be preferable. There is only one correct answer to each question.

3. Work in a systematic manner; do not spend too much time on any one question.

4. You may answer questions even when you are not perfectly sure of the answers. Your score will be based on the number of correct answers you mark. Be sure to mark only one answer to each question. If you mark more than one answer, you will not receive credit for the question.

Instructions for Answer Sheet
Identifying Information
Spaces 1–13

You are now ready to begin filling in the answer sheet for Nursing, Part 1. Before you begin timing your test, fill in the information requests for items 1–13. You will find the corresponding 13 spaces for recording your responses at the top of your answer sheet. Fill in the information according to the instructions that follow.

FOR ITEMS/SPACES 1–5 (ABOVE THE DARK LINE) FOLLOW THESE INSTRUCTIONS:

ITEM/SPACE 1. NAME — Print your name. First print your last name or surname. Then print your first name and your middle name.

ITEM/SPACE 2. TEST CENTER — Print the name of the city and country where you are taking this practice test.

CENTER CODE — When you take the CGFNS Qualifying Exam, the correct code will be given to you. Because this is a practice test, you may use any three numbers between 0 and 9. Write the numbers in the boxes next to the words CENTER CODE. Be careful to put only one number in each box.

ITEM/SPACE 3. FORM — When you take the CGFNS Qualifying Exam, the correct FORM numbers will be given to you. Because this is a practice test, you may use any three numbers between 0 and 9. Write the numbers in the boxes next to the word FORM. Be careful to put only one number in each box.

ITEM/SPACE 4. PART — Fill in the space under the number that is the same as the part of the nursing test you are taking. You will find that number on the cover page of each practice test. The number follows the word "Part."

ITEM/SPACE 5. TEST BOOK NUMBER — When you take the CGFNS Qualifying Exam, the correct

number will be given to you. Because this is a practice test, you may choose any five numbers between 0 and 9. Write the numbers in the boxes next to the words TEST BOOK NUMBER. Be careful to put only one number in each box.

FOR ITEMS/SPACES 6–13 (BELOW THE DARK LINE) FOLLOW THESE INSTRUCTIONS:

ITEM/SPACE 6. CGFNS IDENTIFICATION NUMBER — When you apply to the CGFNS Certification Program, you will be given a permanent identification number. Your identification number will be printed on your exam permit. Because this is a practice test, you may use any seven numbers between 0 and 9. Write one number in each box under the words CGFNS IDENTI-FICATION NUMBER. Be careful to put only one number in each box.

You will see a column of numbers beneath each box. There is a circle around each number. Find the circled number that is the same as the number you have written in the box above the column. Use your pencil to blacken that circle. Fill the circle in completely. Be sure you cover the number in the circle.

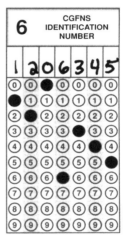

Do the same thing in each of the other six columns. Be sure you fill in one circle in each column. The drawing above shows you how to fill in these spaces correctly.

ITEM/SPACE 7. DATE OF BIRTH — In the boxes below the letters MO., enter the number of the month in which you were born. There are two boxes under these letters. If you were born in a month from January through September, put a 0 in the first box. In the second box, print the number of the month you were born. If you were born in April, for example, you would print 04. If you were born in October, November, or December, print a 1 in the first box. In the second box, print 0, 1, or 2. Remember to put a 0 in the first box if you were born between January and September.

In the boxes beneath the word DAY, enter the day of the month in which you were born. If you were born during the first nine days of the month, put a zero in the first box. If you were born after the ninth day of the month, put one number in each of the boxes. Put the first number in the first box. Put the second number in the second box.

In the boxes beneath the letters YR., enter the last two numbers of the year in which you were born. If you were born in 1965, for example, put a 6 in the first box and a 5 in the second box.

When you have correctly filled in each box, look at the columns of numbers beneath the boxes. There is a circle around each number. Find the circled number that is the same as the number you have written in the box above the column. Use your pencil to blacken that circle. Fill in the circle completely. Be sure you cover the number in the circle. Do the same thing in each of the other five columns. Be sure you fill in one circle in each column.

ITEM/SPACE 8. COUNTRY OF NURSING EDUCATION — In the long box beneath the words COUNTRY OF NURSING EDUCATION, print the name of the country in which you attended nursing school.

Next to the box, you will see the words COUNTRY CODE. The numbers 9 and 0 are already printed in the first and second boxes beneath COUNTRY CODE. When you take the CGFNS Qualifying Exam, you will be told what numbers to put in the other three boxes. These three numbers will be your country code. They will be printed on your exam permit.

Because this is a practice test, you may choose your own COUNTRY CODE. You may choose any three numbers between 0 and 9. Write one of the numbers in each of the boxes that follow the numbers 9 and 0 on your answer sheet. Be sure to put only one number in each box.

Beneath each of the three boxes, you will see a column of numbers. There is a circle around each number. In each column, find the circled number that is the same as the number in the box above that column. Use your pencil to blacken that circle. Completely cover the number in the circle. Be sure to fill in one circle in each column.

ITEM/SPACE 9. SEX — If you are a female, blacken the circle under the word FEMALE. If you are a male, blacken the circle under the word MALE.

ITEM/SPACE 10. IS THIS THE FIRST TIME YOU ARE TAKING THIS TEST? — This is a practice test. Do not answer this question. Do not blacken either circle.

ITEM/SPACE 11. DATE OF GRADUATION — In the first two boxes under the letters MO., print the number of the month in which you graduated from nursing school. If you graduated from nursing

school in a month from January through September, put a 0 in the first box. In the second box, write the number that corresponds to the month you graduated. If you graduated from nursing school in October, November or December, put a 1 in the first box. In the second box, write 0, 1 or 2.

In the boxes beneath the letters YR., enter the last two numbers of the year in which you graduated from nursing school. If you graduated in 1971, for example, you would put a 7 in the first box and a 1 in the second box. Be sure to put one number in each of the two boxes. Do not put any number in the last three boxes. These three boxes are for CGFNS use only.

Beneath each of the numbers you have printed, you will see a column of numbers. There is a circle around each number. In each column, find the circled number that is the same as the number you have printed in the box above the column. Use your pencil to blacken that circle. Completely cover the number in the circle. Be sure to fill in one circle in each column.

ITEM/SPACE 12. TEST FORM — The TEST FORM number is printed on the front of the test booklet (which is available only at the exam center where you will take the CGFNS Qualifying Exam). You will need to write in the TEST FORM number of your test booklet on the answer sheet.

Because this is a practice test, you may choose your own TEST FORM number. You may choose any three numbers between 0 and 9. Write one of the numbers in each of the boxes that follow the numbers 9 and 0 on your answer sheet. Be sure to put only one number in each box.

Beneath each of the numbers you have printed, you will see a column of numbers. There is a circle around each number. In each column, find the circled number that is the same as the number you have printed in the box above the column. Use your pencil to blacken that circle. Completely cover the number in the circle. Be sure to fill in one circle in each column.

ITEM/SPACE 13. SIGNATURE — Sign your name in English characters. Make sure that everything you write is in the line above the box. Do not make any marks below the SIGNATURE box.

Now turn to the appropriate page and begin taking Nursing, Part 1 of a practice test. When you complete Part 1, return to this page to review the instructions below for Nursing, Part 2.

Practice Test
Nursing, Part 2

Instructions For Timing
Nursing, Part 2
Questions 1–110

You will be given one hour and 50 minutes to complete this part of the practice test. If you finish this part of the practice test before it is time to stop, you may use this time to check your answers. You may also go back to answer any questions you have skipped.

If someone is timing your test, ask her/him to tell you when you have only 10 minutes left. You may want to use the remaining 10 minutes to check your answers. You may also want to use this time to return to any questions you have skipped.

When the time allotted for this part of the practice test has expired, you must stop answering questions. Even if you have not answered all the questions, you must stop when the allotted time expires. If you stop at this point, you will see how many questions you will probably be able to answer correctly on the actual CGFNS Qualifying Exam.

When you are ready to start Nursing, Part 2, check to see what time it is. Note the time on the inside cover of your Official Study Guide. Or, set an alarm clock to let you know when to stop answering questions.

General Instructions for Answering
Nursing, Part 2
Questions 1–110

Each question in the test has four possible answers. You are to select only one answer for each question. Read each question through carefully before you decide which one of the suggested answers is correct. Your answers must be marked on the separate answer sheet, not in the test book. You must use a soft lead pencil to mark your answers.

There is one type of question in this part of the test – multiple-choice. Here are two examples with information regarding the use of the answer sheet.

1. This test is designed to measure
   A. reading speed.
   B. cultural background.
   C. general knowledge.
   D. specific nursing knowledge.

2. Which of these procedures should you follow in taking this test?
   A. Select one answer for each question.
   B. Use a pen for marking answers.
   C. Choose an answer before you have read the whole question.
   D. Scribble in your test book.

The correct answer to question one is (D). The correct answer to question two is (A).

When marking the answer sheet, blacken only one circle for each question. Blacken the circle completely. Do not use X's or check marks. If you decide to change your answer, erase your original answer thoroughly. If you do not, your new answer may be scored incorrectly. You must use a soft lead pencil to mark your answers.

Be sure you understand these directions before beginning the test:

1. Read each question carefully.

2. From among the suggested answers provided, select the one answer that best answers the question—even if you think that some other answer, not listed, would be preferable. There is only one correct answer to each question.

3. Work in a systematic manner; do not spend too much time on any one question.

You may answer questions even when you are not perfectly sure of the answers. Your score will be based on the number of correct answers you mark. Be sure to mark only one answer to each question. If you mark more than one answer, you will not receive credit for the question.

CGFNS

Qualifying Exam Practice Exam A

Practice Exam A: Nursing, Part I

You will have two hours and 30 minutes to complete Nursing, Part 1.

1. A patient who is admitted to the hospital gives the nurse an advance directive. The nurse should understand that an advance directive is

   A. a written statement by the patient that defines acceptable care if the patient becomes incapacitated.
   B. the name of the person designated by the patient to make health-related decisions should the patient become incapacitated.
   C. a statement identifying the patient as an organ donor.
   D. a written statement authorizing a particular surgical procedure.

2. A priority nursing intervention for the care of a terminally ill patient diagnosed with metastatic cancer is

   A. maintaining bowel function.
   B. alleviating and relieving pain.
   C. preventing respiratory arrest.
   D. managing chemotherapy.

3. The registered nurse's signature as a witness on an informed consent indicates that the patient

   A. has been informed regarding the procedure.
   B. was medicated for pain before the consent was signed.
   C. can describe how the surgical procedure will be done.
   D. voluntarily agreed to having the procedure performed.

4. When assessing a patient for the potential development of hypovolemic shock, which of the following manifestations would the nurse most likely see first?

   A. Nervousness and apprehension
   B. Decreased urinary output
   C. Systolic blood pressure below 90 mm Hg
   D. Hypoventilation and tachycardia

5. A psychiatric patient continues to disrupt the unit milieu by pacing up and down the hall. The nurse responds by placing the patient in the seclusion room. As a result of her actions, the nurse may be held responsible for which of the following legal implications?

   A. False imprisonment
   B. Battery
   C. Invasion of privacy
   D. Defamation of character

6. An eight-year-old child has cerebral palsy, a tracheostomy, and is oxygen (O2) dependent. During an initial visit to the home, the nurse would include which of the following questions in an environmental safety assessment?

   A. "Are there drafts or air leaks in the home?"
   B. "Are there other children in the home?"
   C. "Does anyone smoke in the home?"
   D. "Are there pets in the home?"

7. A patient is admitted to the clinical unit after having a tracheostomy. When orienting the patient to the room, which of the following explanations would be most important for the nurse to include?

   A. Reason for oxygen collar
   B. Use of call light
   C. Procedure for suctioning
   D. Ways to prevent infection

8. Which of the following instructions should be given to the family to ensure the safety of a patient who recently began experiencing periodic grand mal seizures?

   A. Place a tongue blade in the patient's mouth during a seizure
   B. Physically restrain the patient during the seizure
   C. Remove sharp objects in the patient's immediate environment
   D. Call the emergency medical squad when each seizure begins

9. Staff nurses learn that a patient they have been caring for during the last few weeks has just been diagnosed with tuberculosis. When the nurses express concern about contracting tuberculosis themselves, the charge nurse's response should be based on which of the following statements?

   A. Tuberculosis is easily treated with a short course of antibiotics.
   B. The Mantoux test is used to confirm diagnosis of tuberculosis.
   C. Tuberculosis is not highly infectious when standard precautions are followed.
   D. Vaccination with Bacille Calmette Guerin (BCG) will be used to immunize the nurses against infection.

10. To restrain a three-year-old child in preparation for a lumbar puncture, the nurse should

    A. use soft arm restraints on both hands and legs to stabilize the child.
    B. apply a jacket restraint to prevent sudden movements.
    C. place the child in a flexed side-lying position.
    D. place the child in a supine position on a papoose board.

11. A child with impetigo is to be discharged from the hospital. The nurse's plan of care should include which of the following measures?

    A. Providing high protein meals for the child
    B. Teaching the child and family members about good hand-washing technique
    C. Instructing the child and family members about decreasing playground activity
    D. Providing sun lamp treatments for the child

12. A nurse is providing discharge teaching to the family of an elderly patient who is confused and is taking several oral medications. Which of the following instructions should be given priority?

    A. Administer medications with meals
    B. Withhold medications that the patient refuses
    C. Supervise the patient's medication administration
    D. Allow the patient to self-medicate when possible

13. A 15-month-old child who is postoperative after a cleft palate repair has elbow restraints in place. Which of the following instructions should the nurse include in the patient's plan of care?

    A. Place mittens on the child's hands
    B. Remove the restraints briefly every two hours
    C. Tell the parents that they may remove the restraints while they are in the child's room
    D. Have the parents sign a release form before applying the restraints

14. Which of the following measures is most appropriate for a nurse to take to prevent injury in a patient who is confused?

    A. Apply a soft restraint on the patient's wrist
    B. Administer lorazepam (Ativan) as ordered
    C. Change the patient's environment
    D. Keep the bed in the lowest position

15. A nurse is assigned to all of the following patients. Which patient should the nurse assess first?

    A. The patient requesting medication for chest pain
    B. The patient who has an intravenous medication due in 30 minutes
    C. The patient who has a temperature of 101°F
    D. The patient who is scheduled to go to surgery within the hour

16. When orienting a new nurse to the psychiatric unit, an experienced nurse should provide which of the following explanations regarding the use of patient restraints?

    A. "PRN orders for restraints are unacceptable."
    B. "Documentation must be done every eight hours while a patient is restrained."
    C. "A restraint order, once written, is in effect for the entire hospitalization."
    D. "The vest restraint is the safest type of restraint to use."

17. Which of the following actions should be included in the teaching plan for the parents of a preschool-aged child who has pediculosis capitis?

    A. Administer topical anti-itch medication
    B. Apply calamine lotion or Burow's solution
    C. Comb the child's hair each week
    D. Wash all of the family's clothing and linens

18. Which of the following actions would be most appropriate for the charge nurse to take when caring for a patient who has schizophrenia and a history of violence?

    A. Assign the same staff to care for the patient daily to provide consistency
    B. Assign a staff member of the same sex to care for the patient to provide more open communication
    C. Place the patient on unit restriction to provide disciplinary measures
    D. Place the patient in walking restraints to restrict activity

19. Home safety for an elderly patient whose mobility is impaired should include which of the following measures?

    A. Carpeting stairways
    B. Waxing kitchen floors
    C. Installing handrails next to the tub and toilet
    D. Placing throw rugs in hallways and doorways

20. Which of the following actions would be essential for the nurse to take when caring for a patient in restraints in the psychiatric unit?

    A. Document the events leading to the use of restraints
    B. Check the patient every four hours while restrained
    C. Obtain a physician's order within 24 hours of the restraints being applied
    D. Replace the restraints every 24 hours to ensure proper fit

21. A bone mineral analysis reveals that a patient who is postmenopausal has severe osteoporosis. Which of the following instructions should the nurse give to the patient's family to ensure a safe environment for the patient?

    A. "Disinfect the bathroom weekly."
    B. "Carpet floor surfaces."
    C. "Install handrails on stairways."
    D. "Keep the lights dim."

22. Which of the following nursing measures should be included in the care plan of an elderly patient with bladder incontinence who is identified as a high risk for falls?

    A. Monitor activities every two hours
    B. Toilet every one to two hours
    C. Sedate as needed
    D. Use a chest posey restraint

23. Which of the following reasons, given by a mother who permits her preschool-aged child to sleep in the same bed (co-sleeping) as the parents, requires further investigation by the nurse?

    A. "I am too tired to get up at night to check on the baby in the other room."
    B. "This promotes bonding between us and our child."
    C. "I slept with my parents when I was a small child."
    D. "I can be certain my husband is not being inappropriate."

24. Which of the following questions would be essential in a cultural assessment of a patient?

    A. How many times have you been married?
    B. At what times do you take your medications?
    C. Do you have any siblings?
    D. Are there foods that you cannot eat together?

25. **Which of the following explanations would the nurse give to a patient regarding the role of the case manager?**

    A. The case manager makes daily patient assignments for staff.
    B. The case manager coordinates both inpatient hospitalization and home care.
    C. The case manager negotiates insurance benefits with the hospital.
    D. The case manager decides what treatments are essential.

26. **The nurse should be aware that the correct order for physical assessment of the abdomen is**

    A. Inspect, auscultate, percuss and palpate
    B. Inspect, palpate, auscultate and percuss
    C. Inspect, percuss, palpate and auscultate
    D. Inspect, palpate, percuss and auscultate

27. **When conducting a physical examination of a patient, the nurse should be aware that a pathologic S4 extra heart sound is the result of**

    A. physiologic splitting of the aortic and pulmonic valves with inspiration.
    B. increased resistance to ventricular filling following atrial contraction.
    C. opening of a stenotic mitral valve.
    D. mitral valve prolapse.

28. **An 86-year-old male is admitted to the hospital for renal insufficiency. The first night he becomes extremely disoriented, confused and combative after being given a low dose tricyclic antidepressant. The nurse should be aware that such behavior is indicative of**

    A. dementia.
    B. delirium.
    C. psychosis.
    D. depression.

29. **To accurately assess for jaundice in a patient with dark skin pigmentation, the nurse should examine which body areas?**

    A. Nail beds
    B. Skin on back of the hand
    C. Hard palate of the mouth
    D. Soles of the feet

30. **When caring for a patient with an arteriovenous (AV) fistula, the nurse should assess for which of the following sounds on auscultation?**

    A. Whoosh
    B. Bruit
    C. Echo
    D. Thrill

31. **A newborn is suspected of having patent ductus arteriosus. The nurse should recognize that the newborn is at risk for the development of**

    A. mitral valve prolapse.
    B. inflammation of the pericardium.
    C. pulmonary edema.
    D. bacterial endocarditis.

32. **The nurse should recognize that a patient who is unable to remember being raped by her brother when she was 10 years old is using which of the following ego defense mechanisms?**

    A. Compensation
    B. Repression
    C. Undoing
    D. Regression

33. **Macular degeneration of aging is an important cause of what finding in the elderly patient?**

    A. Poor peripheral vision
    B. Poor central vision
    C. Nystagmus
    D. Lid lag

34. **Which of the following behaviors by a nurse who is suspected of being impaired would support a nursing diagnosis of ineffective individual coping?**

    A. Decreased job performance
    B. Increased food consumption
    C. Verbal manipulation
    D. Frequent illnesses

 *Test A / Part 1*

35. Using eye contact can be an excellent means of calming an anxious patient, but it is a sign of disrespect when caring for a patient of which of the following cultures?

    A. Puerto Rican
    B. Italian
    C. Cuban
    D. Native American

36. A nurse, while doing a physical assessment, shines a light into a patient's right eye and notes pupillary constriction in the left eye. The nurse should chart this response as

    A. a direct reaction.
    B. a consensual reaction.
    C. accommodation.
    D. pupillary convergence.

37. Which electrolyte imbalance would a nurse expect when assessing a patient with bulimia?

    A. Hyperkalemia
    B. Hypokalemia
    C. Hypercalcemia
    D. Hypocalcemia

38. A 79-year-old home health patient with a history of coronary artery disease, diabetes and arthritis tells the nurse, "I'm tired of always having pain in my back and legs from this arthritis, so I made an appointment for massage therapy three times a week." Which of the following actions would be most appropriate for the nurse to take?

    A. Obtain an order from the physician so the patient can receive insurance reimbursement
    B. Make sure the patient has proper transportation since she cannot drive
    C. Encourage the patient to talk to her physician before proceeding with the therapy
    D. Suggest that the patient hold her arthritis medication in order to evaluate the effectiveness of massage

39. An overweight adolescent female asks for information on losing weight. After instructing the patient to decrease her caloric intake, which of the following responses by the nurse would be best?

    A. "You should decrease the amount of vitamins in your diet."
    B. "You should decrease the amount of meals each day."
    C. "You should increase the amount of exercise activities."
    D. "You should increase the amount of fast or easy-to-fix foods in your diet."

40. Evaluation of an elderly patient first day postoperative reveals a temperature of 100.6°F. Which of the following actions should the nurse take first?

    A. Examine the patient
    B. Set up the intravenous antibiotic dose two hours early
    C. Call the physician
    D. Obtain STAT blood cultures

41. A home health nurse is visiting a patient with ovarian cancer. The patient has experienced decreased appetite and a significant weight loss in the past three weeks. Which of the following actions should the nurse take first?

    A. Recommend multiple small feedings of high-protein foods
    B. Plan to include the majority of calories for the day at breakfast
    C. Apply the standard care plan for altered nutrition: less than body requirements
    D. Collect additional information to determine potential causes of the weight loss

42. When informed consent is obtained from the patient, the explanation of the surgical procedure, possible risks, complications and alternatives is the responsibility of the

    A. registered nurse.
    B. surgeon.
    C. admission clerk.
    D. anesthesiologist.

43. The best nursing approach to parents who are displaying anxiety and guilt when their child is hospitalized is to
   A. explain the dangers of excess anxiety and guilt.
   B. distract their attention to something less painful.
   C. anticipate their emotional responses and acknowledge them.
   D. give personal examples that are similar to their situation.

44. The most effective way to manage pain for a patient with terminal cancer is for the nurse to administer pain medication
   A. at eight-hour intervals.
   B. on a continuous, around-the-clock schedule.
   C. as the pain reaches peak level.
   D. when the patient can no longer tolerate the pain.

45. A follow-up home visit is conducted on an elderly patient after a recent hospitalization. The patient reports nocturia. Which of the following patient instructions by the nurse would most effectively address the patient's nocturia?
   A. "Avoid liquids after 5 pm."
   B. "Keep a low-wattage light on in the hallway."
   C. "Wear a disposable undergarment at bedtime."
   D. "Obtain a bedside commode."

46. For nasopharyngeal airway suctioning of a conscious patient with a functional gag reflex, the nurse should place the patient's head in which of the following positions?
   A. Neck hyperextended
   B. Chin to chest
   C. Face toward right shoulder
   D. Face toward left shoulder

47. To which of the following nursing diagnoses would a nurse give priority when caring for a patient who is not eating or bathing and refuses to leave the house since the death of her daughter a year ago?
   A. Anxiety related to fear of death
   B. Self-care deficit related to loss
   C. Anticipatory grieving related to fear of social interaction
   D. Dysfunctional grieving related to loss

48. A 48-year-old patient who has an IV infusing, an epidural drip, and a chest tube attached to wall suction needs to have a bowel movement but does not want to use the bedpan. Which of the following actions by the nurse would be most appropriate?
   A. Offer the patient a bedside commode
   B. Insist that the patient use the bedpan
   C. Assist the patient to the bathroom
   D. Obtain an order to disconnect the wall suction

49. Which of the following observations of a postoperative patient should indicate to the nurse that the patient is experiencing a low pain level?
   A. The patient asked for pain medication five minutes ago but is now asleep.
   B. The patient states her pain is at level two on a 10-point scale.
   C. The patient states that her pain is at level 10 on a 10-point scale.
   D. The patient is lying very still in bed.

50. While orienting a new nurse to the unit, the charge nurse stresses the importance of accurate documentation. The primary reason for a nurse to document care accurately is to
   A. demonstrate responsibility and accountability.
   B. prevent any legal action against the healthcare facility and its staff.
   C. facilitate insurance reimbursement.
   D. be in compliance with individual regulatory agencies.

51. A nurse is teaching a patient about blood pressure measurement in pregnancy. The nurse's teaching should be based on which of the following statements?

    A. Blood pressure can be expected to rise slightly in the second trimester.
    B. Arterial blood pressure is highest when a woman is sitting.
    C. Arterial blood pressure is highest when a woman is supine.
    D. Orthostatic blood pressure readings should be taken at each prenatal visit.

52. The parents of a child diagnosed with a schizoid personality disorder ask the nurse how this diagnosis was made. The nurse should explain that the child exhibited which of the following manifestations?

    A. Inability to experience pleasure
    B. Jealousy and a quickness to react to anger
    C. Insensitivity to the welfare of others
    D. Lack of guilt or social conscience

53. An order on a 3 kg critically ill neonate's chart reads as follows: Give digoxin (Lanoxin) 0.25 mg NG daily. Which of the following nursing actions is appropriate in relation to the prescribed order?

    A. Carry out the order as written
    B. Give the digoxin after checking the apical pulse and potassium level
    C. Hold the drug until a serum digoxin level is obtained
    D. Question the doctor about this order

54. In teaching a mother of an 18-month-old about prevention and safety in the home, the nurse should include which of the following measures in response to accidental ingestion?

    A. Induce vomiting with one dose of ipecac syrup
    B. Call the local Poison Control Center for advice prior to treatment
    C. Give the child several glasses of water to flush the substance
    D. Have the child eat the inner portion of a piece of bread

55. The patient receiving rofecoxib (Vioxx) should be monitored for which of the following side effects?

    A. Tiredness and somnolence
    B. Hypotension and tachycardia
    C. Dyspnea and chest pain
    D. Irritability and agitation

56. Which of the following observations, if made in a patient with a left arm arteriovenous (AV) shunt prior to hemodialysis, should be reported to the physician?

    A. Absence of a palpable thrill over the shunt
    B. Presence of an audible bruit in the left arm
    C. Overbed instructions not to take a blood pressure in the left arm
    D. Overbed instructions that blood specimens are not to be taken from the left arm

57. The nurse caring for a patient in pre-term labor should be aware that the patient may exhibit which of the following side effects when administered intravenous terbutaline sulfate (Brethine)?

    A. Uterine hypertonia
    B. Epistaxis
    C. Tachycardia
    D. Dysuria

58. A nurse notices the mother of a hospitalized one-month-old boy sitting and talking on the telephone while the infant lies in the crib crying. Which of the following statements by the nurse would be most appropriate?

    A. "Your baby is crying and needs your attention now."
    B. "Let's check your baby together to see what he needs."
    C. "Why do you think your baby is crying at this time?"
    D. "When did you last feed your baby?"

59. An 85-year-old is admitted for continuous, cramping pain as the result of intermittent claudication. When conducting an initial physical assessment, the nurse is unable to palpate the pedal pulses. Which of the following actions should the nurse take first?

    A. Notify the physician and anticipate emergency surgery
    B. Assess the apical and radial pulses for any irregularity and notify the physician
    C. Elevate the foot of the bed and apply warm compresses
    D. Obtain a Doppler and recheck the pedal pulses

60. An operating room nurse is opposed to abortion based on moral principles. When assigned to circulate for a pregnancy termination case, the nurse should take which of the following actions?

    A. Discuss her beliefs with the patient
    B. Ask the supervisor to assign another nurse to the case
    C. Request an ethics panel be convened to review the case
    D. Leave the room during the time that the fetus is aborted

61. A patient with a terminal illness is rapidly deteriorating but remains alert, oriented and verbally responsive. He states, "I am tired of being ill. I wish it could end today." The nurse should record this information using which of the following statements?

    A. Patient states, "I am tired of being ill. I wish it could end today."
    B. Patient seems depressed about his illness.
    C. Patient reports being sick all the time and wishes to die.
    D. Patient seems worried about something and states he wants to end it all.

62. A patient is receiving radiation therapy to her right breast. The nurse's teaching plan related to skin care should include which of the following measures?

    A. Completely clean the skin each day to remove ointments and markings
    B. Cover broken skin in the treatment area with a medicated ointment before each radiation treatment
    C. Wear a bra at all times to support the breasts
    D. Protect the breast area from direct sunlight

63. When caring for a patient in restraints, on what area of the bed should the restraints be anchored?

    A. The side rails
    B. The mattress hook
    C. The footboard
    D. The bed frame

64. Which of the following nursing diagnoses should the nurse use to best address the suicidal patient's feelings of despair?

    A. Ineffective coping
    B. Spiritual distress
    C. Anxiety
    D. Dysfunctional grieving

65. An 80-year-old with right-sided weakness following a cerebrovascular accident (CVA) is to ambulate with the aid of a walker. What age-related changes in this individual will increase the risk of injury?

    A. Improved muscle mass and strength
    B. Slowed response to sensory stimuli
    C. Increased cognitive functioning
    D. Development of arcus senilis

66. A child presents in the clinic with iron deficiency anemia. As the nurse, you would expect which of the following symptoms to be present in this patient?

    A. Abdominal pain and vomiting
    B. Poor posture and unclear speech
    C. Bradycardia and dyspnea
    D. Poor muscle tone and decreased activity

67. A patient who is a Jehovah's Witness is scheduled to have a bowel resection for colon cancer. When planning care for the patient, the nurse should be aware that

    A. the resected colon and surrounding tissue will be officially buried.
    B. surgery must be delayed until the curandero visits.
    C. Holy Communion should be given on the day of surgery.
    D. the patient will most likely refuse any blood transfusion.

68. Which of the following statements by a 25-year-old woman indicates that she understands breast self-examination (BSE)?

    A. "I will perform BSE every three months."
    B. "I will wear latex gloves when doing BSE."
    C. "I will do complete BSE on both breasts seven to 10 days after menses onset."
    D. "I will use the palms of my hands to perform BSE."

69. A patient with asthma is producing thick, white secretions. Which of the following nursing measures would be most appropriate for the nurse to include in her plan of care?

    A. Increase fluid intake
    B. Promote exercise
    C. Administer oxygen
    D. Encourage coughing

70. Which of the following behaviors would a patient with borderline personality disorder most likely demonstrate when feeling abandoned by a significant other?

    A. Apathetic
    B. Disoriented
    C. Self-destructive
    D. Psychotic

71. A breast-feeding mother on her third postpartum day states that she is planning on using the lactational amenorrhea method (LAM) for contraception. The most appropriate nursing response would be to inform the mother that

    A. this method can be used for one year.
    B. this method is effective if she is fully breastfeeding and menses has not returned.
    C. she can supplement with formula for the night feedings.
    D. she should check her basal temperature to determine effectiveness of the method.

72. Which of the following actions would be of the highest priority in the treatment of disseminated intravascular coagulation (DIC)?

    A. Maintaining central blood volume
    B. Correcting the triggering cause
    C. Correcting the coagulation deficit
    D. Maintaining strict intake and output

73. A patient is to begin taking alendronate (Fosamax). Which of the following statements should be included in the patient's teaching plan?

    A. Crush the medication and mix with food.
    B. Take the medication with one swallow of water.
    C. Dissolve the medication under the tongue.
    D. Remain upright for 30 minutes after swallowing the medication.

74. The nurse caring for a patient newly diagnosed with glaucoma should include which of the following instructions in the discharge teaching plan?

    A. Do not drive for 15 minutes after using the eye drops.
    B. Keep a reserve bottle of eye drops at home.
    C. Discontinue eye drops when vision improves.
    D. Use only eye drops that dilate the pupil.

75. The nurse accompanies a physician to the room of a newly admitted elderly patient with dementia. Upon examination, the patient has an extremely painful, reddened and enlarged abscess on the right elbow. The physician proceeds to incise the abscess area without anesthetic, and the patient cries out loudly in pain. The most appropriate immediate nursing action is to

   A. provide pain medication after the procedure.
   B. assist in restraining the patient during the procedure.
   C. request that the physician stop the procedure until an anesthetic can be administered.
   D. attempt to distract the patient during the procedure.

76. The nurse is caring for a postoperative patient receiving morphine via patient-controlled analgesia (PCA). The patient complains that he wakes up in severe pain after sleeping. Which of the following actions by the nurse would be most appropriate?

   A. Administer the medication for the patient every hour
   B. Request that the physician order a bolus dose of pain medication
   C. Notify the physician to increase the patient's dosage
   D. Instruct the patient to use the PCA pump every 10 minutes during the hour prior to sleep

77. The nurse provides discharge instructions to a patient with hepatitis B. Which of the following statements, if made by the patient, would indicate the need for further instruction?

   A. "I can never donate blood."
   B. "I can never have unprotected sex."
   C. "I cannot share needles."
   D. "I should avoid drugs and alcohol."

78. In a primigravida, the nurse would suspect cephalopelvic disproportion when

   A. an unopened cervix fails to dilate after 20 hours of contractions.
   B. the cervix remains unchanged for three hours with regular contractions and prior cervical dilatation.
   C. the fetus descends in active labor at a rate of 1.0 cm per hour.
   D. the woman complains of an urge to push at 7-cm dilatation.

79. An elderly patient who is being assessed for postoperative pain, tells the nurse "I don't want to bother you. I'll be okay." Which of the following indicators should the nurse initially use to assess this patient for pain?

   A. Statement of discomfort
   B. Nonverbal indicators of pain
   C. Changes in vital sign parameters
   D. Frequency of pain medication requests

80. A patient is admitted for treatment with a thrombolytic medication. Which of the following patient statements should be reported to the physician?

   A. "I am allergic to ibuprofen."
   B. "I have glaucoma."
   C. "I take aspirin (acetylsalicylic acid) everyday."
   D. "I have had my gall bladder removed five years ago."

81. A patient who is human immunodeficiency virus (HIV) positive is admitted to an isolation unit for treatment of mycobacterium avium complex disease (or infection) and tuberculosis. The nurse observes that the patient has difficulty following instructions, short-term memory loss and difficulty concentrating. The nurse should be aware that these behaviors

   A. will disappear when isolation is no longer required.
   B. are symptomatic of AIDS dementia complex.
   C. are normal for the early stage of HIV infection.
   D. are a result of mycobacterium infection.

82. A primigravida complains to the nurse about dyspnea, nausea and bladder fullness. The nurse should be aware that these symptoms during pregnancy are usually the result of an increase in which of the following hormones?

    A. Estrogen
    B. Melanocyte-stimulating hormone
    C. Progesterone
    D. Follicle-stimulating hormone

83. During periods of illness the nurse should anticipate which of the following occurrences in the patient with diabetes mellitus?

    A. The need for insulin is reduced.
    B. The need for insulin is increased.
    C. There is no need for insulin since the appetite is decreased.
    D. Insulin requirement is not affected by illness.

84. The nurse should be aware that discomfort that occurs during the second stage of labor is most often related to

    A. stretching of the cervix.
    B. distention of the vagina and perineum.
    C. stretching of the lower uterine segment.
    D. the descending shoulder of the fetus.

85. Which of the following behaviors by an adolescent patient suspected of having an anxiety disorder would best support a nursing diagnosis of high risk for violence, self-directed?

    A. Poor impulse control
    B. Criticism of others
    C. Poor concentration
    D. Low achievement in school

86. A one-month-old infant in respiratory distress is brought to the emergency department. The nurse should observe the infant for which of the following signs?

    A. Clubbing of fingers and toes
    B. Jugular venous distension
    C. Nasal flaring and chest retractions
    D. Cool, clammy moist skin

87. Which of the following assessment findings would a nurse expect to identify in an elderly patient with pain?

    A. Increased confusion
    B. Decreased alertness
    C. Increased urinary output
    D. Decreased blood pressure

88. A child with a ventro-peritoneal (VP) shunt presents with signs and symptoms of restlessness, headache, blurred vision, bradycardia, and a widening pulse pressure. The nurse would suspect the child has

    A. a brain tumor.
    B. increased intracranial pressure.
    C. loss of consciousness.
    D. sleep pattern disturbances.

89. A parent of a six-year-old child asks, "Is it safe for my child to ride in the front seat when I have an emergency air bag device in the car?" Which of the following replies should the nurse give?

    A. "Yes, air bags are designed to take the place of safety seats or seat belts."
    B. "Yes, however, you must keep the seat position as close to the front of the car as possible."
    C. "No, children are safest in the middle of the back seat in a manual seat belt."
    D. "No, children should ride in the rear seat behind the driver."

90. A nurse should be aware that for a fetal non-stress test (NST) to be considered reactive, which of the following criteria should be met?

    A. Fetal heart rate baseline is above 110, with no decelerations during fetal movement
    B. Fetal heart rate baseline is above 110, with accelerations noted during fetal activity
    C. Fetal heart baseline is between 110 and 160, with two accelerations of 15 beats for 15 seconds in response to fetal activity
    D. Fetal heart baseline is between 110 and 160, with less than two accelerations during a 20-minute period

91. A patient with anorexia nervosa tells the nurse she has been vomiting after meals. Which of the following responses by the nurse would be most therapeutic?

    A. "You know that it is not good for you to throw-up your meals because you will hurt your body."
    B. "You already are so thin. Why would you want to vomit your meals?"
    C. "It seems like this is difficult for you and that you don't really want to be throwing up."
    D. "Vomiting is unhealthy for you. It is important not to lose nutrients for the health of your body."

92. Which of the following assessment findings would the nurse observe first in a patient who is undergoing peritoneal dialysis and is developing peritonitis?

    A. Dialysate leakage at catheter site
    B. Insufficient flow of dialysate
    C. Cloudy dialysate returns
    D. Increased dialysate returns

93. A patient with a tracheostomy is to be admitted to the unit. As the charge nurse, you should be aware that the most appropriate placement for this patient is

    A. near the nurses station with a patient who had a bowel resection.
    B. in a single room near the elevator.
    C. in a room with a patient who has a compromised immune system.
    D. with a patient who has pneumonia.

94. A patient who has acquired immune deficiency syndrome (AIDS) develops Pneumocystis carinii pneumonia (PCP). The patient asks the nurse, "How did I get this pneumonia?" The nurse's response should be based on which of these statements about PCP?

    A. It occurs in immunosuppressed persons from proliferation of organisms that are normally present in the body.
    B. It is transmitted from close contact with an infected individual who has a suppressed immune system.
    C. It results from exposure to a carrier of the organism who has not taken appropriate precautions.
    D. It is most often acquired from unprotected sex with an infected individual.

95. A patient who is hospitalized with a diagnosis of heart block asks the nurse, "Why is it necessary to put up the side rails of my bed?" The nurse's response should be based on which of these understandings about the physiological changes associated with heart block?

    A. Premature ventricular contractions are likely to occur.
    B. Tetany is an impending problem.
    C. Perfusion of the cerebrum may be impaired.
    D. Kussmaul respirations are a common complication.

96. The family of a dying patient requests that the window remain open in the patient's room. The most appropriate response by the nurse is

    A. "Open windows create a safety hazard."
    B. "You want the window open?"
    C. "It's too cold outside to do this."
    D. "Why would you want the window open?"

97. Which of the following questions should the nurse ask when assessing a 10-year-old patient for type 1 diabetes mellitus?

    A. "Are you going to the bathroom to pass your water more often?"
    B. "Are you sleeping more than 10 hours at night?"
    C. "Are you eating a lot of candy?"
    D. "Are you falling asleep after recess?"

98. The nurse caring for a patient from a culture not her own can increase her cultural sensitivity by

    A. being aware of the patient's social standards.
    B. paying attention to environmental cues.
    C. identifying her personal reaction to the patient.
    D. talking with other staff who have interacted with the patient.

99. The care plan of a patient who has Parkinson's disease should include which of the following measures?

   A. Serving three balanced meals daily to the patient
   B. Providing a full liquid diet for the patient
   C. Allowing the patient to eat at his/her own pace
   D. Assigning an aide or family member to feed the patient

100. A patient who is to undergo surgery will be signing an informed consent. The nurse's main responsibility when informed consent is obtained is to

   A. assure that the patient has not received any sedation two to three hours prior to signing the consent form.
   B. validate that the patient understands the procedure or the treatment.
   C. complete all blank spaces in front of the patient before witnessing.
   D. explain the procedure and any risk factors to the patient thoroughly.

101. Which of the following findings would a nurse suspect when she notices a colleague taking frequent breaks, working extra shifts and having inaccurate drug counts?

   A. The colleague is a victim of domestic violence.
   B. The colleague is abusing a substance.
   C. The colleague has a personality disorder.
   D. The colleague is trying to get out of work.

102. The parents of a six-month-old infant admitted with diarrhea are anxious and concerned. To involve the parents in the child's care, the nurse should first

   A. provide literature on diarrheal causes.
   B. allow the parents to record all diaper changes.
   C. teach the parents how to adhere to standard precautions.
   D. encourage the parents to continue the child's usual diet.

103. When teaching a caregiver in the home about flushing a child's central venous catheter, the nurse should instruct the caregiver to

   A. keep the telephone nearby to call the physician should problems occur.
   B. make certain the child has eaten before the procedure.
   C. use good hand-washing technique before and after the procedure.
   D. have all siblings out of the room during the procedure.

104. The charge nurse should assign the most experienced nurse to the patient who is

   A. depressed.
   B. violent.
   C. psychotic.
   D. manic.

105. A patient planning to become pregnant asks the prenatal nurse for dietary advice. To facilitate normal spinal cord formation in a developing fetus, the nurse should instruct the patient to include foods in her diet that contain

   A. fiber.
   B. calcium.
   C. folic acid.
   D. protein.

106. Before returning a child who is being treated for tuberculosis (TB) to his home, the community health nurse determines

   A. that the child has a private room.
   B. that all family members have been tested.
   C. home school placement.
   D. proper room ventilation.

107. The patient is hospitalized for the treatment of severe preeclampsia. Which of the following clinical manifestations would the nurse consider indicative of progression of the patient's condition?

   A. Generalized edema
   B. Proteinuria
   C. Elevated blood pressure
   D. Seizure activity

108. A nurse planning an educational program for families of patients who have attempted suicide should include which of the following statements in his teaching?

    A. Suicidal patients usually give out many overt clues.
    B. Suicidal patients will often completely isolate themselves immediately prior to the attempt.
    C. Suicidal patients display subtle changes in behavior.
    D. Suicidal patients do not display any changes that might indicate their despair.

109. The nurse is assessing a patient one day post-abdominal surgery. On auscultation, bowel sounds are absent. The nurse should recognize that this is indicative of

    A. ascites.
    B. an obstructed bowel.
    C. peritonitis.
    D. normal postoperative status.

110. A staff nurse observes behaviors in a coworker that suggest chemical impairment. What action should the nurse take first?

    A. Ignore the behavior
    B. Refer the co-worker to Alcoholics Anonymous
    C. Report the observed behavior to the nurse manager
    D. Discuss the nurse's behavior with her co-workers

111. A patient is receiving Total Parenteral Nutrition (TPN) secondary to acute pancreatitis. The nurse is about to administer insulin when the patient states, "Why am I getting insulin? I'm not diabetic." Which of the following responses would be the most appropriate?

    A. "The infection in your pancreas is causing too much insulin to be produced."
    B. "This type of infection stops the production of insulin."
    C. "The TPN solution contains a high amount of glucose."
    D. "The TPN solution interferes with the production of insulin."

112. When developing a teaching plan for a patient who is prescribed a sulfonylurea, the nurse should instruct the patient to avoid which of the following substances?

    A. Green vegetables
    B. Alcohol
    C. Beef products
    D. Caffeine

113. Which of the following nursing diagnoses should the mental health nurse address first in a patient with major depression?

    A. Severe anxiety
    B. Risk for self-directed violence
    C. Self-care deficit
    D. Ineffective coping

114. Which of the following laboratory values would the nurse expect to be elevated in a patient with a parasitic infection who recently immigrated to the United States?

    A. White blood cell count
    B. Reticulocyte count
    C. Eosinophils count
    D. Sedimentation rate

115. The charge nurse on a unit should be aware that which of the following patients may not legally sign an informed consent?

    A. A 55-year-old patient who is crying about the surgery she will be undergoing
    B. A 16-year-old married patient
    C. A 45-year-old patient who has been sedated
    D. An 80-year-old patient

116. Which of the following risk factors should a nurse recognize as the most reliable predictor of patient violence?

    A. Verbal threats
    B. Family history of violence
    C. Pacing behavior
    D. Past history of violence

117. Which of the following assessments should be reported as abnormal in a newborn at eight hours of age?

    A. Acrocyanosis
    B. Caput succedaneum
    C. Epstein's pearls
    D. Yellow sclera

118. A nurse has received an order for Total Parenteral Nutrition (TPN) for a patient admitted with severe malnutrition. Which of the following measures is essential before this order is initiated?

    A. A complete blood count has been obtained.
    B. A subclavian catheter is patent and a chest x-ray is done to confirm placement.
    C. Arm restraints should be in place during catheter insertion.
    D. An antecubital intravenous catheter is started and a baseline chemistry profile has been done.

119. Which of the following statements, if made by a patient who is constipated during pregnancy, indicates a correct understanding of the nurse's self-care instructions?

    A. "I will drink an 8-oz glass of water each day."
    B. "I plan to increase my iron supplements to twice a day now."
    C. "I am so happy that I can now eat four bananas a day."
    D. "I can take a brisk walk for one mile each day."

120. The patient with depression tells the nurse that life just doesn't seem to be worth living and his family would be better off without him. Which of the following interventions should the nurse initially utilize?

    A. Tell the patient that these are normal feelings with depression.
    B. Ask the patient if he is feeling suicidal.
    C. Let the patient know that these feelings will pass.
    D. Ignore the statement and continue with the interview.

121. When assessing a patient for posture and stature, the nurse recognizes that the patient is lying still and complaining of pain. Slight jarring of the bed causes agonizing pain. The nurse assesses that the origin of the pain may be

    A. renal.
    B. biliary.
    C. peritoneal.
    D. meningeal.

122. Which of the following strategies would the nurse manager include in a plan to assist an impaired colleague?

    A. Appoint a team to confront the colleague
    B. Initiate termination of the colleague
    C. Promote professional isolation
    D. Provide covert support of the substance-abusing behavior

123. A 35-week antepartal patient was involved in a two-car motor vehicle crash. The nurse should assess this patient for which of the following complications that would most likely cause both maternal and fetal mortality?

    A. Placenta previa
    B. Premature labor
    C. Spontaneous abortion
    D. Uterine rupture

124. The night nurse admits a six-month-old with acute laryngotracheobronchitis (LTB). The nurse should observe the child for which of the following physical findings?

    A. Drooling, dysphagia, high fever
    B. Hoarseness, stridor, low-grade fever
    C. Restlessness, absent breath sounds, high fever
    D. Low-grade fever, purulent nasal discharge, clear breath sounds

125. **A nurse is part of a multi-disciplinary team discussing an elderly patient's plan of care. The nurse recognizes that her role on the team is to**

A. serve as the group facilitator.
B. identify team members who don't understand the nursing role.
C. assure that her recommendations are adopted in the plan of care.
D. work with other team members to achieve a mutually agreed upon outcome.

126. **Which of the following statements, if made by a parent, would indicate the need for further investigation?**

A. "Whenever my five-year-old disobeys, he is instructed to go into 'time out' for five minutes."
B. "Whenever my 10-year-old fails a test, we ask the teacher to re-teach the information."
C. "Whenever my two-year-old wets the bed at naptime, we withhold fluids for the remainder of the day."
D. "Whenever my one-year-old drops an item, we pick it up."

127. **A patient hospitalized for a physical illness exhibits restlessness, tremors, elevated temperature, elevated blood pressure, complaints of night time leg cramps and diaphoresis within two days of admission. The nurse should recognize that these symptoms suggest**

A. a systemic infection.
B. gastrointestinal hypermotility.
C. alcohol withdrawal.
D. neurologic dysfunction.

128. **A nurse is performing a neurological check on a patient who is one day post-craniotomy. The nurse notices that the patient's eyes are not conjugated when turned right laterally. Which of the following cranial nerves should the nurse suspect is damaged?**

A. Cranial nerve II – optic
B. Cranial nerve V – trigeminal
C. Cranial nerve VI – abducens
D. Cranial nerve VII – facial

129. **A 12-month-old received immunizations at his well-child visit. Fourteen days later, the mother reports that the child has a fire-red maculopapular rash on the trunk and extremities. This rash is most likely due to which of the following vaccines?**

A. DTP (diphtheria, tetanus, pertussis)
B. OPV (oral poliovirus vaccine)
C. MMR (measles, mumps, rubella)
D. Hib (Haemophilus influenzae type b)

130. **When teaching parents first aid for minor burns, a nurse should instruct the parents to**

A. cover the burned area with cotton gauze.
B. apply ice directly to the burned area.
C. coat the burned area lightly with petroleum jelly.
D. immerse the burned area in cool water.

131. **A patient is prescribed chlorpropamide (Diabinese). The nurse should notify the physician if the patient reports being allergic to**

A. aspirin.
B. penicillin.
C. iodine.
D. sulfur.

132. **Under the Good Samaritan Act, a nurse may be held liable for patient abandonment at the scene of an emergency in which of the following cases?**

A. The nurse does not stop to provide assistance.
B. The nurse begins assistance and then abruptly stops.
C. The nurse does not initiate care.
D. The nurse does not perform under the direct order of a physician.

133. **A patient who has cirrhosis of the liver has been treated for hepatic encephalopathy. In preparing the patient for discharge, the nurse discusses dietary protein restrictions. Which of these menu choices, if selected by the patient, would indicate an understanding of foods that are low in protein?**

A. Fruit and cheese platter
B. Tuna fish and tomato sandwich
C. Vegetable soup and tossed green salad
D. Meat loaf with rice

134. During a family therapy session, the nurse notes that the wife is sitting with her arms and legs crossed and her body turned away from her husband. This non-verbal behavior is an example of

    A. incongruence.
    B. distancing.
    C. blocking.
    D. cultural posturing.

135. A nurse is approached by a patient who is experiencing persecutory delusions and requests assistance to escape from the psychiatric unit. Which of the following nursing actions would be most appropriate?

    A. Logically explain the nature of delusions to the patient
    B. Encourage the patient to verbalize the delusions
    C. Attempt to learn the meaning of the delusion to the patient
    D. Point out the false beliefs present in the patient's delusion

136. Which of the following signs would the nurse expect to identify when assessing a patient who has anorexia nervosa?

    A. Decreased heart rate, increased hair loss
    B. Increased body temperature, increased body mass
    C. Increased blood pressure, hyperkalemia
    D. Decreased white blood cells, decreased cholesterol levels

137. During the first year of life, the infant experiences a rapid period of growth and development. At the end of the first year, it is expected that the infant's weight in comparison to birth weight has

    A. doubled.
    B. tripled.
    C. quadrupled.
    D. multiplied.

138. The best method of documenting the physical growth of a three-year-old is to

    A. record the birth weight and current weight.
    B. calculate the body surface area on a nomogram.
    C. plot the child on the Denver II Developmental Screening Test.
    D. use growth charts over time.

139. Because it is highest in protein, the nurse should offer which of the following foods as a between-meal nourishment to a patient recuperating from extensive burns?

    A. Applesauce
    B. Baked custard
    C. Gelatin with fruit
    D. Buttered toast

140. A patient who has a history of being sexually abused is most at risk for developing which of the following disorders?

    A. Attention deficit hyperactivity
    B. Munchausen syndrome
    C. Bipolar disorder
    D. Dissociative reaction

141. Which statement best exemplifies spiritual distress in relation to adult survivors of childhood sexual abuse?

    A. "Life is not fair."
    B. "It was my fault that this happened."
    C. "I don't go to church every week."
    D. "I'm going to pray for the person who did this to me."

142. Which of the following neuromuscular assessments would the nurse expect to find in a healthy term infant?

    A. Absent stepping reflex
    B. Asymmetrical Moro reflex
    C. Positive Babinski reflex
    D. Unilateral grasp reflex

143. A nurse suspects that a psychiatric patient is not taking her oral medication. Which of the following actions should the nurse take?

    A. Obtain an order to change the patient's medication to intramuscular form
    B. Observe the patient for signs of swallowing the medication
    C. Engage the patient in conversation for at least five minutes after she takes the medication
    D. Inspect the patient's mouth after each dose of medication

144. Which of the following behaviors by a 36-month-old child supports a nursing diagnosis of growth and development, altered?

    A. Does not link syllables together
    B. Uses pointing to communicate
    C. Stutters when speaking
    D. Often repeats and hesitates

145. During the flushing of a peripherally inserted central catheter (PICC), the nurse realizes the line will not flush. The nurse's next step would be to

    A. contact the primary practitioner on call.
    B. continue to flush the catheter using a smaller-size syringe.
    C. examine the line for kinks.
    D. hold the medication until the next dose is due.

146. Which of the following questions by the nurse would be most appropriate in responding to a patient's request for pain medication two hours before the next dose is due?

    A. "Have you been dependent on drugs in the past?"
    B. "Are you able to think about something else besides your pain?"
    C. "On the pain rating scale of one to 10, what level of pain are you experiencing?"
    D. "Can you wait two more hours until the next dose of medication is due?"

147. Which of the following psychiatric disturbances are most common among the elderly?

    A. Depression
    B. Anxiety
    C. Bipolar disorders
    D. Personality disorders

148. A patient in the emergency department has multiple fractured ribs and a right-sided tension pneumothorax. The nurse would expect to prepare the patient for which of the following procedures?

    A. Electrocardiogram
    B. Urinary catheter placement
    C. Chest tube insertion
    D. Gastric lavage

149. A patient experiences difficulty falling asleep. Which of the following drinks should the nurse offer to the patient at bedtime?

    A. A cup of coffee
    B. A glass of wine
    C. A glass of milk
    D. A can of soda

150. The physician writes a "DNR" order on a patient's chart. The nurse should understand that DNR stands for

    A. dopamine and nitroglycerin recombination.
    B. diagnostic neurological radiation.
    C. do not resuscitate.
    D. dependent nitrogen re-uptake.

 You have finished the Nursing, Part 1 portion of Practice Test A. Feel free to take a break (a one-hour lunch break will be provided at the Qualifying Exam) before beginning Nursing, Part 2 of Practice Test A. Do not turn the page until you are ready to begin Part 2.

Practice Exam A: Nursing, Part 2

You will have one hour and 50 minutes to complete Nursing, Part 2.

1. Which of the following nursing diagnoses would be appropriate for a patient who has a phobia?

    A. Self-esteem disturbance
    B. Sensory perceptual alteration
    C. Fear related to specific stimulus
    D. Alteration in thought process

2. Which of the following instructions should a nurse provide to a patient who has diabetes and hypertrophic lipodystrophy?

    A. Rotate insulin injection sites
    B. Inject insulin at the edge of the affected area
    C. Withhold injection of insulin until the area heals
    D. Use a longer needle to administer the insulin

3. Which of the following findings would be the best indicator of the severity of a patient's pain?

    A. The patient states that his pain is a nine on the pain intensity scale.
    B. The patient's blood pressure is 160/88 and pulse is 80.
    C. The patient is grimacing and tensing his muscles.
    D. The patient is moaning and crying.

4. During an initial infertility visit, the nurse teaches a patient how to record basal body temperature. Which of the following instructions is appropriate?

    A. "Take your temperature before going to sleep each night."
    B. "Begin taking your temperature on the tenth day of your cycle."
    C. "Take your temperature before arising each morning."
    D. "You need at least four hours of uninterrupted sleep before taking your temperature."

5. Which nursing action should the nurse take first to prevent medication noncompliance in a patient with schizophrenia?

    A. Teach benefits of medication compliance
    B. Build rapport with patient
    C. Give medication in an alternate route
    D. Assure the patient that the medication is safe to take

6. When evaluating an infant's laboratory results for effectiveness of phototherapy, the home health nurse should expect which of the following outcomes?

    A. Decreased serum bilirubin
    B. Increased urine specific gravity
    C. Decreased red blood cell count
    D. Increased platelet count

7. Twelve hours postpartum the nurse assesses uterine involution and documents normal progression when the fundus is palpated

    A. at the level of the umbilicus.
    B. midway between the umbilicus and the symphysis pubis.
    C. one cm above the umbilicus.
    D. two cm below the umbilicus.

8. A patient is in pain following surgery. Which of the following instructions should the nurse give to the patient regarding pain management?

    A. "Try to bear the pain as long as you can."
    B. "Pain should be reported in the early stages."
    C. "Higher levels of pain are easier to reduce than low levels."
    D. "Our goal is to keep you pain free."

9. A patient reports all of the following symptoms. Which one of these symptoms would indicate to the nurse a serious complication of systemic lupus erythematosus?

    A. Fatigue
    B. Hematuria
    C. Joint pain
    D. Oral ulcers

10. Which of the following disorders would a nurse expect to identify when assessing a patient who is experiencing afternoon slumps, carbohydrate craving and weight gain during the fall and winter months that disappear in spring and summer?

    A. Major depressive disorder
    B. Seasonal affective disorder
    C. Dysthymic disorder
    D. Bipolar disorder

11. A nurse caring for a patient who has an ileal conduit (ileal loop) following a cystectomy for bladder cancer should teach the patient that the type of drainage expected from the stoma is

    A. clear urine.
    B. urine streaked with blood.
    C. urine and mucous shreds.
    D. both urine and feces.

12. A physician orders EMLA cream with intravenous (IV) insertion. The nurse plans to

    A. apply the cream to the IV insertion needle.
    B. apply the cream 60 minutes prior to the insertion of the IV.
    C. apply the cream to the insertion site dressing.
    D. apply the cream after cleansing the skin for insertion of the needle.

13. During a home health visit by the nurse, the parent of an 18-month-old states, "I expect my son to be toilet-trained and have no accidents." Which of the following comments by the nurse would be most appropriate?

    A. "At 18 months, your child should be fully toilet-trained."
    B. "Let's talk about your expectations for your son."
    C. "At what age were you toilet-trained?"
    D. "Toilet-training can be a difficult process."

14. Which of the following children would need to be evaluated immediately in an emergency department?

    A. A child who presents with a loud, bark-like cough without swallowing problems
    B. A child who presents with a fever of 102°F for the last two hours
    C. A child who has green, watery-type stools for the last 24 hours
    D. A child who has a low blood pressure, a pulse of 60 beats per minute and petechia on the face and trunk

15. To which of the following nursing diagnoses would a nurse manager give priority when an impaired nurse returns to work?

    A. Ineffective individual coping
    B. Situational low self-esteem
    C. Growth and development, altered
    D. Ineffective family coping: compromised

16. During a non-stress test (NST), the nurse would apply the fetal transducer to the maternal abdomen over the

    A. fetal back.
    B. placenta.
    C. symphysis pubis.
    D. fetal head.

17. A school-aged child with asthma is scheduled to return to school. Which question by the nurse assesses the child's self-care knowledge?

    A. "Do you use your peak expiratory flow meter (PEFM) daily?"
    B. "Do you have stairs to climb at school?"
    C. "Do you drink eight glasses of fluid a day?"
    D. "Do you participate in gym class?"

18. When administering low-dose potassium chloride (KCl) through a peripheral intravenous (IV) to a pediatric patient, the nurse should be aware that the child is at risk for developing which of the following conditions?

    A. Chemical phlebitis
    B. Extravasation
    C. Pulmonary edema
    D. Thrombophlebitis

19. A patient who is in acute renal failure has hyperkalemia. Which of these drugs should the nurse anticipate administering to the patient?

   A. Lactulose (Cephulac)
   B. Sodium polystyrene sulfonate (Kayexalate)
   C. Sodium bicarbonate (NaHCO3)
   D. Phytonadione (vitamin K1)

20. A group of new mothers is attending classes on parenting. The nurse should stress that the most important source of nutrition for infants during the first year is

   A. homogenized whole milk.
   B. iron-fortified homogenized whole milk.
   C. commercial infant formula.
   D. Commercial iron-fortified infant formula.

21. To provide psychiatric home care to a patient, which of the following information would be most important for the nurse to obtain first?

   A. Home-bound status
   B. Payment source
   C. Written orders from a psychiatrist
   D. A chronic mental illness diagnosis

22. During a routine physical examination of a 24-year-old pregnant female, multiple bruises are noted on the abdomen and abrasions on both arms. The patient reports falling down some stairs. Which of the following actions should the nurse take first?

   A. Instruct the patient on proper footwear to prevent falls
   B. Continue the physical assessment to collect information on any injuries
   C. Question the patient about spousal abuse
   D. Evaluate the patient's feelings about her pregnancy

23. A nurse educating a patient on the correct use of a metered-dose inhaler should instruct the patient to

   A. take several short shallow breaths before inhaling the drug.
   B. hold the breath after inhaling the drug.
   C. cough before inhaling the drug.
   D. press the cartridge down before inhaling the drug.

24. When assessing a patient, the nurse notes pallor and mottling of the skin, dyspnea with periods of apnea and a decline in blood pressure. These manifestations are indicative of

   A. imminent death.
   B. a transient ischemic attack.
   C. seizure onset.
   D. a cerebrovascular accident.

25. Which of the following actions may be delegated by the registered nurse (RN) to a licensed practical nurse (LPN)?

   A. Administering oral medications
   B. Evaluating the ability of the patient to perform three-point crutch walking
   C. Developing the nursing care plan
   D. Teaching the patient to administer insulin

26. A patient with chronic schizophrenia is seen monthly by the home health nurse for administration of Prolixin. On one visit, the patient refuses his medication. The nurse should

   A. arrange for another visit to administer the medication.
   B. inform the patient that he must take the medication.
   C. arrange for a relative to add an oral dose of the medication to the patient's morning orange juice.
   D. tell the patient that if he refused the injection, he would have to be hospitalized.

27. A 25-year-old female who recently experienced date rape reports feeling irritable all the time, an inability to fall asleep due to fear of dreaming and loss of interest in finishing her university courses. A nursing diagnosis of rape-trauma syndrome: silent reaction, is made. Which of the following nursing interventions would be most appropriate for the woman?

   A. Establish a contract that she will attend school classes regularly.
   B. Facilitate exploration of primary and secondary gains related to the rape.
   C. Review risks related to denial of traumatic event.
   D. Explore defensive response to physical attack.

28. A woman who is 24 hours postpartum complains to the nurse that she sweated profusely during the night. The nurse's response should be based on the understanding that the woman is experiencing

    A. hypovolemia.
    B. a postpartal infection.
    C. a normal postpartal response.
    D. the initial signs of hyponatremia.

29. Which of the following physical assessment findings would require the nurse to refer a patient for evaluation for breast cancer?

    A. Freely moveable breast lesions
    B. Breast tenderness during or before menstruation
    C. Breast lesions with difficult-to-define edges
    D. Bilateral breast lesions

30. Which of the following behaviors by a 36-month-old child supports a nursing diagnosis of growth and development, altered?

    A. Walks holding onto furniture
    B. Sits down from a standing position
    C. Can push and pull toys
    D. Throws a ball overhead

31. A patient who is scheduled for an abdominal cholecystectomy is given preoperative instructions by a nurse. Which of the following statements by the patient indicates the need for further instruction?

    A. "I will splint my incisional area when coughing."
    B. "I will use an incentive spirometer every one to two hours."
    C. "When I turn, I will need to move my body like a log."
    D. "A few hours after surgery, I will sit up at the bedside."

32. On a second visit to the doctor's office, the nurse weighs a 46-year-old overweight, West African female and tells her that she has lost 10 lbs since her last visit a month ago. The nurse compliments the patient for following her diet plan. The patient begins to cry and states, "I was planning to return to my country in two weeks, now I cannot do so looking this thin." Which of the following nursing diagnoses would be most appropriate?

    A. Ineffective individual coping related to poor self-esteem
    B. Body image disturbance related to physical appearance
    C. Knowledge deficit related to health needs
    D. Powerlessness related to poor judgment

33. An elderly, confused patient who lives alone is admitted to the hospital with hypokalemia. The patient was prescribed a potassium supplement two weeks ago. Which of the following nursing diagnoses would be most appropriate for the patient?

    A. Non-compliance related to lack of teaching
    B. Home maintenance management, impaired related to decreased income
    C. Fluid volume deficit related to sodium excretion
    D. Knowledge deficit related to poor memory

34. The nurse caring for a patient requiring total parenteral nutrition (TPN) should be aware that which of the following substances may be administered piggy-backed to a TPN infusion?

    A. Corticosteroids
    B. Packed cells
    C. Lipids
    D. Osmotic diuretics

35. A patient has begun prenatal care in the first trimester of pregnancy. The nurse should instruct the patient to return for the next visit in how many weeks?

    A. One
    B. Two
    C. Four
    D. Eight

36. When assessing a patient for pain, the nurse observes facial grimacing with movement, and blood pressure and pulse elevation. The patient refuses pain medication. Which of the following measures should the nurse take next?

    A. Realize the patient has the right to refuse medication.
    B. Explain the reasons for taking pain medication.
    C. Tell the patient to notify the nurse when the pain becomes severe.
    D. Leave the medication at the bedside in case the patient desires it later.

37. A two-year-old arrives in the emergency room with an elevated temperature. During the physical examination, the child's color becomes dusky, the body stiffens and the extremities begin to twitch. The nurse should be aware that the child is most probably experiencing

    A. febrile seizures.
    B. respiratory arrest.
    C. a temper tantrum.
    D. shivering.

38. A 19-year-old woman, 5'8" tall and weighing 92 lbs, is diagnosed with anorexia nervosa. In planning her care, the nurse should address which of the following manifestations first?

    A. Body image
    B. Physiological damage
    C. Preoccupation with food
    D. Need for control

39. Which of the following assessment findings would suggest to the home health nurse that the patient is developing congestive heart failure (CHF)?

    A. Orthopnea
    B. Weight loss
    C. Fever
    D. Calf pain

40. The nurse is teaching the parents of a ventilator-dependent child who is living at home about preventing complications. Which of the following measures should be included in the plan?

    A. Encourage increased cold fluids by mouth
    B. Institute infection control methods
    C. Increase playful interactions with other children
    D. Place the child in Trendelenburg position during suctioning

41. A nurse conducts a community education program on child abuse. A primary preventive strategy for child abuse would be that the parents

    A. finish high school.
    B. move in with family.
    C. visit a safe house.
    D. attend a parenting class.

42. A 73-year-old with a history of hepatitis B is being discharged from the outpatient center after an abdominal paracentesis. The patient asks if she can take aspirin for any discomfort. The nurse's response should be based on which of the following statements?

    A. Enteric-coated aspirin would decrease gastric distress.
    B. Aspirin is contraindicated.
    C. Acetaminophen provides more effective pain control.
    D. Pain medication should not be necessary following the procedure.

43. The nurse teaching a patient about the use of transdermal 17ß (beta) estradiol administration during the menopausal period should include which of the following information?

    A. The drug requires once or twice a week dosing.
    B. The drug provides direct delivery of progestin to the bloodstream.
    C. The drug produces a predictable monthly bleeding pattern.
    D. The drug is more cost-effective than other medications.

44. A patient has had a total abdominal hysterectomy. Which of the following instructions would be important to prevent the development of a deep vein thrombosis (DVT)?

    A. Limit intake of fluids
    B. Limit activity for two weeks
    C. Change positions frequently
    D. Massage the incision daily

45. A breast-feeding mother who is eight days postpartum telephones the postpartum unit complaining of a reddened, painful breast and elevated temperature. Which of the following responses by the nurse would be the most appropriate?

    A. "Stop breast-feeding because you probably have an infection."
    B. "Notify your healthcare provider because you may need medication."
    C. "Continue breast-feeding until the pain begins to subside."
    D. "Breast-feed only on the unaffected breast."

46. A patient with diabetes mellitus asks the nurse if he should exercise. The nurse's response should be based on the theory that exercise will

    A. increase blood sugar.
    B. decrease levels of high-density lipoproteins.
    C. decrease the body's need for insulin.
    D. increase total cholesterol.

47. Which of the following comments by a nurse would be most therapeutic when caring for a depressed patient with suicidal ideation who has recently begun to give away cherished personal items?

    A. "You seem to be under stress lately. Would you like to talk about it?"
    B. "You gave away cherished items. Do you have a suicide plan?"
    C. "Is there a reason for giving away your cherished items? Tell me about your feelings."
    D. "Has there been a change in your life?"

48. The nurse caring for a patient with jaundice should expect to see an elevation in which of the following laboratory values?

    A. Serum ammonia
    B. Blood urea nitrogen
    C. Serum albumin
    D. Serum bilirubin

49. A patient taking the drug glipizide (Glucotrol) should be assessed by the nurse for which of the following side effects?

    A. Agranulocytosis
    B. Vitamin B1 deficiency
    C. Hyperlipidemia
    D. Hypernatremia

50. A staff nurse on an oncology unit tells the nurse in charge that he does not want to care for dying patients. The nurse in charge initially should

    A. not assign the staff nurse to care for dying patients.
    B. send the staff nurse to meet with the agency spiritual advisor.
    C. ask the nurse to discuss the reason for his statement.
    D. tell the staff nurse that he should request a transfer to another unit.

51. An eight-month-old infant is carried into the emergency room by a parent. The child recently had a seizure and is now lethargic and bradycardic, and there is a retinal hemorrhage noted on the x-ray. This child is most likely exhibiting signs and symptoms of

    A. mastoid bone fracture.
    B. Munchausen syndrome by proxy.
    C. shaken baby syndrome.
    D. sexual abuse.

52. A patient who is suspected of having hypothyroidism should be expected to have which of these symptoms?

    A. Tachycardia
    B. Weight loss
    C. Hyperthermia
    D. Facial edema

53. When taking a home health history from a depressed patient, which of the following statements should the nurse investigate first?

    A. "I go to day treatment five times a week."
    B. "I go to the psychiatrist twice a month."
    C. "I hear voices telling me to stay home."
    D. "I can't leave my house; I don't have a car."

54. A physician has written all of the following orders for a patient who has a diagnosis of septic shock. Which order should a nurse carry out first?

    A. Obtain culture specimens
    B. Initiate antibiotic therapy
    C. Insert indwelling urinary catheter
    D. Apply antiembolism stockings

55. A pregnant patient's fetus has just been diagnosed with sickle cell anemia. Which of the following interventions by the nurse would be most appropriate?

    A. Provide extensive information regarding the disease process
    B. Allow the patient to be alone if she is crying
    C. Encourage the patient to discuss her concerns
    D. Avoid the topic of the disease altogether until the patient is ready to discuss it

56. An 82-year-old patient is experiencing confusion and forgetfulness. He is diagnosed with vascular dementia. The family asks the nurse for the information about the cause of this disorder. Which of the following statements made by the nurse is correct?

    A. "The cause of this type of dementia is unknown."
    B. "Vascular dementia is the result of many small strokes damaging areas of the brain."
    C. "Vascular dementia is caused by a viral infection."
    D. "The dementia symptoms are caused by the medications he is taking."

57. The purpose of a biophysical profile (BPP) in a 36-week diabetic patient is to

    A. determine fetal lung maturity.
    B. determine gestational age.
    C. determine fetal well-being.
    D. determine maternal uterine activity.

58. A patient is admitted following a motor vehicle accident with a high blood alcohol level. The nurse should monitor the patient for which of the following symptoms of alcohol withdrawal?

    A. Sweating, tremors, nausea and vomiting
    B. Pleasant mood, hyperactivity, increased appetite
    C. Drowsiness, irritability, unsteady gait
    D. Insomnia, decreased blood pressure and heart rate

59. A patient who has poor impulse control and episodic aggression is scheduled for an electroencephalogram (EEG) and magnetic resonance imaging (MRI). The nurse's responsibility in preparing the patient for these tests includes

    A. restricting anything by mouth after midnight.
    B. explaining the procedures and providing reassurance.
    C. withholding all medications for three days prior to the tests.
    D. inquiring about allergies and administering radiopaque dye tablets.

60. A nurse in an inpatient psychiatric unit spends much of her time observing patient activity, talking with patients, and intervening to maintain or restore order when patients become disruptive. This specific example of the intervention step of the nursing process is called

    A. health teaching.
    B. case management.
    C. milieu therapy.
    D. self-care activities.

61. A couple in their 30s seeks out the obstetrician because they have not been able to conceive after 18 months of unprotected intercourse. They do not have children. They are diagnosed with primary infertility. What information supports that diagnosis?

    A. Both partners are in their 30s
    B. They do not have children
    C. They have been trying for 18 months
    D. Both partners are concerned about not conceiving

62. A nurse makes all of these observations of a patient who has acute nonlymphocytic leukemia. Which one should be reported immediately?

    A. Ecchymosis
    B. Fatigue
    C. Hematuria
    D. Pallor

63. An infant is to receive 28 mg of phenobarbital (Luminal) orally per day divided into two equal doses for seizure control. The medication is dispensed as 20 mg per 5 ml. How many milliliters should the nurse administer for each dose?

    A. 2.8
    B. 3.5
    C. 5.6
    D. 7.0

64. Which of the following nursing diagnoses should receive priority for a patient who is hearing voices telling him that he would be better off dead?

    A. Fear related to learned response associated with abuse
    B. Risk for violence: self-directed related to auditory hallucinations
    C. Impaired social interaction related to isolation
    D. Impaired verbal communication related to confusion

65. A physiologic mechanism that results in an increased risk of foot infections in a patient diagnosed with type 1 diabetes mellitus (IDDM) is

    A. hyperglycemia.
    B. hyperkalemia.
    C. renal insufficiency.
    D. gastroperesis.

66. The nurse is instructing a patient and his significant other about the diet for dysphagia. Which of the following food choices should the nurse include in the teaching?

    A. Diced meat
    B. Soft-cooked vegetables
    C. Applesauce
    D. Scrambled eggs

67. Which observation would a nurse expect to make in the home of a patient diagnosed with passive suicidal behaviors?

    A. Farewell letters written to family members
    B. Medication noncompliance
    C. Bills past due for the last six months
    D. An unkempt house and yard

68. A 13-year-old with a leg length discrepancy is being discharged with an Ilizarov external fixator (IEF). Which of the following instructions should the nurse include in the discharge teaching?

    A. Methods to manage bedrest at home until the Ilizarov is removed
    B. Daily observations of the color and movement in both lower extremities
    C. The importance of not touching the pins and keeping the pins free of any moisture
    D. The necessity of returning to the physician for all distractions to be done

69. A pregnant woman is diagnosed with hepatitis A. Supportive care recommended by the nurse should include which of the following measures?

    A. Taking ibuprofen for pain
    B. Eating three large meals a day
    C. Scheduling rest periods throughout the day
    D. Restricting fluids during the acute phase

70. **A nurse is instructing a patient about a mammogram. Which of the following instructions should the nurse include during patient teaching?**

    A. Do not drink fluids for four hours prior to the test.
    B. Do not use deodorant in the underarm area before the test.
    C. The x-ray procedure should be completed within one hour.
    D. No pain or discomfort will be experienced during the procedure.

71. **Which of the following physical assessment findings in an elderly patient should the nurse report to the physician?**

    A. Large pupils
    B. Increased lacrimal secretions
    C. Thickened, yellow lenses
    D. Reddened sclera

72. **Which of the following signs would most likely be observed in a term newborn of a mother who received magnesium sulfate?**

    A. Increased heart rate
    B. Decreased muscle tone
    C. Reflex irritability
    D. Pale color

73. **A patient shares with the nurse that his wife placed a spider web in his wound to promote healing. This is an example of**

    A. herbal medicine.
    B. natural folk medicine.
    C. voodoo.
    D. quackery.

74. **The physician evaluates the most recent set of arterial blood gases (ABGs) of a patient with acute respiratory distress syndrome (ARDS) and orders an increase in the positive end expiratory pressure (PEEP) from 5 cm of H2O to 10 cm of H2O. Based on this change in therapy, the nurse should anticipate which of the following ABG findings?**

    A. decreased PaO2.
    B. increased PaO2.
    C. decreased HCO3.
    D. increased PaCO2.

75. **A staff nurse finds his patient crying because the physician has stated that the patient cannot return home alone and she does not have family nearby. After discussing the patient's concerns, the nurse should contact which of these staff for follow-up?**

    A. Case manager
    B. Social worker
    C. Hospital chaplain
    D. Hospital controller

76. **A symptom related to acute stress is**

    A. bradycardia.
    B. diarrhea.
    C. hyperglycemia.
    D. edema.

77. **The nurse caring for an elderly trauma patient should be aware that which of the following measures should be used to accurately determine fluid volume status?**

    A. Urinary output determination
    B. Serial hemoglobin and hematocrit values
    C. Invasive hemodynamic monitoring
    D. Serial blood pressure readings

78. **To communicate effectively with the parents of a hospitalized child, the nurse should**

    A. understand that non-verbal communication is meaningful.
    B. have empathy with the parents, but realize that the nurse should be in control of the situation.
    C. acknowledge positive comments and ignore negative comments.
    D. present policy and procedures in detail upon admission.

79. **Which of the following patient statements indicates to the nurse a positive outcome at discharge?**

    A. A mastectomy patient states, "I'm anxious to meet the others in the support group next Tuesday."
    B. A patient with end-stage cirrhosis states, "I'm glad I can control the pain with frequent medication."
    C. A newly diagnosed diabetic patient states, "I can now eat all the diet foods I want."
    D. A patient with a recent leg amputation states, "I wish I didn't have to use this wheelchair all the time."

80. Which of the following statements, if made by a patient following education about the use of rofecoxib (Vioxx), would indicate the need for additional instruction?

    A. "I will take the medication with food."
    B. "I guess I will have to have my wife do the driving while I'm on this medication."
    C. "I will report any changes in vision to my doctor."
    D. "I'm glad this new drug is available because I'm allergic to other arthritis drugs."

81. A woman on oral contraceptives presents to the clinic with her third vaginal infection in the past year. Which of the following recommendations should be included in the nurse's teaching of the patient?

    A. Abstain from intercourse for one month after treatment
    B. Soak in a warm water bath twice a day for 10 days
    C. Refrain from douching
    D. Discontinue oral contraception

82. A patient arrives at the emergency department with a history of a fall and a complaint of abdominal pain. Assessment findings are blood pressure 101/68, pulse 116 and regular, respirations 24, capillary refill four seconds, and thirst. The nurse assessing the patient should be aware that these signs and symptoms are indicative of

    A. gall bladder inflammation.
    B. intra-abdominal hemorrhage.
    C. septicemia.
    D. cardiogenic shock.

83. An HIV-positive patient is prescribed zidovudine (AZT) and ganciclovir (Cytovene). The nurse should be aware that both drugs have which of the following side effects?

    A. Peripheral neuropathy
    B. Insomnia
    C. Anticholinergic effects
    D. Bone marrow suppression

84. A patient is using the Lamaze method of childbirth and is 8 cm dilated. Which of the following statements should the nurse anticipate the patient might make during this stage of labor?

    A. "I'm much more comfortable lying flat in bed."
    B. "It feels good to push with my contraction."
    C. "Don't touch my stomach when I have a contraction."
    D. "I don't feel much pain at all."

85. The nurse should carry out which of the following interventions first when caring for a patient experiencing variable decelerations during labor?

    A. Encourage the patient to breathe deeply
    B. Administer oxygen, 2L/min via face mask
    C. Reposition the patient onto her left side
    D. Cleanse the perineum in preparation for delivery

86. When introducing solid foods to infants, the parents should be instructed to

    A. introduce new food between regular meals.
    B. introduce one new food every four to seven days.
    C. mix new food in with infant formula.
    D. mix new food in with infant cereal.

87. Which of the following statements, if made by a patient who has diabetes mellitus, would indicate an understanding of teaching on diabetes and alcohol?

    A. "Alcohol may be taken in moderate amounts with my meals."
    B. "Alcohol will cause an increase in my blood sugar."
    C. "Alcohol will decrease my susceptibility to infections."
    D. "Alcohol intake will cause a decreased need for insulin."

88. Patients with eating disorders should also be assessed for which other psychiatric disorder?

    A. Schizophrenia
    B. Conduct disorder
    C. Depression
    D. Borderline personality disorder

89. A patient is admitted to the hospital with a closed head injury. The nurse observes a yellow ring encircling a clear moist area on the patient's pillow. The nurse should recognize this finding as

    A. an indication of a decrease in cranial pressure.
    B. an indication that the patient had an emesis prior to admission.
    C. a sign of cerebro-spinal fluid drainage.
    D. an indication of an emergency situation requiring the physician to be notified.

90. Which of the following assessment findings would alert the nurse to anticipate the development of jaundice in a full-term newborn?

    A. A negative direct Coombs test result
    B. Presence of a cephalohematoma
    C. Infant blood type of O negative
    D. Maternal rubella status, immune

91. Prior to surgery for a total laryngectomy, the preoperative teaching plan for a patient should include which of the following measures?

    A. How to "log-roll" when turning after surgery
    B. The need to remove spicy foods from the postoperative diet
    C. How to communicate using alternative, nonverbal methods
    D. The need to limit the uses of narcotic medications postoperatively

92. When caring for a patient experiencing status asthmaticus, which of the following signs should alert the nurse to impending respiratory failure?

    A. Audible wheezing
    B. Absence of wheezing
    C. Crackles during expiration
    D. Rhonchi during inspiration

93. When instructing the parents of an infant about enhancing development of walking, the nurse should discuss which of the following methods?

    A. Allowing infants to play in cribs and pull themselves up
    B. Keeping infants in play pens with age-specific toys
    C. Placing infants on floor mats in reach of age-specific toys
    D. Using baby walkers and jumper seats

94. Which of the following nursing diagnoses would be most appropriate for a patient with hyperthyroidism?

    A. Altered nutrition, more than body requirements, related to slowed metabolic rate
    B. Impaired skin integrity related to edema and dryness
    C. Altered comfort related to cold intolerance
    D. Activity intolerance related to fatigue

95. An obese adolescent is seen in the health clinic for a routine examination. The patient expresses a desire to begin a weight reduction plan. Which of the following statements would indicate to the nurse that the child is motivated to lose weight?

    A. "I am just too fat and clumsy."
    B. "I feel tired and am not interested in my school work."
    C. "I often sit home and read or watch television."
    D. "I like to walk and visit with my friends."

96. The physician orders a corticosteroid inhaler (four puffs bid) for a patient with asthma. Which of the following actions by the patient should indicate to the nurse that the patient needs further teaching?

    A. Taking the four puffs in rapid succession
    B. Pausing for one to two minutes between puffs
    C. Rinsing his mouth with water after inhaling
    D. Inhaling the medication slowly

97. A po analgesic is ordered every four hours prn for breakthrough pain for a patient receiving an epidural narcotic. The nurse should be aware that the best time to administer this analgesic is

    A. every four hours around the clock.
    B. when the patient states that he is experiencing a sudden increase in pain.
    C. when the nurse notices increased tolerance to the epidural.
    D. when the patient's family member states that the patient is in pain.

98. Which of the following nursing strategies best promotes communication with a preschool-aged patient?

    A. Use drawings and stories to explain care
    B. Explain care when it is given
    C. Use objects to explain care
    D. Provide written explanations of care

99. Thirty minutes after the nurse removes a nasogastric tube that has been in place for seven days, the patient experiences epistaxis (nosebleed). Which of the following nursing actions is most appropriate to control the bleeding?

    A. Apply pressure by pinching the anterior portion of the nose for five to 10 minutes
    B. Place the patient in a sitting position with the neck hyperextended
    C. Pack the nostrils with gauze and keep the gauze in place for four to five days
    D. Apply ice compresses to the patient's forehead and back of the neck

100. A charge nurse observes that three staff members are arguing about their patient care assignments. Using the democratic style of leadership the charge nurse should

    A. ignore the situation.
    B. facilitate a discussion of which staff member does what tasks.
    C. tell the staff to work out their differences on their own.
    D. meet with each staff member at the end of the workday.

101. A patient has returned to the unit following a bronchoscopy. It is most important that the nurse monitor the patient for

    A. bladder distention.
    B. return of gag reflex.
    C. oral fluid intake.
    D. ability to speak.

102. A home health nurse reviews the dietary history of a patient with congestive heart failure. The nurse should instruct the patient to eliminate which of the following foods to comply with a sodium-restricted diet?

    A. Skim milk and breakfast cereals
    B. Fresh and frozen fruits and vegetables
    C. Lunch meat sandwiches and dill pickles
    D. Baked turkey and fish dinners

103. At 16 weeks' gestation, no fetal heart rate was detected during assessment of a pregnant patient. An ultrasound confirmed a hydatidiform molar pregnancy. Which of the following actions should the nurse tell the patient to expect during her one-year follow-up?

    A. Multiple serum chorionic gonadotropin levels will be drawn.
    B. An intrauterine device will be used to decrease vaginal bleeding.
    C. Pregnancy will be restricted for another year.
    D. Oral contraceptives will not be prescribed because they will increase the risk of cancer.

104. Which of the following nursing diagnoses would be a priority for a patient who has just been admitted with a diagnosis of bipolar disorder, mania?

    A. Decisional conflict related to making health care choices
    B. Self-care deficit, bathing/hygiene, related to lack of attention
    C. Hopelessness related to impending depression
    D. Fatigue related to hyperactivity

Test A / Part 2

105. A young woman is brought to the emergency room following a motor vehicle accident. Assessment findings indicate minor cuts and bruises, sullen mood and guarded responses to questions. The nurse notes multiple old scars on the patient's forearms. Which of the following patient statements would require the nurse to investigate as a priority?

A. "My parents are going to be so mad about the car. I don't know what I will tell them."
B. "I'm glad no one was hurt. The next time I'll have to think of a different way to take care of things."
C. "I don't want to go home. My parents are going to punish me for the car."
D. "I don't like hospitals. When can I go home?"

106. Which of the following symptoms of depression would a nurse most likely observe in children and adolescents but not in adults?

A. Loss of interest in usual activities
B. Significant weight loss
C. Acting-out behavior
D. Feelings of worthlessness

107. Which of the following behaviors by an adolescent patient who is suspected of having a major depression would best support a nursing diagnosis of self-esteem disturbance?

A. Protests that others do not understand him
B. Inconsistent performance in school
C. Poor impulse control
D. Frequent criticism of others

108. A couple with impaired fertility express concern about their inability to conceive. Which of the following statements by the nurse would be most appropriate?

A. "I know how you feel. My cousins went through the same thing."
B. "It's better that this happen while you are young."
C. "It's okay to be angry."
D. "God has something better for you. Just try to have hope."

109. The staff nurse calls a physician regarding an order to administer digoxin (Lanoxin) to a patient with a pulse of 55 and a serum potassium level of 2.9 mEq/L. The physician says to give the medication as ordered. The staff nurse's best response would be

A. "I'll give the medication, but you will still be responsible if anything happens to the patient."
B. "I will not give this medication."
C. "I think we should discuss this with the nursing supervisor."
D. "I'm sorry, but if you want the medication given, you will have to give it yourself."

110. After the completion of an incident report, the nurse places the document in the patient's chart. The nurse should understand that incident reports

A. are not considered legal documents but rather a risk management tool.
B. are maintained by the hospital and used as a staff evaluation tool.
C. will prevent legal action against the nurse.
D. should be reviewed by the patient prior to discharge.

 You have finished Nursing, Part 2 of Practice Test A. You may want to take a break or possibly wait another day before taking Practice Test B.

Rationales – Practice Exam A: Nursing, Part 1

1. **Key: A**   Client Need: _Management of Care_

    A. An advance directive is a written document that contains directives of the person's choices regarding end of life care. A person must have the cognitive and communicative abilities to execute decisions regarding their desires. It includes wishes for treatment options should the person become unable to do so.

    B. A durable power of attorney for healthcare designates an individual to make medical decisions in case the patient is unable to do so.
    C. A statement identifying the person as an organ donor may be included in an advance directive, but it is not the only information in an advance directive. This information would typically be included on an organ donor card.
    D. A written statement authorizing a particular surgical procedure is a consent form.

2. **Key: B**   Client Need: _Management of Care_

    B. Individuals with cancer pain have a right to obtain optimal pain relief. Nurses caring for terminally ill patients with metastatic cancer have an ethical obligation to provide pain relief. A goal is to assist the patient to achieve as comfortable a death as possible.

    A. While constipation may be a problem secondary to pain medications, it is not the priority intervention in the terminally ill cancer patient.
    C. A goal in the care of a terminally ill cancer patient is not to prolong life, but to provide comfort. Preventing respiratory arrest would prolong life.
    D. Many terminally ill patients no longer receive chemotherapy. Managing chemotherapy is the role of an oncologist.

3. **Key: A**   Client Need: _Management of Care_

    A. In order for an informed consent to be valid, three basic criteria must be met. The patient's decision must be voluntary, the patient must be informed, and the patient must be competent to understand the information and alternatives. The registered nurse's signature as a witness indicates these criteria were met.

    B. For an informed consent to be valid, it must be obtained before the administration of the patient's preoperative medication.
    C. The patient needs only to understand the information and alternatives, not describe the procedure.
    D. Making a voluntary decision to have a procedure performed is only part of an informed consent.

4. **Key: A**   Client Need: _Physiological Adaptation_

    A. Early hypoxic and hypocapnic changes result in restlessness, confusion, anxiousness, apprehension, agitation, lethargy and mental cloudiness.

    B. Decreased urinary output is a clinical manifestation of hypovolemic shock, but occurs later than nervousness and apprehension.
    C. During the compensatory stage of shock, the blood pressure is adequate to perfuse the vital organs. The systolic blood pressure does not drop to below 90 mm Hg until the progressive stage of shock.
    D. The heart rate is increased and the depth of ventilation is increased in the early stages of shock to compensate for the lactic acid produced due to anaerobic metabolism.

Test A / Part 1 Answers

5.   **Key: A**   Client Need: *Psychosocial Adaptation*

   A. There is no indication for the use of seclusion with this patient. The use of seclusion or restraint that is not defensible as being necessary and in the client's best interest may result in false imprisonment of the client and liability for the nurse.

   B. Battery is harmful or offensive touching of another person. This is not present in the scenario.
   C. Invasion of privacy would involve sharing of information or discussion of the client's case without permission. There is no evidence that this occurred.
   D. Charges of defamation can be brought if information regarding the client is divulged and that information ultimately harms the client's reputation.

6.   **Key: C**   Client Need: *Safety and Infection Control*

   C. The child is being discharged to home and is oxygen dependent. Oxygen may be administered in the home. Home oxygen therapy requires that a number of safety features should be in place. Because oxygen is a highly flammable gas, precautions must be taken to ensure the safety of the patient and family. Assessing the home for potential fire hazards is necessary. There should be no open flames, electrical sparks or flammable materials present. Smoking in the home by any person when oxygen is in use is contraindicated.

   A. Drafts or air leaks in the home may affect the environmental temperature but would have no direct impact on the care or safety of the child at home who requires oxygen therapy.
   B. Other children in the home do not pose any direct threat to the child who is at home on oxygen. Returning the child to home will reduce the amount of developmental delay or social handicap related to prolonged hospitalization.
   D. Pets in the home could be a potential problem if they shed fine hair. Small particles, such as dust and fine hair, could potentially cause obstruction of the tracheostomy. Keeping the child separate from the family pet should be sufficient to maintain a clear airway.

7.   **Key: B**   Client Need: *Safety and Infection Control*

   B. It is important that the patient knows how to call the nurse. The patient needs to be aware of how to use the call light. Since the patient has a tracheostomy, he is unable to speak. Due to the patient's impaired ability to speak, communication tools should be kept close at hand along with the call light or bell.

   A. The patient may not have an oxygen collar. Not all patients with a tracheostomy require oxygen.
   C. While the procedure for suctioning should be explained to the patient, it is not the most important aspect when orienting the patient to the room.
   D. Preventing infection in a new tracheostomy patient is primarily the responsibility of the nurse. It is not most important when orienting the patient to the room.

8.   **Key: C**   Client Need: *Safety and Infection Control*

   C. Potentially harmful objects should be removed from the immediate environment. This protects the patient from potential injury. The primary nursing outcome is that seizures are controlled and the patient remains free of injury.

   A. Objects such as tongue blades may cause injury to the patient and are not placed in the mouth during seizure activity.
   B. Restraints should never be applied during a seizure.
   D. The family should remain with the patient during seizure activity. Not every seizure will be a medical emergency in the patient with chronic seizures.

9. **Key: C**   **Client Need:** *Physiological Adaptation*

    C. **The infectious stage of tuberculosis declines immediately after effective chemotherapy. The risk of infectious tuberculosis is much higher for persons who are immunosuppressed. Patients need to be taught to cover their mouth when coughing, because tuberculosis is spread by droplets.**

    A. Antimycobacterial therapy is usually prescribed for six to nine months. Short-term use of antibiotics is not effective chemotherapy. The Centers for Disease Control (CDC) recommends a minimum of six months of therapy.

    B. For a definite diagnosis of tuberculosis, a positive sputum culture is necessary. A Mantoux test identifies individuals exposed to mycobacterium tuberculosis. This test does not differentiate between active and dormant infection.

    D. BCG (Bacille Calmette-Guerin) strengthens the body's immune system.

10. **Key: C**   **Client Need:** *Safety and Infection Control*

    C. **A child must be properly restrained when undergoing a lumbar puncture to prevent trauma from an unexpected or involuntary movement. Children are usually controlled best in a side-lying position, with the head flexed and the knees drawn up toward the chest. The child is placed on his/her side with the back close to the edge of the examining table on the side from which the practitioner is working. The nurse maintains the child's spine in a flexed position by holding the child with one arm behind the neck and the other behind the thighs.**

    A. Soft arm restraints or leg restraints are used occasionally when one or more extremity needs to be restrained or limited in motion. However, this type of restraint does not help to maintain the child in the proper position required for a lumbar puncture.

    B. A jacket restraint is sometimes used as an alternative to a crib net to prevent a child from climbing out of a crib or to keep the child from falling out of a chair. This type of restraint fits over the child's torso and would not allow access to the lumbar area. A jacket restraint would interfere with proper positioning of the child.

    D. Placing a child supine on a papoose board (a type of restraint where the child's whole body is usually covered and tied down to prevent any movement) will not allow the practitioner access to the lumbar region. The patient must be in a flexed position in order for the needle to easily enter the lumbar space.

11. **Key: B**   **Client Need:** *Physiological Adaptation*

    B. **Impetigo is a bacterial infection of the skin characterized by reddish macules that become vesicular and can rupture easily, resulting in some drainage. The exudate dries and forms a thick honey-colored crust. The rash may be itchy, but there are minimal systemic affects. The major nursing functions related to bacterial skin infections are to prevent the spread of infection and to prevent complications. Hand-washing is mandatory before and after contact with an affected child. Hand-washing is also emphasized to the child and the family.**

    A. A diet high in protein is not required to treat this illness or promote healing.

    C. There is no need to separate or isolate the child with impetigo. The child can continue normal, age-appropriate play activities that may include outdoor play.

    D. A sun lamp is not considered an appropriate treatment for impetigo. A sun lamp can emit harmful light waves that are not safe for a child's skin.

12. **Key: C**   **Client Need:** *Pharmacological and Parenteral Therapies*

C. **For a confused patient with memory failure, supervision of medication administration is essential. In order for a patient to self-medicate, the patient needs to understand and comprehend drug information. The patient with cognitive changes has difficulty remembering, especially when multiple medications are given.**

A. Not all medications are to be administered with meals. Some medications are better absorbed on an empty stomach.

B. A confused patient does not understand the implications of refusing medications, and therefore the nurse needs to instruct the family how to handle medications for the patient who refuses them.

D. Self-medication, even though it gives the patient control and independence, is not recommended in a confused patient for safety reasons.

13. **Key: B**   **Client Need:** *Safety and Infection Control*

B. **Surgical repair of the cleft palate in a young child results in several important nursing considerations postoperatively, including the child's comfort, positioning, restraints and feeding. Children who have had a cleft palate repair are positioned on their abdomen to facilitate the drainage of secretions from their mouth. Pain medication is important to provide comfort and relief of pain at the surgical site. Elbow restraints are required to prevent the child from touching the mouth. Elbow restraints must be worn at all times except for brief intervals when they can be removed one at a time to exercise arms, provide relief from restriction and observe the skin for signs of irritation. Parents are instructed on the use of restraints prior to the child's discharge.**

A. Placing mittens on the child's hands would not prevent the child from touching the operative site. It is very important that the palate be protected in order to promote proper healing.

C. The restraints should not be removed for long periods of time. This would increase the risk of the child touching the mouth. Removal of the restraints for brief periods, at regular intervals, is sufficient to allow movement of the extremity and assessment of the skin for irritation.

D. Parents need to know the rationale for using elbow restraints as well as how to apply them properly. Children who are discharged to home after a cleft palate repair are required to wear elbow restraints until the surgical site is healed. A physician's order is required for elbow restraints, but a separate parental consent is not required.

14. **Key: D**   **Client Need:** *Safety and Infection Control*

D. **Placing the bed in the low position is an important step in a falls prevention program. The bed should be as low to the floor as possible to decrease falls and prevent injury.**

A. The resident has the right to be free from physical restraints. Physical restraints often increase agitation and restlessness.

B. Lorazepam (Ativan) is a chemical restraint. Residents should not be given psychotropic medications unless they are required to treat the patient's medical condition. Psychotropics may increase confusion and an unsteady gait.

C. Changing a confused patient's environment may increase confusion and the risk for injury

15. **Key: A**   **Client Need:** *Management of Care*

    A. Chest pain could be a sign of a myocardial infarction or life-threatening pulmonary embolus. The nurse should assess the patient for changes in the blood pressure, heart rate, rhythm, and electrocardiogram (EKG). Assessment of accompanying symptoms and precipitating factors to the chest pain should be performed.

    B. The intravenous medication is not due for 30 minutes. The nurse has time to assess the other patients.

    C. A temperature of 101° Fahrenheit should be assessed. However, it is not life threatening. Because chest pain has the potential to be life threatening, it should be assessed first.

    D. Although the preoperative patient needs to be assessed, this situation does not require immediate assessment.

16. **Key: A**   **Client Need:** *Safety and Infection Control*

    A. Physical restraints, usually leather straps, are used to immobilize a person who is clearly dangerous to self or others. In almost all cases, a specific physician's order is required for each episode, as is clearly documented evidence that the restraints were needed. A standing PRN order is not legally sufficient.

    B. Documentation of the patient's status should be done at least every two hours or more often depending on hospital policy. A patient in restraints must be observed and cannot be left alone. All observations should be documented.

    C. The physician must write a restraint order each time the patient is put into restraints. Restraint orders are generally written for 24-hour periods and rewritten as necessary after patient behavior is assessed.

    D. Vest restraints may displace if the patient is agitated, and may cause choking.

17. **Key: D**   **Client Need:** *Prevention and Early Detection of Disease*

    D. Pediculosis capitis (head lice) is an infestation of the scalp caused by a common parasite. Lice infestation is not a major health threat but is highly communicable and may cause embarrassment to the child and family. Lice cause the child to have an itchy scalp. Lice eggs or nits attach to the hair shaft, and the organism lives by feeding on the child's scalp. A teaching plan for the parents should include measures for eliminating the infestation and preventing the spread and reoccurrence of Pediculosis. Machine wash all clothing, towels and bed linens in hot water and dry in a hot dryer for at least 20 minutes. Non-washable clothing should be dry-cleaned.

    A. Administering a topical ant-itch medication is not recommended. Routine treatment consists of the application of pediculicides and manual removal of nit cases. Commonly used medicated shampoos include Nix or RID.

    B. Calamine lotion is a topical application that is used as a protectant and an astringent. Burow's solution is used as an astringent and topical antiseptic. Neither is used in the treatment of head lice.

    C. The child's hair must be combed with a nit comb (fine-toothed comb) to remove the nits from the hair shaft. Hair combing must be performed along with the medicated shampoo treatments. Specific directions for combing and shampooing are included in the product's package directions.

18. **Key: A**   Client Need: *Psychosocial Adaptation*

   A. Patients with schizophrenia may become violent due to alterations in perceptions and suspiciousness. Assigning the same staff member to promote consistency will help the patient to establish trust.

   B. Assigning a member of the same sex to care for a client with schizophrenia would be helpful for assisting the client with self-care activities but is not required to promote consistency of care.
   C. Unit restriction is a measure taken when the patient is not ready or able to handle the stimuli away from the unit. It is not used as a disciplinary measure.
   D. Placing a patient in walking restraints is unacceptable, both ethically and legally. Patients must be cared for in the least restrictive manner.

19. **Key: C**   Client Need: *Safety and Infection Control*

   C. Installing handrails next to the tub and toilet assists in providing balance by giving the patient something to grab onto and reduces the risk of falling. They are used to prevent accidents in patients with mobility impairments.

   A. Carpeting stairways increases the potential for sliding even though it may decrease the amount of injuries by providing padding.
   B. Waxed or slippery surfaces can increase the risk of falling. Waxed floors can produce a glare, which can cause temporary visual impairment.
   D. Throw rugs can be hazardous because of the potential for tripping over them and sliding on them.

20. **Key: A**   Client Need: *Safety and Infection Control*

   A. It is critical to document the events leading up to the use of restraints. Specifically, what was happening immediately before the event and what other measures were attempted before restraints were used. Clear danger to self or others must be evident in the documentation.

   B. The frequency of observation is determined by regulatory agencies and is often set at every 15 minutes. Four hours is too long an interval between observations.
   C. A physician's order is required for the use of mechanical restraints and must be obtained as soon as possible if the client was placed in restraints in an emergency situation. The time required to obtain this order is determined by facility and regulatory agency guidelines.
   D. Proper fit of restraints is checked frequently. Limbs are alternately released from restraints and range-of-motion exercises performed every two hours or according to facility guidelines.

21. **Key: C**   Client Need: *Safety and Infection Control*

   C. Osteoporosis of the hip increases the risk of hip fractures. Decreased bone mass density puts one at high risk for hip fractures. Installing handrails on stairways will improve mobility and prevent falls.

   A. Disinfecting the bathroom does not prevent falls and hip fractures in the patient with osteoporosis.
   B. Carpeting floor surfaces often makes ambulation more difficult.
   D. Poor lighting increases the risk for falling. Areas should be well lit.

22. **Key: B**   **Client Need:** *Safety and Infection Control*

    B. When an elderly patient has bladder incontinence, it is important to establish a bladder routine. The schedule is usually set at least at two-hour intervals throughout the day and every four hours at night. The patient should be encouraged to urinate when the urge arises.

    A. This is irrelevant to the incontinence problem.
    C. The use of sedatives/hypnotics should be limited because they dull the sensation to urinate.
    D. Restraints are not to be used as convenience devices for the prevention of falls.

23. **Key: D**   **Client Need:** *Psychosocial Adaptation*

    D. This statement by the patient may indicate that she suspects her husband of child abuse and does not trust him to be alone with the child. The statement requires further exploration.

    A B and C.
    Co-sleeping, in which the parents allow the child to sleep with them, is a relatively common and accepted practice, especially among Black, Hispanic and Asian families. Other groups that are adopting co-sleeping include single parents, whose need for company may encourage the practice; working parents, who desire the closeness at night that was lost during the day and parents who have had an issue about sleep or separation in their past.

24. **Key: D**   **Client Need:** *Growth and Development*

    D. Ethnic groups tend to vary in their food customs. The nurse should be aware of what foods can be eaten, what foods are forbidden and what foods may or may not be eaten together.

    A. While marriage customs vary among ethnic groups, knowledge of the number of marriages is not essential to patient care.
    B. The broader question that should be addressed in a cultural assessment is the use of folk medicines and herbs.
    C. Family customs regarding health and healthcare rather than the number of siblings are important to identify in a cultural assessment.

25. **Key: B**   **Client Need:** *Management of Care*

    B. Case managers plan, coordinate and monitor services to meet the needs of the client. Case managers pull together available resources to provide the client with the best help. Case management is based on a compilation of services that contains costs and improves the quality of care while reducing fragmentation and duplication of services.

    A. The case manager does not become involved in daily patient assignments. This is the unit manager's responsibility.
    C. Case managers do not negotiate insurance benefits with the hospital. They coordinate care to control costs.
    D. The decision related to what treatments are essential is the responsibility of the medical practitioner.

26. **Key: A**   Client Need: *Prevention and Early Detection of Disease*

    A. Assessment of the abdomen differs from other assessments in that inspection and auscultation precede percussion and palpation. This sequence allows accurate assessment of bowel sounds and delays more uncomfortable maneuvers until last.

    B., C. and D.
    Auscultation of the abdomen before percussion and palpation is preferred.

27. **Key: B**   Client Need: *Prevention and Early Detection of Disease*

    B. S4 may be commonly auscultated because of decreased ventricular compliance following atrial contraction. The fourth heart sound is associated with conditions in which the ventricle is "stiffer" than normal. The ventricle has decreased distensibility or compliance, as seen in ischemia or chronic hypertension.

    A. Split heart sounds (S2) may be normal in adults if heard only during inspiration.
    C. Abnormal heart sounds in mitral stenosis typically include a low-pitched diastolic murmur and an opening snap of the mitral valve.
    D. Clicks (a mid-systolic click) and a late systolic murmur may be heard in mitral valve prolapse.

28. **Key: B**   Client Need: *Pharmacological and Parenteral Therapies*

    B. Delirium has an abrupt onset and usually manifests in impaired orientation, recent and immediate memory impairment and variable psychomotor behavior. In delirium, the causes lie outside the nervous system. The severity of delirium is related to the physiologic disturbance and degree of cerebral edema. Both can occur with renal insufficiency. Symptoms often are worse at night.

    A. Dementia patients have progression of symptoms over time. Their orientation is normal.
    C. Psychosis has an underlying psychologic disturbance. Patients with psychoses usually have illusions, delusions, and hallucinations.
    D. Depressed patients usually have selective disorientation and impairment of intact memory. Symptoms are typically worse in the morning.

29. **Key: C**   Client Need: *Prevention and Early Detection of Disease*

    C. Jaundice is best assessed in the sclera. However, the dark-skinned patient may have normal yellow pigmentation present in the sclera. Inspection of the hard palate for a yellow color can confirm the presence of jaundice.

    A. Cyanosis is best observed in the nail beds.
    B. Skin on the palm of the hand can indicate jaundice, but not skin on the back of the hand.
    D. Jaundice can be assessed on the soles of the feet in a patient with dark skin. However, it is better assessed in the hard palate.

30. **Key: B**   Client Need: *Reduction of Risk Potential*

    B. The nurse must auscultate for a bruit at the access site. A change may indicate thrombus formation or clotting.

    A. The sound of a bruit is a swishing sound caused by turbulent blood flow through a narrowed vessel, not a whoosh.
    C. An echo is not present in an arteriovenous (AV) fistula.
    D. A thrill is palpated, not auscultated, in an arteriovenous (AV) fistula.

31. **Key: C**   **Client Need:** *Reduction of Risk Potential*

    C. Pulmonary edema is common in patients with patent ductus arteriosus (PDA). Both pulmonary edema and cardiomegaly are seen on x-ray due to shunting of blood across the PDA. Patent ductus arteriosus is common in preterm infants.

    A. Mitral valve prolapse is an uncommon finding in the newborn.
    B. Inflammation of the pericardium is usually caused by infection and is not related to fetal circulation.
    D. Bacterial endocarditis is an associated complication of valve replacement surgery in children with congenital heart defects (i.e., tetralogy of Fallot).

32. **Key: B**   **Client Need:** *Coping and Adaptation*

    B. Repression is the exclusion of unpleasant or unwanted experiences, emotions, or ideas from conscious awareness. It is the first psychological defense against anxiety. The client's inability to remember the details of the rape protects her from emotional pain.

    A. Compensation is covering up a real or perceived weakness by emphasizing a trait one considers more desirable. There is no evidence that the client is using compensation.
    C. Undoing is symbolically negating or canceling out an experience that one finds intolerable. This often involves an act that is opposite the experience. There is no evidence that the client is using undoing.
    D. Regression is retreating, in response to stress, to an earlier level of development and the comfort measures used during that period. There is no evidence that the client is using regression.

33. **Key: B**   **Client Need:** *Reduction of Risk Potential*

    B. Central vision for tasks such as reading, driving and performing detailed eye work is controlled by the macula. Damage or degeneration of the macula causes impairment of central vision.

    A. Degeneration of the macula does not affect peripheral vision.
    C. Nystagmus is uncontrolled jerky eye movements. It is not found in macular degeneration. It is found in labyrinthitis and brain tumors.
    D. Lid lag is caused by weakness of the ocular muscles.

34. **Key: A**   **Client Need:** *Psychosocial Adaptation*

    A. Impairment due to substance use results in an inability to function in various roles, including the job. This would result in decreased performance.

    B. Increased food consumption usually does not occur with substance abuse; food consumption is usually decreased.
    C. Verbal manipulation would support a nursing diagnosis of "defensive coping."
    D. Frequent illnesses would support a nursing diagnosis of "risk of infection related to malnutrition and altered immune condition."

35. **Key: D**   **Client Need:** *Coping and Adaptation*

 D. Some Native Americans relate eye contact to impoliteness and an invasion of privacy. Many Native Americans regard eye contact as disrespectful because it is believed that "looking in an individual's eyes" is "looking into an individual's soul."

 A. In the United States, those of the dominant culture, as well as most Mexican Americans, value eye contact as symbolic of a positive self-concept.
 B. Eye contact practices in Italy include frequent, quick eye contact.
 C. Direct eye contact is important in the Cuban culture. Looking away may be interpreted as disrespect or dishonesty.

36. **Key: B**   **Client Need:** *Prevention and Early Detection of Disease*

 B. A consensual pupil response occurs when the client looks straight ahead and each eye is examined from the client's side with a penlight. A normal response is when the pupil opposite the one illuminated constricts simultaneously.

 A. A direct reaction occurs when illuminated pupils constrict.
 C and D.
 Accommodation and pupillary convergence occur when the client stares at an object three to four feet away and when moving the object toward the patient's nose, pupils move together and constrict as the object moves in toward the nose. Pupil responses are uniform.

37. **Key: B**   **Client Need:** *Psychosocial Adaptation*

 B. The purging (vomiting) and/or diuretic use associated with bulimia results in a loss of potassium (hypokalemia), causing diminished reflexes, fatigue and, if severe, cardiac arrhythmias.

 A. Hypokalemia, rather than hyperkalemia, is associated with bulimia.
 C and D.
 Potassium loss due to laxative and diuretic abuse is common in bulimics, rather than calcium abnormalities.

38. **Key: C**   **Client Need:** *Physiological Adaptation*

 C. Many alternative therapies have persisted and grown because people find them useful. Acknowledging the full breadth of services that individuals use and working with them is more productive than ignoring what the client chooses to do in the quest for wholeness and health. The patient should communicate the therapies with his/her professional before embarking on them to make sure there are no deleterious effects.

 A. Insurance companies sometimes do not recognize many of the complementary therapies. The nurse would have to discuss this with the physician.
 B. The patient has already made the arrangements for massage, so she must have her transportation needs addressed.
 D. It would not be wise to hold medication because blood levels need to be maintained. Complementary therapies are most effective when they are used in conjunction with medical practices.

39. **Key: C**   **Client Need:** *Physiological Adaptation*

> **C. An overweight adolescent usually becomes an overweight adult. It is important, therefore, to take measures that would allow the adolescent to be successful in promoting and maintaining weight loss. Decreasing daily caloric intake, reducing portions, and eliminating high-fat foods and junk food are all appropriate measures that would help the teen reach this goal. In addition to modifying the diet, some type of regular physical activity is needed to facilitate weight loss and promote good cardiovascular health. Therefore, teens must incorporate exercise activities into their plans for weight loss.**

- A. Vitamins are an important component of a well-balanced and nutritious diet. Vitamins should not be decreased in a weight reduction diet. Vitamins are essential for normal metabolic activity.
- B. Reducing the quantity of food eaten by preparing smaller portions is a realistic approach for weight loss. The quality of the food is also significant. Substituting low-calorie foods for high-calorie foods and snacks will help the teen lose weight. There is no evidence that decreasing the amount of meals would help decrease the total number of calories consumed. Skipping meals can cause the teen to develop unhealthy eating habits.
- C. "Fast foods" are generally high-fat, high-caloric foods and should be eliminated or eaten infrequently when dieting. Healthy snacks, such as fruit and raw vegetables that are easy to prepare, should be encouraged.

40. **Key: A**   **Client Need:** *Management of Care*

> **A. The patient should be examined for possible causes of the elevated temperature first. Stress, infection, respiratory problems and dehydration are all possible reasons for a temperature elevation on the first postoperative day.**

- B. There is no indication that the patient is receiving antibiotics. Altering the times of antibiotics could change the peak and trough levels.
- C. Calling the physician would not be a first step. Assessment would be first.
- D. Blood cultures are usually not obtained until patient temperature levels are higher.

41. **Key: D**   **Client Need:** *Basic Care and Comfort*

> **D. Collect additional information to determine potential causes of the weight loss. Information derived from interviewing and observing the patient will guide the nurse in the application of her knowledge regarding nutrition. The nurse will need to explore the patient's dietary patterns to discover the unique reasons for the patient's eating behaviors. Assessment is the first step of the nursing process.**

- A. A nutritional assessment should be completed before recommendations are made.
- B. The nurse needs to assess the patient's eating habits before planning calorie distribution.
- C. The patient's plan of care should be individualized. An assessment needs to be completed prior to the institution of a care plan.

42. **Key: B**   **Client Need:** *Management of Care*

> **B. The surgeon must explain the procedure in terms that the patient or surrogate is able to understand. It is the surgeon who is responsible to explain the surgical procedure to the patient.**

- A. The nurse is responsible for ensuring that the patient or surrogate receives honest, fair and accurate information. The nurse may witness the patient's signature.
- C. The admission clerk has no responsibility regarding any surgical procedure and its explanation to the patient or the patient's surrogate.
- D. The anesthesiologist will explain the type of anesthesia that is used for the surgical procedure and obtain consent for anesthesia.

43.   **Key: C**   Client Need: *Coping and Adaptation*

   C. Parents may have a wide range of responses to their child's illness and hospitalization. Following the diagnosis of an illness, they may react with disbelief, anger or guilt. Parents tend to search for self-blame regarding why the child became ill or to project anger at others for some wrongdoing. Fear, anxiety and frustration are common feelings expressed by parents when their child is hospitalized. The best nursing approach to parents is for the nurse to anticipate and recognize these responses and allow parents to verbalize their feelings about their child's illness and hospitalization. Helping parents identify the reasons for their feelings and emphasizing that each is normal, expected and a healthy response to stress provides them with the opportunity to lessen their emotional burden.

   A. Anxiety and guilt are normal parental reactions to a child's hospitalization and the parents should feel free to express their feelings.
   B. Distracting the parent's attention from their feelings about their child's hospitalization to a less painful situation is not appropriate. The parents should be encouraged to express their feelings about the current situation.
   D. Nurses who use therapeutic communication when working with clients and their families should avoid using personal experiences. The nurse should allow the client and family members to express their feelings while actively listening in a non-judgmental manner.

44.   **Key: B**   Client Need: *Physiological Adaptation*

   B. On a continuous around-the-clock schedule. Pain seen in malignancies may require pain-relieving medications routinely. Patients experiencing pain due to cancer may require routine pain-relieving medications. Pain for cancer patients is given on a regular schedule to prevent exacerbations.

   A. Management of cancer pain is in contrast to medications being taken at the time of pain or prn
   C and D.
      Predictable and chronic pain is managed more effectively if the patient maintains a therapeutic blood level of analgesia.

45.   **Key: A**   Client Need: *Basic Care and Comfort*

   A. Excess intake of fluids, especially coffee or alcohol, before bedtime is a cause or associated factor of nocturia. Nocturia is excessive urination at night.

   B. While the nightlight would address safety concerns, the decrease in fluids prior to bedtime would more effectively control the nocturia.
   C. Disposable undergarments may interfere with the patient's self-concept. No soilage of clothing is noted.
   D. There is no report that the patient is having difficulty getting to the bathroom. A report of nocturia does not necessitate a patient having problems with mobility.

46.   **Key: A**   Client Need: *Reduction of Risk Potential*

   A. Hyperextension facilitates insertion of the catheter into the trachea.

   B. This position is used for insertion of a nasogastric tube. This position would inhibit insertion.
   C. Turning the patient's head to the right may help the nurse suction the patient's left main stem bronchus. However, this is after the catheter has been inserted and refers to suctioning, not insertion.
   D. Positioning in some instances, (e.g. turning the patient's head to the left) helps the nurse to suction the patient's right main stem bronchus. However, this would be after the catheter has been inserted and refers to suctioning, not insertion.

47. **Key: D**   **Client Need:** *Management of Care*

    D. Dysfunctional grieving related to loss is the priority nursing diagnosis. This diagnosis includes the presenting symptoms of isolation, self-neglect and social withdrawal.

    A. There is no evidence in this scenario that the patient is anxious about her own death.
    B. Self-care deficit is present, but it is one feature of dysfunctional grieving and is therefore incomplete in itself.
    C. Anticipatory grieving usually refers to the process that begins when a terminal diagnosis is made for either a patient or family member. This is not present in this scenario.

48. **Key: A**   **Client Need:** *Basic Care and Comfort*

    A. One way to promote defecation is to have the patient assume a squatting position. With a bedside commode, the patient will be able to assume the squatting position and this is most like their normal elimination pattern. The nurse should incorporate the patient's elimination routine or habits as much as possible and reinforce those that promote health. The epidural drip can be easily moved and transported. The chest tubes have to remain close to the suction device so as to prevent a pneumothorax.

    B. If the patient is able to get out of bed, he should be permitted to use a commode. This is most like the patient's normal routine and pattern. This patient is unable to go far because he is connected to suction.
    C. With the chest tube, the patient will have to remain connected to suction and there is a limitation in the amount or degree of movement. The nurse does not want to clamp or disconnect the chest tube. It may result in a pneumothorax. Use of the commode is the most realistic option.
    D. Clamping or disconnecting chest tubes is contraindicated. Such actions may result in a tension pneumothorax, which is life threatening.

49. **Key: B**   **Client Need:** *Physiological Adaptation*

    B. The nurse should assess the pain experience from the patient's perspective. Believe the patient in their reports of pain. The patient is the source for evaluating outcomes of pain management. A numerical rating scale requires a patient to rate pain from 0 to 10, 0 being no pain, 10 being severe pain. The patient rates her pain at 2, which is a low pain level.

    A. Sleep or sedation may be mistakenly equated with lack of pain, but even patients with severe pain may sleep. A nurse who is unfamiliar with physiologic and behavioral pain responses may question if a patient has pain if he/she is asleep. If the patient is asleep, the nurse should not conclude that the pain is absent.
    C. A numerical rating scale requires clients to rate pain on a scale of 0 to10, 0 being no pain, 10 being severe pain.
    D. A behavioral indication of the effects of pain may be immobilization.

50. Key: A   Client Need: *Management of Care*

A. Documentation is defined as anything written or printed that is relied on as a record of proof for authorized persons. Effective documentation reflects the quality of care and provides evidence of each healthcare team member's accountability in giving care. Accountability means that the nurse is responsible professionally and legally for the type and quality of nursing care provided.

B. Even though accurate documentation is one of the best defenses against legal claims associated with nursing care, the nurse must function under the Code of Ethics. The nurse is responsible for carrying out nursing responsibilities that provide quality nursing care.

C. Insurance reimbursement requires accurate documentation. However, nurses must remember that they are professionals and must be aware of their professional nursing role.

D. Many regulatory bodies require proper documentation. However, the primary reason for accurate documentation relates to evidence of accountability.

51. Key: B   Client Need: *Growth and Development*

B. The brachial blood pressure is highest when the woman is sitting. The patient should be given a chance to relax and should have her arm at the level of the heart. The blood pressure should be taken with the proper size cuff in the same arm at each visit. If the arm is above the level of the heart, the reading will be falsely low. An arm below the heart produces a falsely high reading.

A. Blood pressure, both diastolic and systolic, decreases in the second trimester.

C. Arterial blood pressure is the lowest in the left lateral position and intermediate in the supine position.

D. Blood pressure should not be taken in the standing position in the pregnant patient.

52. Key: A   Client Need: *Psychosocial Adaptation*

A. Schizoid personality disorder manifests as a pervasive pattern of detachment from social relationships and restricted range of expression. The inability to experience pleasure is one of the characteristic features.

B. Jealousy and quickness to react in anger is not a defining characteristic of any personality disorder.

C. Insensitivity to the welfare of others is a characteristic feature of antisocial personality disorder.

D. Lack of guilt or social conscience is a characteristic feature of antisocial personality disorder.

53. Key: D   Client Need: *Safety and Infection Control*

D. Infants rarely receive more than 1 ml (50 mcg or 0.05 mg) in one dose. A higher dose is an immediate warning of a dosage error. To ensure safety, ask another staff member to check the calculation before giving the drug. This dosage is too high, and the doctor should be questioned.

A. This dosage is too high. The normal dosage for infants is 50 mcg or .05 mg

B. The pulse should be checked. It should not be below 90-110 beats/min in infants or below 70 beats/min in older children. The potassium level should also be checked.

C. The serum digoxin level should be checked for digoxin toxicity. The signs of digoxin toxicity in children are nausea, vomiting, anorexia, bradycardia and dysrhythmias.

54.　**Key: B**　　　　　　　　　　　Client Need: _Safety and Infection Control_

　　B. Poisoning remains a significant health concern for children under six years of age. Most poisonings are caused when children ingest hazardous household substances. When a child accidentally ingests a hazardous substance, the mother or caretaker's first response should be to call the local Poison Control Center. This should be done before initiating any interventions, because instructions on the product label may not give the correct information for treatment.

　　A. Inducing vomiting with syrup of ipecac should be done only if instructed by the poison control center. Do not induce vomiting if the victim is unconscious, convulsing or has an absent gag reflex. Do not induce vomiting if the poison is a low-viscosity hydrocarbon, pesticide, strong acid or alkali.

　　C and D.
　　Attempting to dilute the poison with water or absorb the poison with bread is contraindicated. The poison control center will provide the correct intervention for the type of poison ingested.

55.　**Key: A**　　　　　　　Client Need: _Pharmacological and Parenteral Therapies_

　　A. Fatigue is a side effect associated with rofecoxib (Vioxx).

　　B. Hypertension, rather than hypotension, is a side effect of Vioxx. Tachycardia is unrelated to Vioxx administration.
　　C. Dyspnea and chest pain are associated with cardiac problems rather than Vioxx administration.
　　D. Fatigue is a side effect of Vioxx, but not irritability.

56.　**Key: A**　　　　　　　　　　　Client Need: _Physiological Adaptation_

　　A. Absence of a palpable thrill over the shunt. The patient should be taught to feel for the "thrill" of blood moving through the shunt when it is touched. This should be done daily. The increased pressure in the arterialized vein will create a "thrill".

　　B. A bruit is a blowing sound. This should be heard when an AV shunt is in use. The blood is flowing from the patient's artery through the shunt into the vein.
　　C. The arm with the shunt should be protected, and all healthcare personnel should be reminded that the involved arm with the shunt should not be used for blood pressure.
　　D. The arm with the shunt should be protected, and all healthcare personnel should be reminded that the involved arm should not be used for phlebotomy.

57.　**Key: C**　　　　　　　　　　　Client Need: _Reduction of Risk Potential_

　　C. Tachycardia is listed as one of the primary side effects of Brethine. The mother may report feeling like "her heart is beating out of her chest." The fetal and maternal heart rates should be monitored. Usually, the tachycardia is mild in nature.

　　A. The action of the Brethine is to relax smooth muscles. The uterine muscle is smooth in nature.
　　B. Epistaxis or nosebleeds are not associated with Brethine administration.
　　D. Dysuria or painful urination is associated with urinary tract infections and not with the use of Brethine.

58.   **Key: B**   **Client Need:** *Growth and Development*

   **B. The response by the nurse, "Let's check your baby together to see what he needs." is most
   appropriate because it is non-judgmental and directs the mother to recognize that she
   should respond to the infant's cue. Crying is the infant's first means of verbal communication. It conveys a message of urgency and signals displeasure such as hunger or being wet.
   Parents need to learn to respond to the infant's cry in order to provide physical care and
   emotional security for the infant.**

   A. "Your baby is crying and needs your attention now" sounds harsh and implies that the nurse is
   ordering the mother to pay attention to her baby.
   C. "Why do you think your baby is crying at this time?" is not an appropriate response because the
   caretaker must determine what is causing the baby to cry. This is done by assessing the baby to
   determine if the baby is wet, hungry, cold or in pain. After considering physical needs, it may be
   sufficient to hold the infant to provide emotional support and cuddling.
   D. The response by the nurse, "When did you last feed your baby?" assumes that the only reason
   the baby is crying is because the baby is hungry. The mother must learn to respond appropriately to her infant's crying and to determine what the baby needs.

59.   **Key: D**   **Client Need:** *Management of Care*

   **D. If the nurse has difficulty assessing the pulse, a Doppler is a useful tool. A hand-held
   Doppler permits the assessment of arterial disease through the evaluation of audible arterial signals.**

   A. Sometimes, the pedal pulses may be difficult to palpate, but it does not necessarily mean that
   surgery is indicated.
   B. Apical radial pulses are preformed to assess for pulse deficits, which may indicate an alteration
   in cardiac output.
   C. Elevating the front of the bed will decrease blood flow and exacerbate claudication. Warm compresses may help to reduce edema and improve circulation.

60.   **Key: B**   **Client Need:** *Management of Care*

   **B. Ask the supervisor to assign another nurse to the case. This is an ethical dilemma. The
   nurse has instituted the proper steps to process an ethical dilemma. The nurse has examined and identified her own values, verbalized the problem and then considered
   alternatives (i.e., have another nurse assigned to the case).**

   A. There is no need for the patient to know the nurses' beliefs. The nurse should be non-judgmental and not attempt to place her beliefs on another.
   C. The facility has already made a pro-choice decision and is performing abortions.
   D. The nurse has already made an ethical decision that she is opposed to abortion based on moral
   principles.

61.   **Key: A**   **Client Need:** *Management of Care*

   **A. All facts should be documented exactly as the patient stated. When recording subjective
   data, document the client's exact words within quotation marks.**

   B. The use of such words as appears, seems or apparently is not acceptable when documenting
   because they suggest that the nurse did not know the facts.
   C. The patient's comment is subjective data and should be placed in the patient's own words.
   D. The patient's comment is subjective data and should be placed in the patient's own words.

62. **Key: D**   Client Need: *Reduction of Risk Potential*

    D. The radiated skin should be protected from sunlight and extreme cold. The nurse should instruct the patient to keep the skin dry; not apply lotions, powders, creams, alcohol or deodorants; wear loose-fitting garments; not apply tape, shave with an electric razor; and protect the skin from direct sunlight, chlorinated pools and temperature extremes.

    A. The dark ink markings that outline the radiation field should be left intact. They should not be washed off.
    B. Applying any lotions, perfumes, deodorants or powder to the treatment area is contraindicated.
    C. Non-restrictive cotton clothing should be worn over the treatment area.

63. **Key: D**   Client Need: *Safety and Infection Control*

    D. Restraints should be secured to the bed frame. Hospital bed frames are typically sturdy and immovable and therefore can be safely used in a restraint situation.

    A. Side rails can be easily moved. Restraints anchored to side rails present a danger to both patients and staff.
    B. Restraints may become loosened from mattress hooks and present a hazardous situation.
    C. The footboard of the bed may not be secure enough for restraints, presenting a hazard.

64. **Key: B**   Client Need: *Psychosocial Adaptation*

    B. The nursing diagnosis of spiritual distress is appropriate for the suicidal client who is experiencing a lack of hope for the future and a feeling of despair.

    A. Ineffective coping may describe the individual's lack of problem-solving skills that led to the suicidal ideation or intent, but is not related to feelings of despair.
    C. Anxiety may be appropriate to describe the suicidal client's concerns regarding the future. It may also be a response to a situational crisis. However, it does not best describe the feelings of despair.
    D. Dysfunctional grieving resulting from a loss may contribute to the person feeling isolated and confused and lead to the suicidal feelings. However, spiritual distress better describes the individual's feeling of despair.

65. **Key: B**   Client Need: *Growth and Development*

    B. Normal physiological changes of aging include a decreased rate of voluntary or autonomic reflexes, which increases the risk of injury.

    A. Normal physiological changes of aging include decreased muscle mass and strength.
    C. Normal physiological changes of aging include decreased cognitive ability.
    D. A thin white ring along the margin of the iris is called arcus senilis. This is common with aging but does not increase the risk of injury.

66. **Key: D**   **Client Need:** *Physiological Adaptation*

    D. The basic physiological defect caused by anemia is a decrease in the oxygen-carrying capacity of the blood and, consequently, a reduction in the amount of oxygen available to the cells. When the anemia develops slowly, the child usually adapts to the declining hemoglobin level in his/her body and can function quite well. When the hemoglobin level falls sufficiently low to produce clinical manifestations, the symptoms that result are due to tissue hypoxia. Manifestations include pallor and muscle weakness, and the child becomes fatigued easily. Central nervous system manifestations include headache, light-headedness, dizziness, irritability, slowed thought processes, decreased attention span, apathy and depression.

    A. Abdominal pain and vomiting are not manifestations associated with iron deficiency anemia in a child.

    B. Poor posture and unclear speech are not characteristic of a child with iron deficiency anemia.

    C. Bradycardia is not seen in a child with a low hemoglobin level. Usually the child is tachycardic and has an increased cardiac output to compensate for the low hemoglobin level. Dyspnea on exertion is possible because of the decreased oxygen-carrying capacity of the blood.

67. **Key: D**   **Client Need:** *Physiological Adaptation*

    D. The patient will most likely refuse any blood transfusions. Jehovah's Witnesses are generally opposed to transfusions, including banking their own blood.

    A. In Judaism (orthodox and conservative), amputated limbs, organs or surgically removed tissue should be made available to the family for burial.

    B. In Mexico, the curandero is a spiritual healer who travels about curing those with ailments caused by witches and sorcerers. It is assumed that they also cure regular illnesses as well.

    C. Episcopalians, Methodists, Nazarenes, Presbyterians, Catholics and Lutherans all receive communion. Jehovah's Witnesses do not believe in the concept of Holy Communion.

68. **Key: C**   **Client Need:** *Prevention and Early Detection of Disease*

    C. The best time to do breast self-examination is after your period, when breasts are not swollen or tender.

    A. Breast self-examination should be done after menstruation. If the patient does not have regular periods or sometimes skip a month, breast self-examination should be done on the same day every month.

    B. The finger pads or the top third of each finger should be used to do breast self-examination. It is recommended that the patient do breast self-examination while bathing so that the soapy hands will glide over the wet skin.

    D. The finger pads or the top third of each finger should be used to do breast self-examination.

69. **Key: A**   **Client Need:** *Physiological Adaptation*

    A. Systemic hydration keeps secretions moist and easier to expectorate. Fluids must be given with caution if right or left-sided heart failure is present.

    B. With asthma, there should be a balance between rest and physical activity. Activity levels should be increased as tolerated so that a balance between oxygen supply and demand exists.

    C. Oxygen should be given when the oxygen saturation is less than 95%. Oxygen will have no effect on thinning the secretions.

    D. With asthma, there is a cough with or without mucous production. At times, the mucous is so tightly wedged in the narrow airways that the patient cannot cough it up. The secretions need to be thinner so they can be expectorated.

70. **Key: C**   **Client Need:** _Psychosocial Adaptation_

    C. For individuals with borderline personality disorder, self-destructive behaviors are responses to their sensitivity to present or anticipated stress or loss, particularly related to a significant other. Self-destructive behaviors may manifest as self-mutilation, substance abuse, sexual acting out or other irresponsible behaviors.

    A. Individuals with borderline personality disorder respond to loss with intense affective displays of anger, anxiety and irritability. They rarely display apathy.

    B. There is no evidence that individuals with borderline personality disorder become disoriented in response to loss.

    D. Individuals with borderline personality disorder may display transient paranoid ideation or dissociative symptoms, but psychosis is not a characteristic feature.

71. **Key: D**   **Client Need:** _Growth and Development_

    D. The patient should check her basal temperature to determine the effectiveness of this method because basal temperature changes signal ovulation. The patient will notice a drop in temperature when ovulation occurs. This is followed by a rise that lasts for two to four days prior to menstruation unless pregnancy occurs. If pregnancy occurs, the temperature remains elevated.

    A. This method should not be advised after the sixth month postpartally. A more reliable method should be considered.

    B. Breast-feeding does provide a period of infertility but is not considered effective.

    C. This supplementation with formula feedings will disrupt breastfeeding and increase the likelihood of the menses returning as well as ovulation.

72. **Key: B**   **Client Need:** _Management of Care_

    B. The most important management issue in DIC is treating the underlying cause. The primary prognostic factor is the ability to treat the underlying disease that precipitated the DIC.

    A. Intravenous (IV) fluids, blood, platelets and fresh, frozen plasma are given to replace volume lost through severe bleeding. However, the primary management of DIC involves correction of the underlying cause.

    C. The primary management of DIC involves correction of the underlying cause, which may be removal of a dead fetus, treatment of existing infection, preeclampsia, eclampsia or removal of a placental abruption.

    D. Renal failure is one consequence of DIC. The output is carefully monitored; however, treating the underlying cause is the priority.

73. **Key: D**   **Client Need:** _Pharmacological and Parenteral Therapies_

    D. Fosamax is used to treat osteoporosis in post-menopausal women. The patient should be instructed to remain upright for 30 minutes after taking the dose of Fosamax to prevent esophageal irritation. Gastrointestinal side effects of Fosamax include anorexia, abdominal pain, nausea, vomiting, constipation and esophageal ulceration.

    A. Fosamax should be taken in the morning before food is consumed. It should not be crushed and mixed with food.

    B. Fosamax should be taken with six to eight ounces of water.

    C. Fosamax should not be taken sublingually. It should be taken orally with six to eight ounces of water in the morning before food and other medications.

74. **Key: B**   Client Need: *Management of Care*

   B. **Blindness may occur when glaucoma is ignored or patients are not compliant with medication instructions. Having a second bottle of eye drops available will decrease the likelihood of not having sufficient medication on hand.**

   A. Patients with glaucoma should be instructed to refrain from driving for one to two hours after using eye drops.
   C. Treatment of glaucoma is usually life-long.
   D. Medications that dilate the pupil will prevent aqueous humor from draining through the canal of Schlemm, increasing the intraocular pressure. Patients with glaucoma are treated with eye drops that constrict the pupil.

75. **Key: C**   Client Need: *Management of Care*

   C. **Request that the physician stop the procedure until a local anesthetic can be administered. The nurse needs to be a protector and patient advocate. The nurse helps to maintain a safe environment for the client and takes steps to prevent injury and protect the client from possible adverse effects of diagnostic or treatment measures.**

   A. The patient is in pain now and relief should be immediate.
   B. The procedure should not be allowed to continue until a local anesthetic is given.
   D. The procedure should be stopped and the patient medicated rather than distracted.

76. **Key: B**   Client Need: *Pharmacological and Parenteral Therapies*

   B. **It is crucial that patients be evaluated regularly and their dosages titrated when necessary to maintain adequate analgesic. If the patient is using the PCA pump correctly and still not achieving pain control, the physician should be notified and supplemental boluses given.**

   A. The patient has a PCA pump. The benefits of PCA include the patient having control over their pain, and not being dependent on the nurse's availability to administer medication. The patient, not the nurse, should have control over pain therapy .
   C. Since the patient's pain is controlled during the day, supplementation of medication, rather than increased dosage, is more appropriate.
   D. The nurse should ensure that the patient is using the PCA pump correctly. If the pre-set dosage is not adequate to control pain throughout the night, an order for a bolus of medication should then be obtained by the nurse.

77. **Key: D**   Client Need: *Physiological Adaptation*

   D. **Hepatitis B is an inflammation of the liver by a virus that results in degeneration and necrosis of liver cells. This patient statement indicates need for further teaching. The patient should be instructed that, in order to avoid complications, alcohol should be avoided for six months to one year. Illicit drugs and toxic chemicals should be avoided. Acetaminophen may be taken only when necessary and not beyond the recommended dosage.**

   A. Hepatitis B is transmitted by the serum of infected people. Because all blood and blood products are potential sources of contamination, the patient should not donate blood.
   B. The major source of transmission is via infected serum. It is also transmitted by body fluids such as saliva and semen. The patient should avoid sexual contact until antigen-antibody tests are negative. When sex is allowed to resume, a condom should be worn and sexual contact should be refrained from during menstruation.
   C. All blood and blood products and any instruments that pierce the skin and enter the vascular system are potential sources of contamination. Patients are told not to share needles and to dispose of them properly after single use.

78. **Key: B**   Client Need: *Growth and Development*

   B. **This pattern of labor is referred to as secondary arrest of dilatation. There apparently had been some progress in the labor, but the contractions are no longer strong enough or coordinated to produce further cervical changes necessary for the labor to continue. The problem is also known as hypotonic uterine dystocia and is common in cephalopelvic disproportion.**

   A. This lack of cervical dilatation is referred to as dysfunctional labor. No progress in dilatation or effacement has occurred.
   C. The fetus descending at 1 cm per hour is the usual progression that is necessary for the labor to proceed.
   D. The woman may complain that she wants to push at 7 cm dilation, but she should not be encouraged to do so because it will cause edema to the cervix and possibly cause tissue damage. Pushing should begin when the cervix is dilated to 10 cm.

79. **Key: A**   Client Need: *Physiological Adaptation*

   A. **The patient is the authority on his/her pain. The patient's self report using a pain rating scale (for example zero to 10) is the most reliable indicator of the existence and intensity of pain. Self-report is ranked as the number one hierarchy of importance of basic measure of pain intensity. The patient's not wanting to bother the nurse needs to be discussed further.**

   B. Lack of pain expression does not necessarily mean lack of pain. Even with severe pain, periods of physiological and behavioral adaptations occur, leading to periods of minimal signs of pain.
   C. Physiological measures, such as changes in vital signs, are the least sensitive indicators of pain.
   D. The frequency of pain medication requests would not be a useful indicator of the patient's pain level because of the patient's desire to be "a good patient" and not bother the nurse.

80. **Key: C**   Client Need: *Management of Care*

   C. **Aspirin may increase the risk of bleeding when thrombolytic agents are used, and its use should be reported to the physician.**

   A. Ibuprofen is a non-steroidal, anti-inflammatory drug (NSAID), not a thrombolytic medication. The nurse should inquire about any previous reactions to thrombolytic agents, such as streptokinase. The nurse should assess the patient for rash, dyspnea, fever, changes in facial color, wheezing and swelling around the eyes when the thrombolytic medication is administered.
   B. Glaucoma comprises a group of ocular conditions in which there is increased intraocular pressure (IOP), optic nerve damage and visual field loss. The disease and the treatment are not contraindications for thrombolytic therapy.
   D. Surgery within the last 10 days is a contraindication for thrombolytic medication and should be reported to the physician.

81. **Key: B**   **Client Need:** *Physiological Adaptation*

    B. The symptoms that are associated with HIV encephalopathy, AIDS dementia complex, include cognitive dysfunction, motor problems and behavior changes. The cognitive manifestations include an inability to concentrate, decreased memory, impaired judgment and slow thinking.

    A. Patients who are placed in isolation are at risk for loneliness, depression and sensory deprivation, which are relieved when isolation is discontinued. The patient's cognitive and behavioral changes are related to the disease process.

    C. The symptoms described are in the clinical Category C of the HIV classification system. The conditions in this category are strongly associated with severe immunodeficiency, occur frequently in HIV-infected patients and cause serious morbidity or mortality.

    D. The symptoms described occur in the final crisis phase of HIV infection. It is a result of the continued breakdown and depletion of the immune defenses, increased viral counts and serious opportunistic infections. The clinical signs seen with Mycobacterium tuberculosis infection include fever, chills, weight loss, night sweats, lymphadenopathy, fatigue, dyspnea, chest pain and hemoptysis.

82. **Key: C**   **Client Need:** *Growth and Development*

    C. Due to increasing levels of progesterone, the size of the uterus increases, as does bladder capacity; thus, the patient will often complain of bladder fullness. Progesterone relaxes the smooth muscles of the gastrointestinal (GI) tract and decreases GI motility, causing nausea. Chronic shortness of breath also is associated with increasing levels of progesterone.

    A. Estrogen primarily maintains a blood supply to the uterus, increases growth of the breasts and promotes metabolism of nutrients. It is also responsible for the pliability of connective tissue, allowing the pelvis to accommodate the growing fetus.

    B. Melanocyte-stimulating hormone (MSH) causes a deepening of pigmentation. It is responsible for the mask of pregnancy and linea nigra.

    D. Follicle-stimulating hormone (FSH) is released from the anterior pituitary. FSH is responsible for stimulating the development of ovarian Graafian follicles.

83. **Key: B**   **Client Need:** *Physiological Adaptation*

    B. Diabetes mellitus is a complex chronic disorder of carbohydrate, fat and protein metabolism resulting in hyperglycemia. The hyperglycemia seen is a result of either a decrease in the secretion or the activity of insulin. Both emotional and physical stress can increase the blood glucose levels, thereby increasing the need for insulin. During periods of patient illness the nurse should anticipate monitoring the blood glucose levels more frequently.

    A. Common stress-evoking situations include illness and the controlled stress of surgery. Both examples may cause an increase in blood glucose levels, necessitating increased rather than decreased insulin needs. Extra insulin might be required to maintain glucose control and avoid the complications of diabetic ketoacidosis.

    C. Carbohydrate and fluid intake are important in illness, because the body requires extra energy to handle the stress of illness.

    D. Counter-regulatory hormones released in stress situations elevate blood glucose levels. Adjustments in the diabetes regimen will be necessary to ensure glycemic control.

84. **Key: B**   Client Need: *Growth and Development*

   B. Pain in the second stage of labor is caused by the stretching of perineal tissues to allow for the passage of the fetus. The patient reports a "burning, tearing and stretching pain." Pain impulses are carried from the perineal tissues via the S1 to S4 nerve segments.

   A. Stretching of the cervix, in and of itself, is not painful. During the first stage of labor, the patient often complains of back pain, that radiates toward the abdomen
   C. Stretching of the lower segment of the uterus is associated with the first stage of labor.
   D. Some pain from the descending part may be experienced in the second stage, but it is not the primary complaint in the second stage.

85. **Key: A**   Client Need: *Coping and Adaptation*

   A. Poor impulse control can contribute to self-directed violence because the adolescent may act on maladaptive coping strategies for dealing with anxiety.

   B. Criticism of others may contribute to risk of violence directed toward the patient by others, rather than self-directed violence.
   C. Poor concentration may be a cause of frustration, but it should not be a contributor to self-directed violence.
   D. Low achievement in school may contribute to poor self-esteem in an adolescent.

86. **Key: C**   Client Need: *Reduction of Risk Potential*

   C. Signs of respiratory distress in an infant include tachypnea, nasal flaring, chest retractions (substernal or intercostal retractions) and expiratory grunting. Worsening distress results in cyanosis and respiratory arrest.

   A. Clubbing, a thickening and flattening of the tips of the fingers and toes, is thought to occur because of chronic hypoxemia and polycythemia. Polycythemia is the result of persistent hypoxemia in a child with a congenital heart defect. Polycythemia (increased number of red blood cells) is the body's response to increase the number of red blood cells available to carry oxygen to the tissues.
   B. Jugular vein distension results from consistently elevated central venous pressure and is exhibited in a child with congestive heart failure.
   D. Cool, clammy, moist skin is a sign of hypovolemic shock. Lowered blood volume leads to the body's release of catecholamines to conserve body fluids by causing vasoconstriction. This vasoconstriction causes reduced blood flow to the skin, kidneys, and muscles. Consequently, the skin feels cold and clammy, there is poor capillary refill, and the glomerular filtration rate and urinary output is decreased.

87. **Key: B**   Client Need: *Growth and Development*

   B. The nurse would expect to identify decreased alertness in an elderly patient with pain when she is assessing the patient. Because of the normal processes of aging, the elderly move and react more slowly, and their hearing and visual acuity is diminished. In addition, the associated memory decline seen in aging makes retrieval of information from the mind take longer.

   A. A myth associated with aging is that the elderly experience cognitive decline. Confusion is not a normal assessment finding in the elderly. Harmful effects of unrelieved pain are reduction in cognitive function—mental confusion. However, these changes do not happen only in the elderly.
   C. Harmful effects of unrelieved pain include decreased urinary output, urinary retention, fluid overload and hypokalemia.
   D. Cardiovascular effects of pain include increased heart rate, increased cardiac output, increased vascular resistance and hypertension.

88. **Key: B**   **Client Need:** *Physiological Adaptation*

B. A malfunction of the VP shunt can cause an increase in intracranial pressure (ICP). It is important that the nurse and the caretaker are able to recognize the signs and symptoms of ICP. Early signs of increased ICP in a child include a change in personality or behavior such as irritability, headache, nausea, vomiting, blurred vision or seizures. Other signs include a decline in physical and mental ability, fatigue, weight loss, memory loss, drowsiness, and possible lethargy. Late signs of increased ICP include decreased level of consciousness, alteration in pupil size and reactivity, decerebrate or decorticate posturing, bradycardia and a widening pulse pressure.

A. A brain tumor is a space-occupying lesion in the cranium that can result in an increase in ICP. Typically, signs and symptoms of a brain tumor are dependent on the anatomic location of the tumor. In children, the most common symptoms are headache, especially on awakening, and vomiting. Additional manifestations include neuromuscular changes, behavioral changes, cranial nerve neuropathy and vital sign disturbances.

C. Loss of consciousness or unconsciousness is the inability to respond to sensory stimuli and have subjective experiences. The child's level of consciousness is assessed using the Glasgow Coma Scale, which consists of a three-part assessment: eye opening, verbal response and motor response.

D. Sleep disturbances in children can vary with the child's age. Some typical disturbances include trouble going to sleep, bedtime fears and nightmares or sleep terrors.

89. **Key: C**   **Client Need:** *Safety and Infection Control*

C. The nurse should reply, " No, children are safest in the middle of the back seat in a manual seat belt." Air bags have specific instructions provided by the manufacture that establish minimum weight guidelines for front seat passengers. Most automobiles manufactured prior to 2001 have warnings that only adults be permitted to ride in the front passenger seat if an air bag device is present. Persons weighing less than 120 lbs are at risk for injury when the device is employed due to the force and speed at which it is inflated. Therefore, children should not be placed in the front seat if an air bag is present. Children should be seated in the rear seat. The middle of the car is the safest location. Children should wear safety restraints, as required by state law. Safety restraints consist minimally of a properly worn seat belt and, in some cases, a booster seat that ensures proper positioning of the seat belt. This helps to reduce injury due to the seat belt in the event of a collision.

A. Airbags are designed to be used in conjunction with seat belts and are not intended to be used as the only means for protecting the passenger during a collision. Reports have shown that adults who do not wear seat belts when the airbag is employed can suffer serious injuries. Children are even more susceptible to air bag injuries due to their small size.

B. This statement is false. Sitting closer to the front of the car could put the passenger at greater risk for injury if the airbag is released. Children should not be in the front seat if there is an active air bag present.

D. This statement is only partially correct. The child should ride in the rear seat. However, the middle of the rear seat is preferred, and the child must have a seat belt in place.

90. **Key: C**   Client Need: *Growth and Development*

   C. A fetal heart rate between 110 and 160 beats/min is within normal limits. A non-stress test (NST) is considered reactive when the fetus has two accelerations in heart rate, that are 15 beats per minute above the baseline and last for 15 seconds or more. This is significant because it predicts the fetus' ability to tolerate the labor.

   A. The fetus should not have decelerations in heart rate in relationship to movements.
   B. These criteria do not tell anything about the number of accelerations in a given time period.
   D. The fetal heart rate is within normal limits, but there are less than two accelerations in the 20-minute test.

91. **Key: C**   Client Need: *Psychosocial Adaptation*

   C. The nurse acknowledges the emotional and physical difficulty the client is experiencing to establish a therapeutic alliance. Establishing a therapeutic alliance is a priority and must take place before the client will accept teaching.

   A. A client with anorexia nervosa who is vomiting is already aware that it is hurting her body. This statement by the nurse is not helpful.
   B. The patient does not see herself as thin. The nurse's statement invalidates the patient's perceptions.
   D. This statement would be therapeutic once the client expresses her feelings and a therapeutic alliance is established.

92. **Key: C**   Client Need: *Reduction of Risk Potential*

   C. Peritoneal dialysis is the process by which the body's excess water and nitrogenous wastes are removed, thereby reducing the manifestations of renal failure. Peritonitis is a complication associated with this procedure. Clinical evidence of peritonitis the nurse would observe include fever, rebound abdominal tenderness, nausea, malaise and a cloudy dialysate output.

   A. Fluid leakage may indicate improper catheter function, incomplete healing of the insertion site or excessive installation.
   B. Obstruction of catheter flow is associated with malposition of the catheter, adherence of the catheter tip to the omentum and infection. Constipation may also reduce catheter flow.
   D. Increased dialysate return is not an assessment finding for peritonitis. The purpose of peritoneal dialysis is to remove excess fluid from the body.

93. **Key: A**   Client Need: *Management of Care*

   A. A tracheostomy is a surgical creation of a stoma into the trachea through the overlying skin for airway management. Anxiety, fear and impaired verbal communication are associated with this procedure. Frequent nursing observations are essential interventions to help reduce the patients fears related to the inability to talk and to summon help, fear of suffocating and/or fear of tube dislodgment. Placing the patient near the nursing station would be the appropriate placement.

   B. Isolation precautions are not required for a patient with a tracheostomy. Sharing a room with an appropriate patient may help to reduce some of the fear and anxiety associated with the procedure. A single room is not necessary.
   C. The tracheostomy bypasses the normal upper airway protective mechanisms. In addition, there is a skin incision at the stoma opening. Both areas may become infected. The immunocompromised patient is predisposed to infections. This would not be an appropriate choice.
   D. The infectious types of pneumonia may be spread by droplet transmission. The normal upper airway protective mechanisms are disrupted with a tracheostomy. This would not be an appropriate roommate.

94. **Key: A** Client Need: *Reduction of Risk Potential*

   A. Pneumocystis carinii pneumonia (PCP) is an opportunistic infection that develops in patients with AIDS because the regulators of the immune system are destroyed by the HIV virus. The pathogens responsible for opportunistic infection are ubiquitous. Pneumocystis carinii pneumonia is in the air we breathe. People with intact immune systems do not become sick from this organism. Morbidity and mortality from this complication has been reduced by prophylactic drug treatment.

   B. Most opportunistic infections result from secondary reactivation of previously acquired pathogens rather than from a new or primary infection. Most people become infected with Pneumocystis carinii pneumonia in the pre-school years and the child's intact immune system brings it under control. The organism remains dormant in the person's body and can be reactivated when immunodeficiency occurs.
   C. The pathogen responsible for PCP is airborne and can be found in the lungs of humans and animals. Lifetime suppressive therapy with antibiotics is given to people with PCP to keep the infection under control. Helping patients comply with the antibiotic regimen is an essential part of the nursing care plan.
   D. PCP is an airborne organism. It is not acquired from unprotected sex with an infected individual.

95. **Key: C** Client Need: *Safety and Infection Control*

   C. Atrioventricular (AV) block is a disturbance in conduction arising in the area of the AV junction. Impulses passing through the junction are blocked to varying degrees, thereby causing the conduction of the impulse from the atria to the ventricle to slow or stop entirely, depending on the degree of the block. These dysrhythmias often lead to decreased cardiac output and circulatory impairment. Patients may experience hypotension, chest pain and heart failure and may become confused.

   A. Premature ventricular contractions (PVCs) are usually caused by the firing of irritable pacemaker cells located in the ventricles.
   B. Patients with tetany experience painful muscle spasms, grimacing, tingling of the fingers, laryngospasm and dysrhythmias. Tetany is associated with decreased calcium levels, as seen in hypoparathyroidism. It is not a complication of heart block.
   D. Kussmaul respirations are abnormally deep, very rapid, sighing-type respirations with increased tidal volume and rate. They are associated with diabetic ketoacidosis rather than heart failure.

96. **Key: B** Client Need: *Coping and Adaptation*

   B. The nurse's most appropriate response is to make a clarifying statement. Clarifying is a communication technique used to convey active listening. It is used to validate that the message was interpreted correctly. The nurse tries to restate an unclear or ambiguous message or asks the other person to restate or to further explain.

   A. This is a challenging statement. Challenging statements are blocks to communication. Challenging or arguing against someone's perceptions denies that they are real and valid to the sender.
   C. This is a judgmental statement. Nurses must not impose their own attitudes, values, beliefs and moral standards on others while in the professional role.
   D. Asking "why" is a type of block to communication. These types of responses may imply an accusation and can result in resentment, insecurity and mistrust. If additional information is needed, the nurse needs to phrase the question to avoid using "why."

97. **Key: A**   Client Need: _Growth and Development_

   A. Clinical manifestations of type I diabetes mellitus include the cardinal signs of diabetes: polyphagia, polydipsia and polyuria. Other signs of diabetes in children include abdominal discomfort, weight loss, enuresis, irritability and unusual fatigue. "Are you going to the bathroom to pass your water more often?" allows the nurse to assess for one of the cardinal signs of diabetes—polyuria.

   B. "Are you sleeping more than 10 hours at night?" may be a good question to determine whether or not the child is more tired than usual, but the child's baseline sleeping pattern must also be ascertained.
   C. "Are you eating a lot of candy?" is not pertinent to this assessment. Consumption of sweets does not cause type I diabetes.
   D. "Are you falling asleep after recess?" may be an attempt to determine whether or not the child is experiencing an unusual amount of fatigue. Better questions would be, "Are you taking naps during the day?" or "Are you getting more tired during the day?"

98. **Key: C**   Client Need: _Management of Care_

   C. In order to provide culturally sensitive care, the nurse must be aware of her own ethnocultural heritage, both as a person and as a nurse. Becoming aware of one's own biases and gaining knowledge of other cultures enables the nurse to begin to develop an attitude in which the patient's culture and healthcare beliefs, values and practices are respected and incorporated into the plan of care.

   A. Many variations in socio-economic status and social class can be found within any cultural or ethnic group.
   B. Environmental awareness may provide some clues about a patient's culture, health beliefs, values and practices but it is not the most effective way to increase one's cultural sensitivity.
   D. Talking with others may provide some insight about a patient's culture, health beliefs, values and practices but it is not the most effective way for the nurse to increase his/her cultural sensitivity.

99. **Key: C**   Client Need: _Basic Care and Comfort_

   C. Parkinson's disease is a progressively degenerative disease of the substantia nigra and basal ganglia. It is characterized by the gradual slowing of voluntary movement, muscular rigidity, stooped posture, shuffling gait, resting tremors and diminished facial expression. The goal of care is to promote independence and to encourage maximum participation in self-care activities. Providing sufficient time for the patient to eat promotes independence and participation in the activities of daily living.

   A. Serving small frequent meals composed of soft food and thickened fluids, if needed, are ways to maintain nutritional intake.
   B. The patient needs to be assessed for the ability to chew and swallow. There was no information in the stem of the question that reveals that the patient is having any difficulty with this activity.
   D.   Providing assistance with feeding does not promote independence and participation in self-care activities. There is no information in the stem of the question that indicates that the patient has difficulty with self-feeding.

100. Key: A   **Client Need:** *Management of Care*

A. Informed consent is a person's agreement to allow something to happen, for example, surgery, based on full disclosure of risks, benefits, alternatives and consequences of refusal and the nature of the benefit provided. The person or the surrogate must be capable of understanding the relevant information and must, in fact, sign the consent. The nurse must make sure that the patient has not received any preoperative sedation before the consent is signed. In order for the consent to be legal, the person giving the consent must be mentally and physically competent and legally an adult.

B. The physician must validate that the patient understands the surgery, rather than the nurse.
C. This is not the nurse's main responsibility. The exact procedure for filling in information on the document may vary from institution to institution. Nurses should follow the policies of the employing institution.
D. This is not in the nurse's scope of practice. The nurse assumes the responsibility for witnessing the patient' signature on the consent form. The duty to disclose and obtain informed consent lies with the physician and cannot be delegated to the nurse.

101. Key: B   **Client Need:** *Psychosocial Adaptation*

B. Frequent breaks, working extra shifts and inaccurate narcotic counts may be indicators of substance abuse among nurses. The nurse may be volunteering for extra shifts in an effort to obtain drugs. Other indicators include irritability, absenteeism and deteriorating appearance.

A. Victims of domestic violence present with vague physical complaints, insomnia and headaches. There may be evidence of violence in the form of bruises.
C. The identified symptoms are not defining characteristics of any personality disorder.
D. Individuals trying to get out of work usually do not sign up for extra shifts.

102. Key: C   **Client Need:** *Management of Care*

C. Most infections that cause acute diarrhea are spread by the fecal-oral route; therefore, personal hygiene is extremely important. Meticulous hand-washing, attention to perianal cleansing and proper disposal of diapers is essential. Teaching parents to adhere to standard practices will allow them to learn the proper techniques necessary to prevent the spread of infection and allow them to care for their infant without infecting themselves and others.

A. Providing literature on the cause of diarrhea is important, but it is not the first thing the nurse should do. Parents need to exhibit a readiness to learn, and this will not happen until their anxiety is relieved.
B. Allowing parents to participate in their infant's care is important. They can assist in recording the diaper weights after they have been instructed how to do this by the nurse. Teaching about standard precautions, however, is more important for the parents to learn first.
D. The diet preferred for the infant with acute diarrhea is an oral rehydration fluid, such as Pedialyte. This solution will provide the necessary fluid and electrolytes needed to replace fluid loss due to diarrhea. The parents are taught how to feed this fluid in place of the child's regular diet.

103. Key: C   Client Need: *Reduction of Risk Potential*

C. One of the major complications with the central venous catheter is infection. Hand-washing prior to accessing the device, as well as maintaining aseptic technique when accessing the device, will help to decrease the incidence of infection. Good hand-washing technique before and after the procedure is essential.

A. The location of the phone is not a priority in this situation. A phone should be available in the home so that the physician can be called should the device become dislodged, occlude or develop a leak.

B. The timing of the child's meals is not a consideration when planning care for the catheter or insertion site.

D. Siblings or other visitors may be present in the room when the child is having the central venous line flushed. Only caregivers should have direct contact with the device after they wash their hands properly.

104. Key: B   Client Need: *Management of Care*

B. Resource allocation is the responsibility of the charge nurse. Nursing management of the violent patient requires skill in de-escalation and experience in aggression management to prevent the patient from hurting self or others. Therefore, the patient with a history of violence should be assigned to the most skilled staff member.

A. A patient who is depressed needs social interaction and assessment for suicidal ideation but can be assigned to a less experienced nurse than the violent patient.

C. The patient who is psychotic needs structure and safety but can be assigned to a less experienced nurse than the violent patient.

D. The patient who is manic needs decreased stimulation and increased limit -setting but can be assigned to a less experienced nurse than the violent patient.

105. Key: C   Client Need: *Basic Care and Comfort*

C. Folic acid should be taken prior to conception and during pregnancy to prevent the occurrence of neural tube defects (i.e., spina bifida). The use of folic acid decreases the incidence of neural tube defects by as much as 50%.

A. Fiber is necessary in the diet of all pregnant women to prevent constipation. The recommended dose is 25-30 gm/day. Good sources include vegetables, fruits and grains.

B. Calcium is needed for the healthy development of teeth and bones. The recommended dose is 1000-1300 mg/day.

D. Protein should compose 30% of the total caloric intake in a pregnant patient ,or approximately 60 gm. Increased protein does not prevent neural tube defects.

106. Key: B Client Need: *Safety and Infection Control*

B. Family members who live with the child should be tested for tuberculosis (TB). TB is a communicable disease caused by Mycobacterium tuberculosis, an acid-fast bacillus. Tuberculosis is an airborne infection and is acquired by inhalation of small particles that reach the alveoli. Droplets are emitted from an infected person by coughing, laughing, sneezing or singing. Brief exposure to TB does not usually cause infection. Clients who have repeated close contact with an infected person who has not been diagnosed are more likely to become infected. Therefore, everyone that the client has had contact with should be assessed with a tuberculin skin test.

A. Isolating the child with TB is not necessary.

C. Children who are being treated for TB may return to school.

D. Proper room ventilation is important for all patients and is not specific to TB. Children should learn to cover their mouths when they cough and dispose of soiled tissues properly in waste cans.

107. Key: D Client Need: *Growth and Development*

D. Seizure activity signals the onset of eclampsia. Eclampsia is the gravest complication of pregnancy. Seizures may last 60-75 seconds. The treatment is magnesium sulfate.

A. Generalized edema, especially of the hands, face and abdomen, that is not relieved by 12 hours of bed rest is not considered healthy, but it is not the sign of a progressing condition.

C. A urine dipstick with +2 protein should be repeated within six hours. An increasing proteinuria is not to be ignored, but is not as significant as seizure activity

D. Elevations in blood pressure are also worrisome. They are usually the first sign of preeclampsia and are divided into mild or severe hypertension. No blood pressure (BP) greater than 140/90 mm Hg should be considered acceptable. However, the patient already has severe preeclampsia. Seizure activity would indicate further progression.

108. Key: C Client Need: *Prevention and Early Detection of Disease*

C. Suicidal patients give clues about their intentions. Very subtle clues may be ignored or disregarded by others. These can be verbal statements about problems being solved or behaviors, such as putting personal affairs in order.

A. While suicidal patients may give overt clues, most convey their intentions covertly.

B. Most suicidal patients are ambivalent about the act and may seek assistance prior to the attempt.

D. Suicidal patients may display behaviors that convey their despair. These include confusion, irritability, complaints of exhaustion and feelings of hopelessness.

109. Key: D Client Need: *Reduction of Risk Potential*

D. This is a correct assessment finding for a patient one day post-abdominal surgery. Normal bowel sounds may not return for two or three days following abdominal surgery. This is related to decreased peristalsis from anesthesia, bowel manipulation and immobilization.

A. Ascites is the accumulation of fluid in the peritoneal cavity. The fluid produces abdominal distension, bulging flanks and a downward protruding umbilicus.

B. Rushes of high-pitched bowel sounds are associated with early intestinal obstruction. This sound is called borborygmi. It is not an expected finding postoperatively.

C. Peritonitis is the inflammation of the peritoneal cavity. It causes abdominal distension, abdominal rigidity and decreased bowel sounds. It is not a normal finding.

110. Key: C   **Client Need:** *Management of Care*

C. The nurse needs to report the observed behaviors to the nurse manager. The nurse manager is accountable for maintaining the level of care on the unit. She is also the staff nurses link to administration. The prevalence of substance abuse among nurses parallels that in the general population.

A. Professional nursing promotes accountability, responsibility and advocacy. Legally some State Boards of Nursing require nurses to report unsafe and impaired nurses to the nursing regulatory agency. The issue cannot be ignored, but the first action by the nurse is to report the behavior to the nurse manager.

B. The staff nurse's responsibility is to report the behavior. While Alcoholic's Anonymous (AA) is an intervention used for those with alcohol abuse, it is premature at this time. Denial and rationalization are often used to justify chemical impairment.

D. Discussing the behavior with others violates the nurse's privacy and confidentiality, and it demonstrates a lack of caring and sensitivity. Such discussion might cause defamation of the nurse's character and lead to the charge of slander.

111. Key: C   **Client Need:** *Pharmacological and Parenteral Therapies*

C. TPN is used to maintain nutritional status and prevent malnutrition when the patient is unable to be fed orally or by tube feeding. Glucose is used to supply energy and caloric needs and usually accounts for 50% to 70% of the nutrient prescription.

A. In pancreatitis, 50% of the patients have a transient hyperglycemia due to damage to the beta cells. If the pancreas were producing too much insulin, the patient would experience hypoglycemia. Giving additional insulin would not be the correct intervention.

B. Fifty percent of patients with pancreatitis have interference with insulin release from the beta cells, which may cause hyperglycemia. Not all patients exhibit hyperglycemia.

D. TPN does not interfere with the production of insulin. The goal of therapy is to reduce the secretion of pancreatic enzymes, which stops the inflammatory process. The use of TPN meets the patient's nutritional needs while the patient is taking nothing by mouth (NPO).

112. Key: B   **Client Need:** *Pharmacological and Parenteral Therapies*

B. Sulfonylurea medications are oral anti-diabetic agents used to control blood sugar in type 2 diabetes mellitus. The ingestion of alcohol when these medications are used may result in a disulfiram-like (Antabuse-like) reaction (abdominal cramps, nausea, flushing, headaches and hyperglycemia).

A. Dietary management is an essential part of diabetes management. Dietary guidelines suggest a daily intake of three to five servings of fruits and vegetables, including green vegetables.

C. Diabetics have the same protein requirements as non-diabetic individuals. Approximately 10-20% of total daily calories should be from protein.

D. Caffeine is not contraindicated with sulfonylurea medications.

113. **Key: B**   **Client Need:** *Management of Care*

    B. During the initial assessment, the highest priority is to identify the presence of suicidal risk. Patients with major depression often experience persistent thoughts of death or suicide; therefore, potential for self-harm is a priority concern and protecting the patient from self-directed violence is the most important nursing action.

    A. Anxiety is a common symptom of depression and can range from mild to severe. Tension- relieving activities such as pacing, nail biting and finger tapping convey psychomotor agitation or severe anxiety in the patient with a major depression. Treating anxiety is important but not the most important priority on admission.

    C. Grooming and hygiene are usually neglected by the depressed patient and may necessitate nursing action. Promoting self-activities is important but is not a priority initially.

    D. Teaching adaptive coping methods is a nursing action that is implemented during the course of treatment but cannot be initiated until the patient's readiness to learn has been determined.

114. **Key: C**   **Client Need:** *Reduction of Risk Potential*

    C. Eosinophils are a type of white blood cell that is involved in allergic reactions. They do not respond to bacterial and viral infections. Parasitic infections can stimulate the production of these cells.

    A. This test would not be specific for a parasitic infection. An increase in the total white blood count (WBC) count is usually seen in infection, inflammation, tissue necrosis or leukemic neoplasm.

    B. An increase in the reticulocyte count is an indication of the bone marrow's ability to respond to anemia.

    D. The sedimentation rate is a non-specific test used to detect inflammation associated with acute and chronic infection, inflammation, advanced neoplasm, tissue necrosis and infarction.

115. **Key: C**   **Client Need:** *Management of Care*

    C. This patient may not sign his consent at this time. Adults may sign their own operative permits unless they are unconscious or mentally incompetent. The consent must be signed before the patient receives any medication that may alter consciousness.

    A. Crying behavior does not make the patient unconscious or mentally incompetent. The patient may sign the consent. The nurse, however, should explore the patient's feelings and offer emotional support.

    B. Emancipated minors may legally sign their own consent forms. Emancipated minors are considered to be under the legal age (18) of emancipation but, because of marriage or other circumstances, are independent of parents.

    D. An 80-year-old may sign a consent form. The age of 80 does not make a person incompetent.

116. **Key: D** Client Need: *Coping and Adaptation*

> **D. A past history of violence is the most reliable predictor of patient violence in the assessment of risk factors. Individuals who have used violence in the past as a method to cope with stress are more likely to resort to the use of aggressive behavior in the future.**

> A. Verbal threats convey ineffective coping and the patient's attempt to deal with anxiety through the use of aggressive behavior. Because aggressive behavior does not always follow a verbal threat, it is not the single most reliable predictor of violence.
> B. A history of family violence is identified as one of several predisposing factors for patient violence. Individuals who have witnessed the use of violence in their family are more prone to use violence because of learned behavior. However, a past history of violence by the patient is the best indicator of future violence.
> C. Pacing is one of several predictive behaviors that convey the pre-assaultive tension state. Pacing that is accompanied by verbal threats, increased voice tone and clenched fists is more indicative of impending violence than when it occurs alone. However, a past history of violence is a more reliable indicator of future violence.

117. **Key: D** Client Need: *Growth and Development*

> **D. Yellow sclera is associated with hyperbilirubinemia. Jaundice, if seen in the first 24 hours of life, is considered pathologic. Other areas where jaundice may be obvious are the skin and the mucous membranes. If left untreated, pathologic jaundice may lead to a condition known as kernicterus, which results in severe brain damage. Treatment initially would be phototherapy.**

> A. Acrocyanosis is a normal finding in the first day of life. It is the cyanotic coloring of the hands and feet due to vasomotor instability.
> B. Caput succedaneum is generalized edema of the scalp, usually found in the occipital region. It crosses the suture lines and is associated with prolonged pushing during labor or with vacuum-assisted deliveries.
> C. Epstein's pearls are occlusion cysts on the gums of a newborn. They are considered a normal finding.

118. **Key: B** Client Need: *Management of Care*

> **B. TPN is indicated to maintain nutritional needs and prevent malnutrition in patients who cannot be fed orally or by tube feedings. TPN solutions are highly concentrated mixtures. TPN administration requires central vascular access into a high flow vein. Before the initiation of the TPN solution, the placement of the catheter tip must be confirmed by a chest x-ray.**

> A. Metabolic profile blood work, including blood chemistry and electrolytes, is needed for this patient.
> C. It is not necessary to restrain a patient for subclavian catheter insertion. Should the patient become agitated, the nurse may hold the patient's arms. Restraint will only further agitate the patient.
> D. This is not the correct type of venous access. TPN cannot be infused through a peripheral line because of the concentrated dextrose solutions that are used. Baseline metabolic profiles should be done.

119. Key: D   Client Need: *Growth and Development*

D. Constipation is a normal complaint in the gravid patient. The decrease in gastric motility and the use of iron supplements contribute to the problem. The patient should increase roughage in her diet and increase her exercise.

A. One 8-oz glass of water is not sufficient. Six glasses of water per day are recommended.
B. Iron supplements may be constipating and should not be increased above the recommended dose of 30 mg per day.
C. While the patient should increase consumption of fruits and vegetables that are good sources of fiber, four bananas a day may be excessive. Bananas are higher in calories than most other fruits and vegetables and could contribute to excess weight gain in the pregnant woman.

120. Key: B   Client Need: *Psychosocial Adaptation*

B. The patient's statement is a verbal clue suggesting the presence of suicidal thoughts and feelings. The nurse should always make overt what is covertly expressed. It is extremely important to assess for the presence of suicidal thoughts and a suicidal plan by asking specific questions.

A. Although thoughts of suicide and death frequently occur in patients with major depression, they should not be considered normal. This nursing response is inappropriate and conveys a lack of concern for the patient's feelings of despair and hopelessness.
C. Telling the patient that these feelings will pass is non-therapeutic because the nurse is communicating false reassurance. Thoughts of suicide may disappear eventually with appropriate treatment or may result in a successful suicide attempt.
D. Ignoring the patient's statements is non-therapeutic and conveys a lack of empathy. Verbal and behavioral clues of suicide must be explored to assess for suicidal risk and the potential for self-directed violence.

121. Key: C   Client Need: *Prevention and Early Detection of Disease*

C. This pain may be of peritoneal origin. This type of pain is well-localized pain that causes rigidity of the abdominal muscles. The pain increases with any pressure or motion. Patients breathe shallowly and keep movement to a minimum to reduce pain.

A. Pain of renal origin begins in the flank area and may radiate to the lower abdomen and groin.
B. Pain of biliary origin is right upper quadrant pain that may radiate to the right shoulder.
D. Pain of meningeal origin is associated with headache, nuchal rigidity, and stiff neck. Pain is present when the neck is flexed toward the chest.

122. Key: A   Client Need: *Management of Care*

A. The nurse manager needs to assist an impaired nurse in obtaining treatment for his/her substance abuse. The treatment process can be initiated when a team of colleagues confronts the nurse and offers him/her assistance in seeking treatment.

B. Termination of an impaired nurse will protect the safety of the patients, but does not assist the nurse in obtaining necessary treatment. The nurse should be removed from his/her role until he/she has received and responded successfully to treatment. Termination only serves to promote the growth of the problem. The nurse often can obtain employment in another healthcare facility.
C. The impaired nurse needs to be removed from the professional duties and responsibilities of his/her job but should not be professionally isolated. The professional future of the impaired nurse should be considered and a humane system of intervention and treatment provided.
D. By providing covert support, the nurse manager not only is promoting the growth of the problem in the impaired nurse but also is jeopardizing the safety of patients and increasing the risk for health care employers.

123. Key: D   **Client Need:** *Growth and Development*

> **D. Fetal death is common with a high energy, direct blow to the abdomen. Maternal death is found in 10% of cases, but when it does occur, it is the result of massive injuries as well as uterine rupture.**

A   Placenta previa is associated with a placenta that is attached in the lower segment of the uterus, .sometimes covering the cervical os. Bleeding may be the result of a previa if it occurs after 24 weeks. It is not a result of trauma.

B. Preterm labor should be evaluated via an electronic fetal monitor whenever the patient states that she thinks she is having regular contractions. Trauma does increase the incidence of preterm labor, but preterm labor does not usually cause both maternal and fetal mortality.

C. The incidence of spontaneous abortion is also increased by trauma to the mother. Spontaneous abortion does not usually increase maternal mortality.

124. Key: B   **Client Need:** *Physiological Adaptation*

> **B. Laryngotracheobronchitis (LTB) is the most common type of croup experienced by children under five years of age that results in hospitalization. Inflammation of the mucosal lining of the larynx and trachea causes narrowing of the airway, resulting in the child having difficulty inhaling air past the narrowed structures of the lungs. The child will have a classic inspiratory stridor and suprasternal retractions. Hoarseness and a cough that sounds like a barking seal may also be present. The child frequently has a low-grade fever.**

A. Drooling, dysphagia and high fever are signs of acute epiglottitis.

C. Restlessness, absent breath sounds and high fever are abnormal assessment findings. Collectively, they are not indicative of a particular illness.

D. A low-grade fever may indicate that an infection is present. Purulent nasal drainage is commonly seen in children with an upper respiratory infection. Clear breath sounds may be heard in a child with an upper respiratory infection, but more commonly there are abnormal breath sounds such as coarseness or wheezing present.

125. Key: D   **Client Need:** *Management of Care*

> **D. The healthcare team is made up of nurses, physicians, allied health professionals and specialists. The registered nurse is most often responsible for coordinating and integrating services, because the nurse has the opportunity to interact with all team members.**

A. Serving as group facilitator is not the role of the nurse on the health team. The purpose of the team is to discuss the patient's plan of care. The nurse will bring to the discussion the plan of care that identifies the patient's nursing care needs.

B. The purpose of team discussion is the elderly patient's plan of care. It is not the role of the nurse to identify members who don't understand the nursing role. It is the nurse's role to contribute to the professional development of colleagues and to share knowledge and skills.

C. Collaborating with other health team members, rather than promoting one's own recommendations, is key to preventing fragmentation of the elderly patient's plan of care.

126. Key: C   Client Need: *Growth and Development*

C. The age at which children achieve urinary continence varies widely. Control of anal and urethral sphincters is gradually achieved with complete myelination of the spinal cord. The physiological ability to control the sphincters probably occurs between ages 18 and 24 months. By 18 months many children are able to retain urine for up to two hours. It would be detrimental to withhold fluids and risk the child's not receiving their maintenance fluid amounts.

A. This is an appropriate parental response. Time-out, a non-physical disciplinary approach, removes the reinforcing attention the child receives for misbehavior and places the child in an unstimulating and isolated place. Current recommendations include one minute of time-out for every year of age (for example: three years old = three minutes of time-out).

B. School-aged children strive developmentally to be productive in their work, and to keep up with peers. It is possible to become discouraged and frustrated with failures. The teacher may need to vary or adjust teaching style to the learning needs of the child. Reteaching, or other opportunities for success, will enhance the 10-year-old's self-esteem and possibly provide the motivation to continue the studies.

D. Although the majority of children have mastered the thumb-finger grasp and the ability to pull to a standing position by approximately 10 months of age, only about 50% of children possess the gross motor ability to stoop and recover an object at one year of age.

127. Key: C   Client Need: *Psychosocial Adaptation*

C. A patient suffering from alcohol withdrawal will begin to experience symptoms within 12 to 48 hours after his/her last drink. Some of the signs and symptoms of alcohol withdrawal are restlessness, tremors, diaphoresis, increased pulse, blood pressure and respirations fever and hyperreflexia (which could cause leg cramping).

A. A systemic infection would not typically include nighttime leg cramps.

B. Gastrointestinal hypermotility would probably include abdominal cramping and diarrhea, not leg cramping.

D. A neurologic dysfunction known as restless legs syndrome (RLS) is manifested by pain and tingling in the legs. You would not expect this disorder to be accompanied by the other symptoms mentioned.

128. Key: C   Client Need: *Prevention and Early Detection of Disease*

C. Cranial nerves III, IV and VI, deal with movement of the eye. The abducens functions specifically as a motor nerve ennervating the lateral rectus muscle of the eye. A right lateral deviation would indicate damage to this nerve.

A. Cranial nerve II, the optic nerve, is a sensory nerve responsible for vision.

B. The ophthalmic branch of cranial nerve V, the trigeminal nerve, provides sensation only to the forehead, eye and superior nasal cavity.

D. The cranial nerve VII is the facial nerve, which ennervates the muscles of expression and the cheek muscles.

129. Key: C   Client Need: _Growth and Development_

   **C. The MMR vaccine is most likely responsible for the child's symptoms. The measles compo-
   nent of the vaccine can cause anorexia, fever, malaise, and rash seven to 10 days after
   immunization.**

   A. Common reactions to the DTP vaccine include fever and soreness, redness and swelling at the
      injection site.
   B. The OPV vaccine does not produce a rash on the trunk and extremities. Vaccine-associated
      paralysis is a rare side effect that occurs within two months of immunization.
   D. A local reaction at the injection site and a low-grade fever are the only reactions found to the Hib
      vaccine.

130. Key: D   Client Need: _Physiological Adaptation_

   **D. Flushing a burn with tap water is the acceptable first aid for a small, minor burn. If done
   within one minute, the tap water will minimize the depth of injury. After the burn has
   been cooled, it is acceptable to apply a small amount of antibiotic ointment and a light
   dressing to keep the area clean.**

   A. Gauze may stick to the wound and cause further pain when removed.
   B. Ice is never applied directly to a burn. It could cause further tissue damage by freezing the area.
   C. Applying petroleum jelly to a burn will not permit interruption of the burning and may lead to
      deeper tissue injury.

131. Key: D   Client Need: _Pharmacological and Parenteral Therapies_

   **D. Diabinese is a sulfonamide, a sulfur-based drug, used to treat type 2 diabetes. It would be
   contraindicated in a patient with an allergy to sulfur. Therefore, the physician should be
   notified.**

   A. Aspirin is a non-steroidal anti-inflammatory drug. It is a salicylate and not related to sulfur-based
      medications.
   B. Penicillin is a broad-spectrum antibiotic and is frequently the next choice of drug to treat bacter-
      ial infections when the patient is allergic to sulfur.
   C. Iodine is a nonmetallic element that aids in the development of the thyroid gland. It is used to
      treat goiter.

132. Key: B   Client Need: _Management of Care_

   **B. If a nurse chooses to stop and give aid at the scene of an emergency, the Good Samaritan
   Act provides the following guidelines. The nurse should give care that any reasonable, pru-
   dent person would consider first aid. Do not do what you don't know. Offer assistance; do
   not insist. Do not leave the scene until the injured victim leaves or another qualified person takes over.**

   A. There are only a few US states that mandate stopping to give aid at the scene of any emer-
      gency. The Good Samaritan Act covers those who choose to give aid.
   C. The nurse, like anyone else, is only accountable for first aid as described in the above state-
      ment. The nurse should not initiate care if he/she is unsure of the appropriate care.
   D. When acting as a "Good Samaritan," the nurse is not expected to perform under the direct
      orders of a physician.

133. Key: C   Client Need: *Basic Care and Comfort*

C. Meat, fish, poultry, eggs and dairy products are foods high in protein. Fruits and vegetables have only a small to scant amount of protein. Therefore, vegetable soup and tossed green salad would be a complex carbohydrate, low-protein meal, and an excellent choice for someone on a protein-restricted diet.

A. A fruit and cheese platter would be high in carbohydrates, protein and fat since cheese is a high-fat, high-protein food.

B. A tuna fish and tomato sandwich would be high in protein and carbohydrates.

D. Meat loaf with rice is also high in protein and carbohydrates.

134. Key: B   Client Need: *Coping and Adaptation*

B. Crossed arms and legs and turning away from a person are nonverbal behavioral signs that convey an unwillingness to communicate with another. The use of this closed body language is one way the wife conveys that she is distancing herself from a meaningful conversation.

A. The term, incongruence, is applied when nonverbal behavior does not correspond or agree with the verbal message expressed by an individual. Because the question does not provide the verbal message that the wife is communicating along with this nonverbal behavior, the presence of incongruence cannot be determined.

C. The term, blocking, relates to an abnormal thought process that occurs when there is a sudden cessation of thought in the middle of a sentence. The person is unable to continue the train of thought or introduces a new idea.

D. Cultural posturing refers to nonverbal behavior, gestures, and spatial determinants that are customary for a given culture. The meaning of nonverbal communication must be understood from a cultural perspective to accurately interpret the meaning of verbal communication. The family's cultural background is not provided in the question.

135. Key: C   Client Need: *Psychosocial Adaptation*

C. Delusions are fixed, false beliefs that result from misperceived cognitive stimuli but have meaning to a person expressing them. The nurse needs to attempt to see the world as it appears through the eyes of a patient in order to better understand his delusional experience. It is important for the nurse to understand the patient's feelings and the meaning of the delusion.

A. A logical explanation about the nature of a delusion will not alter the paranoid patient's sense of reality. Explaining the nature of a delusion can increase the patient's level of anxiety that could in turn lead to further delusional thinking.

B. The nurse should not focus on the delusion or get drawn into a conversation regarding it's content. Encouraging the patient to talk about the delusion can reinforce the false beliefs.

D. Delusional thinking is defensive and is a response to anxiety. Pointing out that the patient's beliefs are false will increase anxiety further and prevent the patient from disclosing his thoughts and feelings.

136. **Key: A**   **Client Need:** *Psychosocial Adaptation*

    A. The patient with anorexia nervosa experiences the complications of a decrease in heart rate, a decrease in cardiac output and increased hair loss. These physical changes occur due to inadequate nutritional intake that leads to fluid and electrolyte imbalances.

    B. A decrease in body temperature and body mass are physical changes that occur in a patient with anorexia nervosa. These changes result from the inadequate intake of food and the fluid and electrolyte imbalances that develop.

    C. Blood pressure decreases in anorexia nervosa due to the decreased cardiac output. Hypokalemia results from fluid and electrolyte imbalances.

    D. Although serum cholesterol levels are decreased due to decreased fat absorption and digestion, there is a decrease in red blood cells, not white blood cells, in response to an inadequate intake of iron. The immune system is affected in the anorexic patient, increasing the patient's susceptibility to infection and causing an increase in white blood cells.

137. **Key: B**   **Client Need:** *Growth and Development*

    B. By one year of age, an infant's birth weight has tripled to an average weight of 21 lbs (9.75 kg).

    A. The first half of infancy is characterized by very rapid growth. Birth weight has doubled by approximately age four to seven months.

    C. At the end of the first year, an infant's weight has tripled, not quadrupled, compared with the birth weight.

    D. Although the infant's birth weight triples at approximately one year of age, this answer is not very specific. To say the "weight has multiplied" does not provide the specific information about the amount of weight gain.

138. **Key: D**   **Client Need:** *Growth and Development*

    D. Because growth is a continuous but uneven process, the most reliable evaluation lies in comparing growth measurements over a prolonged period of time. The National Center of Health Statistics has available growth charts to assess height, weight, head circumference and height for weight for ages birth to 36 months and ages two to 20 years.

    A. As physical growth is an uneven process, assessing the pattern of growth over time is more valuable than comparing a current weight with birth weight. Also, weight alone is not sufficient, as length is required, as well, to assess body surface area (BSA), body mass index (BMI), and determinants of normal weight for height.

    B. The West Nomogram, used for the determination of BSA, is the most reliable method for determining children's medication dosages. Unlike growth charts, the nomogram results are not associated with norms for various ages.

    C. The Denver Developmental Screening Test II is a screening test identifying what tasks most children can normally perform at a specified age. The four categories of the test are personal-social, fine motor adaptive, language and gross motor. This test does not address physical growth.

139. Key: B   Client Need: *Basic Care and Comfort*

B. The burn patient is in a hypermetabolic and highly catabolic state. It is necessary for this patient to have a high-protein, high-carbohydrate diet to meet the high caloric needs created by his metabolic state. Since baked custard is high in milk and eggs (high-protein foods), this would be the best choice for a snack.

A. Applesauce is a carbohydrate with no measurable protein.
C. Gelatin with fruit is also a carbohydrate food without any protein value.
D. Although bread has a few grams of protein per slice, it would not be the best choice for a high-protein snack. Butter is considered a fat.

140. Key: D   Client Need: *Psychosocial Adaptation*

D. A predisposing factor for a dissociative reaction is a set of traumatic experiences that overwhelm the patient's capacity to cope. These experiences usually take the form of severe physical, sexual or psychological abuse by a parent or significant other in the child's life.

A. A history of sexual abuse is not identified as a predisposing factor for attention deficit hyperactivity. Genetic links, biochemical theories and prenatal influences, such as maternal smoking and alcohol use, are identified as possible causes for attention deficit hyperactivity disorder.
B. Munchausen syndrome is considered a form of child abuse. The caregiver, usually the mother, reports that her child has symptoms of an illness, causing the child to have unnecessary medical tests. A history of sexual abuse is not identified as a predisposing factor for this illness.
C. Factors that predispose an individual to bipolar disorder include genetic links, biochemical influences and possible disruption of ego development during childhood. A history of sexual abuse is not identified as a predisposing factor for this illness.

141. Key: C   Client Need: *Psychosocial Adaptation*

C. Statements made by a patient that focus on God, prayer, faith, church or religious topics are used to assess for spiritual distress. The nursing diagnosis of spiritual distress is the state in which the individual experiences or is at risk for experiencing a disturbance in the belief or value system that provides strength, hope and meaning to life.

A. This statement does not relate to spiritual distress in the adult survivor of childhood sexual abuse. It reflects the individual's feelings of powerlessness that are commonly experienced by the adult survivor of abuse.
B. This statement reflects the individual's feelings of guilt associated with the sexual abuse. This would support a diagnosis of self-esteem disturbance.
D. Praying for the person is often healing in nature and does not indicate disturbance in one's belief system.

142. Key: C   Client Need: *Growth and Development*

C. A positive Babinski reflex is a normal finding in a newborn. It does disappear by the first year of life. If, on examination, the Babinski reflex is absent, it is significant and should be followed up with a neurology consult.

A. A stepping reflex is expected in a newborn up to three to four weeks of age.
B. An asymmetrical Moro reflex is indicative of muscle or nerve damage during the delivery. All reflexes should be symmetrical.
D. Unilateral grasp reflex may be indicative of a fractured clavicle or damage to the brachial plexus sustained during delivery.

143. **Key: D**   **Client Need:** _Psychosocial Adaptation_

   D. Psychiatric patients need to be checked after administering oral medications to ensure that they have swallowed pills and not "cheeked" them. Patients can retain a pill under the tongue or in the cavity of the cheek; therefore, it is important that the nurse inspect the patient's mouth after each dose of medication.

   A. Administration of a medication via the intramuscular route will ensure that the patient has received it. However, it is not the preferred route of administration, because it often produces pain and anxiety in the patient. Many psychiatric medications are manufactured only in pill or liquid form.
   B. A patient can appear to have swallowed a pill, while holding it under the tongue or in the cheek cavity. Signs of swallowing do not ensure that the medication has in fact been ingested.
   C. Engaging the patient in conversation for five minutes after she takes medication does not ensure that the patient has swallowed a pill.

144. **Key: A**   **Client Need:** _Growth and Development_

   A. According to the Denver Developmental Screening Test II-Revised (DDST-R) 50% of children combine syllables by the age of nine months and 90% do so by the age of 10 months. Almost all children combine words by the age of 24 months. A 36-month-old child who does not link syllables together is exhibiting an alteration in normal growth and development.

   B. The child may be using pointing as a method of communicating his/her desires or needs in order to compensate for the discrepancy that often exists between the receptive language (understanding the spoken word) and expressive language (speaking in words). Also, toddlers are often shy around strangers and may use hand gestures.
   C. Receptive speech surpasses expressive speech for the majority of early school years. For this reason, stuttering is considered normal until five or six years of age. Stuttering occurs when expressive speech cannot keep pace with the child's thoughts and intentions to speak.
   D. Repeating words and hesitating while speaking are characteristic of a 36-month-old's speech patterns.

145. **Key: C**   **Client Need:** _Pharmacological and Parenteral Therapies_

   C. There are two major classifications for PICC line occlusions, thrombotic or non-thrombotic. A non-thrombotic occlusion may be caused by a kinked or clamped catheter; an obstruction of the in-line filter; pinch-off syndrome; catheter rupture; catheter malposition or migration; or drug and mineral precipitates or lipid residue. The first step in trouble-shooting an occlusion is to assess the situation. Therefore, examining the line for kinks would be the next step.

   A. After assessing the problem, the nurse should contact the primary physician on call. Anything other than releasing a kink or unclamping the line and replacing a clogged in-line filter would require a physician's order.
   B. Attempting to flush a line after meeting resistance could cause life-threatening dislodgement of a thrombus and should never be done.
   D. If a line will not flush, waiting until the next dose is due will almost assuredly create a larger obstruction, necessitating the possible removal and reinsertion of a new line. It is unacceptable to hold a medication without a physician's order to do so.

146. Key: C Client Need: *Pharmacological and Parenteral Therapies*

C. When a patient has not gotten the pain relief expected from the medication, the cause is usually not enough medication or not frequent enough administration to control the pain. When this occurs, the next step for the nurse is to reevaluate the patient's pain by asking, "On the pain rating scale of one to 10, what level of pain are you experiencing?" This enables the nurse to make an accurate report to the physician so that the dose, medication or interval can be adjusted to meet the patient's needs.

A. It is not acceptable to assume that the patient has been dependent on drugs simply because the patient did not receive adequate pain relief.

B. While doing a comprehensive pain assessment and patient teaching, it would be acceptable to suggest adjuncts to pain management, (e.g., distraction), but not in place of medication in this instance.

D. Expecting the patient to wait two hours for another dose of medication without reassessing the patient's pain and contacting the physician is contrary to good pain management.

147. Key: A Client Need: *Psychosocial Adaptation*

A. The most common psychiatric disturbances in the elderly population are depression and dementia. Depression is the most common affective psychiatric disorder that occurs after the middle years.

B. Although some disorders appear for the first time after the age of 60, most anxiety disorders begin in early to middle adulthood.

C. Bipolar disorders usually begin in early adulthood.

D. Personality disorders are uncommon in the elderly population, with an incidence of 5% or less after the age of 65. Depression is the most common affective disorder among this age group.

148. Key: C Client Need: *Management of Care*

C. A tension pneumothorax is a medical emergency. If the tension in the pleural space is not relieved by insertion of a chest tube, the patient is likely to die from inadequate cardiac output or hypoxia. Therefore, the nurse should expect to prepare for chest tube insertion.

A. After the patient's breathing status is stabilized, an electrocardiogram would be in order but would not be the immediate concern under these circumstances.

B. Further assessment would be needed to determine if placement of a urinary catheter is necessary.

D. Gastric lavage is not part of treatment for either fractured ribs or pneumothorax. It would be done to wash out stomach contents, particularly in cases of toxic ingestion, deliberate or accidental.

149. Key: C   Client Need: *Basic Care and Comfort*

> **C. As long as there are no medical contraindications, a glass of milk would be the best drink to offer a patient who is having difficulty falling asleep. The dietary amino acid L-tryptophan found in milk is believed to aid in the induction of sleep. Milk also has a good nutritional value, unlike the other choices.**

A. Coffee is a stimulant that disrupts rapid eye movement (REM) sleep, delays onset of sleep and may cause frequent awakenings due to its mild diuretic effects.

B. Wine is an alcoholic beverage that also disrupts REM sleep, delays onset of sleep and could cause nightmares and daytime drowsiness. It is also a controlled substance, which would require a physician's order.

D. A can of soda would not be a good choice because it has no sleep-inducing properties and its high sugar content could act as a mild stimulant.

150. Key: C   Client Need: *Safety and Infection Control*

> **C. DNR is the medically acceptable abbreviation for "do not resuscitate." A DNR order is written by the physician after discussion with the patient or family regarding withholding resuscitative measures such as CPR, defibrillation and intubation in the event of a terminal illness.**

A. Dopamine and nitroglycerin recombination is a cardiac medication. Medications must always be spelled out and ordered with a dose, route and frequency.

B. Diagnostic neurological radiation is a radiographic test. It is not a common procedure and would have to be written out in its entirety to avoid an error in transcribing the order.

D. Dependent nitrogen re-uptake is another example of an infrequently ordered test. It also involves the administration of a drug and would therefore require dose, route and frequency. It would not be acceptable to abbreviate.

Rationales-Practice Exam A: Nursing, Part 2

1.   **Key: C**   Client Need: *Psychosocial Adaptation*

   C. The most appropriate diagnosis for a patient who has a phobia is fear related to specific stimulus. The essential feature of a phobia is a marked, persistent and excessive or unreasonable fear when in the presence of, or when anticipating an encounter with, a specific object or situation. The individual recognizes the fear as excessive or unreasonable.

   A. The nursing diagnosis of self-esteem disturbance is defined as a negative self-evaluation about self or self-capabilities, which may be directly or indirectly expressed. Although an individual with a phobia may also experience a disturbance in self-esteem, fear is the primary underlying process.
   B. The nursing diagnosis of sensory perceptual alteration is defined as a state in which an individual experiences a change in the amount or interpretation of internal or external stimuli accompanied by absent, diminished, exaggerated, distorted or impaired response to such stimuli. The patient with a phobia does not have deficits related to the five senses, nor does he misperceive external stimuli.
   D. An alteration in thought process is defined as a disruption in the thinking process. Defining characteristics of this diagnosis include disorientation to time, place, person or events; decreased ability to grasp ideas; impaired ability to make decisions; solve problems or reason; distractibility; inappropriate or non-reality-based thinking; and an inaccurate interpretation of the environment. Such symptoms are not commonly associated with a phobia.

2.   **Key: A**   Client Need: *Pharmacological and Parenteral Therapies*

   A. Hypertrophic lipodystrophy occurs when the same injection sites are used frequently. The patient should rotate insulin injection sites and avoid using the affected area for six months. This will allow the thickened subcutaneous tissue to regress.

   B. Injecting insulin at the edge of the affected area could result in erratic absorption of the insulin.
   C. Withholding insulin for any length of time without a specific physician order is illegal. Since the site could take up to six months to heal, the patient would certainly go into diabetic ketoacidosis (DKA) and die without appropriate intervention.
   D. Since insulin is injected into subcutaneous tissue, a longer needle would bypass this tissue and alter the absorption rate of the insulin. Also, only regular insulin can be given via the intramuscular route. This is done when immediate action is desired.

3.   **Key: A**   Client Need: *Prevention and Early Detection of Disease*

   A. The person with the pain is the expert. Pain intensity can be measured on a one to 10 scale and is an excellent measurement if the patient is able to use such a scale. Since the patient has reported his pain is a nine on this scale, this would be the best indicator of the severity of his pain.

   B. Blood pressure alone is not a good indicator of pain intensity. Blood pressure may go up with increased pain, but persons with low or normal vital signs could be in extreme pain.
   C. Grimacing and tensing of muscles may be an indication that the patient is in pain. It would require further questioning and evaluation by the nurse because some people are reluctant to report pain. However, this would not be the best indicator.
   D. Crying and moaning also requires further investigation by the nurse. These signs alone may not be the result of pain.

4. **Key: C**   Client Need: _Growth and Development_

    C. The basal body temperature should be taken prior to any activity. The patient is instructed to take her temperature prior to arising, utilizing a basal thermometer. The temperature should be recorded daily. A dip followed by an increase indicates ovulation.

    A. The temperature must be taken after a night's sleep.
    B. The temperature is plotted throughout the month to establish the presence of ovulation.
    D. A full night's sleep is necessary prior to taking the basal body temperature.

5. **Key: B**   Client Need: _Psychosocial Adaptation_

    B. The impaired ability to form and maintain interpersonal relationships is the major characteristic of schizophrenia. The major focus of nursing actions centers on helping the patient enter into meaningful socializations. Building rapport and establishing trust are the primary goals to achieve before teaching can be effective.

    A. Teaching the benefits of medication compliance is an important nursing action. Teaching, however, will be effective only after a therapeutic nurse-patient relationship has been established.
    C. Giving medication via an alternate route will not increase medication compliance. Compliance only occurs when the patient has developed a clear understanding of the beneficial and adverse effects of medication on thought processes and sensory perceptual alterations.
    D. Offering a patient reassurance that a medication is safe to take is non-therapeutic and not an effective nursing action for improving medication compliance.

6. **Key A**   Client Need: _Reduction of Risk Potential_

    A. The goal of phototherapy is to decrease serum bilirubin levels. The serum bilirubin levels increase until the third to fifth day of life before beginning to decrease. Home phototherapy is accomplished with the use of a fiberoptic blanket. The ultraviolet light is effective in breaking down bilirubin at the skin level.

    B. Increased specific gravity is not related to hyperbilirubinemia.
    C. Decreased red blood cell (RBC) count is a not associated with hyperbilirubinemia. The RBC count of a newborn stays the same until two months of age when it decreases, but this is a normal occurrence.
    D. Increased platelet count is not a normal finding in a newborn. The newborn has a platelet count similar to that of an adult.

7. **Key: A**   Client Need: _Growth and Development_

    A. The fundus is palpated at the level of the umbilicus from the first hour postpartum until the end of the first 24 hours.

    B. The fundus can be palpated midway between the umbilicus and the symphysis pubis immediately after the delivery.
    C. After the first 24 hours, the fundus will decrease one centimeter or fingerbreadth per day until the 10th day, when it dips below the symphysis bone and is no longer palpable.
    D. The fundus can be found at two centimeters below the umbilicus at the third day.

8.   **Key: B**   **Client Need:** *Physiological Adaptation*

   B. Medicating before pain begins will require less medication. Therefore, the nurse should advise the postoperative patient that pain should be reported in the early stages to best manage the pain.

   A. Trying to bear the pain as long as possible will only require more medication and/or greater frequency to get the pain under control.
   C. Higher levels of pain are not easier to reduce than low levels.
   D. It is not always realistic to expect to keep the patient totally pain free at all times. But, through frequent assessment, reassessment and proper intervention, the nurse should be able to manage the patient's pain throughout the healing process until pain relief is no longer needed.

9.   **Key: B**   **Client Need:** *Reduction of Risk Potential*

   B. Systemic lupus erythematosus (SLE) is characterized by alternating periods of remissions and exacerbations. Normal symptoms of SLE include fatigue, joint pain and oral ulcers. Almost half of SLE patients have some renal involvement, which can include microscopic hematuria, that the patient would not see. Therefore, if the patient reports hematuria, it should be considered a serious complication.

   A. Excessive fatigue is a general complaint preceding an exacerbation of SLE and would not be considered a serious complication.
   C. Joint pain is a general complaint associated with SLE.
   D. Oral ulcers are associated with SLE and not considered a serious complication.

10.   **Key: B**   **Client Need:** *Psychosocial Adaptation*

   B. People with seasonal affective disorder report a craving for, and increased consumption of, carbohydrates, weight gain, fatigue and irritability during the winter months. A reversal of these symptoms occurs in the spring and summer, with elation, increased social activity, decreased appetite and weight loss occurring.

   A. A major depressive disorder is diagnosed when one or more episodes of major depression occur without a history of a manic or hypomanic episode. Other symptoms include a decrease in appetite with weight loss. The occurrence of a major depressive disorder does not fluctuate with the changes of the seasons.
   C. A dysthymic disorder is a chronic rather than episodic disorder. Symptoms of either overeating or a poor appetite occur. Symptoms are usually present for a period of two years before the diagnosis is made.
   D. Symptoms of bipolar disorder include a history of one or more major depressive episodes in addition to one or more manic episodes in which the mood is elevated, expansive or irritable.

11.   **Key: C**   **Client Need:** *Reduction of Risk Potential*

   C. Urine and mucous shreds are the expected drainage from an ileal conduit. The mucous is present in the urine because it is excreted by the intestines as a result of the irritating effect of the urine.

   A. Clear urine would be expected when collected from a healthy bladder.
   B. Urine streaked with blood is not normal and would indicate possible injury or infection.
   D. Urine or feces would not be expected from an ileal conduit. It may be expected in patients with a ureterosigmoidostomy because the ureters are implanted into the sigmoid colon near the rectum.

12. **Key: B**   Client Need: _Pharmacological and Parenteral Therapies_

    B. EMLA cream consists of lidocaine 2.5% and prilocaine 2.5%. It is a topical anesthetic for use on normal intact skin or genital mucous membranes. For intravenous insertion, 25 grams of the cream is applied to the skin surface at least one hour prior to the procedure. It is then covered with an occlusive dressing.

    A. Any substances applied to the IV insertion needle would contaminate the needle and break asepsis.

    C. The cream is applied at least one hour before the procedure to anesthetize the skin. It will be of no use if applied after the procedure.

    D. Once the skin is prepared for IV insertion, nothing else should touch the skin except the IV needle in order to maintain asepsis.

13. **Key: D**   Client Need: _Growth and Development_

    D. This non-judgmental, open-ended statement acknowledges that the toilet-training process can be a challenge. This statement will begin the discussion and elicit the parent's beliefs regarding toilet-training. If unrealistic expectations are presented, the nurse can then clarify misconceptions and provide education.

    A. The age at which children achieve urinary continence varies widely. Control of the urethral sphincters is gradually achieved with complete myelination of the spinal cord. The physiological ability to control the sphincter probably occurs somewhere between age 18 and 24 months. It is unlikely physiologically that a child aged 18 months would be expected to be fully toilet-trained.

    B. Although this information regarding expectations may reveal unrealistic toilet-training issues, it is not as specific as a discussion focused on toilet training itself. This broad open-ended discussion may even occur and omit the issues related to toilet-training.

    C. This response is irrelevant, even if the parent is knowledgeable about the age at which they were toilet-trained. Further, if the parent believes that they achieved control early, unrealistic or undue pressure may be placed on the child.

14. **Key: D**   Client Need: _Management of Care_

    D. Low blood pressure is a circulatory concern in this child. More worrisome is the fact that the child is bradycardic and in a state of impending circulatory collapse. Usually when a patient is in shock, the heart rate increases in an attempt to improve tissue perfusion and increase cardiac output. A fall in blood pressure is a very late sign of shock in children. Petechiae, the result of intradermal or submucosal hemorrhage, may indicate sepsis. When dealing with a child in shock, the ABCs of resuscitation are employed immediately (airway, breathing, circulation), followed by more specific treatments.

    A. The child with symptoms consistent with a viral croup syndrome will not likely need immediate evaluation. The child is exhibiting a loud, bark-like cough and is therefore moving air across the vocal cords in a sufficient amount. Further, there is no difficulty in swallowing. This child is unlikely to rapidly progress to having a narrowed airway. A child with epiglottitis, evident by difficulty swallowing, drooling and difficulty breathing, would need immediate attention.

    B. Fever is a normal physiological response to infection. It is a protective mechanism employed by the body. Children often exhibit fevers with even mild viral illnesses. The most important factor to assess in the child with a fever is behavior. A child who is lethargic with a fever of 99° F is markedly more worrisome than a child whose fever is 102° F but is actively involved in normal play.

    C. Diarrhea is a common gastrointestinal complaint of children and has many and varied causes. The most important factor to assess in the child with diarrhea is hydration status. If the child's hydration status is adequate, he/she will not require immediate evaluation.

15.   **Key: A**   **Client Need:** *Management of Care*

A. **The impaired nurse has difficulty in coping with stress and has abused substances as a means to reduce stress and anxiety. The nurse manager should closely monitor the recovering nurse's ability to manage stress and utilize effective coping methods. Recognizing the use of ineffective coping is a priority concern.**

B. Situational low self-esteem is defined as negative self-appraisal in a person with a previous positive self-evaluation. Individuals who abuse substances have experienced low self-esteem and a negative self-concept. Over a long period of time, therefore, a recovering nurse's low self-esteem is not related specifically to returning to work.

C. Altered growth and development is identified as a predisposing factor that is associated with substance abuse disorders but is not a relevant diagnosis for the recovering nurse.

D. The diagnosis of ineffective family coping compromised, is inappropriate in this situation and in relation to the role of the nurse manager.

16.   **Key: A**   **Client Need:** *Growth of Development*

A. **Placement over the fetal back is the position of choice for the transducer because it can easily pick up the fetal heart tones. The transducer emits low-energy, high-frequency ultrasound waves and directs them through the abdominal wall toward the fetal heart. The waves hit the fetal heart wall and are deflected back through the abdominal wall where the transducer receives them. They are then transmitted to the fetal monitor.**

B. Placing the transducer over the placenta will emit the maternal pulse rate, not the fetal heart rate.

C. The transducer will not be able to pick up fetal heart tones over the bony prominence of the symphysis.

D. The transducer will work better if it is not over a bone.

17.   **Key: A**   **Client Need:** *Growth and Development*

A. **The peak expiratory flow meter (PEFM) is an objective measure of forced expiratory volume (maximum amount of air expired) at one second. This device is used by patients to monitor their degree of airway narrowing. It provides an early and objective measure of airway status. Anti-inflammatory and bronchodilator medications can then be adjusted according to the established medical plan. Often the plan includes a "traffic light" approach with the "green" zone being within 80-100% of the child's own personal best PEFM reading; the "yellow" zone within 50-80% of the personal best, and the "red" zone representing under 50% of the child's personal best.**

B. This question by the nurse does not address the child's self-care knowledge regarding asthma. Regardless of the child's answer, "yes" or "no", self-care knowledge is not assessed. Further, when self-care knowledge is accurate, airway symptoms should be controlled, and the child should have no restrictions on physical activities.

C. Regular consumption of adequate fluid intake is important for good health. Further, an adequate hydration status is the most important factor in maintaining thin secretions of the respiratory tract. Based on a child's weight, though, the actual amount of fluid maintenance will vary. Consumption of fluid does not specifically address asthma self-care knowledge.

D. When asthma symptoms are well controlled, there should be no restrictions on physical activity, including gym classes. In fact, regular physical activity, while airway symptoms are controlled, is beneficial to respiratory, cardiovascular and overall health and well-being.

18. **Key: A**   **Client Need:** *Pharmacological and Parenteral Therapies*

    A. Chemical phlebitis is the inflammation of a vein by irritating solutions or medications, particularly when very small veins are used. Many antibiotics, chemotherapeutic agents, potassium chloride and diazepam cause irritation to the vein and promote chemical phlebitis. This complication is one of the most common hazards associated with intravenous practices. KCL can produce severe venous inflammation. Associated signs and symptoms include redness and warmth at the site, and local swelling.

    B. Extravasation is the infiltration of a vesicant medication or solution. Vesicants cause the formation of blisters with sloughing of tissues occurring from tissue necrosis. The most harmful vesicant medications are antineoplastic agents, potassium chloride in high doses, calcium, and sodium bicarbonate in high concentrations. These medications must be administered with sufficient dilution according to manufacturer's directions.

    C. Pulmonary edema denotes an abnormal accumulation of fluid in the lungs. It is often caused by fluid overload or by too rapid infusion of fluids. Patients at risk for pulmonary edema are those with cardiovascular disease or renal disease and the elderly. Initial signs and symptoms include restlessness, shortness of breath, cough and a slow increase in pulse rate. Later signs include hypertension, severe dyspnea and coughing up frothy fluid or secretions.

    D. Thrombophlebitis encompasses a two-part injury: thrombosis and inflammation of the vein. The inflammation develops in response to the thrombosis. A chemical phlebitis can precipitate a thrombophlebitis. Thrombophlebitis is often related to the use of leg veins for infusions, or the use of hypertonic or highly acidic solutions.

19. **Key: B**   **Client Need:** *Pharmacological and Parenteral Therapies*

    B. Hyperkalemia is a condition in which serum potassium levels are elevated. Kayexalate therapy removes 1 mEq of potassium per gram of the drug. It produces osmotic diarrhea so that potassium rich stool can be evacuated from the colon, the primary site for potassium exchange. In renal failure, Kayexalate provides a more prolonged correction of elevated potassium.

    A. Lactulose is a laxative frequently used to relieve constipation and decrease elevated blood ammonia levels as seen in hepatic encephalopathy.

    C. Sodium bicarbonate ($NaHCO3$) is given intravenously in a medical emergency to correct acidosis and causes a shift of potassium into cells. This would not be the drug of choice for ongoing treatment of hyperkalemia.

    D. Phytonadione (vitamin K1) is a fat-soluble vitamin used as a nutritional supplement, an antidote for drug-induced hypoprothrombinemia and as an agent to prevent hemorrhage (antihemorrhagic agent). It is essential for the normal clotting of blood.

20. **Key: D**   **Client Need:** *Basic Care and Comfort*

    D. An acceptable alternative to breast-feeding is commercial iron-fortified formula. Like human milk, it supplies all the nutrients needed by the infant for the first six months of life.

    A. Whole milk may cause occult gastrointestinal bleeding and iron deficiency anemia in infants.

    B. According to the American Academy of Pediatrics, whole milk should not be introduced until at least one year of age.

    C. Iron stores are depleted by four to six months; therefore, non-fortified infant formula would not meet the infant's nutritional requirements.

21. **Key: C**   Client Need: *Management of Care*

    C. **The nurse should obtain written orders from a psychiatrist before providing home care to a psychiatric patient. The nurse should know the reason for home care and the medications the patient is to receive before a visit is made.**

    A. Medicare, a U.S. government insurance plan, pays for the majority of home healthcare. The first criteria that must be met for a patient to qualify for psychiatric home care under Medicare is certification by a physician that the client is home bound.
    B. The source of payment for home care is important information that the home health agency needs before a nurse is assigned to a home visit. Pre-authorization for psychiatric home care is required by most managed care agencies.
    D. Although the chronically medically ill is the predominant population that benefits from psychiatric home care, the diagnosis of an acute psychiatric illness or acute exacerbation of such an illness is required for payment.

22. **Key: B**   Client Need: *Growth and Development*

    B. **All patients should be assessed for physical abuse factors. If physical findings suggest abuse, further questioning is needed to protect the mother and the fetus.**

    A. A fall must be ruled out. Thus, further assessment is necessary.
    C. The patient should be questioned about her relationship with her spouse or the father of the baby. These questions should extend beyond those who are at risk or who have a history as battered women.
    D. A thorough history at the first prenatal visit should include questions regarding the patient's feeling about her pregnancy. If there is evidence of abrasions, further information should be obtained.

23. **Key: B**   Client Need: *Pharmacological and Parenteral Therapies*

    B. **Even with breath-holding, only 10-15% of the inhaled medication reaches the lungs. Therefore, it is important to hold your breath for a count of 10, if possible, after inhaling the drug to promote maximum benefit.**

    A. After removing the cap and shaking the inhaler, you should breathe OUT all the way.
    C. Before inhaling the drug, you should breathe slowly through your mouth. You should not cough.
    D. The cartridge is depressed as you are breathing in slowly.

24. **Key: A**   Client Need: *Reduction of Risk Potential*

    A. **Signs of impending death include mottling and cyanosis of extremities, slowing of the circulation and changes in respirations. The patient's decline in blood pressure is an example of circulatory slowing and dyspnea and apneic periods are changes in respirations.**

    B. Transient ischemic attacks (TIAs) are transient episodes of cerebral dysfunction. They usually present with a sudden loss of motor, sensory or visual function. They may last from minutes to hours but not more than 24 hours.
    C. Any seizure is an involuntary contraction or series of contractions of muscles caused by abnormal cerebral stimulation.
    D. A cerebral vascular accident is commonly known as a stroke or, more recently, a brain attack. It is an onset of neurologic dysfunction from a disruption in the blood supply to the brain. Depending on its location, the signs and symptoms may include paralysis of one side of the body, and/or impairments in speech, discrimination, language, math, comprehension, judgment, and time concepts.

25. **Key: A** Client Need: *Management of Care*

    A. The RN may delegate tasks and procedures to the LPN. Administering oral medications would come under this heading. Assessment, evaluation and nursing judgment are the responsibility of the RN and may not be delegated.

    B. Evaluating the ability of the patient to perform three-point crutch walking falls under evaluation. The RN may not delegate this.
    C. Developing a nursing care plan involves assessment and may not be delegated to the LPN.
    D. Teaching the patient to administer insulin also involves assessment and evaluation and may not be delegated to the LPN.

26. **Key: A** Client Need: *Pharmacological and Parenteral Therapies*

    A. Patients have the right to refuse treatment. Nurses need to explore the reason for refusal and evaluate the situation on a case-by-case basis. In this case, there is no evidence that the patient is a danger to himself or others and, therefore, forcing medication is not warranted. The nurse may be able to develop trust with the patient and administer the medication on a return visit.

    B. The nurse cannot tell the patient that he must take the medication, as she has no authority to back up this statement. In order to coerce treatment, the patient must be evaluated to be dangerous to self or others and further evaluated to be incompetent to make decisions.
    C. Adding medication to food without the patient's knowledge violates the patient's right to informed consent.
    D. A patient cannot be hospitalized for refusal to take medication unless there is clear evidence of danger to self or others.

27. **Key: C** Client Need: *Psychosocial Adaptation*

    C. The nurse offers anticipatory guidance regarding the common reactions experienced by survivors of rape. This assists the survivor to anticipate reactions and understand them as part of recovery.

    A. It is important for the survivor to resume a normal routine. Establishing a contract to attend classes may be appropriate at a later point in the therapy.
    B. The concepts of primary and secondary gain are appropriate for conversion disorders, not rape-trauma syndrome.
    D. Defensive responses to physical attack may be more useful for survivors who have been violently assaulted and are afraid of a repeat attack. In this situation, it is not the priority intervention.

28. **Key: C** Client Need: *Growth and Development*

    C. Within the first 12 hours of birth, the woman may begin to lose excessive fluids which have been stored in the tissues during pregnancy. Profuse diaphoresis is common, especially at night, for the first two to three nights.

    A. Hypovolemia is associated with severe postpartum hemorrhage and is not related to the normal blood loss experienced at delivery.
    B. Postpartum infection can occur anytime within the first 28 days following delivery. The patient presents with fever first, but not usually diaphoresis.
    D. Hyponatremia is not associated with a normal puerperium or postpartum course.

29. **Key: C**   **Client Need:** *Prevention and Early Detection of Disease*

   C. Breast cancer is the leading cause of cancer incidence and death in Black and Caucasian women. Neoplasms are usually singular, hard, and irregularly-shaped with poorly defined edges. Finding a lump with difficult-to-define edges would require the nurse to refer this patient for evaluation of breast cancer immediately.

   A. Freely moveable lesions are indicative of fibrocystic changes, not cancer.
   B. Breast tenderness during or before menses is due to fibrocystic changes and not cause for alarm.
   D. Most neoplasms occur unilaterally. Bilateral symptoms are most likely benign.

30. **Key: A**   **Client Need:** *Growth and Development*

   A. By 12 to 13 months of age a toddler can walk alone. A 36-month-old who requires support for ambulation would be considered to have altered growth and development.

   B. A child can sit down from a standing position without help at 12 months.
   C. The ability to use pull and push toys occurs by 18 months.
   D. An 18-month-old can throw a ball overhead without falling.

31. **Key: C**   **Client Need:** *Reduction of Risk Potential*

   C. Abdominal cholecystectomy involves removal of the gallbladder through a midline abdominal or right subcostal incision. It may also involve exploration of the biliary ducts for stones. "Log-rolling" technique for turning is necessary for patients who have had lumbar disc, not abdominal, surgery to avoid twisting the spine during movement. The patient's statement indicates a need for further instruction.

   A. A non-pharmacologic intervention for pain management and to help the patient overcome the fear that his incision might open is to assist and teach him to splint his incision when coughing. This is an appropriate statement by the patient.
   B. Postoperatively, incentive spirometry is prescribed every one to two hours to increase lung expansion while providing the patient visual results of his efforts. This is a correct interpretation of instructions.
   D. All patients must be encouraged to get out of bed and walk as soon as possible after surgery to prevent pulmonary complications and the formation of thrombi and emboli. Gradual position changes postoperatively give the patient's circulatory system time to adjust, preventing orthostatic hypotension. This is an appropriate statement by the patient.

32. **Key: B**   **Client Need:** *Coping and Adaptation*

   B. Disturbed body image is a state in which an individual experiences confusion, embarrassment or revulsion in the way she perceives her physical self. This patient is expressing shame about her thinner body that is not in line with her native cultural experience.

   A. Ineffective coping is a state in which an individual experiences an inability to manage stressors as evidenced by aggression or destructive behavior. This individual is not displaying these behaviors.
   C. This overweight female lost 10 lbs in a month, implying she correctly learned and implemented the diet plan given to her by the nurse. This behavior does not meet the defining characteristics for the nursing diagnosis "knowledge deficit."
   D. While this individual may feel powerless, or without control, over her countrymen's perception of her since she lost weight, there is no evidence that she has used poor judgment.

33. **Key: D**   **Client Need:** _Pharmacological and Parenteral Therapies_

   D. The nursing diagnosis "knowledge deficit" is characterized by incorrect performance of a prescribed health behavior. Evaluation of the success of a teaching plan includes direct assessment of the patient's status. Confusion is a mental state marked by altered thinking and followed by problems in comprehension. The nurse may conclude that the patient is still hypokalemic because confusion impaired his/her ability to learn self-administration of the newly prescribed potassium supplement.

   A. Non-compliance describes a person who desires to comply but certain factors prevent him from doing so, such as inadequate teaching. There is no indication this patient received inadequate teaching.
   B. There is no indication that decreased income prevented the patient from obtaining the pre-scribed potassium supplement.
   C. Hypokalemia refers to a decreased serum level of potassium, not of sodium. It commonly results from inadequate potassium intake. There is no indication of a fluid volume deficit.

34. **Key: C**   **Client Need:** _Pharmacological and Parenteral Therapies_

   C. TPN refers to amino acid-dextrose formulas. Fat emulsions (lipids) are often infused simul-taneously with TPN through a Y-connector. Such a mixture provides enough nitrogen and calories to meet the patient's daily nutritional needs.

   A. Additional components of TPN include electrolytes, vitamins and trace elements. Insulin (because TPN contains a high glucose concentration) and heparin (to prevent clot formation on the tip of the catheter) may be added. If corticosteroids are required, additional venous access would be needed.
   B. Hemolysis of red blood cells occurs if packed red blood cells are administered piggyback into any solution except normal saline.
   D. Osmotic diuretics are not piggy-backed into TPN. Additional venous access is required.

35. **Key: C**   **Client Need:** _Growth and Development_

   C. Prenatal visits should be scheduled once a month for the first and second trimesters. At 28 weeks, the patient should be seen every two weeks until 36 weeks, when she is seen every week till delivery.

   A. In a healthy patient, there is no need to be seen every week during the first trimester.
   B. The patient is not seen every two weeks until 28 weeks' gestation.
   D. Prenatal care every two months is not often enough to closely monitor the mother or fetus.

36. **Key: B**   **Client Need:** _Pharmacological and Parenteral Therapies_

   B. Regardless of its source, pain that is inadequately treated has harmful effects beyond the discomfort it causes. Unrelieved pain affects various body systems, including the cardio-vascular system, and can initiate the stress response, resulting in increased pulse and blood pressure and a distressed appearance. By providing an explanation such as this, the nurse can help the patient to accept the drugs needed to relieve pain.

   A. Patients have the right to refuse therapy. The nurse can play an important role in determining the reason for refusal and should first make that attempt before accepting refusal.
   C. A general principle for administering analgesics is to administer them before pain increases in severity.
   D. Medications should never be left at the bedside for the patient to take later.

37.　**Key: A**　　　　　　　　　　　　　　　**Client Need:** *Reduction of Risk Potential*

　　A. Febrile seizures are transient disorders of childhood that occur in association with a fever. One of the most common neurological disorders of childhood, most febrile seizures occur after about six months of age and usually before three years, with increased frequency in children younger than 18 months. They usually accompany a gastrointestinal (GI) tract infection or an acute respiratory illness and are usually self-limiting and benign in nature.

　　B. Respiratory arrest is cessation of breathing and does not occur with febrile seizures.
　　C. Although a child holding his/her breath in a temper tantrum may cause fainting from decreased oxygen supplies, the increased level of carbon dioxide will stimulate the respiratory center and the child will begin breathing again.
　　D. Parents are discouraged from using a tepid bath to lower elevated temperatures, because the resulting shivering increases metabolic output.

38.　**Key: B**　　　　　　　　　　　　　　　**Client Need:** *Psychosocial Adaptation*

　　B. The client who is 5'8" and weighs 98 lbs is below 80% of ideal body weight and is suffering from severe malnutrition. Physiological damage is the priority concern and must be assessed and addressed first.

　　A. Once the client has attained some degree of nutritional stabilization, issues of body image distortion can be addressed.
　　C. Obsession and preoccupation with food are common in the client with anorexia nervosa. These behaviors decrease as the physiological effects of starvation are treated.
　　D. Need for control is common among clients with anorexia nervosa. Decision-making regarding choice of foods is part of the treatment; however, physical concerns should be addressed first.

39.　**Key: A**　　　　　　　　　　　　　　　**Client Need:** *Reduction of Risk Potential*

　　A. Heart failure is a physiological state in which the heart cannot pump enough blood to meet the body's metabolic (or oxygen) needs. It is characterized by manifestations of volume overload, inadequate tissue perfusion and poor exercise tolerance. Orthopnea develops because the supine position increases the amount of blood returning to the heart and lungs from the lower extremities, causing pulmonary congestion and decreased vital capacity.

　　B. As cardiac output falls, decreased renal blood flow results in a lowered glomerular filtration rate, with increased sodium and water retention. This is reflected by weight gain, rather than weight loss.
　　C. Congestive heart failure results in tachycardia, tachypnea and hypertension or hypotension. It does not produce fever.
　　D. Congestive heart failure causes edema of the lower extremities. Calf pain is typically associated with deep vein thrombosis.

40. **Key: B**   Client Need: *Reduction of Risk Potential*

    B. Because of respiratory infections, half of all children discharged on mechanical ventilation will require re-hospitalization. Respiratory syncytial virus (RSV) is a frequent cause. Practical advice for the parents to follow in order to avoid hospitalization and infection include: avoiding sibling contact if suspicious for infection, watching for signs of infection such as irritability, low-grade fever, nasal congestion, cough, tachypnea or wheezing, and maintaining flu shots for parents and routine immunizations for siblings.

    A. Due to risk of aspiration, most liquids are administered via a gastrostromy tube (g-tube).
    C. Play is a child's work. Ventilated or not, a child must have playtime scheduled into his/her awake time of day. As long as parents follow infection control procedures when screening visitors, parallel and group play are essential for normal growth and development.
    D. Trendelenburg position may be used for percussion and postural drainage of the lower lung lobes, but not for suctioning.

41. **Key: D**   Client Need: *Prevention and Early Detection of Disease*

    D. Primary prevention interventions are interventions that protect children from diseases or injuries. Some examples are well childcare clinics, immunization programs, safety programs, nutrition programs, safety measures and community parenting classes.

    A. No one factor is predictive of abuse, including completion/non-completion of high school.
    B. If a large percentage of child abusers were abused themselves, moving in with the extended family might not be safe.
    C. Parenting skills are learned by example, repetition, practice and positive reinforcement.

42. **Key: D**   Client Need: *Pharmacological and Parenteral Therapies*

    D. Paracentesis involves draining fluid accumulated in the peritoneum (ascites) via an aseptically inserted trocar. Ascites can develop when hepatitis B becomes chronic, resulting in liver failure. The major complications of paracentesis are hypovolemia and shock. Pain is not expected after paracentesis.

    A. While gastritis can occur with liver disease, aspirin, even if enteric-coated, should be avoided because of its hepatotoxic properties
    B. Medications such as aspirin and acetaminophen are given as infrequently as possible to patients with hepatitis because of their hepatotoxic properties.
    C. Acetaminophen does not have greater analgesic effects than does aspirin, and it has hepatotoxic properties.

43. **Key: A**   Client Need: *Pharmacological and Parenteral Therapies*

    A. Transdermal 17-beta estradiol is an estrogen hormone used to prevent or treat menopausal symptoms. The transdermal form is applied to the skin once or twice a week.

    B. Estradiol is an estrogen, not a progestin. The transdermal route allows for systemic absorption of the drug through the skin. The intravenous route provides direct delivery into the bloodstream.
    C. Common adverse effects of estradiol include vaginal spotting, breakthrough bleeding and amenorrhea.
    D. The transdermal dosage form is more expensive than the oral form of estrogen.

44. **Key: C**   Client Need: *Reduction of Risk Potential*

   C. Deep vein thrombosis (DVT) is clot formation in a deep vein. Because of positioning during surgery, postoperative edema and immobility, the patient who has had a total abdominal hysterectomy is at risk for DVT. To minimize the risk, the patient is assisted in changing positions frequently.

   A. Dehydration is a risk factor for the development of DVT. Adequate hydration is an important preventive measure.
   B. Discharge teaching to prevent DVT includes avoiding prolonged sitting in a chair and avoiding immobility.
   D. DVT occurs in a deep vein, often in the lower extremities. At times, hidden bleeding occurs beneath the skin at the surgical site. Massage would aggravate this hematoma and would not improve venous return from the lower extremities.

45. **Key: B**   Client Need: *Growth and Development*

   B. Mastitis is an infection of the breast that presents with fever, chills and painful reddened area on the breast. It is generally unilateral in nature. It requires antibiotic therapy and is usually caused by Staphylococcus aureus bacteria.

   A. Pumping to continue lactation is necessary, but after 24 hours of antibiotic therapy breast-feeding can begin again.
   C. Pain will diminish with the help of anti-inflammatory agents. Breast milk should be discarded until antibiotic therapy has been in effect for 24 hours.
   D. If both nipples are cracked, there is a chance that they will both be exposed to the bacteria. Both breasts should be pumped and the breast milk discarded for 24 hours.

46. **Key: C**   Client Need: *Physiological Adaptation*

   C. The main goal of diabetes management is to normalize insulin activity and blood glucose levels to reduce the development of vascular and neuropathic complications. Exercise is an important factor in managing diabetes, because it increases the uptake of glucose by body muscles and improves insulin utilization.

   A. Exercise lowers blood glucose. It does not increase it.
   B. Exercise alters blood lipids, decreasing total cholesterol and triglyceride levels.
   D. Exercise alters blood lipids, increasing, not decreasing, levels of high-density lipoproteins.

47. **Key: A**   Client Need: *Psychosocial Adaptation*

   A. When there is a change in behavior in a patient with known suicidal ideation, the patient should be assessed directly for suicide intent and means.

   B. This statement does not directly address the patient's level of suicide ideation.
   C. While it is important to address the client's feelings, it is more important to be direct in the assessment of suicide.
   D. This statement is too broad and does not specifically question the patient's suicide intent.

48. **Key: D**   **Client Need:** *Reduction of Risk Potential*

   D. Jaundice produces (or results in) a yellow color of the skin, sclera and mucous membranes resulting from liver and gallbladder disease, certain anemias and hemolysis of red blood cells. Jaundice becomes clinically evident when the serum bilirubin level exceeds 2.5 mg/dL.

   A. Elevated serum ammonia occurs when a failing liver is no longer able to detoxify and convert the ammonia to urea.
   B. Blood nitrogen levels are increased in kidney disease and decreased in liver disease.
   C. Albumin, a protein formed in the liver, is decreased in liver disease, one of the causes of jaundice.

49. **Key: A**   **Client Need:** *Pharmacological and Parenteral Therapies*

   A. Glipizide is a second-generation sulfonylurea agent used to treat type 2 diabetes mellitus in patients with some pancreatic beta-cell function remaining. While hypoglycemia is the most common side effect, this drug can also cause hematologic reactions such as agranulocytosis.

   B. Vitamin B1 deficiency is not a side effect of glipizide.
   C. Hyperlipidemia is not a side effect of glipizide.
   D. Hypernatremia is not a side effect of glipizide.

50. **Key: C**   **Client Need:** *Management of Care*

   C. About 50% of patients with cancer (oncology) will eventually die of their disease. When working on an oncology unit, caring for patients who are dying would, therefore, be common. A problem exists for the charge nurse when a staff member says he does not want to care for dying patients on this unit. Before problem-solving can occur, perceptions must be clarified. Questioning, which is central to problem-solving, identifies issues and examines reasoning.

   A. Before a solution to the problem is implemented, the nature of the problem must be clarified and a variety of options identified. Further, it is unrealistic to not assign an oncology nurse to dying patients.
   B. Having the staff nurse talk with a spiritual advisor may be part of the implementation step of problem-solving. Assessment of the problem must occur first.
   D. The staff nurse may function more effectively on another unit but transfer should not occur as initial pressure. An assessment of the nurse's concerns should occur first.

51. **Key: C**   **Client Need:** *Reduction of Risk Potential*

   C. The hallmark of Shaken Baby Syndrome (SBS) is the retinal hemorrhage. Violent shaking of children can cause fatal intracranial trauma without signs of external head injury. Nurses should suspect SBS in infants less than one year of age who present with subdural and/or retinal hemorrhage in the absence of external signs of trauma.

   A. A mastoid fracture is more consistent with a fall or bump to the head.
   B. Signs and symptoms of this disease will only present in the parent's presence.
   D. Bruises, bleeding, lacerations or irritation of external genitalia, anus, mouth or throat would be suggestive of sexual abuse.

52.   Key: D   **Client Need:** *Prevention and Early Detection of Disease*

D. Hypothyroidism is a deficiency of thyroid hormone resulting in slowed metabolism, decreased heat production and decreased oxygen consumption by body tissues. Among the many clinical manifestations of hypothyroidism are fluid retention with periorbital, facial and pretibial edema.

A. Tachycardia occurs with hyperthyroidism.
B. Weight loss occurs with hyperthyroidism.
C. Hypothyroidism results in decreased heat production.

53.   Key: D   **Client Need:** *Psychosocial Adaptation*

D. Hallucinations are serious symptoms that present in severely depressed patients. These can progress to voices commanding the patient to commit suicide. This symptom warrants immediate investigation.

A. A client attending day treatment five days a week is compliant with treatment. No further investigation is needed.
B. A client seeing a psychiatrist twice a month is receiving regular assessment and treatment. No immediate investigation is needed.
C. The situation of being housebound can be explored further and support systems established. This does not, however, constitute an immediate concern.

54.   Key: A   **Client Need:** *Management of Care*

A. Sepsis is the systemic response to infection. Septic shock results when large amounts of toxins and endotoxins produced by bacteria are secreted into the blood, causing a whole-body inflammatory reaction. Treatment of septic shock begins with identifying the cause of infection by collecting specimens of urine, blood, sputum and wound drainage for culture.

B. After cultures are obtained and until the infecting organism is known, treatment with broad-spectrum antibiotics is begun.

C. Urine output provides important information about renal perfusion and is monitored closely following insertion of an indwelling catheter. However, identification of the source of the sepsis and beginning treatment hold priority.
D. Antiembolism stockings encourage venous return to the heart and help prevent thrombus development. They should be applied after other treatment modalities are begun.

55.   Key: C   **Client Need:** *Coping and Adaptation*

C. Encouraging the patient to discuss her concerns about the fetus will enable the patient to ventilate and the nurse to plan appropriate therapeutic interventions.

A. Providing information about the disease would not be done until the patient's readiness to learn is determined.
B. The nurse can provide support by just sitting with the patient while she cries.
D. The nurse should address the patient's feelings and readiness to learn. The nurse should not wait until the patient introduces the topic.

56. **Key: B**   Client Need: *Physiological Adaptation*

   B. Vascular (or multi-infarct) dementia is second only to Alzheimer's disease in incidence. Multiple small cerebral infarctions, or small strokes, result in multi-infarct dementia. Cerebral damage occurs because of disruption of blood supply to the brain.

   A. The cause of this type of dementia is multiple small cerebral infarcts.
   C. Vascular dementia is caused by multiple small cerebral infarctions, not by a virus.
   D. Medications have not been identified as an etiologic factor in vascular dementia.

57. **Key C**   Client Need: *Growth and Development*

   C. A biophysical profile (BBP) is used to determine fetal well-being. It is a method of fetal risk surveillance, that scores five categories: fetal movement, fetal breathing movement, fetal tone, fetal heart rate and amniotic fluid volume. A score of 8-10 is considered normal. The presence of a positive BBP shows an intact nervous system.

   A. Fetal lung maturity is measured by the lecithin/sphingomyelin (L/S) ratio. Amniotic fluid is analyzed for a 2:1 L/S ratio, which signifies mature fetal lungs.
   B. Gestational age is measured by ultrasonography.
   D. Contractions or uterine activity is measured by electronic fetal monitoring.

58. **Key: A**   Client Need: *Psychosocial Adaptation*

   A. Autonomic activity (sweating, increased pulse), nausea or vomiting, tremors, anxiety and psychomotor agitation are all signs of alcohol withdrawal. Clients with recent heavy drinking must be observed for these symptoms.

   B. Pleasant mood, hyperactivity and increased appetite are not associated with substance withdrawal. Pleasant mood and hyperactivity are associated with amphetamine use.
   C. Drowsiness, irritability and unsteady gait are not associated with substance withdrawal. These symptoms are associated with alcohol intoxication.
   D. Insomnia and decreased blood pressure and heart rate are not associated with substance withdrawal.

59. **Key: B**   Client Need: *Reduction of Risk Potential*

   B. An EEG is a graphic recording of the electrical activity of the brain. The MRI is a non-invasive diagnostic scanning study that provides information about the body's anatomy. Both studies would be useful in determining the cause of the patient's symptoms. To assure patient understanding and cooperation, the nurse should provide information and reassurance about the studies.

   A. Neither an EEG nor an MRI requires the patient to be fasting.
   C. While certain medication, such as sedatives and hypnotics, must be withheld prior to an EEG, it is not necessary to withhold all medications. It is not necessary to withhold medications before an MRI.
   D. Administration of radiopaque tablets is not part of patient preparation for an EEG or an MRI. Nothing is administered during an EEG, so an allergic response is not an issue.

60. **Key: C**   **Client Need:** *Psychosocial Adaptation*

    C. Milieu therapy is a scientific structuring of the environment in order to effect behavioral changes and to improve the psychological health and functioning of the individual. The goal of milieu therapy is to manipulate the environment so that all aspects of the patient's hospital experience is therapeutic.

    A. Health teaching refers to activities that the nurse conducts to bring about behavioral change in the patient. The focus of the behavioral change is usually the acquisition of knowledge or technical skills. Health teaching is a component of milieu therapy.

    B. Case management is a nursing care delivery method in which the case manager is responsible for tracking the patient's health progress from home, to hospital and back home. Case management strives to organize patient care throughout an episode of illness so that specific clinical and financial outcomes are achieved within an allotted time frame.

    D. A self-care activity refers to a standard of psychiatric nursing practice in which the nurse structures activities of daily living to foster self-care and mental and physical well-being. This standard is one of several nursing practice standards that are applied in structuring milieu therapy.

61. **Key: B**   **Client Need:** *Growth and Development*

    B. They do not have children. Primary infertility is diagnosed when the couple cannot conceive. The fact that this couple has no living children makes them a candidate for primary infertility.

    A. The fact that both partners are in their 30s does not contribute to the diagnosis. Age is not a determining factor.

    C. The couple should have an infertility work-up after one year of unprotected intercourse.

    D. The fact that both partners are concerned should be addressed but does not contribute to the diagnosis.

62. **Key: C**   **Client Need:** *Management of Care*

    C. Acute nonlymphocytic leukemia results from a defect in the stem cell that differentiates into monocytes, granulocytes, erythrocytes and platelets. Most of the signs and symptoms of the disease result from insufficient production of normal blood cells, including platelets, which are important in blood clotting. Risk of bleeding is a priority nursing diagnosis. Hematuria implies active or persistent bleeding.

    A. Ecchymosis in the patient with leukemia also has bleeding as an underlying cause. However, the skin is not a site of major hemorrhage

    B. Fatigue is a common manifestation of leukemia and its associated anemia. While it can be oppressive, it is not as critical as active bleeding.

    D. Pallor of the skin, conjunctiva and nailbeds commonly occurs as a result of the anemia associated with acute leukemia.

63. **Key: B**   **Client Need:** *Pharmacological and Parenteral Therapies*

   B. The 28 mg of Luminal should be divided into two 14-mg doses, one to be given in the morning and one in the evening. The nurse should administer 3.5 ml per dose. The calculation is as follows:

$$\frac{20 \text{ mg}}{5 \text{ ml}} = \frac{14 \text{ mg}}{x}$$

$$20x = 70$$

$$x = 3.5 \text{ ml}$$

   A. This volume, 2.8 ml, would result in 11.2 mg of Luminal being administered per dose. The infant would be undermedicated.
   C. This volume, 5.6 ml, would result in 22.4 mg of Luminal being administered per dose. The infant would be overmedicated.
   D. This volume, 7.0 ml, would result in 28.0 mg of Luminal being administered per dose. The infant would be overmedicated.

64. **Key: B**   **Client Need:** *Management of Care*

   B. A client hearing voices stating that he would be better off dead is at high risk for suicide. The nursing diagnosis, risk for violence: self-directed related to auditory hallucinations, is most appropriate. It requires that nursing staff take immediate measures to assure client safety.

   A. The nursing diagnosis, fear related to learned response associated with abuse, would be appropriate for an individual who has experienced abuse or trauma.
   C. The nursing diagnosis, impaired social interaction related to social isolation, would be appropriate for individuals who are very isolated from others.
   D. The nursing diagnosis, impaired verbal communication related to confusion, would be appropriate for a client with dementia or delirium.

65. **Key: A**   **Client Need:** *Reduction of Risk Potential*

   A. Long-term complications of type 1 diabetes mellitus can affect almost every body system. One diabetic complication that contributes to increased risk of foot infections is immunocompromise. In poorly controlled diabetics, hyperglycemia impairs the ability of leukocytes to destroy bacteria, thereby lowering resistance to infection.

   B. Hyperkalemia is not associated with foot infections in diabetic patients. If hyperglycemia is severe enough to cause diabetic ketoacidosis, hypokalemia can occur.
   C. Renal insufficiency occurs in diabetics because of microvascular complications, which impair circulation to the nephrons.
   D. Gastroperesis occurs in diabetics because of neuropathy of the autonomic nervous system. It does not affect risk of foot infection.

66. **Key: C**   **Client Need: *Basic Care and Comfort***

   C. Patients with dysphagia have difficulty swallowing foods and liquids. A common cause of dysphagia is stroke. Swallowing difficulties place the patient at risk for aspiration, pneumonia and malnutrition. Thick liquids or pureed foods, such as applesauce, are easier to swallow without aspirating than are thin liquids or regular foods for the patient with dysphagia.

   A. Diced meats are not cohesive and could pose a choking hazard for the patient with dysphagia.
   B. Soft-cooked vegetables would be appropriate for the patient whose dysphagia is nearly resolved and who is able to swallow most foods very well.
   D. Scrambled eggs are appropriate for patients with Stage II (less severe) dysphagia who have chewing and swallowing difficulties with some food textures.

67. **Key: A**   **Client Need: *Psychosocial Adaptation***

   A. Passive suicidal behavior pertains to an action that indirectly suggests a person is having suicidal thoughts and may have developed a suicide plan. These thoughts are not directly expressed and are conveyed indirectly through actions or word. Examples of behavioral clues include farewell letters written to family members, getting financial affairs in order and giving away prized possessions.

   B. Medication noncompliance can occur due to a variety of reasons and does not specifically connote passive suicidal behavior. Patients may be noncompliant due to a lack of knowledge and understanding about the benefits of the medication or a lack of financial resources to purchase the medication, or they may decide not to take the medication due to side effects.
   C. Overspending for the last six months is not specifically indicative of suicidal thoughts and may result due to other psychological problems. For example, the patient's judgment may be impaired due to mania and grandiosity or the patient may have a personality disorder that results in compulsive spending.
   D. An unkempt house and yard does not indicate suicidal behavior and can be due to symptoms of depression, such as a lack of interest in normal activities, fatigue and a lack of energy.

68. **Key: B**   **Client Need: *Reduction of Risk Potential***

   B. The Iligarer external fixator (IEF) uses a system of wires, rings and telescoping rods that permits limb lengthening to occur by manual distraction. Manual distraction is accomplished by manipulating the rods to increase the distance between the rings. A special osteotomy involves cutting only the cortex of the bone while preserving its blood supply, bone marrow, endosteum and periosteum. Capillary blood flow to the transected area is essential for proper bone growth. Therefore, circulation checks must be done daily.

   A. Partial weight bearing is allowed, and the child needs to learn to walk with crutches. Since the device is external, the child and family need to be prepared for the reaction of others. Camouflaging the device with wide-leg jeans or breakaway pants may help in the immediate return to school phase.
   B. Children are involved in learning to adjust the device to accomplish distraction.
   D. Follow-up care is essential to maintaining appropriate distraction until the desired bone length is achieved. The device is removed surgically after the bone has consolidated.

69. **Key**   **Client Need:** *Reduction of Risk Potential*

    C. The patient with hepatitis needs considerable rest during the acute phase of the illness. Activity should be based on the amount of fatigue and severity of the disease. Rest periods should be interspersed throughout the day and patient care scheduled to allow for uninterrupted periods of napping and relaxation.

    A. Ibuprofen is detoxified in the liver and should be avoided.
    B. Eating frequent, small meals is usually better tolerated then eating large meals.
    D. The patient diagnosed with hepatitis A requires 3000 ml/day of fluids during the acute phase of the disease because of the loss of fluids due to fever and vomiting. Fluids should not be restricted.

70. **Key: B**   **Client Need:** *Prevention and Early Detection of Disease*

    B. Mammography is an x-ray examination of the soft tissue of the breast used to identify cancers. Often these cancers can be detected before they become palpable lesions. Talcum powder, creams and underarm deodorant can give the impression of calcification within the breast and should not be applied prior to the study.

    A. No fasting is required prior to a mammogram
    C. A radiology technologist performs mammography in approximately 10 to 15 minutes.
    D. Some discomfort or pain will be experienced because of the pressure required to compress the breast tissue while the x-ray films are being taken.

71. **Key: D**   **Client Need:** *Prevention and Early Detection of Disease*

    D. The sclera, or "white of the eye," is a dense fibrous structure that makes up the posterior 5/6th of the eye. It helps maintain the shape of the eyeball and protects its contents from trauma. The sclera appears slightly bluish in young children, dull white in adults, and slightly yellowish in the elderly. Reddened sclera is abnormal and can indicate infection, closed angle glaucoma or the presence of a foreign body.

    A. The pupils generally become smaller with aging, although certain medications may cause them to dilate.
    B. A decrease in tear secretions commonly occurs in the elderly.
    C. With age, the thickness and density of the lens increase and the lens becomes progressively yellowed.

72. **Key: B**   **Client Need:** *Growth and Development*

    B. Decreased muscle tone in the infant is an associated complication if the mother received Magnesium Sulfate. Muscle flaccidity is the only complication for the newborn.

    A. Increased heart rate or tachycardia is associated with maternal fever or the use of Brethine, a tocolytic, for the treatment of preterm labor.
    C. Reflex irritability is one of the five parts of Apgar scoring. Reflex irritability is elicited by a slap on the infant's foot. A good cry is noted in an infant with an intact neurological system.
    D. Pale color is usually the result of anemia, due to blood loss when the cord is cut or to Rh incompatibility.

73. **Key: B**   **Client Need:** *Physiological Adaptation*

    B. Natural folk medicine involves the belief that health is a gift from God and illness is a punishment from God or a retribution for sin and evil. The most prevalent need expressed by people who practice folk medicine is to protect a given person and prevent "evil" from harming this person or to remove the "evil" that may be the cause of the health problem. The use of a spider web to promote wound healing is an example of folk medicine.

    A. Herbal medicine involves the use of plants or natural herbs to heal the body and treat or prevent illness. St. John's Wort, Ginseng, Ginkgo, and Echinacea are examples of herbal remedies commonly used today.

    C. Voodoo is a practice in which the followers believe in one supreme being. Each person has a protector spirit who rewards the individual with wealth and punishes with illness.

    D. Quackery is defined as the practice of an individual who misrepresents his/her ability and experience to diagnose or treat an illness or the effects to be achieved by the treatment.

74. **Key: B**   **Client Need:** *Reduction of Risk Potential*

    B. Based on the change in therapy, the nurse should anticipate an increased PaO2. PEEP causes a constant increase in the pressure in the airways and alveoli, helping them to stay open. PEEP is usually needed to maintain adequate blood oxygen levels in acute respiratory distress syndrome (ARDS).

    A. Increasing PEEP will keep the alveoli open. This will increase, not decrease, PaO2 levels.

    C. Decreased bicarbonate is not directly related to an increase in positive end expiratory pressure. Bicarbonate is more directly affected by metabolic, rather than respiratory, function.

    D. As the pressure in the airways is increased, carbon dioxide levels will decrease, not increase.

75. **Key: A**   **Client Need:** *Management of Care*

    A. Case management is a care delivery mode that incorporates concepts of continuity in addressing physical, psychological and social needs of clients. The case manager follows the client through the entire health care system and back into the community.

    B. The social worker addresses specific concerns, including those identified by the case manager. Further assessment of this problem is necessary before the nurse consults the social worker.

    C. The chaplain is fundamental in spiritual care and support and may help to comfort the patient, but the nurse needs to facilitate solving the problem that is causing the patient's distress. The chaplain may assist in comforting the patient, but not in providing follow-up care in this situation.

    D. The hospital controller is concerned with the management of the hospital, rather than individual patients.

76. **Key: C**   Client Need: *Physiological Adaptation*

   C. **Hyperglycemia is a symptom of acute stress. An increase in blood glucose occurs in acute stress due to the flight or fight response. The endocrine system and the sympathetic branch of the autonomic nervous system are triggered by emotional arousal.**

   A. Bradycardia, or a decreased heart rate, occurs when the parasympathetic branch of the autonomic nervous system triggers the relaxation response. An increase in heart rate occurs in response to acute stress.
   B. A decrease in the motility of the gastrointestinal tract occurs in response to acute stress. Diarrhea results from an increase in gastrointestinal motility.
   D. Edema occurs when an excess of body water combined with an increase in sodium produces retention of fluid within the interstitial spaces. Aldosterone and the antidiuretic hormone are released during acute stress to increase blood volume and blood pressure and maintain body fluid within the cells.

77. **Key: C**   Client Need: *Reduction of Risk Potential*

   C. **Hemodynamic pressure monitoring provides information about blood volume, fluid balance and how well the heart is pumping. The earliest changes in the circulatory system that are not yet clinically detectable can be seen with invasive monitoring.**

   A. Urinary input determination provides the nurse with limited information about the critically ill patient's fluid volume status.
   B. The consecutive examination of hemoglobin and hematocrit provides the nurse with information that aids in the assessment of fluid volume status but does not indicate immediate changes.
   D. Serial blood pressure readings provide limited information about fluid volume.

78. **Key: A**   Client Need: *Coping and Adaptation*

   A. **Through everyday interactions, the family develops and uses its own patterns of verbal and non-verbal communications. These patterns give insight into the emotional exchange within a family and are reliable indicators of interpersonal functioning. Family members not only react to the communication or actions of other family members, but also interpret and define them. Observation of non-verbal behavior will assist the nurse in determining who is the decision-maker, enable the nurse to assess readiness to learn and provide guidelines to follow in communication of complex clinical information.**

   B. Although it is important that the nurse be able to empathize with the parents of a hospitalized child, the secret to success in pediatric nursing is acceptance that the nurse is caring for the entire family. Nurses are privileged to participate in the identification and meeting of the child's clinical needs based on nursing assessments, selection of nursing diagnosis and provision of appropriate nursing interventions. Although the nurse may determine certain priorities of action, this does not place him/her in control of the situation, the child or the parents.
   C. All comments from parents are valuable. Negative comments might communicate a misunderstanding of previously delivered care information and must be clarified. This could be true of positive comments as well. Although the nurse does not wish to remove parent's feelings of hope in desperate circumstances, the reality of the patient's condition cannot be withheld.
   D. When a child is admitted to the hospital, the nurse must address the emotional state of the parents, as well as their anxiety levels and their readiness to absorb policies and procedures in detail. Basic information, such as how the call bell works or use of the telephone, may be given but more complex information should wait until the parents are more adjusted to their child's hospitalization and better able to process information.

79.   **Key: A**   **Client Need:** *Physiological Adaptation*

    A. The patient's statement indicates that she doesn't seem to be self-conscious about her appearance, but rather is looking forward to meetings others in a similar situation.

    B. This statement indicates that the patient is not aware of the role of the damaged liver in medication detoxification. It does not indicate a positive outcome.

    C. This patient statement indicates that the patient needs additional dietary instruction. It is not indicative of a positive outcome at discharge.

    D. Use of a wheelchair is not necessary for the mobility of a patient with a recent leg amputation. This statement does not indicate a positive discharge outcome.

80.   **Key: D**   **Client Need:** *Pharmacological and Parenteral Therapies*

    D. Cross-sensitivity may occur with other nonsteroidal anti-inflammatory drugs that are commonly given for pain management in arthritis. Rofecoxib is contraindicated in patients who have a history of allergic reactions to aspirin or other arthritis medications. It is important that the patient be taught about this important potential side effect.

    A. This medication may be taken without regard to food.

    B. This medication may occasionally cause dizziness. Driving is avoided until the individual response is known; however, driving would not have to be given up all together.

    C. While this medication is not known to directly cause problems with vision, it is possible that difficulty with visual acuity may occur with dizziness.

81.   **Key: C**   **Client Need:** *Physiological Adaptation*

    C. Chemical irritants, such as those found in douche preparations, may be a cause of vaginal infection, as with bubble baths, deodorant pads, tampons and contraceptive sponges. The nurse should teach the patient with recurrent vaginal infections to refrain from douching.

    A. While intercourse may cause irritation of the vagina, abstaining from intercourse for one month after treatment for an infection will not guarantee that the infection will not return. The nurse should not recommend this intervention.

    B. Soaking in a bath will not cure an infection. If soap is in the bath water, it is likely to contribute to the problem. The nurse should not include this in teaching the patient with vaginal infections.

    D. Oral contraceptives do not place a woman at increased risk for vaginal infections. The nurse would not teach the patient to discontinue this method of contraception.

82.   **Key: B**   **Client Need:** *Physiological Adaptation*

    B. Hemorrhage may produce fluid volume deficits. Common causes of blood volume loss are internal bleeding sites, including various injuries to abdominal structures. The patient usually presents with a recent fall or blunt force trauma and complaints of pain. Because bleeding causes fluid volume loss, the patient presents with tachycardia, tachypnea, hypotension, and delayed capillary refill longer than two seconds. As the bleeding continues, the patient may develop thirst as a compensatory mechanism to the fluid volume deficit caused by the bleeding.

    A. Gall bladder inflammation can cause pain in the abdominal region; however, prolonged capillary refill and thirst are not common symptoms of this disorder.

    C. Septicemia is an infection in the blood. Although this may cause a lowered blood pressure and increased pulse rate, it does not usually occur until the patient progresses to septic shock.

    D. Cardiogenic shock results from the impaired muscle action of the heart. Thirst is not necessarily an assessment finding with this disorder. Abdominal pain usually does not occur in this condition, unless there is right-sided heart failure causing venous congestion of organs.

83. **Key: D**   Client Need: _Pharmacological and Parenteral Therapies_

   D. Both AZT and Cytovene may cause bone marrow suppression, resulting in the depletion of blood cell production. The nurse should assess for, and intervene in, this potential side effect.

   A. Neuropathies are not known to be side effects of these medications. AZT has been known to cause myopathy.
   B. AZT has been known to cause insomnia. However, Cytovene does not specifically cause this complication.
   C. Anticholinergic effects include increasing heart rate and decreasing nausea and vomiting. Both AZT and Cytovene may cause nausea and vomiting, rather than decrease it.

84. **Key: D**   Client Need: _Growth and Development_

   D. The Lamaze method of prepared childbirth uses a pain conditioned response. Focusing on a favorite object takes the focus off the painful stimuli and places it on something more pleasant. The mother is taught to relax other muscles while the uterus is contracting.

   A. Lying flat in the bed is uncomfortable for the mother because the weight of the gravid uterus on the vena cava makes breathing difficult.
   B. No pushing should be done until the cervix is completely dilated.
   C. This is a common response from a patient who is experiencing the transition phase of labor.

85. **Key: C**   Client Need: _Growth and Development_

   C. Repositioning the patient should be the first intervention by the nurse because variable decelerations are caused by cord compression. Turning the patient allows the weight of the gravid uterus to shift and may move the fetus off of the cord.

   A. Encouraging the patient to deep breathe may help to relax the patient, but repositioning is the first nursing measure.
   B. Administration of oxygen may be helpful but is not the first nursing action to be taken.
   D. Although the perineum is cleansed prior to delivery, it is not the action of choice in this situation. There is no indication that delivery is imminent. Repositioning should be the first nursing intervention.

86. **Key: B**   Client Need: _Physiological Adaptation_

   B. The parents should be taught to introduce one new food at a time, usually at intervals of four to seven days to allow for identification of food allergies. Since the first introduction of food is a new experience, spoon-feeding of the food should be attempted before or after ingestion of a small amount of breast milk or formula to associate this new experience with a pleasurable and satisfying experience.

   A. Solid foods should be introduced when the child is hungry. Proper nutritional habits are learned in the home, and prevention of early childhood obesity is essential in this day of decreased physical activities, increased computer reliance and round-the-clock television programming, as well as portable video games.
   C. Food should not be mixed in the bottle and fed through a nipple with a large hole. This deprives the child of the pleasure of learning new tastes and developing a discriminating palate.
   D. Introducing new foods in cereal may prevent identification of allergies, and deprive the child of learning new tastes. If the child is accustomed to immediately swallowing the cereal, problems with poor chewing of food later in life could occur because this experience would be lacking.

87.   **Key: A**   **Client Need:** *Physiological Adaptation*

    A. Alcohol may be taken in moderate amounts in patients with diabetes mellitus. Since alcohol tends to produce hypoglycemia, it should be taken with food. Alcohol may produce an increase in triglyceride levels. Therefore, only moderate amounts should be calculated in the meal plan.

    B. Alcohol tends to produce hypoglycemia, not hyperglycemia.
    C. Alcohol may increase, rather than decrease, the patient's susceptibility to infection.
    D. Only patients with type1 diabetes mellitus use insulin. Because alcohol tends to promote hypoglycemia, only moderate amounts of alcohol should be consumed.

88.   **Key: C**   **Client Need:** *Psychosocial Adaptation*

    C. Depression, phobias, addictive disorders and a range of obsessive-compulsive behaviors are often present in individuals with eating disorders. Individuals with eating disorders typically have a distorted self-concept, low self-esteem and self-depreciating thoughts that predispose them to depression. Between 50-75% of eating disorder patients have a lifetime history of a major depressive disorder.

    A. Schizophrenia is a psychiatric disorder that is characterized by a loss of contact with reality, psychotic symptoms, communication impairment and a deterioration in self-care functioning. These symptoms are not associated with eating disorders.
    B. A conduct disorder is characterized by a persistent pattern of behavior in which the rights of others and the rules of society are disrupted and violated. This disorder usually occurs in childhood and is not associated with eating disorders.
    D. A borderline personality disorder is characterized by a pattern of intense and chaotic relationships with marked shifts in mood and fluctuating attitudes toward other people. These individuals are impulsive, self-destructive and lack a clear sense of identity.

89.   **Key: C**   **Client Need:** *Reduction of Risk Potential*

    C. Fluid leaking through the nose or ears may be cerebrospinal fluid. Cerebrospinal fluid has a high glucose content, so the nurse should assess for glucose using a TesTape or Dextrostix. No cleaning of the ears or nose, or suctioning of the nose, is allowed because it could increase the leakage of cerebro-spinal fluid.

    A. Leakage of cerebrospinal fluid is seen in increased intracranial pressure.
    B. Emesis prior to admission should not be on the patient's pillow following admission. Emesis would not have a yellow circle with a clear center.
    D. Leaking of cerebrospinal fluid in a patient with a head injury is not an emergency situation, but does need to be monitored and reported.

90.   **Key: B**   **Client Need:** *Growth and Development*

    B. The presence of a cephalohematoma is of concern because the accumulation of blood in the periosteum will break down slowly over the next few weeks. This will cause an increase in serum bilirubinemia.

    A. A negative direct Coombs test is okay as was. The positive direct Coombs test is indicative of an ABO incompatibility.
    C. A blood type O negative in the fetus should not be of concern. A problem may arise when the mother is Rh-negative and her fetus is Rh-positive.
    D. Maternal rubella status has no bearing on the development of jaundice.

91. **Key: C**   **Client Need:** *Physiological Adaptation*

  C. Communication using alternative, non-verbal methods is a priority in a patient with a laryngectomy. The occupational therapist or speech therapist should be consulted preoperatively to help establish a communication system that can be used immediately after surgery during voice rest and to prepare the patient for postoperative rehabilitation. For example, the patient may try to use electronic voice devices.

  A. Log-rolling is done for a laminectomy or spinal surgery patient, not a laryngectomy patient.
  B. Spicy foods are not a problem with a laryngectomy patient. They may be a problem with a patient who has gastrointestinal surgery or ulcer disease.
  D. Narcotics should be given postoperatively for pain control. As the patient nears discharge, analgesics such as acetaminophen (Tylenol) are used. After discharge from the hospital, many patients continue to require pain medication as they become more active.

92. **Key: A**   **Client Need:** *Reduction of Risk Potential*

  A. A major symptom of status asthmaticus is audible wheezing. Wheezing may be audible without auscultation. As bronchial constriction becomes more severe, audible wheezing is more pronounced.

  B. Wheezing occurs in status asthmaticus and respiratory failure. Absence of wheezing is not indicative of status asthmaticus.
  C. Crackles are usually heard during inspiration and indicate fluid in the airway.
  D. Rhonchi are caused by mucus or fluid in the large airways and are usually heard during expiration.

93. **Key: C**   **Client Need:** *Growth and Development*

  C. At nine months of age, infants can creep on their hands and knees. A safely placed floor mat, adorned with age-specific toys, will encourage the infant to move about in search of a favored or new object. At 11 months, a sitting child will pivot to reach back to pick up an object. These skills will assist the infant in learning how to walk.

  A. At 12 months, children may attempt to stand alone momentarily, may attempt their first step alone, with one hand held, or utilizing the crib rail. However, the presence of such a rail will not enhance the development of walking.
  B. Children less than 12 months of age cannot be left unsupervised on an adult or child mattress. Playpens can present safety hazards as well and do not support walking development.
  D. Baby walkers and jumper seats are a safety hazard and can lead to falls and head and limb injuries. They also do not support development of walking and should be removed from the home as part of child-proofing and injury prevention.

94. **Key: D**   **Client Need:** *Physiological Adaptation*

  D. Patients with hyperthyroidism often feel driven to be constantly active, yet they are chronically fatigued. Activity intolerance related to muscle fatigue is a common nursing diagnosis. An expected outcome is to perform activities of daily living without experiencing excessive muscle fatigue.

  A. The metabolic rate is increased in hyperthyroidism. Therefore, the patient's caloric needs are increased. The nursing diagnosis would be altered nutrition: less than body requirements, related to an intake less than metabolic needs, secondary to an excessive metabolic rate.
  B. The skin is moist in hyperthyroidism. It is dry and edematous in hypothyroidism.
  C. The patient with hyperthyroidism has heat intolerance due to an increased metabolic rate. The patient with hypothyroidism has intolerance to cold.

95. Key: D   **Client Need:** *Basic Care and Comfort*

D. Pressure for time and commitments to activities adversely affect the adolescent's eating habits. If an obese adolescent indicates both the time and the desire to engage in normal activities within their peer group, the nurse can presume that the motivation for weight reduction is present.

A. This statement could indicate discomfort with the adolescent growth spurt, being taller or shorter than classmates or concern with fat deposition and body image adjustment. It does not communicate the energy to initiate a weight reduction regimen.

B. Although American children are generally overscheduled, fatigue might be due to boredom, poor nutritional habits, anemia or depression – all of which must be investigated by the health clinic.

C. Inactive parents can raise sedentary children. Although reading is strongly encouraged, an adolescent's day should be a mix of school, active play, private and family time and sleep. This statement does not include any "change my behavior" energy.

96. Key: A   **Client Need:** *Pharmacological and Parenteral Therapies*

A. Taking four puffs in rapid succession would indicate the need for further teaching. The patient should be taught to inhale slowly and deeply through the mouth while pressing down on the inhaler, and to continue to breathe in slowly and hold the breath for 10 seconds, or as long as possible. The patient should wait at least one minute between puffs.

B. The patent should pause one to two minutes between puffs.

C. Rinsing the mouth out after inhaling each dose will aid in reducing local side effects.

D. The patient should inhale the medication slowly.

97. Key: B   **Client Need:** *Pharmacological and Parenteral Therapies*

B. When the patient is experiencing a sudden increase in pain, this is breakthrough pain. The nurse should instruct the patient to request the prn medication before the pain becomes severe.

A. Prn means as necessary and not around the clock. The epidural analgesia is continuous.

C. Breakthrough pain does not necessarily mean an increased tolerance to epidural analgesia.

D. Pain is subjective and should be addressed by the patient, not the family.

98. Key: B   **Client Need:** *Growth and Development*

B. Preschool children need to have care interventions explained in simple terms before, during and after all nursing procedures. Caution should be used with phrases like "I would like to take your temperature," which can communicate that you are taking something away from the child and not giving it back. Preferred would be "I am going to check your temperature and listen to your heart. Would you like to listen to your heart first?"

A. A preschooler is unable to work with abstractions. Their major fear is loss of control and the sense of their own power.

C. This age group may communicate through transient objects. Acknowledge the child's fear and anxieties, and encourage the parents to leave the child's favorite toys and some tangible evidence of their love.

D. Although information sheets and teaching handouts should be provided to the parents, this age group cannot read, and would not be able to fulfill such a self-care requisite.

99. **Key: A**   **Client Need:** *Reduction of Risk Potential*

    A. Pressure should be applied to the nose for five to 10 minutes. Patients require coaching in mouth breathing while pressure is applied.

    B. If not contraindicated, the patient is positioned with the head of the bed elevated. The neck should not be hyperextended. When the neck is hyperextended, blood can drain into the airway, putting the patient at risk for aspiration.

    C. Nasal packing is done by a physician, rather than by a nurse.

    D. Ice compresses aid in vasoconstriction. However, they are placed directly on the nose and not on the forehead and back of the neck. Placing ice compresses on the back of the neck could restrict blood flow to the brain.

100. **Key: B**   **Client Need:** *Management of Care*

    B. The democratic management style encourages staff participation in decision-making and involves the staff in planning and developing. Research has shown that staff nurses' job satisfaction increases as the involvement in decision making and problem solving increases.

    A. An autocratic management style would ignore subordinates' ideas or suggestions. Autocratic leadership is an approach wherein the leader retains all authority and is primarily concerned with the task accomplishment.

    C. A laissez-faire leadership style would be one in which the charge nurse would provide no guidance or direction and little or no feedback.

    D. A characteristic of a democratic leadership style is to be concerned with team work on human relations; however, this should be accomplished at the time the incident is taking place, not at the end of the workday.

101. **Key: B**   **Client Need:** *Reduction of Risk Potential*

    B. Before beginning oral fluids, the nurse should assess that the client's gag and swallow reflex is intact, in order to prevent aspiration of food or fluids.

    A. A local anesthetic and intravenous sedation are used to suppress the cough reflex and relieve anxiety. A topical anesthetic is also sprayed on the back of the throat. There should be no problems with bladder distention because general anesthesia is not used.

    C. Nothing is given by mouth until the cough and swallow reflexes have returned—normally in about one to two hours.

    D. This test should not produce any nerve damage, so it would not be necessary to monitor the patient's ability to speak.

102. **Key: C**   **Client Need:** *Basic Care and Comfort*

    C. One ounce of luncheon meats equals about 250 mg of sodium per serving. One medium dill pickle equals 928 mg of sodium. This equals approximately 1178 mg of sodium. This diet option has the greatest amount of sodium.

    A. Skim milk equals 126 mg of sodium. Breakfast cereal is about 250 mg per serving. This choice equals approximately 376 mg of sodium.

    B. A one to two-cup serving of fresh and frozen vegetables equals less than 50 mg of sodium per serving. This choice equals approximately 100 mg of sodium.

    D. Fresh meats, chicken and fish equal less than 50 mg of sodium per serving. This choice equals approximately 100 mg of sodium.

103. Key: A   **Client Need:** *Growth and Development*

> **A. Frequent serum chorionic gonadotropin levels will be needed until the level falls below normal and stays there for three weeks. Monthly levels will be drawn for six months, and then bi-monthly levels are drawn for the remainder of the year.**

B. The intrauterine device (IUD) may cause increased bleeding and will not be recommended for use.
C. Another pregnancy can be planned after one year of normal chorionic gonadotropin levels.
D. Oral contraceptives are effective in preventing an unwanted pregnancy, but they may give falsely high chorionic gonadotropin levels by inhibiting lutenizing hormone.

104. Key: D   **Client Need:** *Psychosocial Adaptation*

> **D. A patient with a bipolar disorder displays excessive and constant motor activity and is unable to sleep or eat for several days. Fatigue related to hyperactivity is a priority concern for this patient, and nursing care must be directed towards preventing exhaustion and cardiac collapse.**

A. Decisional conflict is often present in the patient with bipolar disorder, manic type, due to alteration in thought processes. Although judgment tends to be impaired, this diagnosis is not a priority concern on admission.
B. Self-care deficits are related to the manic patient's hyperactivity that impairs ability to eat and sleep. Hygiene and grooming may be neglected. Dress may be disorganized, flamboyant or bizarre, and the use of excessive makeup and jewelry is common. Nursing care should be directed towards assisting the patient in hygiene and grooming during the course of treatment, but it is not a priority on admission.
C. Hopelessness related to impending depression is not an appropriate diagnosis for the patient with mania. Grandiosity, or inflated self-regard, occurs, and hopelessness is more commonly experienced by the patient with depression.

105. Key: B   **Client Need:** *Psychosocial Adaptation*

> **B. Suicide is the third leading cause of death in adolescents between 15 and 24 years of age. Immediate referrals to mental health professionals need to be made when assessment suggests that adolescents may be considering suicide. "I'll have to think of a different way" should alert the nurse to the possibility of suicide and requires further investigation as a priority. This patient statement should be investigated, but it does not have to be a priority.**

A. A technique that could be used is focusing. "This point seems worth looking at more closely. Perhaps you and I can discuss it together," is a means of getting the patient to focus on the concerns behind the statement.
C. "Tell me more about your home situation." The nurse will need to explore this statement more with the patient, and this could be an appropriate response by the nurse. However, suicide assessment should be done first, and the nurse may have to question the patient regarding abuse later.
D. This is a normal question from someone in the hospital. A correct time should be given to the patient.

106. Key: C   **Client Need:** *Coping and Adaptation*

     C. Acting-out behavior is a common symptom of depression in children and adolescents that is not seen in adults. Feelings of anger and hostility may be expressed through running away, delinquency, substance abuse and sexual acting out.

     A. Individuals with depression in all age groups commonly experience a loss of interest in their usual activities.

     B. Significant weight loss is a common symptom of depression for all age groups that results from a decrease in appetite.

     D. Feelings of worthlessness commonly occur in children, adolescents and adults who have a depressive disorder.

107. Key: A   **Client Need:** *Psychosocial Adaptation*

     A. A disturbance in self-esteem has several defining characteristics. The adolescent patient may protest that others do not understand him, deny problems that are obvious to others, project blame or responsibility for problems on others or rationalize personal failures.

     B. Inconsistent performance in school is a symptom of depression in children and adolescents that is related to lack of interest in normal activities and poor concentration.

     C. Poor impulse control is a symptom more frequently seen in adolescent explosive disorders. The patient experiences an irresistible impulse to lash out through violence without any apparent provocation. The degree of aggressiveness expressed is out of proportion to any precipitating psychosocial stressor. Poor impulse control is more commonly associated with ineffective coping methods.

     D. The adolescent with a major depression is hypersensitive to criticism and typically does not frequently criticize others.

108. Key: C.   **Client Need:** *Coping and Adaptation*

     C. It is important that the nurse be able to really listen and validate the couple's frustration and anger related to their current inability to conceive. They must work their way through the anger and move on to planning differently or whatever action they choose.

     A. The nurse's focus should remain on the client and should not be detoured to the nurse's family.

     B. This comment by the nurse is closed-ended and does not allow for the couple to express their feelings.

     D. This statement by the nurse does not encourage the couple to ventilate their feelings or express their concerns.

109. Key: B   **Client Need:** *Safety and Infection Control*

     B. When administering digoxin, the nurse should monitor the apical pulse and withhold the dose and notify the physician if the pulse rate is below 60 beats per minute in an adult, below 70 in a child or below 90 in an infant. Digitalis toxicity can develop in patients with hypokalemia. The nurse should document both findings and not administer the digoxin.

     A. When administering a medication to a patient, the nurse accepts the responsibility that the medication, or the nursing actions in administering the medication, will not harm the patient in any way.

     C. The professional nurse is autonomous. Autonomy means that a person is reasonably independent and self-governing in decision-making and practice. The nurse caring for the patient should make the decision not to give the digoxin. The supervisor may be informed of the action.

     D. This is an aggressive statement. Aggressive behavior often leads to conflict and seldom to resolution or effective communication.

110. Key: A   Client Need: *Management of Care*

    A. Nurses are legally bound to report critical incidents to nursing management. A form called an incident report (or an unusual occurrence report) is completed and forwarded to nursing administration as well as hospital or agency administration. The document is used as a risk management tool but does not become part of the patient's legal document, (i.e., the patient chart).

    B. Incidents are reported and sent to the risk management department or to hospital and nursing administrators. They should not be used as a means of staff evaluation.

    C. Because state laws vary as to whether the incident report may be "used" by the plaintiff's attorney in a lawsuit, specific guidelines of the hospital or agency should be followed.

    D. Incident reports are not reviewed with the patient during hospitalization or at discharge.

CGFNS

Qualifying Exam Practice Exam B

Practice Exam B: Nursing, Part 1

You will have two hours and 30 minutes to complete Nursing, Part 1.

1. A child who has acute lymphocytic leukemia is receiving chemotherapeutic drugs and has an order for allopurinol (Zyloprim). The nurse should recognize that the purpose of Zyloprim for the child is to

   A. stimulate erythropoieti c activity.
   B. promote the deposit of calcium in the long bones.
   C. interfere with the production of leukemic cells.
   D. inhibit uric acid production.

2. A teenager with acne says to the nurse in the physician's office, "Look at my face! No matter how often I clean my face, I still get pimples." The nurse should explain to the teenager that a contributing cause of acne in adolescents is

   A. eating a large amount of foods high in fat.
   B. eating foods that are high in complex carbohydrates.
   C. an increase in secretions of the sebaceous glands.
   D. an increase in secretions of the adrenal glands.

3. When assessing a six-month-old baby girl, the nurse should expect the infant to exhibit which of the following abilities indicative of normal development?

   A. Creeping on her hands and knees
   B. Pulling herself to a standing position
   C. Waving bye-bye
   D. Turning over completely

4. A mother makes all of the following comments about her 14-month-old son's behavior. Which behavior should the nurse discourage?

   A. "My son loves to feed himself slices of peeled apple."
   B. "My son takes his favorite blanket with him whenever he leaves the house."
   C. "My son gets up on his knees and rocks himself to sleep."
   D. "My son takes a bottle of juice to bed with him and sucks on it if he wakes during the night."

5. A nurse would instruct a patient who has had an ileostomy to avoid which of the following foods?

   A. Potatoes
   B. Beef
   C. Popcorn
   D. Yogurt

6. A 12-year-old girl has a long leg cast applied to her left leg. She is being instructed in crutch-walking with no weight bearing on her left leg. Which of the following observations indicates that the girl needs further teaching?

   A. She is using the three-point gait.
   B. Her elbows are slightly flexed.
   C. She places the crutches approximately six to eight inches (15 to 20 cm) in front of her with each step.
   D. She is supporting her weight on the axillary bars and hand pieces of the crutches.

7. A 26-year-old woman is brought to the psychiatric unit because of suicidal thoughts. To determine if one-to-one observation is indicated for the woman, the nurse should determine if

   A. anyone in the woman's family has attempted suicide.
   B. the woman has a plan for suicide.
   C. the woman has had a recent loss.
   D. the woman has a social support system.

8. In which of the following ways should the nurse intervene when a patient repeatedly talks about the past?

   A. Help the patient to establish goals for the future
   B. Give the patient a diversional activity
   C. Ask the patient to think of recent pleasures
   D. Encourage the patient to share memories

9. A patient who has begun taking a tricyclic antidepressant is given instructions regarding its use. Which of the following comments would indicate that the patient understands the information?

    A. "I like active exercise, but I won't be able to do it while I'm on this medicine."
    B. "This medicine will make my ears ring, but I guess I can tolerate that."
    C. "I won't eat cheese if one of my visitors brings me some."
    D. "I don't feel any better, but I've only been taking the medicine for a week."

10. A woman who is dependent on alcohol is admitted to the detoxification unit. The answer to which of the following questions is essential for the nurse to obtain from the patient immediately?

    A. How does her husband react to her problem?
    B. When did she have her last drink?
    C. How old she was when she began to drink?
    D. What did she eat in the past four hours?

11. When discussing methods of stress reduction with a patient, the nurse should use which of the following approaches first?

    A. Explain to the patient the physiological effects of stress
    B. Teach the patient relaxation techniques that reduce stress
    C. Determine if the patient is able to identify sources of stress
    D. Describe to the patient the benefits of active exercise in coping with stress

12. In the immediate postoperative period following a hip replacement, the patient should be assisted to perform which of the following exercises on the affected extremity?

    A. Leg raising
    B. Dorsiflexion and extension of the foot
    C. Flexion and extension of the knee
    D. Quadriceps setting

13. Diazepam (Valium) is prescribed for a patient with low back pain. The desired therapeutic action of Valium in this situation is to

    A. reduce anxiety levels.
    B. eliminate pain sensation.
    C. suppress the inflammatory process.
    D. lessen muscle spasticity.

14. A patient admitted to the hospital with a diagnosis of chronic renal failure should be assessed for which of the following manifestations?

    A. Hypotension
    B. Fatigue
    C. Flushed skin
    D. Painful urination

15. Following a prostatectomy, the pathology report reveals that the patient has cancer of the prostate. Which of the following blood test results would support this diagnosis?

    A. Decreased uric acid
    B. Decreased creatinine
    C. Elevated bicarbonate
    D. Elevated acid phosphatase

16. Which of the following plans is particularly important in the care of a patient who has Alzheimer's disease?

    A. Using behavior modification techniques
    B. Assessing the patient's abilities on an ongoing basis
    C. Helping the patient explore emotional conflicts
    D. Implementing a bowel training program

17. A patient who has a spinal cord transection is in spinal shock. On assessment, the nurse would expect the patient to describe which of the following findings in the lower extremities?

    A. Loss of sensation
    B. Complaints of tingling
    C. Excessive diaphoresis
    D. Constant tremors

18. Which of the following observations of a patient who has pernicious anemia would indicate that the goal of care has been achieved?

    A. The patient's skin has no petechiae.
    B. The patient's tongue has lost its beefy red color.
    C. The patient has no dependent edema.
    D. The patient has a good appetite.

19. To screen for the presence of neural tube defects in the fetus, a nurse would expect a pregnant woman to have which of the following tests performed?

    A. Serum alpha-fetoprotein
    B. Biophysical profile
    C. Amniocentesis
    D. TORCH titers

20. If a four-year-old child's growth and development is age-appropriate, a nurse would expect to observe which of the following behaviors?

    A. Talking with an imaginary playmate
    B. Drawing a stick figure with at least six parts
    C. Walking down stairs, one step at a time
    D. Counting backwards from the number 10

21. An elderly man who has Alzheimer's disease calls the nurse by his wife's name. Which of the following measures by the nurse would be appropriate?

    A. Responding to whatever name he calls the nurse
    B. Asking him to remember the nurse's name
    C. Stating the nurse's name at each contact with him
    D. Allowing him extra time in which to remember the nurse's name

22. A nurse would expect a patient to describe the symptoms of arterial insufficiency in the lower extremities in which of the following ways?

    A. "My legs feel weak when I get up to walk."
    B. "My legs hurt when I walk, but they feel better when I sit down."
    C. "My feet and ankles become swollen after walking."
    D. "My feet burn if I walk on a hard surface."

23. A patient who has a borderline personality disorder asks the nurse on a psychiatric unit if she may stay up beyond the designated bedtime. When the nurse says no, the patient says, "The nurse on duty last night let me stay up late." Which of the following responses by the nurse would be therapeutic?

    A. "You shouldn't have been given that privilege."
    B. "Everyone is required to go to bed now."
    C. "You can stay up for one more hour."
    D. "Why do you want to stay up?"

24. When a woman who is at 34 weeks' gestation has non-reactive results to successive non-stress tests, a nurse would prepare the woman for

    A. an emergency cesarean delivery.
    B. induction of labor.
    C. internal fetal monitoring.
    D. a biophysical profile.

25. A six-year-old child who is admitted to a hospital for suspected sexual molestation tells a nurse, "I do not like it when my stepdad takes a bath with me." Based on this information, which of the following actions should the nurse take?

    A. Ask the child to explain to you what takes place during bath time
    B. Interview the child further by using anatomically correct dolls
    C. Contact the facility's designated child abuse interviewer
    D. Approach the stepfather to clarify the child's statement

26. Which of the following comments would a patient with an antisocial personality be most likely to make?

    A. "The police are always arresting me for nothing."
    B. "I'm feeling guilty because I've disappointed my family."
    C. "I'm becoming very anxious."
    D. "I've learned my lesson, and I'll never do that again."

27. A patient who has ulcerative colitis does not respond to the prescribed therapy and is admitted to the hospital for a total colectomy and creation of an ileostomy. Which of the following measures should be given priority in the patient's preoperative care plan?

    A. Promoting the patient's acceptance of an ileostomy
    B. Monitoring the patient's emotional state
    C. Preventing the patient from developing pressure sores
    D. Correcting the patient's fluid imbalance

28. A patient is to be transfused with a unit of whole blood. If the patient were to develop an allergic reaction, the nurse would expect to administer which of the following drugs?

    A. Diphenhydramine hydrochloride (Benadryl)
    B. Chlorpheniramine maleate (Chlortrimeton)
    C. Pseudoephedrine hydrochloride (Sudafed)
    D. Promethazine hydrochloride maleate (Phenergan)

29. A patient who has had an ileostomy says to the nurse, "I will have to be isolated for the rest of my life because no one will be able to stand this terrible odor." Which of the following responses by the nurse would most likely be reassuring?

    A. "The odor will gradually become less noticeable."
    B. "I can understand your concern, but remaining in isolation does not reduce the odor."
    C. "There are techniques that can reduce the odor."
    D. "The odor is a normal part of your condition and will not offend people."

30. A patient who has been given a prescription for daily thyroid extract also should be given which of the following instructions?

    A. "You may have a skin irritation due to the medication."
    B. "You may become sluggish if the medication dosage is too high."
    C. "You will take the medication for the rest of your life."
    D. "You will need to take the medication with food."

31. A nurse should recognize that cardiac arrest in a previously healthy infant is usually preceded by

    A. ventricular arrhythmias.
    B. respiratory failure.
    C. generalized seizures.
    D. distributive shock.

32. Because a woman is receiving magnesium sulfate for pregnancy-induced hypertension, it is essential for the nurse to assess the woman's

    A. urine chemistry.
    B. platelet count.
    C. apical heart rate.
    D. respiratory rate.

33. A patient has a laryngectomy with a laryngeal tube in place. When suctioning the laryngeal tube, which of the following measures is correct?

    A. Suctioning the laryngeal tube for about 10 seconds
    B. Using a clean technique when suctioning the tube
    C. Applying suction while inserting the catheter into the tube
    D. Turning the patient's head to suction one side and then the other side

34. While a patient who has Hodgkin's disease is receiving chemotherapy, it is important to assess the patient for symptoms of

    A. thrombus formation.
    B. ascites.
    C. infection.
    D. splenomegaly.

35. When a patient who has diabetes mellitus experiences peripheral neuropathy, the priority nursing diagnosis should be

    A. altered health maintenance.
    B. altered urinary elimination.
    C. risk for impaired skin integrity.
    D. noncompliance.

36. **Which of the following approaches would a nurse take first when preparing to insert an intravenous catheter into an eight-year-old boy?**

    A. Have an assistant restrain the boy for the procedure
    B. Request that the parents leave the room during the procedure
    C. Explain to the boy what he will feel during the procedure
    D. Reassure the boy that the procedure will be over quickly

37. **Following a subtotal gastrectomy, a patient has a nasogastric tube attached to low, intermittent suction. Eight hours after surgery, the patient complains of being nauseated. The nurse should take which of the following actions first?**

    A. Instruct the patient to take deep breaths
    B. Apply a cool cloth to the patient's forehead
    C. Administer antiemetic medication to the patient
    D. Determine the patency of the patient's nasogastric tube

38. **A patient is to receive heparin sodium, 20,000 units in 1000 ml of solution intravenously. The fluid is to be regulated to deliver 50 ml of solution each hour. At this rate, the patient should receive how many units of heparin each hour?**

    A. 500
    B. 1000
    C. 1500
    D. 2000

39. **A nurse suspects that a six-month-old infant has cystic fibrosis. Which of the following tests would confirm the diagnosis?**

    A. Quantitative collection of stool for fecal fat
    B. Pulmonary function studies
    C. Serum sample for human leukocyte antigen
    D. Sweat chloride analysis

40. **A woman who is in preterm labor is receiving magnesium sulfate for which of the following purposes?**

    A. To enhance fetal lung maturity
    B. To prevent seizures
    C. To improve urine output
    D. To control uterine contraction patterns

41. **A 27-year-old man is admitted to the psychiatric unit after striking his wife with a cooking utensil. He is hyperactive and is in handcuffs. Which of the following behaviors would indicate that the patient needs continued restraints?**

    A. He pushes the attendant out of his way.
    B. He shouts curses at the nurse.
    C. He tears up his chart.
    D. He makes obscene gestures.

42. **A patient is brought to the psychiatric unit. Which of the following activities would be performed by the registered nurse rather than the licensed practical nurse?**

    A. Administering a stat dose of lorazepam (Ativan), 2 mg intramuscularly (IM)
    B. Admitting the patient to the psychiatric unit
    C. Asking the patient whether he hears voices other people do not hear
    D. Drawing a blood sample for a lithium level

43. **A community health nurse makes a home visit to evaluate a mother's understanding of discharge instructions for her five-month-old infant who has chronic gastroesophageal reflux. Which of the following actions, if taken by the mother, indicates a correct understanding of the instructions?**

    A. The mother is restricting the child's fluids.
    B. The mother is burping the infant at the end of a 6-oz (180 ml) feeding.
    C. The mother is administering prescribed cisapride (Propulsid) to the infant 15 minutes prior to feeding.
    D. The mother is placing the infant in a recumbent position 15 minutes after feeding.

44. A patient is taking theophylline (Theo-Dur) for the management of asthma. A nurse would advise the patient to report which of the following symptoms?

    A. Weight gain
    B. Excessive thirst
    C. Red-orange urine
    D. Heart palpitations

45. The nurse should expect a patient who has chronic renal failure to be given epoetin alfa (Epogen) to

    A. elevate the white blood cell count.
    B. enhance the maturation of thrombocytes.
    C. increase the production of platelets.
    D. stimulate the synthesis of red blood cells.

46. Because a woman who is confirmed to be at 30 weeks' gestation has sudden painless bright red vaginal bleeding, a nurse would suspect the woman is experiencing

    A. abruptio placentae.
    B. an ectopic pregnancy.
    C. placenta previa.
    D. a molar pregnancy.

47. A five-year-old child who has celiac disease is being assessed in a pediatric clinic. To which of the following nursing diagnoses would a nurse give priority in the child's long-term care plan?

    A. Activity intolerance
    B. Self-concept disturbance
    C. High risk for ineffective family coping
    D. Impaired skin integrity

48. A hospitalized patient has recovered from an acute exacerbation of his chronic mental illness and is demanding release. In planning the patient's discharge, the nurse should take into consideration that the patient

    A. is used to being homeless and does not need much assistance.
    B. cannot be discharged until a suitable living arrangement is identified.
    C. will receive adequate aftercare at the community mental health center.
    D. has the right to be discharged.

49. To which of the following nursing diagnoses would a nurse give priority for a patient who has an elevated serum carbon dioxide (CO_2) level following surgery?

    A. Urinary retention
    B. Impaired skin integrity
    C. Ineffective airway clearance
    D. Impaired physical mobility

50. Which of the following instructions would a nurse include in the teaching plan for a patient who is taking furosemide (Lasix)?

    A. "Restrict foods that are high in cholesterol."
    B. "Take supplemental calcium."
    C. "Decrease complex carbohydrates."
    D. "Increase your dietary intake of potassium."

51. A six-year old child has a short arm cast placed on the right extremity. While assessing the fingers during the immediate period after casting, a nurse would report which of the following finding?

    A. Mild edema
    B. Pain on movement
    C. Slight coolness of the cast when touched
    D. Capillary refill greater than three seconds

52. Which of the following medications would a nurse have available when administering an injection of heparin sodium to a patient?

    A. Naloxone hydrochloride (Narcan)
    B. Protamine sulfate
    C. Phytonadione (AquaMEPHYTON)
    D. Phentolamine mesylate (Regitine)

53. The treatment plan for a 14-year-old child who has ulcerative colitis includes chronic use of high-dose corticosteroids. Because of the use of this medication, the child is at risk for

    A. growth retardation.
    B. peripheral neuropathy.
    C. muscular degeneration.
    D. hyperkalemia.

 *Test B / Part 1*

54. When obtaining vital signs on a sleeping three-month-old infant, which of the following assessments would a nurse obtain first?

 A. Respiratory rate
 B. Apical pulse
 C. Axillary temperature
 D. Blood pressure

55. A nurse would assess a woman in labor who is receiving continuous epidural analgesia for

 A. temperature instability.
 B. urinary retention.
 C. persistent headache.
 D. uterine hyperstimulation.

56. The nursing staff on a psychiatric unit consists of registered nurses, licensed practical nurses and unlicensed assistive personnel. Which of the following activities can most safely be assigned to unlicensed assistive personnel?

 A. Observing a patient after electroconvulsive therapy (ECT)
 B. Monitoring a patient who is on suicide precautions
 C. Co-conducting an activity group
 D. Doing an intake interview of a new patient

57. The most common adverse effect of electroconvulsive therapy (ECT) for which the nurse must plan interventions is

 A. arrhythmia.
 B. physical injury.
 C. severe hypertension.
 D. memory loss.

58. When caring for a patient who is receiving mechanical ventilation with positive end-expiratory pressure (PEEP), which of the following blood test results would indicate to a nurse that the treatment is having the desired effect?

 A. PaO2, 88 mm Hg
 B. pCO2, 50 mm Hg
 C. Oxygen saturation, 86%
 D. HCO3 20 mEq/L

59. A patient who has acquired immune deficiency syndrome (AIDS) has a nursing diagnosis of altered nutrition, less than body requirements. The nurse should instruct the patient to eat a diet that is

 A. high in protein.
 B. high in potassium.
 C. low in saturated fat.
 D. low in sodium.

60. Which of the following toys would a nurse select for a two-year-old child?

 A. A 10-piece jigsaw puzzle
 B. A push-pull vacuum cleaner
 C. A paint-by-numbers set
 D. A hand-held electronic game

61. Which of the following measures would a nurse encourage a patient in the acute stages of gout to take in order to minimize complications?

 A. Drinking a minimum of 3000 ml of fluid per day
 B. Eating a minimum of 2500 calories per day
 C. Walking at least three miles per day
 D. Resting at least three hours per day

62. A nurse would expect a patient who has ulcerative colitis to report which of the following manifestations of the disease?

 A. Abdominal distention
 B. Bloody diarrhea
 C. Esophageal reflux
 D. Flank pain

63. A patient says to the nurse, "I have something important to tell you, but you must promise not to tell anyone else." The nurse's best response would be to

 A. explain that the patient should share this information with her physician instead.
 B. explain that the information may need to be shared with the treatment team but will be held confidential.
 C. commit to keeping the confidence.
 D. commit to conditionally keeping the confidence.

64. A nurse performs a physical assessment of a two-month-old infant. Which of the following findings would require further investigation?

    A. Closed anterior fontanel
    B. Bilateral strabismus
    C. Multiple Mongolian spots
    D. Prominent extrusion reflex

65. Solid foods can be started in infants at four months of age because by this time, the

    A. Moro reflex has disappeared.
    B. tonic neck reflex is stronger.
    C. swallowing reflex has matured.
    D. rooting reflex has receded.

66. An infant who weighs 11 lb (5 kg) is to receive 750 mg of antibiotic in a 24-hour period. The liquid antibiotic comes in a concentration of 125 mg per 5 ml. If the antibiotic is to be given three times each day, how many milliliters would the nurse administer with each dose?

    A. 2
    B. 5
    C. 6.25
    D. 10

67. Which of the following instructions would a nurse include in the discharge plan for a patient who had a transurethral resection of the prostate (TURP)?

    A. Limit the intake of caffeinated beverages
    B. Resume normal activities of daily living
    C. Maintain a diet low in fiber
    D. Strain urine with each voiding

68. An 18-month-old infant has received a diphtheria, tetanus toxoid and pertussis (DTP) vaccine in the anterior thigh. A nurse would instruct the infant's parent to contact the physician if the infant

    A. displays a decreased interest in usual activities.
    B. refuses to walk.
    C. cries inconsolably.
    D. develops a rectal temperature of 102°F (38.9°C).

69. When administering oral liquid medication to a six-month-old infant, the nurse would

    A. mix the drug in the infant's formula and offer with the next feeding.
    B. sweeten the drug with honey and give from a teaspoon.
    C. quickly squirt the drug from a syringe to the back of the mouth.
    D. slowly squirt the drug from a syringe into the cheek pocket.

70. Which of the following clients would the nurse prepare for an emergency cesarean delivery?

    A. A woman who has a prolapsed cord
    B. A woman with a twin gestation
    C. A woman who has meconium-stained amniotic fluid
    D. A woman who has a nonreactive non-stress test

71. A nurse is leading a community meeting on an inpatient psychiatric unit. One of the group members complains that the hospital visiting hours are too short. The most appropriate action for the nurse is to

    A. explain the reason for the visiting hours policy.
    B. explore with the patient why he is so upset.
    C. invite the nurse manager to the group to explain the policy.
    D. ask the other group members if they have similar concerns.

72. The best time to administer prn lorazepam (Ativan) to a patient who is aggressive is when the patient

    A. starts to pace in the hallway.
    B. stops pacing and starts making verbal threats.
    C. stops threatening and actually performs a violent act.
    D. is placed in restraints.

73. Which of the following statements, if made by a patient scheduled for a lumpectomy, indicates that the patient understood the preoperative teaching?

    A. "A portion of the growth will be excised and examined."
    B. "A needle will be inserted into the tumor and cells will be withdrawn."
    C. "The suspicious area and some normal surrounding tissue will be removed."
    D. "The underarm lymph nodes will be surgically removed and sent for analysis."

74. Which of the following statements, if made by a four-year-old child whose brother just died of cancer, would be age-appropriate?

    A. "I know I'll never see my brother again."
    B. "I'm glad my brother isn't crying anymore."
    C. "I can't wait to go get pizza with my brother."
    D. "I know where my brother is buried."

75. To which of the following nursing diagnoses would a nurse give first priority in caring for a patient who has sustained serious facial and neck burns?

    A. Fluid volume deficit
    B. Body image disturbance
    C. Ineffective thermoregulation
    D. Ineffective airway clearance

76. The nurse is caring for a patient who is diagnosed with glaucoma. Which of the following medications, if ordered for this patient, should the nurse question?

    A. Atropine sulfate ophthalmic solution, two drops in both eyes at hour of sleep
    B. Pilocarpine ophthalmic solution, one drop in both eyes every 12 hours
    C. Timolol maleate (Timoptic), one drop every 12 hours
    D. Diamox, 250 mg, one tablet, po, every 12 hours

77. To promote the skin integrity of a patient who is in Russell's traction, which of the following measures should be included in the care plan?

    A. Having the patient lie on the right side for 20 minutes every two to three hours
    B. Placing pillows under the patient's sacral and scapular areas
    C. Massaging the patient's back and buttocks frequently
    D. Applying an antiseptic solution to the patient's bony prominences after bathing

78. A woman who is at 32 weeks' gestation has had ruptured membranes for 26 hours. A nurse would assess the woman for which of the following manifestations?

    A. Proteinuria
    B. Dependent edema
    C. Constipation
    D. Elevated temperature

79. A six-year-old child is experiencing a series of absence seizures. Which of the following actions would the nurse take?

    A. Insert a padded tongue blade between the child's teeth
    B. Place the child in a side-lying position
    C. Administer oxygen to the child via face mask
    D. Monitor the nature of the child's behavior

80. A patient develops stomatitis secondary to radiation therapy for oral cancer. Which of the following nursing instructions would be most helpful?

    A. Gargle with mouthwash and rinse thoroughly after each meal
    B. Use ice cold liquids such as tea or cola to relieve discomfort
    C. Use a toothbrush soaked in saline to clean the mouth
    D. Drink citrus juices and broth

81. A nurse is observed taking all of the following actions when suctioning a patient who has a newly placed tracheostomy tube. Which of the following actions require intervention?

    A. Applying suction for less than 15 seconds at one time
    B. Administering 100% oxygen prior to starting suctioning
    C. Utilizing negative pressure of 120 mm Hg during suctioning
    D. Deflating the tracheostomy cuff for three minutes before initiating suction

82. Three hours after receiving an insulin injection (regular insulin), a patient is diaphoretic. Which of the following actions should the nurse take first?

    A. Help the patient to put on a dry nightgown
    B. Ask the patient for a urine specimen
    C. Give the patient a glass of juice to drink
    D. Instruct the patient to stay in bed until seen by the physician

83. The bowel retraining program for a patient who has had a cerebrovascular accident should include which of the following measures?

    A. Checking for impaction daily
    B. Increasing the intake of milk products
    C. Utilizing incontinent pads until control is achieved
    D. Establishing a consistent time for elimination

84. A nurse evaluates a three-month-old, developmentally-delayed infant for manifestations of cerebral palsy. Which of the following findings would a nurse report?

    A. Exaggerated arching of the back
    B. Absence of the extrusion reflex when fed from a spoon
    C. Head circumference measurement less than the 50th percentile
    D. Slight head lag when pulled to a sitting position

85. Diphenoxylate hydrochloride with atropine sulfate (Lomotil) is prescribed for a patient. When the patient returns to the clinic, the nurse should evaluate the therapeutic effectiveness of Lomotil by assessing the patient's

    A. weight.
    B. number of daily bowel movements.
    C. amount of daily food intake.
    D. skin turgor.

86. A two-month-old infant who was born with Down syndrome, has been recently diagnosed with a ventricular septal defect. Based on a diagnosis of congenital heart disease, the nurse would instruct the parent to report which of the following manifestations in the infant immediately?

    A. Mottling with environmental temperature changes
    B. Nasal congestion when recumbent
    C. Brow-sweating during feedings
    D. Tongue-thrusting during episodes of crying

87. Following a left modified radical mastectomy, which of the following nursing measures should be implemented to prevent complications in the affected area?

    A. Using sequential compression devices on the arm
    B. Applying warm soaks to the arm
    C. Immobilizing the arm with armboard
    D. Elevating the arm on two pillows

88. A pregnant woman has varicosities of her legs and is instructed about wearing elastic stockings. Which of the following comments, if made by the woman, indicates that she understood the instructions?

    A. "I put the stockings on when my legs begin to swell."
    B. "I put the stockings on before I get out of bed in the morning."
    C. "I remove the stockings if I get cramps in my legs or feet."
    D. "I remove the stockings only when I bathe."

89. A patient who has had a laryngectomy is being prepared for discharge. Which of the following questions, if asked by the patient, would indicate an understanding of the instructions?

    A. "What type of humidifier would you recommend?"
    B. "What are the best foods for a high-fiber diet?"
    C. "How long would you suggest that I keep the plug for the laryngectomy tube in a disinfectant?"
    D. "How long do I have to worry that I may aspirate food?"

90. The purpose of performing a biophysical profile on a woman who is experiencing a high-risk pregnancy is to

    A. identify the location of the placenta.
    B. evaluate the well-being of the fetus.
    C. validate the expected date of birth.
    D. detect the presence of fetal abnormalities.

91. A patient who has hyperthyroidism is taking methimazole (Tapazole) and attends the clinic regularly. To evaluate the effectiveness of Tapazole therapy, the nurse should consider which of the following questions?

    A. Has the patient's vision improved?
    B. Has the patient's appetite improved?
    C. Has the patient's need for sleep decreased?
    D. Has the patient's pulse rate decreased?

92. A patient who comes to the physician's office is suspected of having hypertrophy of the prostate. The nurse should expect that he will probably have which of the following symptoms?

    A. Residual urine of more than 50 ml
    B. Pain radiating to the scrotum
    C. Urethral excoriation
    D. Stress incontinence

93. Prior to surgery for correction of congenital hip dysplasia in a four-month-old-infant, which of the following home-care instructions would a nurse include in the teaching plan for the infant's family?

    A. "Apply double diapers when changing the infant."
    B. "Perform passive range-of-motion on the lower extremities."
    C. "Support the legs in an adducted position with pillows during sleep."
    D. "Avoid placing the infant in an upright position."

94. A parent of a five-year-old child who was recently diagnosed with type 1 diabetes asks a nurse when the child can begin to self-administer insulin. The nurse would recommend that the child begin this procedure at age

    A. six.
    B. nine.
    C. twelve.
    D. fifteen.

95. An infant is born at 30 weeks' gestation. A nursing assessment of the newborn is most likely to reveal

    A. defined pinnae that recoil quickly.
    B. extremities that abduct when lying supine.
    C. sole creases that extend over the entire foot.
    D. 5-mm bilateral breast buds.

96. A patient who has Alzheimer's disease is told by the nurse to brush his teeth. He shouts angrily, "Tomato soup!" Which of the following actions by the nurse would be correct?

    A. Focusing on the emotional reaction
    B. Clarifying the meaning of his statement
    C. Giving him step-by-step directions
    D. Doing the procedure for him

97. A patient whose ventilation is inadequate should be observed for early symptoms of hypoxia, which include

    A. pallor.
    B. restlessness.
    C. mottling of the extremities.
    D. disorientation.

98. **Which of the following statements about arm protection measures, if made by a patient who has had a right lumpectomy and axillary node dissection, indicates a need for further teaching?**

    A. "I plan to get a good tan so that I will look healthy."
    B. "I will wear rubber gloves whenever I wash dishes."
    C. "I will tell lab personnel to draw blood from my left arm."
    D. "I will watch for signs of redness in my right arm."

99. **Which of the following observations would be most definitive when assessing a patient who has posttraumatic stress disorder?**

    A. Substance abuse
    B. Aggression
    C. Flashbacks
    D. Depression

100. **An eight-year-old child who has type 1 diabetes wants to play soccer. Which of the following recommendations would a nurse make to the child?**

    A. "It would be best for you to play a non-contact sport."
    B. "Take extra insulin an hour before playing."
    C. "Eat an extra sugar exchange during the game."
    D. "Drink at least a quart of water after the game."

101. **A patient who has a left frontal lobe tumor has a craniotomy. Four hours after surgery, the following data are obtained by the nurse. Which of the following data would be most indicative of increasing intracranial pressure?**

    A. The patient's blood pressure is 160/94 mm Hg; up from 140/90 mm Hg.
    B. The patient is difficult to rouse.
    C. The patient's Babinski reflex is negative.
    D. The patient is incontinent of urine.

102. **A patient who has had a total gastrectomy is given instructions on measures to prevent the development of dumping syndrome. Which of the following statements, if made by the patient, would indicate a correct understanding of the instructions?**

    A. "I will have a bedtime snack."
    B. "I will rest one hour before each meal."
    C. "I will avoid concentrated sugars."
    D. "I will include high-fiber foods in my diet."

103. **An infant is born at 39 weeks' gestation. An initial newborn assessment is most likely to reveal**

    A. vernix caseosa in axillary and inguinal areas.
    B. a 1-mm surface area of the nipple and areola.
    C. lanugo covering the front and back of the trunk.
    D. slight yellowish hue to the skin and sclera.

104. **A patient is admitted to the emergency department following a sexual assault. Which of the following assessments should a nurse recognize as most pertinent to crisis intervention?**

    A. The patient's past history
    B. The patient's perception of the event
    C. The patient's behavior prior to the assault
    D. The patient's understanding of sexually-transmitted diseas

105. **Which of the following adolescents is able to sign the consent form in a situation that requires emergency surgery?**

    A. An adolescent male who lives at home
    B. An adolescent female who is in foster care
    C. An adolescent male who is in juvenile detention
    D. An adolescent female who is married

106. **Which of the following observations should be most significant to a nurse when assessing the condition of a six-week-old infant who is suspected of having pyloric stenosis?**

    A. Loose stools
    B. Hiccoughs
    C. Projectile vomiting
    D. Distended abdomen

107. Which of the following patient outcomes should indicate to a nurse that treatment with mannitol (Osmitrol) has been effective for a patient who has increased intracranial pressure?

    A. Decreased level of consciousness
    B. Increased urinary output
    C. Elevated body temperature
    D. Slowed pupillary response

108. A nurse should assess a patient who is receiving aminophylline for which of the following side effects of the medication?

    A. Agitation
    B. Bradycardia
    C. Tinnitus
    D. Ecchymosis

109. Which of the following recommendations should a nurse make to a patient who has a diagnosis of chronic prostatitis?

    A. "Daily sitz baths will provide comfort."
    B. "Cold scrotal compresses will reduce inflammation."
    C. "A week of antibiotic therapy should be effective."
    D. "Sexual activity should be curtailed."

110. A 12-year-old child who has been diagnosed with scoliosis is to be treated with a Milwaukee brace. To which of the following nursing diagnoses would a nurse give priority?

    A. Skin integrity
    B. Self-care deficit
    C. Impaired gas exchange
    D. Sleep pattern disturbance

111. During the one-minute Apgar assessment, a newborn has a heart rate of 120 beats/minute, lusty cry, acrocyanosis and minimal flexion of extremities. A nurse would give the newborn an Apgar score of

    A. 6.
    B. 7.
    C. 8.
    D. 9.

112. Which of the following factors would best support a diagnosis of substance abuse?

    A. Daily substance use
    B. Spending money on drugs
    C. Interference with activities of daily living
    D. Legal complications related to substance use

113. A nurse is counseling a parent whose 11-year-old child has attention deficit hyperactivity disorder. The parent reports that the child is disruptive at home. Which of the following approaches should the nurse suggest that the parent take?

    A. Confine the child to the bedroom
    B. Establish a specific schedule for activities
    C. Explain to the child why the behavior is disturbing
    D. Vary the methods by which rewards are given

114. A nurse has given home care instructions to the parent of a child who has head lice. Which of the following statements, if made by the parent, indicates that the instructions are correctly understood?

    A. "I must keep my child at home at least one week after treatment."
    B. "I must wash my child's hair with an antibacterial shampoo."
    C. "I must discard all of my child's personal linens."
    D. "I must ensure that all family members receive treatment."

115. A patient who has autism demonstrates a high level of anxiety following the rearrangement of furniture in the room. A nurse should understand that the patient's behavior is the result of a need for

    A. trust.
    B. privacy.
    C. constancy.
    D. independence.

116. A nurse should teach a patient who is taking chlorpromazine hydrochloride (Thorazine) to avoid

    A. exposure to the sun.
    B. swimming in a chlorinated pool.
    C. drinking fluids high in sodium.
    D. eating foods such as chocolate and aged cheese.

117. A child is being discharged from the emergency department with a diagnosis of acute glomerulonephritis. Which of the following measures would a nurse include in the home care plan?

    A. Restrict fluid intake
    B. Weigh daily
    C. Maintain strict bed rest
    D. Limit visitors

118. Which of the following statements, if made by a patient who has tuberculosis, would indicate a correct understanding of disease transmission?

    A. "The disease can be acquired from breast milk."
    B. "The disease does not spread beyond the lungs."
    C. "I contracted the disease through bird droppings."
    D. "I can be infected more than once with this disease."

119. Which of the following nursing diagnoses would be given priority in the care plan of a newborn at one hour of age?

    A. Risk for infection
    B. Altered nutrition
    C. Ineffective thermoregulation
    D. Impaired skin integrity

120. A nurse observes a mother administering ear drops to her four-year-old child who has acute right-sided otitis media. Which of the following actions, if taken by the mother, indicates the administration was performed correctly?

    A. Removing wax in the affected ear with a cotton swab prior to the procedure
    B. Pulling the pinna of the affected ear upward and back when administering the drug
    C. Placing the ear drop container under cool, running water prior to the procedure
    D. Placing the child in a recumbent position for several minutes after the procedure

121. Which of the following guidelines should a nurse include in the teaching plan for a patient who has osteoarthritis?

    A. Achieve ideal body weight
    B. Increase daily calcium intake to 1500 mg
    C. Maintain a high-fiber diet
    D. Sleep at least 10 hours each day

122. Which of the following findings in a patient taking levothyroxine sodium (Synthroid) for hypothyroidism would indicate that the medication is producing the desired effect?

    A. Weight gain
    B. Slowed pulse
    C. Increased alertness
    D. Decreased salivation

123. The nurse assessing an elderly patient should recognize which of the following findings as characteristic of the normal aging process?

    A. Decrease in reasoning ability
    B. Elevation in body temperature
    C. Loss of subcutaneous tissue
    D. Increase in bladder tone

124. A nurse observes a new mother breast-feeding her newborn. Which of the following actions would indicate to a nurse that the mother has a correct under-standing of breastfeeding techniques?

    A. Cleansing the breasts with soap and water prior to feeding the newborn
    B. Scheduling the newborn to feed every six hours around the clock
    C. Initiating the newborn's feeding on the same breast for each feeding
    D. Placing the nipple and areola into the newborn's mouth

125. A newborn receives vitamin K (AquaMEPHYTON) to

    A. protect the eyes from infection.
    B. prevent bleeding problems.
    C. boost the immune response.
    D. stimulate growth of gastrointestinal flora.

126. Which of the following responses by a 16-year-old boy, who has acute streptococcal pharyngitis, indicates he understands the nurse's instructions?

    A. "I won't get close to my girlfriend until I finish taking all of my medication."
    B. "I will not take any over-the-counter pills while I am taking the antibiotics."
    C. "I will have to take these antibiotic pills until all the medicine is finished."
    D. "I'll rest in bed for the first two days while taking this medication."

127. When discharging an 18-month-old child who has laryngotracheobronchitis (LTB) from the emergency department, a nurse would give the parent which of the following instructions for home care?

    A. "Situate the child in a cool, mist-filled environment if the symptoms recur."
    B. "Restrict the child's visitors to immediate family members for 72 hours."
    C. "Give the child non-prescription cough suppressants at bedtime."
    D. "Avoid giving the child dairy products until the cough subsides."

128. Which of the following action measures should a nurse include in the care plan of a patient who has a borderline personality disorder?

    A. Supporting the patient when arguments arise
    B. Encouraging the patient to develop the care plan
    C. Channeling all patient requests through one nurse per shift
    D. Administering psychotropic medication upon the patient's request

129. Which of the following laboratory values should a nurse expect to be elevated in a patient who has pancreatitis?

    A. Red blood cell count
    B. Blood urea nitrogen (BUN)
    C. Glycosylated hemoglobin
    D. Serum amylase

130. Which of the following instructions should a nurse give to a patient who has gas pains following a laparoscopic chole-cystectomy?

    A. "Increase your fluid intake."
    B. "Get up and move around."
    C. "Eat foods that are high in fiber."
    D. "Lie on your abdomen."

131. Which of the following statements, if made by a patient who has had a chole-cystectomy, would indicate a correct understanding of dietary instructions?

    A. "I should limit my intake of citrus products."
    B. "I must avoid carbonated beverages."
    C. "I will increase high-fiber foods in my diet."
    D. "I can eat whatever I can tolerate."

132. To which of the following measures should a nurse give priority when caring for a patient who has acute hepatitis B?

    A. Using disposable dishes for the patient
    B. Placing the patient in a private room
    C. Promoting bed rest
    D. Limiting fluid intake

133. An Rh-negative mother would need to receive Rho(D) immune globulin (RhoGAM) within 72 hours after delivery if her newborn had which of the following blood test results?

    A. Rh negative, Coombs positive
    B. Rh negative, Coombs negative
    C. Rh positive, Coombs negative
    D. Rh positive, Coombs positive

134. Which of the following instructions should a nurse include in the discharge teaching for a patient who has been diagnosed with hepatitis B?

    A. "Avoid alcoholic beverages."
    B. "Consume a diet low in fat."
    C. "Stay in a darkened room."
    D. "Take acetaminophen (Tylenol) for headache."

135. Which of the following statements should a nurse include when preparing a female patient for a cone biopsy?

    A. "You may experience vaginal bleeding after the procedure."
    B. "Take nothing by mouth for eight hours prior to the procedure."
    C. "There will be a catheter in your bladder after the procedure."
    D. "Douche with vinegar the evening before the procedure."

136. To which of the following nursing diagnoses should a nurse give priority in the care of a patient who has cirrhosis of the liver and an elevated serum ammonia level?

    A. Risk for infection
    B. Colonic constipation
    C. Altered thought processes
    D. Ineffective thermoregulation

137. A nurse would assess a three-year-old child who has Hirschsprung disease (HD) for which of the following manifestations?

    A. Prolapsed rectum and mucous stools
    B. Tight rectal sphincter and watery stools
    C. Periumbilical pain and clay-colored stools
    D. Abdominal distention and ribbon-like stools

138. To which of the following nursing diagnoses should a nurse give priority in the care of a patient who is receiving chemotherapy for treatment of breast cancer?

    A. Risk of infection
    B. Stress incontinence
    C. Altered sexuality patterns
    D. Impaired physical mobility

139. A six-year-old child who sustained a fracture has a long leg cast applied to the left leg. Which of the following statements, if made by the parent, would indicate the need for further teaching?

    A. "I will call the clinic if my child complains of sudden pain in his foot."
    B. "I will check the skin temperature of my child's toes at least once each day."
    C. "I should not expect my child to have sensation in the toes while the cast is on."
    D. "I should not let my child put anything inside the cast to relieve itching."

140. Spasms of the neck muscles develop in a patient who is taking phenothiazine (Nemazine). Which of the follow prn medications should the nurse administer?

    A. Hydroxyzine hydrochloride (Vistaril)
    B. Acetaminophen (Tylenol)
    C. Acetylsalicylic acid (Aspirin)
    D. Benztropine mesylate (Cogentin)

141. Shortly after a transfusion is started, the patient complains of lower back pain. Which of the following actions should the nurse take first?

    A. Notify the physician
    B. Check the patient's apical pulse
    C. Discontinue the transfusion
    D. Monitor the patient's temperature

142. The nurse should instruct a patient who is receiving an intravenous potassium chloride (KCL) infusion to report the development of adverse effects, which include

    A. burning at the insertion site.
    B. hot flushes.
    C. lightheadedness.
    D. blurring of vision.

143. The nurse gives instructions about dietary modification to a patient who is receiving continuous ambulatory peritoneal dialysis. Which of the following statements, if made by the patient, would indicate the need for further teaching?

    A. "I should limit my fluids to three glasses of water per day."
    B. "I must increase my intake of high-fiber foods."
    C. "I can have ice cream in the evening."
    D. "I will avoid adding salt to my food."

144. The nurse caring for a patient with renal disease should be aware that one of the most common factors contributing to renal failure is

    A. diabetes mellitus.
    B. alcohol abuse.
    C. morbid obesity.
    D. bile stones.

145. Because a newborn is diagnosed with Down syndrome, a nurse would anticipate that the infant is at high risk for developing

    A. altered thermoregulation.
    B. generalized infections.
    C. feeding problems.
    D. pathologic jaundice.

146. Which of the following statements, if made by a patient who is taking atenolol (Tenormin), should indicate to a nurse that the patient is experiencing adverse effects of the drug?

    A. "I can feel my heart pounding."
    B. "I feel dizzy when I get out of bed."
    C. "I am urinating more frequently."
    D. "I have a severe headache."

147. Which of the following statements, if made by a parent of a one-year-old child recently diagnosed with celiac disease, supports a nursing diagnosis of knowledge deficit?

    A. "I won't have to make any major dietary changes until my child reaches puberty."
    B. "I have to keep my child on a gluten-free diet to prevent episodes of diarrhea."
    C. "I should learn to read labels on any processed foods I offer to my child."
    D. "I will need to notify my child's school about special dietary requirements."

148. Which of the following nursing interventions should a nurse include in the care plan for a patient who is taking a tricyclic antidepressant medication?

    A. Teach the patient to check for blood in the stool
    B. Prepare the patient for excessive urinary output
    C. Offer the patient frequent sips of water for dry mouth
    D. Instruct the patient to avoid tyramine-rich foods

149. Which of the following measures is important for a nurse to include in the care of a patient who has septic shock?

    A. Promoting ambulation
    B. Restricting dietary protein
    C. Limiting sensory stimulation
    D. Increasing fluid intake

150. Because a newborn is suspected of having necrotizing enterocolitis (NEC), which of the following assessments is it essential that a nurse perform?

    A. Probe the anus for patency
    B. Percuss the liver to determine size
    C. Palpate the abdomen for rebound tenderness
    D. Check the stool for occult blood

 You have finished the Nursing, Part 1 portion of Practice Test B. Feel free to take a break (a one-hour lunch break will be provided at the Qualifying Exam) before beginning Nursing, Part 2 of Practice Test B. Do not turn the page until you are ready to begin Part 2.

Practice Exam B: Nursing, Part 2

You will have one hour and 50 minutes to complete Nursing, Part 2.

1. A two-year-old child who experienced a head trauma and is receiving mechanical ventilation suddenly develops increased intracranial pressure. Which of the following actions would a nurse take first?

   A. Suction the endotracheal tube
   B. Position the child in Trendelenburg
   C. Increase the oxygen concentration
   D. Hyperventilate the child

2. A nurse places a patient in four-point restraints following orders from a physician. Which of the following measures should the nurse include in the patient's care plan?

   A. Socialize with other patients once a shift
   B. Check circulation periodically
   C. Provide stimulating diversional activities
   D. Assess rectal temperature frequently

3. Which of the following findings, if identified in a patient who is being treated for hypovolemic shock, should indicate to the nurse that the treatment is having the desired effect?

   A. Central venous pressure of 4 mm Hg
   B. Pulse oximeter reading of 98%
   C. Urine output of 50 ml/hr
   D. Temperature of 98.6°F (37°C)

4. A patient who has severe burns is receiving H2 receptor antagonist therapy. The nurse should explain to the patient that the purpose of the therapy is to

   A. prevent stress ulcers.
   B. enhance gas exchange.
   C. facilitate protein absorption.
   D. block prostaglandin synthesis.

5. A nurse conducts discharge teaching with a patient who is in cervical traction with a halo apparatus. Which of the following statements indicates that the patient needs further instruction?

   A. "I will need to wear the halo for several months."
   B. "I should remove the halo when I shower."
   C. "I plan to take a walk every day."
   D. "I will continue my previous diet."

6. Which of the following instructions is appropriate for a nurse to give to a patient who has gastroesophageal reflux disease?

   A. "Take prescribed antacids before eating."
   B. "Place blocks under the legs of the head of the bed."
   C. "Eat a high-fat, low-protein diet."
   D. "Lie down for one hour after eating."

7. Which of the following statements would a nurse include in discharge instructions to the parent of an eight-year-old boy has been diagnosed with a concussion?

   A. "Call your healthcare provider if your child has repeated episodes of vomiting."
   B. "Don't give your child any non-prescription analgesics for 48 hours."
   C. "Limit your child's diet to clear liquids for 24 hours."
   D. "Keep your child in a quiet and darkened room while he is recovering."

8. A patient says to a staff nurse, "Give me your home telephone number so I can call you when I'm discharged from the hospital." Which of the following responses by the nurse would be appropriate?

   A. "I'll give it to you when you're ready to leave."
   B. "Give me your telephone number and I'll call you."
   C. "Our relationship will end when you go home."
   D. "If you called me, I wouldn't know what to say to you."

9. Neuroleptic malignant syndrome (NMS) is a potentially lethal complication of treatment with antipsychotic drugs. Which of the following manifestations should the nurse recognize as an early sign of NMS?

   A. Difficulty swallowing
   B. Unstable blood pressure
   C. Muscle stiffness
   D. Respiratory depression

10. To which of the following nursing diagnoses would a nurse give priority in caring for a patient who has inflammatory bowel disease?

   A. Social isolation
   B. Risk of impaired skin integrity
   C. Constipation
   D. Altered nutrition: less than body requirements

11. A patient who has ulcerative colitis is scheduled for surgery for creation of an ileostomy. The patient asks a nurse why the surgery is necessary. The nurse would respond that the purpose is to

   A. remove the diseased portion of the bowel.
   B. prevent the development of colon cancer.
   C. limit the spread of disease in the intestine.
   D. reduce the loss of nutrients from the gut.

12. Prior to assisting with electroconvulsive therapy, the nurse notices the signature of the patient's significant other on the consent form. Which of the following actions should the nurse take first?

   A. Check to verify the legal guardianship for this patient
   B. Ask the patient to explain why the form doesn't have the patient's own signature
   C. Proceed with the treatment
   D. Call a third party to witness the signature

13. When a child is to be discharged after having a tonsillectomy, the child's care at home is discussed with the mother. Which of the following comments by the child's mother indicates a need for additional teaching?

   A. "I won't be surprised if my child's throat is sore for a week or so."
   B. "I have an ice collar for my child if she will use it."
   C. "I'll have my child gargle with warm salt water a couple of times a day for a week."
   D. "I'll give my child liquids and soft foods for the next week."

14. An 85-year-old patient who lives alone and has major depression is being prepared for discharge. Which of the following nursing actions would be most therapeutic initially?

   A. Contact the patient's religious group to obtain a visitor pass
   B. Arrange for food delivery by a home-delivered meals program
   C. Enroll the patient in a day care center
   D. Refer the patient to social services

15. Which of the following preoperative instructions should a nurse give to a patient who is scheduled for a laparoscopic cholecystectomy?

   A. "You will be able to return to work in one month."
   B. "You will have four small incisions on your abdomen."
   C. "You will be on bed rest for 48 hours after surgery."
   D. "You will need to permanently restrict your fat intake."

16. A patient returns to the unit following the surgical creation of a double-barrel colostomy. Which type of drainage from the patient's bowel would a nurse expect to find postoperatively?

   A. Mucoid drainage from the distal stoma
   B. Fecal material from the distal stoma
   C. Black, tarry stool from the rectum
   D. Bright red blood from the rectum

17. A patient tells the nurse, "I'm too depressed to talk to you. Leave me alone." Which of the following responses by the nurse would be most therapeutic?

   A. "I'll be back in two hours."
   B. "Why are you so depressed?"
   C. "I'll sit here with you for a moment."
   D. "Call me when you feel like talking to me."

18. A nurse would assess a patient who has undergone a total gastrectomy for symptoms of dumping syndrome, which include

   A. diaphoresis and lightheadedness.
   B. facial flushing and paresthesia.
   C. disorientation and vomiting.
   D. diarrhea and abdominal distention.

19. **Which of the following patient outcomes is appropriate for a patient who has a nursing diagnosis of altered urinary elimination following creation of an ileal conduit?**

    A. The patient practices Credé's maneuver.
    B. The patient performs self-catheterization.
    C. The patient monitors for skin irritation.
    D. The patient demonstrates stoma irrigation.

20. **Which of the following instructions should a nurse give to a patient who is taking cyclophosphamide (Cytoxan) tablets at home?**

    A. "Report tingling in your hands and feet."
    B. "Store the drug in the refrigerator."
    C. "Take the medication one hour after meals."
    D. "Monitor your intake and output after treatment."

21. **A woman who is one hour postpartum after a vaginal delivery is experiencing heavy vaginal bleeding. Which of the following actions would a nurse take first?**

    A. Initiate a perineal pad count
    B. Assess the location of the bladder
    C. Obtain vital signs
    D. Massage the uterine fundus

22. **To which of the following nursing measures should a nurse give priority in the care of a patient who is receiving vincristine sulfate (Oncovin)?**

    A. Limiting environmental stimuli
    B. Observing for gum hyperplasia
    C. Monitoring for cardiac dysrhythmias
    D. Increasing dietary fiber content

23. **Neuroleptic malignant syndrome (NMS) is a potentially lethal complication of treatment with antipsychotic medications. Which of the following manifestations should the nurse recognize as an early sign of NMS?**

    A. Difficulty swallowing
    B. Unstable blood pressure
    C. Muscle stiffness
    D. Respiratory depression

24. **A patient who has had a right hip replacement should be instructed to carry out which of the following techniques when turning in bed?**

    A. Bring both knees to the chest before turning
    B. Keep an abductor wedge between the legs
    C. Maintain flexion of the affected hip
    D. Move the affected leg with the unaffected foot

25. **Which of the following statements would a nurse make to a patient who is scheduled for a computerized axial tomography (CAT) scan?**

    A. "You will experience minimal discomfort."
    B. "You will be exposed to a magnetic field."
    C. "You will be required to lie still for an hour after the study."
    D. "You will need to drink eight glasses of water before the test."

26. **Which of the following findings would indicate to a nurse that a patient who is administered phenytoin sodium (Dilantin) is experiencing an adverse effect of the drug?**

    A. Gingival hyperplasia
    B. Tunnel vision
    C. Paresthesia
    D. Hypertension

27. **A 15-year-old child is suspected of having Hodgkin's disease. It is most important that a nurse perform which of the following assessments during the initial physical examination?**

    A. Inspection of the mucous membranes
    B. Percussion of the kidneys
    C. Palpation of the lymph nodes
    D. Auscultation of the bowel sounds

28. A two-year-old child being treated for leukemia has the following blood count:
RBC: 3.8 million cells/cu mm
HGB: 11.5 g/dL
HCT: 32%
PLT: 150,000 cells/cu mm
WBC: 2,000 cells/cu mm
Which of the following nursing diagnoses should be given priority in this child's nursing care?

A. Altered nutrition: less than body requirements
B. Fluid volume deficit
C. Altered oral mucous membranes
D. Risk of infection

29. A woman is eight hours postpartum after a vaginal delivery. The fundus is at the level of the umbilicus and displaced to the right. Which of the following actions would a nurse take first?

A. Evaluate the characteristics of the lochia
B. Assess the location of the bladder
C. Insert a Foley catheter
D. Massage the uterus

30. A patient who has returned to the neurosurgery unit following a frontal craniotomy has all of the following orders in the chart. Which order should a nurse question?

A. Provide oxygen at 2 L/min
B. Administer dexamethasone (Decadron), 4 mg every six hours
C. Infuse intravenous fluids at 150 ml/hr
D. Elevate head of bed 30 degrees

31. A patient who has sustained a head injury is administered vasopressin (Pitressin). Which of the following responses would indicate to the nurse that the drug is effective?

A. Decreasing intracranial pressure
B. Increasing level of consciousness
C. Blood pressure of 130/90 mm Hg
D. Urinary output of 50 ml/hr

32. A patient who has a head injury has a urine output of 200 ml/hr for three consecutive hours. Which of the following nursing measures is most appropriate in the care of the patient?

A. Palpating the bladder
B. Offering additional fluids
C. Monitoring renal function tests
D. Measuring urine specific gravity

33. Which of the following pieces of equipment would a nurse order when planning the homecare needs of a patient who has myasthenia gravis?

A. Suction apparatus
B. Oxygen cylinder
C. Sequential compression device
D. Alternating pressure mattress

34. A nurse instructs the parent of a two-year-old child who has phenylketonuria (PKU) about acceptable foods to include in the child's diet. Which of the following foods, if selected by the parent, indicates a correct understanding of the teaching?

A. Chocolate milkshake
B. Scrambled eggs
C. Peanut butter sandwich
D. Animal-shaped crackers

35. A nurse would expect a patient who has Ménière's disease to have which of the following findings?

A. Distention of the abdomen
B. Swelling of the ankles
C. Shortness of breath
D. Loss of balance

36. A nurse answering the telephone of a suicide hotline should assess which of the following patient comments as highest priority?

A. "My husband has end-stage cancer, and I can't stand the thought of losing him."
B. "I have a loaded gun and I'm thinking of using it."
C. "If things don't get better, I'm going to drive my car over a cliff."
D. "I'm so unhappy. I can't go on."

37. A nurse gives discharge instructions to the parent of a two-month-old infant who was hospitalized and treated for acute bacterial meningitis. The best indication that the teaching has been effective is that the parent

A. keeps the infant confined to the home.
B. feeds the infant 24-calorie per ounce soy-based formula.
C. makes an appointment for the infant to have an audiology screening test.
D. keeps a daily diary of the infant's temperature.

38. A nurse is instructing a patient who has multiple sclerosis. Which of the following instructions should the nurse stress?

A. Avoid extremes of heat and cold
B. Eat red meat
C. Exercise vigorously daily
D. Avoid eating shellfish

39. Which of the following nursing interventions is most appropriate in the care of a patient who has peripheral venous insufficiency?

A. Elevating the legs
B. Increasing the fluid intake
C. Limiting the activity level
D. Massaging the extremities

40. Which of the following nursing measures is appropriate when caring for a patient who has undergone a right, above-the-knee amputation?

A. Ambulating the patient in the hallway with crutches
B. Placing the patient in a chair during waking hours
C. Keeping the patient's stump elevated on a pillow
D. Encouraging the patient to lie prone in bed

41. It is most essential that a nurse include which of the following assessments in the care of a woman who has had a cesarean delivery 12 hours ago?

A. Palpating pedal pulses
B. Auscultating bowel sounds
C. Checking perineal incision status
D. Measuring urine specific gravity

42. Which of the following nursing measures best illustrates the primary concept of a therapeutic milieu?

A. Encouraging patient participation in competitive activities
B. Promoting social interactions among patients
C. Planning daily therapy sessions with a psychiatrist
D. Using containment as the primary method of controlling patient behavior

43. During a well-child visit, a nurse gives instructions to the parent of an 18-month-old child who has strabismus. The best indication that the teaching has been effective is that the parent

A. purchases sunglasses for the child.
B. makes an appointment for the child with an ophthalmologist.
C. patches the child's affected eye.
D. applies antibiotic ointment to the child's affected eye at bedtime.

44. When planning care for a 14-year-old female who is pregnant, a nurse should recognize that the adolescent is at risk for

A. glucose intolerance
B. fetal chromosomal abnormalities
C. incompetent cervix
D. iron deficiency anemia

45. Which of the following menus would best meet the nutritional requirements of a patient who has major burns?

A. Cottage cheese, fruit salad, a roll and tea
B. Spaghetti with meatless sauce, green salad, garlic bread and coffee
C. Roast beef, mashed potatoes with gravy, green beans, fruit salad and milk
D. Pork chops, French fries, applesauce and iced tea

46. When planning discharge instructions for a patient who has had a laryngectomy, a nurse should include which of the following measures?

A. Chest percussion techniques
B. Ventilator management
C. Swallowing techniques
D. Communication strategies

47. When caring for a patient who has a chest tube connected to a water seal drainage system, a nurse observes that the fluid in the chest tube is not fluctuating. Which of the following nursing interventions is most appropriate?

   A. Assessing for breath sounds
   B. Reinforcing the occlusive dressing
   C. Emptying the drainage catheter
   D. Clamping the chest tube

48. Which of the following observations of a mother who delivered a healthy baby 48 hours ago indicates that the woman is developing a positive attachment to the newborn?

   A. She requests that the nurse feed the newborn.
   B. She expresses difficulty in finding a name for the newborn.
   C. She touches the newborn using her fingertips.
   D. She allows the newborn to cry for several minutes.

49. A patient is receiving treatment for hypovolemic shock. Which of the following findings would indicate that the treatment has been successful?

   A. Heart rate, 100 to 120 beats/minute
   B. Central venous pressure, four to six cm of H20
   C. Capillary refill time, eight seconds
   D. Urine output, 210 ml in eight hours

50. Which of the following dietary changes would a nurse implement with a two-year-old child who is in the acute stage of nephrotic syndrome?

   A. Increase iron
   B. Increase calcium
   C. Decrease sodium
   D. Increase protein

51. Following an adrenalectomy, a patient is to take steroid therapy after discharge from the hospital. Which of the following instructions should be given to the patient?

   A. "You should anticipate loss of hair."
   B. "You should test your urine for glucose daily."
   C. "You should avoid taking cathartics."
   D. "You should call the physician if you have a temperature elevation."

52. A patient who is dependent on secobarbital (Seconal) is in the detoxification unit and receiving phenobarbital (Luminol) in decreasing amounts. Which of the following outcomes is expected as a result of the administration of phenobarbital?

   A. The patient will not experience convulsions.
   B. The patient will not develop polyneuritis.
   C. The patient will accept the withdrawal of secobarbital.
   D. The patient will be optimistic about remaining drug-free.

53. A patient who is having eye pain is suspected of having glaucoma. The answer to which of the following questions would provide additional information?

   A. "Do your eyes water a lot?"
   B. "Do you see floating spots in front of your eyes?"
   C. "Does everything look hazy to you?"
   D. "Do you see halos around lights?"

54. A child who is receiving cancer chemotherapy has a platelet count of 50,000 cu ml. Based on this information, the child's parents should be instructed to

   A. maintain strict bed rest until the child's blood levels return to normal.
   B. use a soft-bristled toothbrush for the child's oral hygiene.
   C. anticipate the need for a red blood cell transfusion for the child.
   D. eliminate spicy foods from the child's diet.

55. It is essential that a nurse take which of the following measures when caring for a child who is in the acute phase of nephrotic syndrome?

   A. Weigh the child every day
   B. Obtain the child's hematocrit level every 12 hours
   C. Measure the child's abdominal girth every two hours
   D. Dipstick the child's urine every hour

56. It is essential that a nurse take which of the following measures prior to discharging a woman who is at high risk for postpartum depression?

   A. Encourage the woman to make an appointment with a psychologist
   B. Explore the need for prophylactic antidepressant agents
   C. Arrange for a visit to the woman's home within the next 48 hours
   D. Tell the woman to restrict her social activities until her first post-delivery check-up

57. All of the following prn medications are prescribed for a patient hospitalized for alcoholism. Which drug should be administered by the nurse to ease the symptoms of withdrawal?

   A. Chlordiazepoxide hydrochloride (Librium)
   B. Bisacodyl (Dulcolax)
   C. Acetaminophen (Tylenol)
   D. Prochlorperazine maleate (Compazine)

58. A parent of an infant who has a small atrial septal defect makes all of the following comments. Which one indicates an accurate understanding of the infant's condition?

   A. "I won't let my baby get upset and cry."
   B. "My baby needs to have heart surgery immediately."
   C. "My baby may need to rest more so than other infants while feeding."
   D. "I understand that my baby will grow at a slower pace."

59. Which of the following comments by the nurse would be used to encourage a patient who is schizophrenic and withdrawn to participate in activity therapy?

   A. "You must go to group right now."
   B. "I'll walk with you to activity therapy."
   C. "If you don't go to group, you'll be put in seclusion."
   D. "If you go to activity therapy, I'll increase your unit privileges."

60. If a patient were to develop thrombophlebitis at an intravenous infusion site, which of the following early findings should the nurse expect to observe?

   A. Pallor and swelling
   B. Erythema and heat
   C. Mottling and coolness
   D. Leakage of fluid and numbness

61. Which of the following measures should be included in the care plan of a patient whose left leg is in traction?

   A. Checking the feet for the presence of ankle clonus
   B. Noting the color of the toenails after applying temporary pressure
   C. Assessing the femoral arteries for equality of pulses
   D. Percussing the knee for a patellar reflex

62. Which of the following manifestations supports a nursing diagnosis of fluid volume excess in an eight-year-old child who has acute glomerulonephritis?

   A. Polyuria
   B. Periorbital edema
   C. Nocturnal diaphoresis
   D. Jugular vein distention

63. A patient who is diagnosed with the human immunodeficiency virus (HIV) is complaining of weakness and fatigue. The patient's nursing diagnosis is altered nutrition: less than body requirements. Which of the following measures should a nurse include in the patient's care plan?

   A. Offering raw fruits and vegetables
   B. Limiting the amount of oral fluids
   C. Obtaining daily weights
   D. Increasing the patient's activity level

64. A pregnant woman who has tested positive for the human immunodeficiency virus (HIV) is admitted to the labor unit. Which of the following statements, if made by the woman, would indicate that she has an accurate understanding of labor management?

   A. "I will receive antibiotics during my labor."
   B. "My baby will be delivered by cesarean section."
   C. "My baby will have to be monitored internally."
   D. "I plan to have an epidural to help ease the pain."

65. Which of the following patients should a nurse identify as being at highest risk for developing a cerebrovascular accident (CVA)?

   A. A 35-year-old female who has migraine headaches
   B. A 49-year-old male with a history of myocardial infarction
   C. A 65-year-old female with a history of transient ischemic attacks (TIAs)
   D. A 70-year-old male who has adult-onset diabetes mellitus

66. A 28-year-old woman who is seven weeks pregnant has had insulin-dependent diabetes mellitus (type 2) since she was 16 years old. A common symptom of pregnancy that could lead to problems for this pregnant woman is

   A. urinary frequency.
   B. breast enlargement.
   C. the presence of chorionic gonadotropin in the urine.
   D. nausea.

67. At 36 weeks of pregnancy, a woman is to have a lecithin/sphingomyelin (L/S) ratio performed. She should be instructed that the purpose of this test is to determine

   A. the amount of fetal muscle mass.
   B. whether the fetal kidneys are mature enough to excrete creatinine.
   C. fetal pulmonary maturity.
   D. the functioning of the fetal-placental unit.

68. A primigravida who has had no prenatal care is admitted to the hospital in active labor. Her cervix is eight centimeters dilated. She starts to push with a contraction. During her next contraction, the nurse should take which of the following actions?

   A. Instruct the patient to take short, rapid breaths
   B. Tell the patient to take a deep breath, hold it and then bear down
   C. Help the patient to assume a semi-sitting position and to hold her knees in a flexed position while bearing down
   D. Apply firm pressure to the patient's lower back

69. A nurse gives a postpartal woman instructions about the use of diaphragms. Which of the following comments, if made by the woman, indicates the need for further instruction?

   A. "I have a diaphragm that I can start to use as soon as I'm ready to have intercourse."
   B. "I always wash my diaphragm with soap and water."
   C. "I use a spermicidal jelly with the diaphragm."
   D. "I leave my diaphragm in place at least six hours after intercourse."

70. A newborn develops jaundice shortly after birth and receives phototherapy. While the newborn is receiving phototherapy, which of the following measures should be included in the newborn's care plan at regular intervals?

   A. Testing the newborn's urine for glucose
   B. Changing the newborn's position
   C. Assessing the newborn for symptoms of dependent edema
   D. Applying an emollient to the newborn's skin

71. **The most important factor the registered nurse should consider when delegating patient care to a nursing assistant is**

    A. the individual's competence with patient assessment.
    B. the level of skill needed to care for the patient.
    C. the nursing assistant's response to being observed by a registered nurse.
    D. the nursing assistant's ability to communicate with other members of the health team.

72. **When crowning is observed during the second stage of labor, a nurse would take which of the following actions?**

    A. Position the woman on her left side
    B. Have the woman hold her breath and push
    C. Encourage the woman to take short breaths
    D. Prepare the woman for immediate delivery

73. **A woman who is postpartum would be instructed to perform Kegel exercises for which of the following purposes?**

    A. To strengthen the vaginal muscles
    B. To promote uterine involution
    C. To strengthen the pelvic ligaments
    D. To prevent urinary tract infection

74. **An eight-year-old child is admitted to the hospital for acute glomerulonephritis. The nurse would expect the child's history to reveal which of the following findings?**

    A. Otitis media
    B. Gastroenteritis
    C. Strep throat
    D. Viral pneumonia

75. **A nurse is instructing a patient about gastroesophageal reflux disease (GERD). Which of the following instructions should the nurse stress?**

    A. Reduce intake of caffeine beverages
    B. Eat three large meals a day
    C. Drink milk as a bedtime snack
    D. Take antacids directly after a meal

76. **A 61-year-old male is admitted to the hospital with a right-sided cerebrovascular accident. In discussing the patient's medical history with his wife, the nurse obtains all of the following information. Which information most strongly indicates that the patient has had previous transient ischemic cerebral attacks?**

    A. He has throbbing frontal headaches when he becomes emotionally upset.
    B. He has often been very fatigued after returning from work.
    C. He has recently been irritable and less happy than usual.
    D. He has occasionally been forgetful and appeared to be in a daze during their conversations.

77. **A patient who is manic has been monopolizing group time, and the nurse has been setting limits on this behavior. If the patient is benefiting from this intervention, the nurse should expect the patient to**

    A. arrive on time for group.
    B. dress appropriately.
    C. raise a hand before speaking.
    D. remain seated throughout the session.

78. **A patient whose ventilation is inadequate should be observed for early symptoms of hypoxia, which include**

    A. pallor.
    B. restlessness.
    C. mottling of the extremities.
    D. disorientation.

79. **A nurse teaches new coping skills to a patient who abused cocaine. Which of the following comments, if made by the patient, would indicate that the teaching was effective?**

    A. "I'm staying off cocaine one day at a time."
    B. "I'm going to discourage my friends from using cocaine."
    C. "I will try to sleep more so I don't think of cocaine."
    D. "I'm going to take a tranquilizer whenever I feel the urge to use cocaine."

80. A nurse therapist uses systematic desensitization in the treatment of a patient who has a phobia about flying in airplanes. Which of the following patient outcomes indicates a favorable response to the treatment?

    A. The patient visits an airport.
    B. The patient understands the reasons for his fear of flying.
    C. The patient uses methods of transportation other than airplanes.
    D. The patient cancels all travel plans.

81. A male patient has an arteriovenous fistula created in his left forearm. Which of the following behaviors would indicate that the patient needs instruction in self-care?

    A. He wears sleeveless shirts.
    B. He keeps a dry dressing on his left arm.
    C. He wears a watch on his left wrist.
    D. He prefers to take a shower rather than a tub bath.

82. Following a hip replacement, the patient should have the affected hip placed in which of these positions?

    A. Extended, with a wedge between the legs
    B. Flexed, with the knee supported on sandbags
    C. Elevated, with pillows under the leg from the knee to the ankle
    D. Rotated externally, with a trochanter roll in place

83. A patient is scheduled for a bronchoscopy. To prepare the patient for the procedure, the nurse should give which of the following instructions?

    A. "A small needle will be inserted through the skin into the lung tissue."
    B. "Food and fluids will be withheld for one to two hours following the procedure."
    C. "It will be uncomfortable to breathe deeply following the procedure."
    D. "You will cough up some of the dye during the next few days."

84. A patient's serum lithium carbonate (Eskalith) level is 1.9 mEq/L. The nurse should

    A. administer the lithium with an antacid.
    B. administer the next dose of lithium at the prescribed time.
    C. ask the physician for an order to increase the lithium dose.
    D. withhold the lithium and report the lithium level to the physician.

85. A child who has received injectable contrast media during a computerized axial tomography (CAT) scan should be closely observed for which of the following untoward effects?

    A. Malignant hypothermia
    B. Diaphragmatic irritability
    C. Urticarial rash
    D. Generalized edema

86. During the night shift report, the charge nurse learns that an elderly patient has become very confused and is shouting obscenities and undressing himself. Which of the following actions is the most appropriate initial nursing response?

    A. Restrain the patient with a Posey jacket
    B. Medicate the patient with haloperidol (Haldol) as ordered
    C. Notify the physician
    D. Complete a nursing assessment of the patient

87. To which of the following assessments of a patient who had a recent myocardial infarction would the nurse give the highest priority?

    A. Moderate levels of anxiety
    B. Bibasilar rales
    C. Chest pain
    D. Ventricular dysrhythmias

88. A two-year-old child who has a tracheostomy is being discharged in one or two days. Which of the following statements by the parent indicates the need for further assessment of the parent's readiness to provide care at home?

    A. "Someone from the equipment company showed me how to use the oxygen tank."
    B. "The homecare nurse will visit us the day of discharge."
    C. "I feel that I can do the tracheostomy care."
    D. "I'm not sure what to do if the power goes out."

89. The nurse accompanies a newborn's parents to their car following discharge from the birthing center. The car seat has been placed in the front seat. The father states, "We want the baby where we can see her." The most appropriate response of the nurse would be

    A. "That is all right. Newborns should be watched closely."
    B. "Placement of the car seat is a matter of preference as long as it is securely fastened."
    C. "This is fine for today, but later you should move the seat to the rear."
    D. "I know that you like to watch her closely, but the safest place for the baby is in the back center seat."

90. A client who is postpartum has had a fourth-degree episiotomy and repair. Which intervention would be most important for dealing with possible complications?

    A. Administering docusate (Colace) capsules, one at hour of sleep (hs)
    B. Giving intramuscular analgesics as ordered
    C. Instructing the patient in the use of a Fleet enema
    D. Encouraging the patient to continue her prenatal vitamins

91. A patient was admitted to a psychiatric unit after she assaulted her landlord, because she thought the landlord was putting bad ideas in her head. When determining if the patient is ready for discharge, it would be most appropriate to ask the patient,

    A. "What would you do if the same situation came up again?"
    B. "Do you understand that these ideas about the landlord are part of your stress?"
    C. "What do you see as the reason you were admitted to the hospital?"
    D. "Would you be willing to come back to the hospital for further treatment if you needed it?"

92. A woman who has been identified as a victim of domestic violence is seen by the community mental health nurse. The priority outcome is for the client to

    A. explore her relationship with her parents.
    B. make a personal safety plan.
    C. accept responsibility for her role in the abusive relationship.
    D. develop conflict resolution skills.

93. A middle-aged patient says to the nurse, "I don't deserve to live." The most therapeutic initial response by the nurse would be to

    A. continue to listen to the patient while maintaining direct eye contact.
    B. remain with the patient until she states she feels better.
    C. say to the patient, "You sound depressed," and lean toward her.
    D. ask the patient what she means by "I don't deserve to live."

94. A patient who made 12 calls to the police reporting that someone was trying to poison him is being admitted to the psychiatric unit. Which of the following actions by the nurse would be most therapeutic at this time?

    A. Explaining that the fear is not reasonable
    B. Delaying the admission interview until the patient is medicated
    C. Helping the patient to identify the alleged poisoner
    D. Acknowledging the patient's fear

95. A patient who has emphysema complains of a non-productive cough and dyspnea that is steadily worsening. A nurse should include which of the following nursing diagnoses in the patient's care plan?

   A. Ineffective thermoregulation
   B. Activity intolerance
   C. Chronic pain
   D. Non-compliance

96. A patient being treated for schizophrenia has his medication changed from fluphenazine (Prolixin) to clozapine (Clozaril). Because of the change to Clozaril, the nurse should be more vigilant in assessing the patient for

   A. dry mouth.
   B. seizures.
   C. orthostatic hypotension.
   D. constipation.

97. Which of the following test results would confirm a diagnosis of cystic fibrosis?

   A. Reduced serum calcium
   B. Reduced hemoglobin
   C. Elevated serum amylase
   D. Elevated sweat sodium

98. A patient receiving pharmacological treatment for a psychotic disorder exhibits restlessness and sits down for only a few minutes at a time. The nurse would recognize that this behavior

   A. needs to be further assessed to rule out a medication side effect.
   B. is common in psychotic patients.
   C. results from internal conflicts the patient is experiencing.
   D. will subside as the patient improves.

99. A parent of a child who has sickle cell anemia tells the nurse, "It is all my fault that my child has this problem." The nurse should initially respond to this statement by

   A. reassuring the parent that no one is at fault.
   B. referring the parent for genetic counseling.
   C. having the parent clarify the meaning of the statement.
   D. acknowledging the validity of the parent's statement.

100. Which of the following children are at high risk for developing lead poisoning?

   A. The toddler who lives in a house built before 1960
   B. The preschooler who takes a daily vitamin pill with iron
   C. The infant who drinks formula prepared with well water
   D. The school-aged child who likes to build model cars

101. A nurse should assess a postoperative patient for which of the following early manifestations of hypovolemic shock?

   A. Hypotension
   B. Restlessness
   C. Oliguria
   D. Dyspnea

102. For which of the following procedures would the nurse expect to prepare a patient who has adult respiratory distress syndrome (ARDS)?

   A. Endotracheal intubation
   B. Chest tube insertion
   C. Incentive spirometry
   D. Ventilation-perfusion scan

103. An 18-year-old primigravida is admitted at 34 weeks' gestation with preeclampsia. The nurse should observe her carefully for manifestations of eclampsia, which include

   A. convulsions, seizures and coma.
   B. a diastolic blood pressure of 90 mm Hg or more.
   C. proteinuria of 3+ g/day.
   D. a rise in systolic blood pressure of 30 mm Hg or more.

104. A 15-year-old boy has undergone a spinal instrumentation at the level of T4 to T5 for scoliosis. Because there is an order to maintain strict bed rest, a nurse should use which of the following techniques when repositioning the boy?

A. Assist the patient in pulling himself up with the overhead trapeze bar
B. Turn the patient's head to one side, then have him reach for the rail to turn
C. Place the bed in Trendelenburg position, then have the boy roll to one side
D. Use an assistant and logroll the patient to the desired side

105. A nurse would assess a patient who has undergone a lumbar laminectomy for which of the following post-surgical complications?

A. Deep vein thrombosis
B. Urinary frequency
C. Intermittent claudication
D. Flank pain

106. A 10-year-old child is receiving therapeutic doses of acetylsalicylic acid (aspirin) for treatment of Kawasaki disease. Which of the following findings indicates to the nurse that the drug therapy needs to be modified?

A. Temperature of 97.8°F (36.6°C)
B. Bilateral tinnitus
C. Platelet count of 240,000 cells/cu mm
D. Desquamation of the palms

107. For which of the following substances should a nurse test to determine if nasal drainage contains cerebro-spinal fluid (CSF)?

A. Glucose
B. Blood
C. Albumin
D. Bicarbonate

108. A patient who has Parkinson's disease is admitted to the hospital for medication control. In addition to presenting with muscle rigidity, the nurse should expect that the patient will have

A. a mask-like facial expression.
B. tremors of the knees when resting.
C. bilateral nystagmus.
D. long-term memory loss.

109. A registered nurse is assigned to the following patients. Which one should the nurse see first after shift report?

A. A 32-year-old postoperative appendectomy patient of five hours who is complaining of pain
B. A 44-year-old myocardial infarction (MI) patient who is complaining of nausea
C. A 24-year-old patient admitted for dehydration whose intravenous (IV) has infiltrated
D. A 62-year-old postoperative abdominal hysterectomy patient of three days who's incisional dressing is saturated with serosanguinous fluid

110. When a woman is 18 weeks pregnant, it is determined that she has a twin pregnancy. Which of the following additional findings would be consistent with the diagnosis?

A. Rapid uterine growth
B. Low hematocrit
C. Decreased amniotic fluid
D. Urinary frequency

 You have finished Nursing, Part 2 of Practice Test B. You may want to take a break or possibly wait another day before taking Practice Test C.

Rationales – Practice Exam B: Nursing, Part 1

1. **Key: D**   **Client Need:** *Pharmacological and Parenteral Therapies*

    D. Zyloprim reduces uric acid synthesis and is indicated for hyperuricemia associated with malignancies. Antileukemic drugs can cause a rapid breakdown in the malignant cells, which raises the uric acid load that must be handled by the kidney. This increased load, combined with a state of dehydration caused by poor fluid intake and vomiting, causes renal injury.

    A. Zyloprim does not stimulate red blood cell formation.
    B. Zyloprim accelerates the excretion of uric acid and reduces the risk of kidney stone formation. It does not promote the deposit of calcium in the long bones.
    C. Zyloprim controls hyperuricemia. It does not interfere with the production of leukemic cells.

2. **Key: C**   **Client Need:** *Prevention and Early Detection of Disease*

    C. Acne develops at puberty when the secretion of sebum takes place. The sebum accumulates in the pilosebaceous unit forming comedones, which may be invaded by bacteria. This results in overgrowth and inflammation.

    A. Eating large amounts of fat in the diet is associated with obesity and heart disease. It has not been implicated in the development of acne.
    B. Dietary habits, such as eating complex carbohydrates, chocolate, ice cream and candy, has not been scientifically linked to development of acne.
    D. The adrenal glands secrete steroids and catecholamines. These have not been implicated in the development of acne.

3. **Key: D**   **Client Need:** *Growth and Development*

    D. The six-month-old can roll from back to abdomen and may sit alone without support.

    A. Creeping on the hands and knees is seen at nine months of age.
    B. Pulling self to a standing position is seen at nine to 10 months of age.
    C. Waving bye-bye is seen in the infant at 10 months of age.

4. **Key: D**   **Client Need:** *Growth and Development*

    D. Giving the child a juice bottle at night encourages the formation of dental caries. Water would be a better choice of solution rather than a glucose-based fluid. At 15 to 18 months of age the child should be totally weaned.

    A. Feeding self is normal at 14 months of age and should not be discouraged.
    B. Items such as favorite blankets provide security for the child and should not be discouraged.
    C. Rocking helps to calm the child and is normal behavior in the 14-month-old.

5. **Key: C**   **Client Need:** *Basic Care and Comfort*

    C. Foods which can cause a potential obstruction in an ileostomy include nuts, raisins, popcorn, seeds, chocolate, raw vegetables, celery and corn.

    A, B and D.
    These foods are not contraindicated for patients who have an ileostomy.

6. **Key: D**   Client Need: *Reduction of Risk Potential*

    D. The axilla should not rest on the crutches. Such pressure may cause discomfort and nerve damage. The weight of the body should be borne by the hands. The girl needs further instruction in this area.

    A. Since the child is not allowed weight bearing on her left leg, a three-point gait is used for crutch-walking. The child should advance one crutch and then the other, followed by the unaffected leg. The unaffected leg should be advanced only as far as the crutches. Moving beyond the crutches can cause the child to lose her balance.
    B. Elbows should be flexed when using crutches and the weight of the body should be borne by the hands. The girl is using proper crutch-walking technique.
    C. The crutches should not be advanced further than six to eight inches in order to prevent loss of balance and falls. The girl is using proper crutch-walking technique.

7. **Key: B**   Client Need: *Psychosocial Adaptation*

    B. A patient with a well-thought-out plan and the means to carry out the plan is at extremely high risk for suicide.

    A. A family history of suicide increases an individual's risk, but the plan is a better indicator of suicidal intent.
    C. Experiencing a recent loss also increases an individual's risk of suicide. However, the plan is the better indicator of suicidal intent.
    D. Having a support system that one can rely on during periods of crisis decreases the risk for suicide.

8. **Key: D**   Client Need: *Coping and Adaptation*

    D. Encouraging the patient to share memories can provide a way of working through unresolved issues from the past. The nurse can validate the patient's feelings and help the patient come to terms with painful issues. This helps the patient attain a sense of positive identity.

    A. The patient needs to resolve issues from the past before he/she can set goals for the future.
    B. Giving a diversional activity minimizes the importance of the patient's feelings.
    C. Asking the patient to think of recent pleasures also minimizes the importance of what the patient wants to focus on with the nurse.

9. **Key: D**   Client Need: *Pharmacological and Parenteral Therapies*

    D. It takes two to four weeks for tricyclic antidepressants to achieve therapeutic blood levels. The patient demonstrates that he understands that he will not feel better until therapeutic levels are reached.

    A. Exercise is not contraindicated for patients taking tricyclic antidepressants.
    B. Ringing in the ears is a symptom of aspirin toxicity and is not a side effect of tricyclic antidepressant therapy.
    C. Food restrictions are indicated for the patient taking monoamine oxidase inhibitors for depression, but are not indicated for those on tricyclics.

10. **Key: B**   **Client Need:** *Psychosocial Adaptation*

    B. Alcohol withdrawal begins within four to six hours of cessation of, or reduction in, heavy and prolonged alcohol use. By knowing when the patient had her last drink, the nurse can anticipate withdrawal symptoms and intervene appropriately.

    A. This information will be of use when the individual begins counseling. If the patient has a husband who enables her drinking, it will be much more difficult for her to quit.

    C. Knowing how old the patient was when she started drinking provides information on the length of her addiction. However, it is not a question that needs to be asked immediately.

    D. The nurse should be aware of what the patient has eaten prior to admission since food may slow down the absorption of alcohol and thereby delay withdrawal. However, the most essential assessment for the nurse to make is determining when the patient had her last drink.

11. **Key: C**   **Client Need:** *Coping and Adaptation*

    C. The patient should be able to identify signs and symptoms of stress or anxiety so that the techniques of stress reduction can be used effectively.

    A. Explaining the physiological effect of stress might be done in a later teaching session. The first priority is helping the patient to identify the manifestations of stress.

    B. Teaching relaxation exercises is part of stress management but the patient must be able to recognize the signs and symptoms of stress so that he/she is aware of when to use the techniques.

    D. Active exercise is a means of controlling stress. However, identification of stressors should take priority.

12. **Key: B**   **Client Need:** *Reduction of Risk Potential*

    B. In the immediate postoperative period following hip replacement, the patient should dorsiflex and extend the foot to prevent thrombosis, which is a serious complication following joint surgeries.

    A. One day postoperatively, the patient should begin exercises to restore strength and tone in the hip muscles, such as leg raising and abduction exercises.

    C. Using a postoperative abduction pillow following hip replacement interferes with flexion and extension of the knee.

    D. In addition to leg raises and abduction exercises, patients with a hip replacement should begin quadriceps and gluteal muscle setting exercises.

13. **Key: D**   **Client Need:** *Pharmacological and Parenteral Therapies*

    D. Diazepam (Valium) is prescribed for a patient with low back pain to decrease muscle spasms.

    A. Valium is an antianxiety agent and may be used to reduce anxiety. However, in this situation, its purpose is to lessen muscle spasms.

    B. Valium has no direct effect on pain sensation.

    C. Valium does not affect the inflammatory process.

14. **Key: B**   **Client Need:** *Physiological Adaptation*

     B. Anemia occurs in renal failure due to the decreased production of erythropoietin. This leads to fatigue in the patient.

     A. Hypertension, which is usually caused by sodium retention and increased extracellular fluid volume, is present in chronic renal failure, and not hypotension.

     C. The most noticeable change in the integumentary system is a yellowish discoloration of the skin that results from the absorption and retention of urinary chromogens that normally give the characteristic color to urine.

     D. The patient with chronic renal failure has oliguria or anuria rather than dysuria.

15. **Key: D**   **Client Need:** *Reduction of Risk Potential*

     D. Acid phosphatase is elevated in advanced Paget's disease, cancer of the prostate and hyperparathyroidism.

     A. Uric acid levels are decreased with the administration of uricosuric drugs.

     B. Creatinine levels are increased in renal failure.

     C. Bicarbonate is elevated in metabolic alkalosis.

16. **Key: B.**   **Client Need:** *Physiological Adaptation*

     B. Since Alzheimer's disease progresses from a subtle deterioration in memory to a more profound memory loss, it is important to do an ongoing assessment of the patient's abilities.

     A. The patient with Alzheimer's disease who experiences memory loss is unable to participate in a behavior modification program.

     C. Since recent events and new information cannot be recalled, helping the patient to explore emotional conflicts would be difficult.

     D. Implementing a bowel-training program is beyond the cognitive abilities of the Alzheimer's patient.

17. **Key: A.**   **Client Need:** *Physiological Adaptation*

     A. A patient with a spinal cord transection has no movement or feeling below the level of the injury.

     B. The patient with a spinal cord injury loses feeling and sensation below the level of the injury. Therefore, the patient would not have complaints of tingling.

     C. The patient with autonomic dysreflexia has marked diaphoresis above the level of the lesion.

     D. The patient with a spinal cord injury is unable to move below the level of the injury; therefore, the patient would not have tremors.

18. **Key: B.**   **Client Need:** *Physiological Adaptation*

     B. Pernicious anemia is the absence of the intrinsic factor secreted by the gastric mucosa. It produces a beefy, red tongue. When treatment has been effective, the tongue loses this appearance.

     A. Patients with pernicious anemia do not have alterations in their platelet count and do not have petechiae.

     C. Patients with pernicious anemia do not characteristically develop dependent edema.

     D. Patients with pernicious anemia do not generally experience loss of appetite.

19. **Key: A**   **Client Need:** *Growth and Development*

    A. Alpha-fetoprotein (AFP) is found in the fetal circulation, amniotic fluid and maternal fluid. Elevated levels have been found to reflect open neural tube defects such as spina bifida and anencephaly.

    B. A biophysical profile is an assessment of fetal well-being.
    C. Amniocentesis would provide information on neural tube defects but is far more risky and invasive.
    D. TORCH titers will give information regarding exposure to viral infections. The TORCH group of infectious diseases are those that can cause serious harm to the developing fetus. These diseases include toxoplasmosis (T), other infections such as syphilis (O), rubella (R), cytomegalovirus (C) and herpes simplex virus type 2 (H).

20. **Key: A**   **Client Need:** *Growth and Development*

    A. Imaginary companions usually appear between the ages of two and three years. They are often relinquished when the child enters school.

    B. A four-year-old's drawing of a human is just pictorial, a head with two arms attached. The child would not draw a stick figure with parts.
    C. At 24 months, the child can go up and down stairs alone with two feet on each step. This behavior would not be appropriate for a four-year-old.
    D. At age seven, the child can repeat three numbers backward and at age eight to nine can count backward from 20. The four-year-old would not be able to do this.

21. **Key: C**   **Client Need:** *Psychosocial Adaptation*

    C. Since the patient with Alzheimer's disease has problems with memory, it is important for the nurse to state his or her name at each contact with the patient.

    A. Responding to whatever name the patient calls the nurse does not provide reality orientation for the patient.
    B. Since the patient has difficulty with memory, especially short-term memory, asking him to remember a name is not appropriate.
    D. Allowing extra time to remember will not enable the patient to recall the name and may agitate the patient since he has difficulty with memory.

22. **Key: B**   **Client Need:** *Physiological Adaptation*

    B. A patient with arterial insufficiency develops intermittent claudication, which is pain in the calf muscles when walking. The pain subsides with rest.

    A. Weakness in the legs is often related to neuromuscular disease.
    C. Dependent edema may be a sign of congestive heart failure or peripheral vascular disease.
    D. Tendonitis may occur from walking or running on hard surfaces.

23. **Key: B**   **Client Need:** *Psychosocial Adaptation*

    B. The patient with borderline personality disorder engages in splitting of the staff or "playing" one staff member against another. The nurse should not respond directly to the patient's comment but, instead, should consistently enforce unit rules.

    A. This response focuses on the other nurse's behavior rather than the patient's.
    C. Consistency in carrying out the treatment plan, which includes adherence to unit rules, is essential to prevent manipulation of the staff by the patient.
    D. This response allows the patient to think that he will be allowed to break the unit rules. The best response is to remind the patient of the rules and that they are in place for all patients.

24. **Key: D**   **Client Need:** *Growth and Development*

    D. A reactive pattern to a non-stress test (NST) demonstrates fetal well-being. Due to the high false positive rate for nonreactive findings, a biophysical profile also should be done.

    A. An emergency Cesarean section is not indicated at this time.
    B. Induction will be instituted only after the healthcare team is sure that there is a nonreactive fetus.
    C. Internal fetal monitoring can be accomplished only after the patient's membranes have ruptured.

25. **Key: C**   **Client Need:** *Psychosocial Adaptation*

    C. Children's reports may vary from contradictory stories to unwavering versions of the experience. While their stories may sound contradictory, this may reflect the child's experiences in several instances of abuse. Also, children who repeatedly tell identical facts may have been prompted to do so. Increasing evidence suggests that the types of interrogation that children are exposed to following reports of sexual abuse shape their thinking. In interviewing the child, every effort is made to coordinate the number of interviewers and to assign a primary professional to work with the child. Videotaping or audiotaping can be used to limit the number of traumatic events.

    A. The nurse should contact the designated interviewer to interview the child.
    B. Controversy exists over the validity of using anatomically correct dolls. Findings have shown that the interviewer could influence and shape the child's behavior with these dolls. In addition, some studies have shown that children who have not been abused may manipulate the dolls in sexually suggestive ways.
    D. When children report sexually abusive experiences, their reports need to be taken seriously, but also cautiously, to avoid harming the child or falsely accusing a person.

26. **Key: A**   **Client Need:** *Psychosocial Adaptation*

    A. Patients with an antisocial personality disorder fail to conform to social norms with respect to lawful behaviors. They see themselves as victims and do not accept the consequences of their behavior.

    B. Patients with antisocial personality disorders do not experience guilt over their behavior or the effects of their behavior on others.
    C. Patients with antisocial personality disorders do not experience anxiety because of their behavior. They do have a low tolerance for frustration, and can become furious and vindictive if thwarted. When things go their way, they can be cheerful, gracious and charming.
    D. Patients with antisocial personality disorders do not learn from experience. They act impetuously and are unable to delay gratification.

27. **Key: D**   **Client Need:** *Reduction of Risk Potential*

    D. Patients who have ulcerative colitis with severe diarrhea develop fluid and electrolyte imbalance. Therefore, it is important to correct any imbalances prior to surgery.

    A. Promoting acceptance of the ileostomy should be instituted preoperatively, but fluid and electrolyte balance would be the priority.
    B. The patient's emotional state can influence the outcome of the surgery and should be attended to preoperatively. But again, the priority of care would be fluid and electrolyte balance.
    C. Since the patient with ulcerative colitis is not usually on bedrest, pressure areas are unlikely to develop.

28. **Key: A**   **Client Need:** *Pharmacological and Parenteral Therapies*

    A. Benadryl is an antihistamine that is used in the treatment of allergic reactions. It can be administered intravenously for a quick response.

    B. Chlortrimeton is used for allergy symptoms and rhinitis.
    C. Sudafed has its primary effects on the respiratory mucosal membrane. It is a nasal deconges-
       tant that can be used with antihistamines.
    D. Phenergan is used for control of motion sickness and nausea. It also is used to potentiate the
       effects of medications such as Demerol.

29. **Key: C**   **Client Need:** *Basic Care and Comfort*

    C. There are techniques that the nurse can use to reduce the odor of the ileostomy, such as placing charcoal in the ileostomy bag. The charcoal will absorb the odor in the bag.

    A. The odor does not gradually become less noticeable unless steps are taken to reduce it.
    B. While it is important to help the patient ventilate, this response does not address the issue
       of the odor.
    D. This statement is not necessarily true. Others may be offended by the odor. Teaching the patient
       measures that will help to reduce the odor will be most beneficial.

30. **Key: C**   **Client Need:** *Pharmacological and Parenteral Therapies*

    C. Thyroid hormone replacement is necessary for the duration of the patient's life. Stopping the medication will result in recurrence of the hypothyroidism.

    A. Skin irritation is not identified as a side effect of thyroid extract.
    B. Insomnia, headache and tremors are central nervous system side effects of thyroid extract. The
       patient should be told to report anxiety, irritability and excitability since they may indicate too
       high a dose of the medication.
    D. There is no indication that this medication should be taken with food.

31. **Key: B**   **Client Need:** *Reduction of Risk Potential*

    B. Cardiac arrest in the pediatric population is less often of cardiac origin than from pro-longed hypoxemia secondary to inadequate oxygenation, ventilation and circulation.

    A. Ventricular arrhythmias are rare in children. They are more common in adults.
    C. Generalized seizures are rare in children.
    D. Distributive shock results from a vascular abnormality that produces maldistribution of blood sup-
       ply throughout the body. Common causes are neurogenic shock, anaphylactic shock and septic
       shock. All may result in cardiac arrest but are less common a cause than respiratory etiology.

32. **Key: D**   **Client Need:** *Pharmacological and Parenteral Therapies*

    D. Because magnesium sulfate is a central nervous system (CNS) depressant, the nurse should assess for signs and symptoms of magnesium toxicity, including loss of knee jerk reflexes, respiratory depression, oliguria, respiratory arrest and cardiac arrest. The woman's blood pressure, pulse and respiratory status are monitored every 15 minutes.

    A. Urine chemistry is not routinely done. Urine dipstick for protein would be appropriate.
    B. The platelet count will be assessed along with the routine complete blood count (CBC).
    C. The apical heart rate does not have to be assessed. Measurement of the radial pulse rate is
       acceptable. Vital signs should be taken every 15 minutes.

33. **Key: A**   **Client Need:** *Safety and Infection Control*

    A. The laryngeal tube should be suctioned for 10 seconds. Suctioning for longer periods can result in hypoxia.

    B. This is an incorrect measure. Sterile technique should be used when suctioning the laryngectomy tube to prevent infection.

    C. This is an incorrect measure. Suction should not be applied when inserting the suction catheter in order to prevent trauma to surrounding tissue.

    D. This is an incorrect response. Turning the head is done when suctioning a tracheostomy. It does not have to be done for the patient who has a laryngectomy.

34. **Key: C**   **Client Need:** *Reduction of Risk Potential*

    C. Immunosuppression is an adverse reaction to chemotherapy; therefore, it is important to assess the patient for infection.

    A. Due to the thrombocytopenia secondary to chemotherapy, bleeding is a more common side effect than thrombus formation.

    B. Ascites is not usually a side effect of chemotherapy, but is an indication of obstructive manifestations caused by the disease.

    D. If the chemotherapy is effective, the patient should not have splenomegaly.

35. **Key: C**   **Client Need:** *Management of Care*

    C. Sensory neuropathy leads to loss of pain and pressure sensation. Autonomic neuropathy leads to increased dryness and fissuring of the skin. The typical sequence of events in the development of a diabetic foot ulcer begins with a soft-tissue injury of the foot and formation of a fissure between the toes or in an area of dry skin.

    A, B and D.
    While these options may be potential nursing diagnoses for the patient with diabetes mellitus, they are not the priority when a patient has peripheral neuropathy.

36. **Key: C**   **Client Need:** *Management of Care*

    C. Preparing children for procedures decreases their anxiety, promotes their cooperation, supports their existing coping skills and may teach them new ones and facilitates a feeling of mastery in experiencing a potentially stressful event.

    A. The nurse can suggest ways for the school-age child to maintain control during procedures (deep breathing, relaxation, counting). Restraining should be a last resort.

    B. The nurse should provide privacy from peers during procedures on school-age children to maintain self-esteem. Parents should be allowed to remain with their child.

    D. The nurse should emphasize the end of the procedure and any pleasurable events afterward. Be honest with the child about unpleasant aspects of the procedure. It is best not to tell the child that a procedure will be over quickly because the child's perception of time may not be that of the nurse's.

37. **Key: D**   *Client Need: Management of Care*

   D. The purpose of a nasogastric tube following a subtotal gastrectomy is to drain the stomach or intestinal tract to prevent postoperative vomiting, obstruction of the intestinal tract and distention of the stomach or intestinal tract caused by fluid or gas. The first action when a patient complains of nausea would be to determine the patency of the patient's nasogastric tube.

   A. Instructing the patient to take deep breaths does not relieve nausea caused by abdominal distention. It may cause the patient to swallow more air leading to increased abdominal distention.
   B. A cool cloth to the patient's forehead is a treatment to relieve a headache, not nausea.
   C. Administering an antiemetic medication is an appropriate nursing intervention. However, determining the patency of the patient's nasogastric tube would be the first action.

38. **Key: B**   *Client Need: Pharmacological and Parenteral Therapies*

   B. First determine the amount of Heparin in 1 ml.

$$\frac{20000 \text{ units}}{1000 \text{ ml}} = \frac{x \text{ units}}{1 \text{ ml}}$$

$$1000x = 20000$$

$$x = 20 \text{ units/ml}$$

   Then multiply by the number of ml to be given. The patient is to receive 50 ml/hr. The total amount of heparin received in one hour is 1000 units.
   50 ml/hr x 20 units/ml = 1000 units/hr.

39. **Key: D**   *Client Need: Reduction of Risk Potential*

   D. The only reliable and valid test for cystic fibrosis (CF) is the sweat test by pilocarpine iontophoresis followed by the Gibson-Cooke quantification of chloride concentration.

   A. Quantitative collection of stool for fecal fat is not a definitive test for cystic fibrosis. It merely indicates malabsorption.
   B. Pulmonary function studies would aid in assessing lung function but would not diagnose cystic fibrosis.
   C. Human-leukocyte antigen is not diagnostic of cystic fibrosis.

40. **Key: D**   *Client Need: Pharmacological and Parenteral Therapies*

   D. Magnesium sulfate decreases uterine activity. It is used as a tocolytic agent because it is safer for the woman than ritodrine.

   A. Fetal lung maturity is enhanced with the administration of betamethasone, not magnesium sulfate (MgSO4). Magnesium sulfate is used to prevent seizures in patients with eclampsia.
   B. A preterm labor patient does not routinely exhibit seizures. They are associated with eclamptic patients.
   C. Urine output must be monitored for decreases in hourly output. MgSO4 will not increase urine output. Rather, the patient may have retention of urine as a sign of MgSO4 toxicity.

41. **Key: A**   **Client Need:** *Psychosocial Adaptation*

    A. A patient may be restrained who poses a threat of harm to self or others. Generally, less restrictive measures are tried initially, such as verbal intervention (talking the patient down) and chemical restraint (antianxiety or antipsychotic medication). Since this patient is not able to maintain control and pushes the attendant, restraints are indicated.

    B. Shouting curses would not warrant restraints. Redirection should be tried initially.
    C. Tearing up his chart indicates a greater loss of control than shouting curses. The patient should be watched carefully and prn medication should be given to control severe anxiety.
    D. Making obscene gestures is behavior that requires redirection and possibly chemical restraint in the form of medication, if the patient's anxiety warrants.

42. **Key: C**   **Client Need:** *Coping and Adaptation*

    C. The mental status examination, done as part of the admission interview, should be conducted by the registered nurse rather than the licensed practical nurse. Part of the mental status examination is determining if the patient is in touch with reality or is delusional and/or hallucinating.

    A. The licensed practical nurse and the registered nurse can both administer medications.
    B. The licensed practical nurse can admit the patient, take vital signs and orient the patient to the unit. The registered nurse must conduct the mental status examination.
    D. The registered nurse and the licensed practical nurse can draw a blood sample for a lithium level.

43. **Key: C**   **Client Need:** *Pharmacological and Parenteral Therapies*

    C. Propulsid is indicated for the treatment of heartburn from reflux esophagitis.

    A. Adequate calories and fluids are needed for growth and hydration. The mother should be instructed in the nutritional needs of the infant.
    B. Burping of the child should occur after every ounce of fluid is given. The mother should be instructed in the principles of feeding the infant.
    D. The head-elevated position helps to reduce episodes of reflux. The mother should be instructed in positioning techniques.

44. **Key: D**   **Client Need:** *Pharmacological and Parenteral Therapies*

    D. Adverse effects of theophylline include heart palpitations, headache, dizziness, nervousness, nausea, vomiting and epigastric pain.

    A. Weight gain is not a side effect of theophylline administration. The nausea and vomiting associated with theophylline may cause weight loss.
    B and C.
       Excessive thirst and red-orange urine are not adverse effects of theophylline.

45. **Key: D**   **Client Need:** *Pharmacological and Parenteral Therapies*

    D. Erythropoietin is a glycoprotein that stimulates red blood cell (RBC) production. It is produced in the kidneys and stimulates bone marrow production of RBCs. Epogen, a form of erythropoietin, is used to elevate the hemoglobin of patients with anemia secondary to chronic renal failure.

    A, B and C.
       There is no indication that Epogen has an effect on white blood cells or platelets.

46. **Key: C**   **Client Need: *Growth and Development***

    C. Manifestations of placenta previa include minimal to severe bright red blood from the vagina and absence of pain.

    A. Abruptio placentae is manifested by uterine tenderness or pain and dark red or absent bleeding.
    B. Pain and dark red or no vaginal bleeding also is associated with a ruptured tubal pregnancy.
    D. Molar pregnancy is a uterine growth that contains no fetus, placenta or amniotic sac. Vaginal bleeding occurs in 45% of patients. The vaginal discharge may be dark brown or bright red, either scant or profuse. It may continue for a few days, or continue intermittently for weeks.

47. **Key: C**   **Client Need: *Management of Care***

    C. Because of the prolonged onset of celiac disease, the parents' ability to cope with the situation may be severely altered.

    A. Activity intolerance would be a concern at the time of diagnosis if the child is malnourished, but it is not a long-term problem.
    B. Self-concept disturbance is not a priority in the care of the patient with celiac disease.
    D. Impaired skin integrity would cause concern at the time of diagnosis, if the child does dehydrate at the time of malnourishment. It should not be a long-term problem.

48. **Key: D**   **Client Need: *Management of Care***

    D. By law a patient has the right to appropriate treatment in the least restrictive setting. Liberty may be restricted only to the extent required by treatment needs. This patient has recovered from the acute exacerbation of his illness and has the right to be discharged.

    A. This is a false assumption on the part of the nurse. Because of the physical and psychological problems that accompany homelessness, the patient may require greater assistance.
    B. Staff should find suitable placement for the patient as he is eligible for discharge.
    C. The nurse should not assume that the patient will continue care post-discharge.

49. **Key: C**   **Client Need: *Reduction of Risk Potential***

    C. After anesthesia and surgery, patients experience a reduction in pulmonary function including a reduction in lung volume secondary to pain, anesthesia and immobility. There is also a decrease in the clearance of mucus secondary to anesthesia and narcotics.

    A, B and D.
    All of these nursing diagnoses may be applicable to the postoperative patient who has an elevated CO2 level. However, effective airway clearance should take priority.

50. **Key: D**   **Client Need: *Pharmacological and Parenteral Therapies***

    D. The patient taking Lasix should be instructed to eat a diet high in potassium since Lasix causes excretion of potassium.

    A, B and C.
    Dietary alterations for a patient taking furosemide include restriction of sodium and an increase in dietary potassium.

51. **Key: D** **Client Need:** *Reduction of Risk Potential*

    D. Capillary refill greater than two seconds indicates vascular compromise or pressure from the immobilizing device.

    A. Edema is usually present after injury or surgery and is most evident in uncasted, dependent areas. Mild edema usually does not need to be reported. Excessive edema, however, may indicate constriction of vessels from an immobilizing device and should be reported.
    B. Some pain is normal after trauma or surgery but the pain should decrease when the bone is immobilized.
    C. Plaster casts set rapidly, but take several hours to dry completely and feel cool to the touch. Promoting the circulation of warm, dry air around a damp cast can enhance moisture evaporation and speed the drying process.

52. **Key: B** **Client Need:** *Pharmacological and Parenteral Therapies*

    B. Protamine sulfate is the antidote for heparin toxicity and overdose.

    A. Narcan is a narcotic antagonist and is used to reverse respiratory depression due to narcotic overdose.
    C. AquaMEPHYTON, or vitamin K, is the antidote for Coumadin overdose.
    D. Regitine is used to treat hypertension secondary to pheochromocytoma.

53. **Key: A** **Client Need:** *Pharmacological and Parenteral Therapies*

    A. High dose corticosteroids can cause bone demineralization and impair cell division. They are decreased as soon as possible to minimize side effects such as altered body composition, growth retardation, osteoporosis and adrenal suppression.

    B. Peripheral neuropathy is not a side effect of steroid therapy.
    C. Steroids can cause muscular atrophy.
    D. High dose corticosteroids can cause hypokalemia.

54. **Key: A** **Client Need:** *Coping and Adaptation*

    A. This is the least intrusive assessment. The nurse does not have to touch the patient so the rate will be more accurate.

    B, C and D.
    All of these assessments necessitate touching the patient and possibly disturbing the patient. This will decrease the accuracy of vital signs as the three-month-old infant may fuss and cry.

55. **Key: B** **Client Need:** *Reduction of Risk Potential*

    B. With an epidural block, the woman loses the sensation of her bladder filling. The nurse should remind the woman to void every two hours, monitor her intake and output and palpate her bladder for distention.

    A. Temperature instability is not generally associated with epidural blocks.
    C. Spinal headaches occur rarely after epidural anesthesia since those headaches are caused by leakage of cerebrospinal fluid from, or the instillation of air into, the cerebrospinal space. The cerebrospinal space is not entered with this technique.
    D. Uterine hyperstimulation is not a complication of epidural anesthesia.

56. **Key: C**   Client Need: *Management of Care*

    C. Unlicensed assistive personnel can conduct selected activity groups under the guidance of professional staff.

    A. Post-ECT care requires patient assessment and should not be delegated to unlicensed assistive personnel.
    B. Monitoring a patient on suicide precautions requires in-depth assessment of the physical and psychological needs of the patient and should not be performed by unlicensed assistive personnel.
    D. The intake interview is conducted when a patient is admitted to the psychiatric unit. It includes a mental status examination that should be conducted by the professional nurse.

57. **Key: D.**   Client Need: *Psychosocial Adaptation*

    D. Confusion and memory loss are the most common side effects of electroconvulsive therapy (ECT). The memory loss and confusion increase as the number of treatments increases. The nurse should plan interventions that address appropriate safety measures.

    A. Medical complications, such as arrhythmias, laryngospasm and circulatory insufficiency are infrequent and occur in approximately one out of 1400 treatments. ECT is contraindicated for patients with severe cardiac conditions.
    B. With the use of general anesthesia and muscle relaxants during ECT, physical injury is minimized. Injury can result from the confusion that occurs post-ECT.
    C. ECT is contraindicated for patients with severe hypertension.

58. **Key: A**   Client Need: *Reduction of Risk Potential*

    A. Monitoring a patient receiving PEEP ventilation for signs of improvement would include assessment of PaO2 levels within normal limits of 75-100 mm Hg.

    B. The normal pCO2 is 38-42 mm Hg. The patient's reading is high.
    C. An oxygen saturation of 86% indicates hypoxia.
    D. A bicarbonate reading of 20 mEq/L is decreased from the normal of 24-26 mEq/L.

59. **Key: A**   Client Need: *Basic Care and Comfort*

    A. The nurse should encourage the nutritional intake of high-protein and high-caloric foods to prevent weight loss and malnutrition and to enhance immune function.

    B. The diet of the AIDS patient does not require an increase in potassium.
    C. A diet low in saturated fat is essential for patients with cardiac disease. It is not required for a patient with AIDS.
    D. The diet of the patient with AIDS does not have to be sodium-restricted. High-protein and high-caloric foods are recommended for patients with AIDS.

60. **Key: B**   Client Need: *Growth and Development*

    B. Children of this age enjoy toys that encourage motor-like activity. A push-pull toy would be appropriate.

    A. This puzzle has too many pieces for a two-year-old.
    C. A paint-by-numbers set is too complicated for a two-year-old.
    D. A hand-held electronic game is too complex for a child this age.

61. **Key: A**   Client Need: *Reduction of Risk Potential*

   A. In addition to purine restriction, the patient requires at least 3000 ml of fluid per day to discourage the formation of renal stones.

   B. Dietary restrictions include avoiding foods containing purine and alcohol. Weight control is also recommended.
   C. During acute attacks the patient is placed on bed rest.
   D. During acute attacks bed rest and joint immobilization are maintained.

62. **Key: B**   Client Need: *Physiological Adaptation*

   B. The major manifestations of ulcerative colitis are bloody diarrhea and abdominal pain.

   A, C and D.
   Abdominal distention, flank pain and esophageal reflux are not indicators of ulcerative colitis.

63. **Key: B**   Client Need: *Management of Care*

   B. Confidential information may be shared with the treatment team directly involved in the care of the patient.

   A. This purpose implies that only the physician should be told confidential information, rather than the treatment team.
   C. The nurse needs to make the patient aware of the fact that she will share information pertinent to the care of the patient with the treatment team.
   D. The nurse should not conditionally agree to keep a confidence and should inform the patient that she cannot do so. The patient can then determine if he wishes to share confidential information that the nurse may have an obligation to share with other members of the treatment team.

64. **Key: A**   Client Need: *Growth and Development*

   A. The anterior fontanel closes between 12 and 18 months. A closed anterior fontanel at two months of age would require further investigation.

   B. Strabismus is a normal finding because of the lack of binocularity in the newborn.
   C. Mongolian spots are usually noted in the sacral and gluteal regions and are seen predominantly in newborns of African, Native American, Asian and Hispanic descent.
   D. This is a normal finding. When an infant's tongue is touched or depressed, the infant responds by forcing the tongue outward. This reflex disappears by age four months.

65. **Key: C**   Client Need: *Growth and Development*

   C. Swallowing movements facilitating the ingestion of solid foods occur by four to six months of age. By this time, the oral cavity has grown and mature sucking and jaw motions have developed, indicating readiness to start solids.

   A. The Moro reflex or startle response is elicited by startling the infant with a loud noise. It does not determine when solid food should be introduced.
   B. The tonic neck reflex simulates the position assumed by someone preparing to fence. It disappears at about age six months. It does not determine the introduction of solid foods.
   D. The rooting reflex occurs when the infant's cheek is lightly stroked on the side of the mouth. It stimulates the infant to turn its head in that direction in order to find food. This reflex disappears at nine to 12 weeks of age.

66. **Key: D**   **Client Need:** *Pharmacological and Parenteral Therapies*

    D. First calculate how many milligrams of antibiotic should be given for each dose:

$$\frac{750 \text{ mg}}{24 \text{ hr}} \quad = \quad \frac{x \text{ mg}}{8 \text{ hr}}$$

$$24x \quad = \quad 6000$$

$$x \quad = \quad 250 \text{ mg/dose}$$

Now calculate the number of milliliters needed for each dose:

$$\frac{\text{Dose Desired}}{\text{Dose on Hand}} \quad X \quad \text{solution} \quad = \quad \text{number of milliliters per dose}$$

$$\frac{250 \text{ mg}}{125 \text{ mg}} \quad X \quad 5 \text{ ml} \quad = \quad \text{ml/dose}$$

$$\frac{1250}{125 \text{ mg}} \quad = \quad \text{ml per dose}$$

$$\quad = \quad 10\text{ml/dose}$$

67. **Key: A**   **Client Need:** *Reduction of Risk Potential*

    A. The patient should be instructed to use alcohol, caffeinated beverages and spicy foods in moderation to avoid overstimulation of the bladder.

B. Strenuous activities should be avoided for at least two to three weeks.

C. Dietary intervention and stool softeners are important in the postoperative period to prevent the patient from straining while moving his bowels. A diet high in fiber facilitates the passage of stool.

D. This option is not identified as part of postoperative management following a prostatectomy. It is indicated for patients with renal calculi.

68. **Key: C**   **Client Need:** *Reduction of Risk Potential*

    C. Crying uncontrollably could indicate possible neurological complications from the vaccine.

A. It is not unusual to observe behavioral changes and decreased interest in usual activities in a child after vaccination. These effects are temporary.

B. Often the child refuses to walk because of pain at the injection site. Such pain is an expected reaction.

D. A temperature of 102°F would be normal after immunization.

69. **Key: D**   **Client Need:** _Growth and Development_

    D. Allowing the infant to suck the drug that has been placed in an empty nipple or inserting the syringe or dropper into the side of the mouth, parallel to the nipple, while the infant nurses are methods of giving liquid drugs to infants. The syringe is best placed along the side of the infant's tongue and the drugs given slowly.

    A. Drugs are not added to an infant's formula feeding.
    B. The nurse should not mix drugs with high-sugar content foods, such as honey, when giving drugs to infants because of the risk of botulism.
    C. Quickly squirting a drug from a syringe to the back of the mouth can lead to aspiration.

70. **Key: A**   **Client Need:** _Growth and Development_

    A. A prolapsed umbilical cord is an indication for cesarean birth.

    B. Twin gestation is not necessarily an indication for a cesarean section.
    C. Stained amniotic fluid is to be monitored carefully along with fetal well-being, but this is not automatically an indication for cesarean section.
    D. A nonreactive, non-stress test is a concern, but a biophysical profile should be done prior to delivery to document poor fetal well-being.

71. **Key: D**   **Client Need:** _Coping and Adaptation_

    D. This response is an attempt to validate that the length of visiting hours is a group concern and not an individual issue.

    A. This response does not allow for exploration of group concerns.
    B. There is no mention that the patient is very upset.
    C. Inviting the nurse manager to explain the policy to the group shifts responsibility away from the nurse and also does not allow for exploration of group concerns.

72. **Key: A**   **Client Need:** _Psychosocial Adaptation_

    A. The patient's behavior should be carefully monitored and Ativan, an antianxiety agent, administered before the patient escalates. Pacing that becomes more rapid is a sign of increased agitation in the patient.

    B, C and D.
    Ativan should be administered before the patient's behavior becomes threatening.

73. **Key: C**   **Client Need:** _Reduction of Risk Potential_

    C. Breast conservation surgery (lumpectomy) involves the removal of the entire tumor along with a margin of normal tissue.

    A. The entire area and normal surrounding tissue will be removed, not just a portion for examination.
    B. This option describes a needle biopsy rather than a lumpectomy.
    D. Underarm lymph nodes are not removed in a lumpectomy.

74. **Key: C**   **Client Need:** *Growth and Development*

   **C. The principles of magical thinking and omnipotence affect preschoolers when a sibling
   becomes critically ill or dies. They conceive of illness as a punishment for their thoughts
   or actions. If they are in any way accused or suspected of harboring ill feelings toward the
   sibling, they may feel guilty and responsible for the sibling's death.**

   A and B.
   Anger and jealousy are not predominant feelings in a child whose sibling is ill.
   D. A four-year-old child may have experiences of guilt from past wrongs, but the child is too young
   to have remorse.

75. **Key: D**   **Client Need:** *Management of Care*

   **D. The patient with facial and neck burns is at high risk for ineffective airway clearance relat-
   ed to possible upper airway edema, secondary to inhalation of superheated air, smoke or
   noxious chemicals.**

   A, B and C.
   Immediate care of the patient following a burn involves maintaining a patent airway. In pre-hos-
   pital care the primary response of the medical team follows the ABCs of emergency
   management: A = airway, B = breathing and C = circulation. While body image, ineffective thermoregulation and fluid volume deficit are all appropriate nursing diagnoses for the patient with
   serious facial and neck burns, airway is the priority in this patient.

76. **Key: A**   **Client Need:** *Safety and Infection Control*

   **A. Glaucoma is an increase in intraocular pressure due to either excess production of aque-
   ous humor or obstruction of the drainage of aqueous humor in the eye. The goals of
   therapy are to improve drainage and decrease production of aqueous humor. Atropine sulfate causes pupillary dilation, which further obstructs the drainage of aqueous humor. The
   nurse should question this order.**

   B. Pilocarpine is a miotic agent that causes pupillary constriction and improves the drainage of
   aqueous humor.
   C. Timoptic is a beta-adrenergic blocker that decreases aqueous humor production.
   D. Diamox is a carbonic anhydrase inhibitor that decreases aqueous humor production.

77. **Key: C**   **Client Need:** *Basic Care and Comfort*

   **C. Massaging the patient's back and buttocks frequently promotes skin integrity and should
   be included in the care plan of a patient in traction.**

   A. The patient in Russell's traction is not able to turn on the side for 20 minutes.
   B. Placing pillows under the patient's sacral and scapular areas will interfere with the line of traction.
   D. Using antiseptic solutions would dry the skin, increase the chances of the skin cracking and lead
   to open areas.

78. **Key: D**   **Client Need:** *Growth and Development*

   D. After spontaneous rupture of membranes, maternal temperature and vaginal discharge are assessed every one to two hours for early identification of infection.

   A. Proteinuria is not relevant if the patient does not have pregnancy-induced hypertension (PIH), preeclampsia. It is not associated with rupture of the membranes.
   B. Dependent edema is associated with pregnancy and, in and of itself, is not worrisome.
   C. Constipation is a normal complaint of pregnancy and is not related to rupture of membranes.

79. **Key D**   **Client Need:** *Physiological Adaptation*

   D. The onset of absence seizures is abrupt and characterized by a brief loss of consciousness that appears without warning and lasts about five to 10 seconds. Absence seizures may occur up to 20 times or more daily. Slight loss of muscle tone may cause the child to drop objects, but the child is able to maintain postural control. An episode can be mistaken for inattentiveness or daydreaming, especially during a group activity.

   A. Inserting a padded tongue blade between the child's teeth is not recommended for generalized seizures because of the danger of injuring the teeth.
   B. The child experiencing an absence seizure is not at risk for respiratory problems.
   C. There is no cyanosis with this type of seizure.

80. **Key: B**   **Client Need:** *Reduction of Risk Potential*

   B. Iced liquids tend to have a soothing effect on the mucosal lining and should be encouraged.

   A and D.
   Gargling with mouthwash and drinking citrus juices will further irritate stomatitis and should be avoided.
   C. Using a toothbrush with saline to cleanse the mouth also will cause further irritation of the oral mucosa.

81. **Key: D**   **Client Need:** *Safety and Infection Control*

   D. As a general rule the cuff on a tracheostomy tube should be kept inflated to prevent dislodgment of the tube.

   A. Applying suction for less than 15 seconds is appropriate. Suctioning for longer than that amount of time may lead to hypoxia in the patient.
   B. Administering 100% oxygen is appropriate prior to suctioning.
   C. This is an appropriate pressure setting for suctioning.

82. **Key: C**   **Client Need:** *Management of Care*

   C. Regular insulin peaks in two to four hours. Since diaphoresis is a symptom of hypoglycemia, a glass of juice or skim milk should be given to the patient to raise blood sugar levels.

   A. Helping the patient to put on a dry nightgown can be done after the patient is given a carbohydrate to drink.
   B. When hypoglycemia occurs, a urine test for glucose is negative. However, a negative test does not always indicate hypoglycemia.
   D. Staying in bed until seen by a physician is not the first action to be taken and frequently is not indicated once a carbohydrate is given to correct the hypoglycemia.

83. **Key: D** Client Need: *Basic Care and Comfort*

    D. Bowel retraining is established by providing a consistent time for evacuation each day.

    A. Checking for impaction daily is not indicated and can interfere with sphincter control.
    B. Fluids should be increased to at least 3000 ml per day, unless contraindicated by cardiac or renal disease. High-fiber foods such as oat bran, fruits and vegetables should be encouraged. Milk products are not high in fiber.
    C. Using incontinent pads does not help in bowel retraining and may encourage incontinence.

84. **Key: A** Client Need: *Management of Care*

    A. Increased or decreased resistance to passive movement is a sign of abnormal muscle tone. The child with cerebral palsy may exhibit opisthotonic postures (exaggerated arching of the back) and may feel stiff on handling or dressing.

    B. Other significant signs of motor dysfunction are poor sucking and feeding difficulties with persistent tongue thrust.
    C. Head circumference measurement less than the 50th percentile is a normal finding for a three-month-old infant. The National Center for Health Statistics' growth charts use the fifth and 95th percentiles as criteria for determining which children are outside the normal limits for growth.
    D. When pulled to a sitting position, the child with cerebral palsy may extend the entire body, rigid and unbending at the hip and knee joints. This is an early sign of spasticity. Slight head lag is expected in a three-month-old infant.

85. **Key B:** Client Need: *Pharmacological and Parenteral Therapies*

    B. Lomotil inhibits gastric motility by acting on mucosal receptors responsible for peristalsis. It is used for acute nonspecific and acute exacerbation of chronic functional diarrhea.

    A. Lomotil does not affect weight unless the patient abuses the drug.
    C. Lomotil has no direct effect on daily food intake.
    D. When the patient's diarrhea improves, the dehydration should improve. Skin turgor also will improve, but this is a secondary effect of Lomotil.

86. **Key: C** Client Need: *Reduction of Risk Potential*

    C. The early signs of heart failure are tachycardia (especially during rest and slight exertion), tachypnea, profuse scalp sweating (especially in infants), fatigue, irritability, sudden weight gain and respiratory distress.

    A. Mottling due to a decrease in environmental temperature or stress is common in the newborn.
    B. Nasal discharge/congestion is commonly associated with respiratory infections in infants.
    D. Upon inspection, the infant's tongue is enlarged and may protrude. This is a normal finding. Protrusion of the tongue is often seen in children with mental retardation.

87. **Key: D** Client Need: *Reduction of Risk Potential*

    D. Positioning will help to promote venous lymphatic drainage. The affected arm is elevated to promote fluid drainage via the lymphatic and venous pathways.

    A, B and C.
    Elevation of the arm so that it is level with or above the heart, diuretics and isometric exercises may be recommended to reduce fluid volume in the arm. The patient may need to wear an elastic pressure gradient sleeve during waking hours to maintain volume reduction, but the initial action by the nurse would be elevating the arm.

88. **Key: B**   Client Need: _Growth and Development_

   B. Elastic stockings provide venous support to the legs. Therefore, the patient should elevate the legs prior to putting on the stockings to promote venous return. The stockings should be put on prior to getting out of bed.

   A. Elastic stockings are worn to prevent edema. They should be put on prior to the swelling.
   C. Cramps in the legs are due to arterial insufficiency, not venous insufficiency. The patient should be instructed to keep the stockings on.
   D. The stockings also should be removed at night when the patient goes to bed.

89. **Key: A**   Client Need: _Physiological Adaptation_

   A. Since the nose normally humidifies the air, supplemental humidification is indicated for the patient with a laryngectomy.

   B. There are no dietary restrictions for the patient with a laryngectomy.
   C. Laryngectomy tubes are not plugged.
   D. There is no risk for aspiration by the laryngectomy patient, since there is no connection between the esophagus and the respiratory tract.

90. **Key: B**   Client Need: _Growth and Development_

   B. The biophysical profile is performed as a fetal risk assessment. It can be viewed as giving the fetus a physical examination and measures fetal breathing movements, gross body movements, heart tones and amniotic fluid volume.

   A. The placenta will be visualized via ultrasound but it is not the basis for the testing.
   C. Biophysical profiles are done to assess fetal well-being. Fetal age assessments are performed using ultrasound.
   D. Fetal abnormalities can be detected in the biophysical profile but are not the basis for the testing.

91. **Key: D**   Client Need: _Pharmacological and Parenteral Therapies_

   D. Tapazole is used to decrease iodine use and inhibit the synthesis of thyroid hormones. Therefore, metabolic activity will be decreased if the treatment is effective.

   A. Tapazole does not improve vision.
   B. The patient's appetite should decrease secondary to decreased metabolic rate.
   C. The patient should have more restful sleep when the metabolic rate is decreased.

92. **Key: A**   Client Need: _Physiological Adaptation_

   A. Hypertrophy of the prostate causes urinary outflow problems. The patient experiences retention of urine with overflow that produces dribbling of urine. When the patient is catheterized for residual urine, moderate amounts of urine are obtained.

   B. There is usually no pain associated with benign prostatic hypertrophy. Pain radiating to the scrotum is found in infections such as epididymitis.
   C. Urethral excoriation is not a manifestation of hypertrophy of the prostate.
   D. Stress incontinence is involuntary urination as a result of increased pressure, such as when sneezing or coughing. It is usually related to weakness of sphincter control.

93. Key: A   Client Need: *Reduction of Risk Potential*

A. Multiple diapers can be used prior to surgery to effectively separate the child's legs and hold the legs in an abducted, externally rotated position.

B. Passive range-of-motion is not indicated. The infant's legs should be abducted using extra diapers.
C. The legs should be abducted, rather than adducted, to keep the hip in alignment.
D. The child may be placed in an upright position and does not have to remain flat in bed.

94. Key: B   Client Need: *Growth and Development*

B. From about nine years of age, children can be taught to administer their own insulin. At this age they are able to understand the principles behind administration and determine the dosage of insulin.

A. A child of six does not have the manual dexterity to administer the insulin or the ability to calculate the dosage.
C and D.
    Children can begin self-administration of insulin by age nine. They do not have to wait until ages 12 or 15.

95. Key: B   Client Need: *Growth and Development*

B. A 30-week-old fetus is in a slightly flexed position. With increasing maturity comes more flexion.

A. Quick recoil of the ears is a sign of a mature infant.
C. Soles of the feet with creases indicate a mature infant.
D. A five-millimeter breast bud is consistent with a preterm infant.

96. Key: C   Client Need: *Psychosocial Adaptation*

C. Patients with Alzheimer's disease require structure and direction to complete tasks. It is appropriate to give them step-by-step directions.

A. Since Alzheimer's disease is a type of dementia that is characterized by progressive deterioration in memory and other aspects of cognition, it is inappropriate to focus on the emotional reaction.
B. Since recent events and new information cannot be recalled, the meaning of the statement is unimportant.
D. The goal of care for patients with Alzheimer's disease is to have them maintain independence in the performance of activities of daily living for as long as possible.

97. Key: B   Client Need: *Reduction of Risk Potential*

B. Restlessness is one of the earliest symptoms of hypoxia. Poor concentration and tachycardia also are early clinical manifestations of hypoxia.

A. Pallor is a manifestation of hypoxia that occurs when PaO2 levels fall below normal.
C and D.
    Mottling of the extremities, disorientation, stupor, lethargy and depressed tensor reflexes are late signs of hypoxia.

98. **Key: A**   Client Need: *Reduction of Risk Potential*

   A. Patient education includes avoiding lymphedema and sunburn. This statement by the patient indicates the need for additional teaching.

   B. The patient should be instructed to wear protective gloves when gardening and when using strong detergents.
   C. The patient is correct in telling lab personnel not to draw blood from the right arm.
   D. The patient should observe her right arm for signs of lymphedema.

99. **Key: C**   Client Need: *Psychosocial Adaptation*

   C. Criteria for the diagnosis of posttraumatic stress disorder include acting or feeling as if the traumatic event were recurring. This phenomenon is termed "flashback."

   A, B and D.
   Aggression, substance abuse and depression are commonly seen as concurrent behaviors in posttraumatic stress disorder patients who have limited coping skills for dealing with the anxiety caused by the trauma.

100. **Key: C**   Client Need: *Physiological Adaptation*

   C. Hypoglycemia can develop with rigorous exercise. To avoid this, a child is instructed to take an additional carbohydrate exchange.

   A. It is not necessary for the child to restrict his activities to non-contact sports.
   B. Extra insulin would further decrease the blood sugar during strenuous activity.
   D. Fluids should be encouraged but the essential element in the teaching is that the child eat an extra carbohydrate exchange to counteract the hypoglycemia that can occur with strenuous exercise.

101. **Key: B**   Client Need: *Physiological Adaptation*

   B. As intracranial pressure increases, the patient becomes less alert and more difficult to rouse. This change in consciousness is one of the earliest signs of increased intracranial pressure.

   A. The patient's pulse pressure widens with increased intracranial pressure, causing a larger gap between the systolic and diastolic pressures than is seen in this patient.
   C. A patient with increased intracranial pressure may develop a positive Babinski reflex but this is not an early sign of increased intracranial pressure.
   D. Incontinency of urine does not necessarily indicate increased intracranial pressure. There are other reasons for incontinency.

102. **Key: C**   Client Need: *Reduction of Risk Potential*

   C. The diet that will prevent dumping syndrome in a patient who has had a gastrectomy is low in carbohydrate, restricted in refined sugar and moderate in amounts of protein and fat.

   A. The diet should consist of six small dry feedings rather than three large meals. Fluids should be taken in between meals.
   B. The patient should rest at least 30 minutes after each meal.
   D. Moderate amounts of protein and fat should be including in the diet, not high-fiber foods.

103. Key: A   **Client Need:** *Growth and Development*

     A. The skin covering of newborns that is whitish, cheesy and odorless is called vernix caseosa. Increased amounts are found in creases and folds of the skin.

     B. Breast nodules of the newborn are generally six millimeters in a term infant. The range is three to 10 millimeters.

     C. Lanugo, a fine downy hair, is usually present over shoulders, pinnae and the forehead in a term infant.

     D. No jaundice should be present in the first 24 hours of life. If it is present, it is considered pathologic.

104. Key: B   **Client Need:** *Psychosocial Adaptation*

     B. No single event affects all people the same way. Each victim's perception of the event is unique to the victim. Assessing the patient's perception of the event and available coping mechanisms helps the nurse and patient to plan realistic goals.

     A. While a past history of abuse may influence how the patient perceives the sexual assault, the past abuse will not be dealt with during crisis intervention. Crisis intervention addresses only the current problem(s) causing the crisis.

     C. The patient's behavior prior to the assault is not necessary to help the patient set realistic goals. Questioning implies that the victim may be responsible for the attack.

     D. Although the patient's understanding of sexually transmitted disease is part of the nursing assessment for a victim of sexual assault, it is not more important than assessing the patient's perception of the event.

105. Key: D   **Client Need:** *Psychosocial Adaptation*

     D. Minors become emancipated by pregnancy, marriage, high school graduation, living independently or military service.

     A, B and C.
     Minors living at home, in foster care or in juvenile detention are not considered emancipated.

106. Key: C   **Client Need:** *Physiological Adaptation*

     C. Vomiting usually starts in the second or third week of life and becomes forceful and projectile when pyloric stenosis is present.

     A. Loose stools are not an indication of pyloric stenosis.

     B. Hiccoughs generally do not occur with pyloric stenosis.

     D. The child's abdomen may or may not become distended, but the most significant sign of pyloric stenosis is projectile vomiting following feedings.

107. Key: B   **Client Need:** *Pharmacological and Parenteral Therapies*

     B. Effectiveness of therapy can be demonstrated by a urine output of at least 30-50 ml/hr or an increase in urine output.

     A. A decreasing level of consciousness is a classic sign of increased intracranial pressure, not an expected outcome of therapy.

     C. Change in body temperature may be noted with increased intracranial pressure due to pressure on the hypothalamus. However, it is not an expected outcome of treatment with mannitol.

     D. Change from a brisk to a sluggish pupillary response indicates increasing intracranial pressure.

108. **Key: A**   **Client Need:** *Pharmacological and Parenteral Therapies*

 A. Side effects of aminophylline administration include nervousness, restlessness and irritability.

 B. Tachycardia, not bradycardia, is a side effect of aminophylline therapy.
 C. Tinnitus is not listed as an adverse effect of aminophylline.
 D. Ecchymosis is not listed as an adverse effect of aminophylline. It may occur with use of anticoagulant drugs.

109. **Key: A**   **Client Need:** *Physiological Adaptation*

 A. Therapeutic management of chronic prostatitis may include long-term administration of antibiotics and anti-inflammatory agents, frequent prostatic massage and ejaculations, sitz baths and stool softeners.

 B. Hot, rather than cold, compresses are indicated to reduce inflammation.
 C. Usually long-term administration of antibiotics is required, and not a seven to 10-day course of treatment. However, in non-bacterial prostatitis, antibiotics are not indicated.
 D. Activities that drain the prostate, such as intercourse, masturbation and prostatic massage, are often helpful in the long-term management of prostatitis.

110. **Key: A**   **Client Need:** *Management of Care*

 A. Alteration in skin integrity is the priority nursing diagnosis. Skin excoriation can occur if the leather and plastic pads of the brace touch the child's skin. The brace can be worn over a tee shirt.

 B and C.
 Self-care deficit and impaired gas exchange are not nursing diagnoses applicable to the patient wearing a Milwaukee brace.
 D. Since the brace is worn for 23 of 24 hours in the day, the patient's sleep may be affected. However, this would not be the priority nursing diagnosis.

111. **Key: C**   **Client Need:** *Growth and Development*

 C. Heart rate > 100 = 2, lusty cry = 2, acrocyanosis = 1, minimal flexion = 1, reflex irritability = 2. Total Apgar score = 8.

 A, B and D.
 None of these scores corresponds to the assessment findings.

112. **Key: C**   **Client Need:** *Psychosocial Adaptation*

 C. Drug abuse is the maladaptive and consistent use of a drug despite social, occupational, psychological or physical problems exacerbated by the drug.

 A, B and D.
 Although any of these problems may be associated with substance abuse, interference with daily functioning defines the disorder.

113. Key: B   Client Need: *Psychosocial Adaptation*

   B. Consistency and fostering a highly structured environment can help the child to be more successful.

   A. Confining the child to the bedroom is not an appropriate action.

   C. Explaining why the behavior is disturbing will not necessarily change the behavior. A consistent and structured environment will help the child to maintain control.

   D. Consistency, rather than variety, will help the child gain greater control.

114. Key: D   Client Need: *Prevention and Early Detection of Disease*

   D. The parent should be advised that anyone can get lice. Since it is transmitted from one person to another, all family members should receive treatment.

   A. The child does not have to be contained once treatment is completed.

   B. The shampoo is a pediculocide. Head lice are not bacteria.

   C. Linens should be washed in hot water but do not have to be discarded.

115. Key: C   Client Need: *Psychosocial Adaptation*

   C. The patient with autism finds it difficult to adapt to any change. Change can exacerbate stereotypical behaviors.

   A, B and D.
   Sameness is an overwhelming need of patients with autism. The need for trust, privacy and independence are not as crucial as controlling anxiety.

116. Key: A   Client Need: *Pharmacological and Parenteral Therapies*

   A. Many patients who take phenothiazines, such as chlorpromazine, experience the side effect of photosensitivity resulting in severe sunburn. Chlorpromazine causes photosensitivity more often than any other phenothiazine. The nurse should teach the patient to wear sun block and protective clothing when he/she cannot avoid the sun.

   B. There is no contraindication for swimming, but if swimming in the sun, the patient must wear sun block and limit exposure time.

   C. Patients need to maintain a fluid intake of 2000 to 3000 milliliters per day while taking chlorpromazine. There is no contraindication to including water as a fluid.

   D. Patients taking monoamine oxidase inhibitors must avoid foods containing tyramine, such as chocolate, aged cheese and red wine.

117. Key: B   Client Need: *Physiological Adaptation*

   B. There is no specific treatment available for acute glomerulonephritis, but recovery is spontaneous and uneventful in most cases. Management consists of general supportive measures, and early recognition and treatment of complications. Children who have normal blood pressure readings and satisfactory urine output can generally be treated at home. A record of daily weight is the most useful means of assessing fluid balance.

   A. Water restriction is seldom necessary unless the output is significantly reduced.

   C. Bed rest may be recommended during the acute phase, but ambulation does not appear to have an adverse effect.

   D. Acute glomerulonephritis is a post-streptococcal complication and therefore, the patient is no longer contagious. Visitors do not have to be limited.

118. **Key: D**   Client Need: *Reduction of Risk Potential*

   D. To prevent recurrence of the infection, the patient must maintain proper nutrition and comply with the treatment regimen and follow-up care.

   A and C.
   Mycobacterium tuberculosis is transmitted via aerosolization, or the airborne route.
   B. Disseminated tuberculosis can occur and typically can be seen in the brain, liver, kidneys and bone marrow.

119. **Key: C**   Client Need: *Safety and Infection Control*

   C. During all procedures with the newborn, care must be taken to avoid heat loss. Cold stress is detrimental to the newborn. It increases the need for oxygen and can upset the acid base balance. The infant may react by increasing its respiratory rate and may become cyanotic. An axillary temperature should be taken every hour until the newborn's temperature stabilizes. Initial temperatures as low as 96.8˚F are not uncommon. By the 12th hour, the newborn's temperature should stabilize within the normal range. Good hand-washing between infants is the single most important factor in preventing infection. Cover gowns are not necessary.

   A. Infants who are at risk for infection must be monitored closely but this is not the priority nursing diagnosis in the first hour of life.
   B. Infants as of one hour of age are not routinely fed unless they have low serum glucose or are infants of a diabetic mother.
   D. Infants normally do not have an impairment of their skin integrity. This is not a priority nursing diagnosis.

120. **Key: B**   Client Need: *Pharmacological and Parenteral Therapies*

   B. Otic drops in a child older than three years are administered by pulling the pinna of the affected ear upward and back when instilling the drug.

   A. Cotton swabs should not be used in the ear canal.
   C The solution should be instilled at room temperature.
   D. The child does not have to be placed in a recumbent position following administration of eardrops.

121. **Key: A**   Client Need: *Physiological Adaptation*

   A. Nutritional counseling for weight reduction may be necessary to eliminate excessive strain on the joints of a patient with osteoarthritis.

   B. Calcium prevents osteoporosis, but not osteoarthritis.
   C. There is no indication for a high-fiber diet in osteoarthritis.
   D. While patients are encouraged to balance rest and activity, 10 hours of sleep are not necessary.

122. **Key: C**   Client Need: *Pharmacological and Parenteral Therapies*

   C. Thyroxine (Synthroid) is used as replacement therapy for absent or diminished thyroid function. Indications that the medication is producing the desired effect would include an improvement in mental processes.

   A, B and D.
   A continuation of weight gain, a slow pulse rate and a decrease in salivation indicate that the symptoms of hypothyroidism persist and the medication is not producing the desired effect.

123. Key: C. Client Need: *Growth and Development*

C. **Expected aging changes in the gerontologic patient include collagen and subcutaneous fat decrease.**

A. For the majority of healthy older adults, there is no noticeable decline in mental abilities.
B. The older adult has a decrease in body temperature due to decreased metabolic rate.
D. There is a decrease in bladder smooth muscle, elastic tissue and sphincter control.

124. Key: D Client Need: *Growth and Development*

D. **The baby should be put to breast by guiding the nipple and areolar tissue into the infant's mouth and over the tongue. Compress the breast with fingers above and thumb below the areola to permit the infant to latch on effectively.**

A. Daily washing of the breasts with water is sufficient for cleanliness.
B. Newborns need to be fed every two to three hours for a total of eight to 12 times each 24 hours for at least one month.
C. The mother will be able to tell which breast to start with next time by feeling the weight of the breast. The heaviest one has the most milk and should be used for that feeding.

125. Key: B Client Need: *Pharmacological and Parenteral Therapies*

B. **A single parenteral dose of vitamin K given soon after birth prevents hemorrhagic disorders. Vitamin K is produced in the gastrointestinal tract soon after microorganisms are introduced.**

A. Vitamin K is not related to eye prophylaxis. Erythromycin is the drug of choice to protect the eyes from infection.
C. Vitamin K does not boost the immune system.
D. Vitamin K is produced in the bowel by means of bacterial flora that are initially low in number in newborns and continue to be so in those infants being breastfed.

126. Key: C Client Need: *Physiological Adaptation*

C. **Therapeutic management of strep throat involves a 10-day course of penicillin (PCN). PCN usually produces a prompt response within 24 hours. However it should be continued for 10 days to eliminate organisms that might initiate rheumatic fever and to reduce spread of certain strains of strep to family members or contacts. Children with strep are noninfectious to others 24 hours after initiation of antibiotics, and may return to school.**

A. The patient should continue the full course of antibiotics but is non-infectious after 24 hours of treatment.
B. Pain may be managed with Tylenol, as well as with throat lozenges.
D. During the acute phase of strep throat some children may experience fatigue and discomfort, but bed rest is not required.

127. Key: A   Client Need: *Physiological Adaptation*

A. Acute laryngotracheobronchitis (LTB) is the most common type of croup experienced by children less than five years of age. Inflammation of the mucosal lining of the larynx and trachea causes narrowing of the airway. Cervical manifestations include inspiratory stridor, retractions, "barky" or "brassy" cough and hoarseness. Therapeutic management involves high humidity with cool mist, which provides symptomatic relief for most children.

B. Laryngotracheobronchitis is usually caused by viral agents. Isolation is not required.

C. Cough suppressants are not recommended since airway obstruction is due to pathologic change and irritation.

D. Controversy exists over whether dairy products increase mucus or not. Laryngotracheobronchitis is an inflammatory process not a mucous product or problem.

128. Key: C   Client Need: *Psychosocial Adaptation*

C. The most accepted theory that explains the behavior of the borderline patient is that independence by the patient as a toddler was punished by emotional abandonment by the mother or mother figure. To the borderline patient, any person encouraging independence is "bad" and the patient then mobilizes to convince others of the same, while desperately searching for someone new to whom they can cling. This action, called "splitting," causes much chaos among staff and other patients. A nursing intervention that helps prevent this situation is to channel all patient requests and problems to one nurse per shift. All staff must be aware of and follow through with this intervention for it to be effective. This forces the patient to maintain a relationship with that nurse, for at least the shift, and realize that the nurse will not abandon the patient no matter what behavior the patient exhibits.

A. The borderline personality patient constantly seeks a dependent, clinging relationship to prevent abandonment, but then sabotages this relationship when encouraged to be independent by the person with whom they've developed a relationship. Borderline patients want proof that a person will not abandon them when problems arise. The ultimatum that borderline patients give to staff members with whom they have developed a relationship is that if the staff member really cares about the patient, that person will take the side of the patient in any argument, no matter what the circumstance. This can leave the staff member in a no-win situation.

B. Care plans for any patient require input from the nurse and the patient. With a borderline patient the nurse must be firm and very clear about the behaviors that are acceptable, those that are not acceptable and the consequences for performing either type of behavior.

D. The nurse should first assess the need for psychotropic medications and then explore with the patient other ways to handle anxiety.

129. Key: D   Client Need: *Reduction of Risk Potential*

D. The primary diagnostic tests for pancreatitis are serum amylase, serum lipase and urinary amylase levels. Serum amylase is elevated in pancreatitis.

A. The red blood cell count is elevated in polycythemia.

B. Blood urine nitrogen (BUN) is elevated in renal failure, dehydration and starvation.

C. Glycosylated hemoglobin is a measurement that is useful in determining glycemic levels over time.

130. **Key: B**   **Client Need: *Reduction of Risk Potential***

 B. To relieve pain the nurse should encourage ambulation to increase the body's absorption of the gas used in the laparoscopy.

 A and C.
 These options are not identified as measures to relieve pain following laparoscopic cholecystectomy.
 D. CO_2 can irritate the phrenic nerve and diaphragm. Placing the patient in Sim's position (left side with right knee flexed) helps move the gas pocket away from the diaphragm.

131. **Key: D**   **Client Need: *Basic Care and Comfort***

 D. After stone removal, a low-fat diet should be followed for several weeks until fat digestion is normalized. Thereafter, a normal diet is usually well tolerated and should be encouraged.

 A. Citrus products are not contraindicated following cholecystectomy.
 B. Carbonated beverages are not usually a problem for a patient pre- or post-cholecystectomy.
 C. A high-fiber diet is not indicated for a patient following a cholecystectomy. No dietary restrictions are needed other than to eat nutritious meals and avoid excessive fat intake.

132. **Key: C**   **Client Need: *Management of Care***

 C. The patient with hepatitis B will need considerable rest during the acute phase of the illness. The level of physical activity allowed will be individually determined on the basis of the amount of fatigue and severity of the disease.

 A. Hepatitis B is spread by percutaneous or permucosal routes through infected blood or body fluids introduced by contaminated needles and sexual contact. There is a much lower risk of transmission through kissing and sharing of food items. Hepatitis A is transmitted by the oral-fecal route.
 B. A private room is not indicated for a patient with hepatitis B. A patient with hepatitis A should be placed in a private room if the patient is incontinent of stool and has poor personal hygiene.
 D. During the acute phase of the illness, the patient needs 3000 ml/day of fluids because of the increased fluid needs associated with febrile illness and vomiting.

133. **Key: C**   **Client Need: *Pharmacological and Parenteral Therapies***

 C. RhoGAM is given to the mother if the baby is Rh positive and the Coombs negative.

 A. Rh-negative offspring are in no danger since there is no incompatibility with the mother. Postpartally, Rho (D) immune globulin is administered to all Rh-negative, antibody (Coombs) negative mothers who give birth to Rh-positive babies. There is no danger because both the mother and baby have Rh-negative blood.
 B. There is no danger because both the mother and baby have Rh-negative blood.
 D. RhoGAM is not given to an Rh-positive baby with a positive Coombs test.

134. Key: A   **Client Need:** *Physiological Adaptation*

   A. The patient with hepatitis B should avoid alcoholic beverages because they are metabolized in the liver.

   B. The diet should be planned with the patient so it is appealing. Frequent, small meals are usually better tolerated than larger meals. Fats may need to be restricted if poorly tolerated. Intolerance to fatty foods can occur if bile obstruction is severe.

   C. There is no indication for a darkened room except to promote relaxation during the acute phase if headache is present. The use of general comfort measures, such as relaxing baths, backrubs, fresh linen on the bed and a quiet, dark environment, may help to make the patient more comfortable if the patient has headaches or arthralgia.

   D. Essentially all analgesics are metabolized in the liver and, therefore, are given only sparingly to people with liver dysfunction.

135. Key: A   **Client Need:** *Reduction of Risk Potential*

   A. The patient is instructed to report excessive bleeding and to leave the packing in place until the physician removes it, usually 24 hours later.

   B, C and D.
   A cone biopsy is done as an outpatient surgery, and involves the excision of a small portion of the cervix for pathological examination. There is no particular preparation identified for this procedure. The patient does not have to be fasting, a catheter is not inserted and douching prior to the procedure is not recommended.

136. Key: C   **Client Need:** *Management of Care*

   C. Portal-systemic encephalopathy, also called hepatic encephalopathy, is one of the major complications of cirrhosis. It results from several metabolic derangements including increased blood ammonia levels. Portal-systemic encephalopathy results in alterations in the state of consciousness, intellectual function, behavior, and personality and in neuromuscular dysfunction. Alteration in thought processes is the most appropriate diagnosis.

   A, B and D.
   These nursing diagnoses are not related to an elevated serum ammonia level.

137. Key: D   **Client Need:** *Physiological Adaptation*

   D. The symptoms of Hirschsprung disease (HD) include constipation, passage of ribbon-like, foul-smelling stools and abdominal distention. Fecal masses may be palpable and fecal impactions recur frequently.

   A. Prolapsed rectum is not associated with Hirschsprung disease. The child's stool may have mucus if chronic constipation or enterocolitis develops.

   B. A tight rectal sphincter is associated with Hirschsprung disease but stool, whether watery or formed, would not be able to pass through the sphincter.

   C. Abdominal pain secondary to obstruction occurs but is usually located in the lower abdominal area. Stool color reflects oral intake. With Hirschsprung disease the stool may contain blood if enterocolitis develops.

138. Key: A   **Client Need: *Management of Care***

    A. The nursing diagnosis that should take priority when caring for a patient undergoing chemotherapy is risk of infection. Use of chemotherapeutic agents results in leukopenia and a depressed immune system. Exposure of the patient with a compromised immune system to microorganisms may cause infections.

    B. Stress incontinence is not generally a nursing diagnosis for the patient receiving chemotherapy.

    C. Altered sexuality patterns may be a nursing diagnosis due to the breast cancer but it would not take priority over risk for infection.

    D. Impaired physical mobility is not usually associated with chemotherapy administration. Fatigue and lethargy may be seen and are related to the decrease in red blood cells caused by chemotherapeutic agents.

139. Key: C   **Client Need: *Reduction of Risk Potential***

    C. This statement indicates a need for further teaching. The child should have sensation while the cast is in place. Observations such as pain, swelling, discoloration of the exposed portions, lack of pulsation and warmth and the inability to move the exposed part are reported immediately.

    A. Sudden pain may indicate ischemia, which can occur if a cast is too tight.

    B. Skin temperature should be monitored and the toes should be warm.

    D. Items should not be placed inside the cast because the irritation will cause skin breakdown.

140. Key: D   **Client Need: *Pharmacological and Parenteral Therapies***

    D. Dystonia, characterized by spasms of the head and neck, is an extrapyramidal effect of antipsychotic medications. Commonly used drugs in the treatment of dystonia include Cogentin, Artane, Benadryl and Symmetrol.

    A, B and C.
    These drugs are not effective in the management of dystonia. Tylenol or aspirin may alleviate residual muscular pain and Vistaril can relieve the anxiety associated with experiencing extrapyramidal symptoms. Most patients do not require these drugs once the dystonia is relieved.

141. Key: C   **Client Need: *Pharmacological and Parenteral Therapies***

    C. While administering blood to a patient, the nurse should carefully observe the patient for a reaction to the transfusion. A sign of a hemolytic reaction is low back pain. Should the patient complain of low back pain while receiving a transfusion, the blood should by stopped immediately, vital signs taken and the physician notified.

    A. The physician should be notified, but stopping the transfusion is the first priority.

    B. Vital signs should be taken after the transfusion is stopped and reported to the physician.

    D. The patient's temperature is monitored for febrile reactions caused by leukocytic incompatibility. However, stopping the transfusion should be the nurse's first action.

142. Key: A   **Client Need:** *Pharmacological and Parenteral Therapies*

    A. Potassium chloride (KCL) is never administered by push or in concentrated amounts by any route. Extreme care should be taken to prevent extravasation and infiltration. At the first sign of such a complication, discontinue the infusion and immediately remove the needle or catheter.

    B, C and D.
    Adverse effects of potassium chloride include nausea, vomiting, diarrhea, abdominal distension, pain and lethargy. Hyperkalemia, mental confusion, irritability listlessness, paresthesia of extremities, muscle weakness and heaviness of limbs, difficulty in swallowing, flaccid paralysis, anuria, respiratory distress, hypotension, bradycardia, cardiac depression, arrhythmias or arrest also may occur.

143. Key: A   **Client Need:** *Basic Care and Comfort*

    A. Individuals need to be instructed on the importance of maintaining an adequate fluid intake each day, and should drink at least two liters of fluid daily.

    B, C and D.
    Patients on peritoneal dialysis should have their sodium intake restricted. They should be allowed freedom in choosing foods within limitations, eat frequent small meals and manage or prevent constipation through the use of high-fiber foods.

144. Key: A   **Client Need:** *Physiological Adaptation*

    A. Hypertension and diabetes mellitus are the most common causes of renal failure, accounting for over 60 percent of patients seen on dialysis.

    B. Alcohol abuse can lead to liver dysfunction, such as hepatitis and cirrhosis.
    C. Morbid obesity contributes to multisystem failure, however it is not the leading cause of renal failure.
    D. Bile stones cause cholecystitis rather than renal failure.

145. Key: C   **Client Need:** *Reduction of Risk Potential*

    C. Inadequate drainage and pooling of mucus in the nose can interfere with feeding. When eating solids, the child may gag on the food because of the mucus in the oral pharynx. The protruding tongue interferes with feeding, especially of solid foods.

    A. Down syndrome patients are not at high risk for problems with thermoregulation.
    B. Down syndrome patients are prone to upper respiratory infections due to decreased muscle tone that compromises respiratory expansion. In addition, the under-developed nasal bone causes a chronic problem with inadequate mucous drainage. The constant stuffy nose forces the child to breathe through the mouth, which dries the oropharyngeal membranes and increases susceptibility to upper respiratory infection.
    D. Down's syndrome patients are not prone to pathological jaundice.

146. Key: B   Client Need: *Pharmacological and Parenteral Therapies*

B. Adverse effects of atenolol include dizziness, vertigo and syncope. The nurse should caution the patient about rising to a standing position too quickly.

A. Atenolol causes bradycardia rather than tachycardia.
C and D.
    Atenolol does not cause infertility or affect the reproductive system.

147. Key: A   Client Need: *Physiological Adaptation*

A. This statement indicates a knowledge deficit. The parent needs further education about the disease. Celiac disease is a disorder of the small intestine characterized by abnormal mucosa with permanent intolerance to gluten. Symptoms usually begin between the ages of one and five years. There is usually a delay of several months between introduction of gluten-containing foods and the onset of symptoms. Treatment is aimed at eliminating wheat, barley, oats, rye and any other gluten-containing foods. Most children who comply with the diet remain healthy and symptom free.

B. Clinical manifestations of celiac disease include diarrhea, anorexia and abdominal distention. They appear when glutens are introduced into the diet. The parent's statement indicates an understanding of the treatment protocol.
C. The favorite foods of many children contain gluten, including bread, cake, cookies and crackers, pies, pasta, luncheon meats and selected candies. The nurse should advise the parent of the necessity of reading all food labels carefully. The parent is aware of this and does not have a knowledge deficit.
D. Luncheon preparation away from home is particularly difficult since bread, luncheon meats and instant soups are not allowed on the diet. The parent is aware of the need to speak with the school dietician about the child's requirements.

148. Key: C   Client Need: *Pharmacological and Parenteral Therapies*

C. Dry mouth is a common side effect of tricyclic antidepressants. Nursing measures for relief of dry mouth include frequent sips of water, frequent mouth care, offering chewing gum and sugarless candy, and applying lip balm.

A. There is no indication that tricyclic antidepressants cause gastrointestinal bleeding.
B. Urinary retention, not excessive urination, is a side effect of tricyclic antidepressants.
D. Avoidance of tyramine-rich foods is indicated for antidepressants of the monoamine oxidase inhibitor type but not the tricyclic type.

149. Key: D   Client Need: *Physiological Adaptation*

D. Interventions for the patient experiencing septic shock should focus on correcting the conditions contributing to shock and the prevention of complications. Fluid volume deficit is associated with septic shock and is controlled by increasing the rate of IV fluid delivery.

A, B and C.
    These measures are generally not included in the care plan of a patient in septic shock. The patient is usually on bed rest, and sensory stimulation does not have to be limited nor dietary protein restricted.

150. Key: D   Client Need: _Reduction of Risk Potential_

    D. Necrotizing enterocolitis (NEC) is a multifactorial disorder involving ischemic necrosis of the alimentary tract in the absence of predisposing anatomic or functional abnormalities. The manifestations range from feeding intolerance to evidence of sepsis, shock and peritonitis. The usual presentation includes abdominal distention, bilious vomiting and bloody stools.

    A. Patency of the anus is not related to NEC. However, the anus should be inspected for fissures when blood is found in the stool, to determine the etiology of the blood.
    B. The abdomen may be distended and the liver not palpable.
    C. The abdomen may not be tender, even if the child has NEC.

Rationales-Practice Exam B: Nursing, Part 2

1. **Key: D**   **Client Need:** *Management of Care*

    D. Carbon dioxide has a potent vasodilating effect and will increase cerebral blood flow and intracranial pressure. Cerebral hypoxia may result if intracranial pressure is elevated. Hyperventilation, because it decreases carbon dioxide levels, may be induced to decrease the intracranial pressure.

    A. Suctioning stimulates coughing, which creates hypoxia and the Valsalva maneuver, both of which acutely elevate intracranial pressure. If suctioning is required, it should be preceded by hyperventilation with 100% oxygen and performed quickly to minimize hypoxia. Suctioning is poorly tolerated and therefore contraindicated unless there are concurrent respiratory problems.
    B. Trendelenberg position will increase blood flow to the brain and therefore increase intracranial pressure. The head of the bed should be elevated 15-30° and supported in a midline position to facilitate venous drainage.
    C. Maintaining the airway and providing appropriate mechanical ventilation is important, but additional oxygen has no benefit and may damage lung tissue.

2. **Key: B**   **Client Need:** *Safety and Infection Control*

    B. Restraints encircle the limbs, placing the patient at risk for circulation being restricted to the distal areas of the extremities. Checking the patient's circulation every 15-30 minutes will allow the nurse to adjust the restraints before injury from decreased blood flow occurs. The nurse must document the time of the check and the degree of capillary refill.

    A. Placing the restrained patient with other patients violates the restrained patient's right to privacy. Seeing a patient in restraints is often upsetting to other patients. This may put the restrained patient at risk for injury since he is unable to defend himself due to the restraints.
    C. Stimulating activates may agitate the patient. A calm atmosphere will help to reduce agitation.
    D. Vital signs are important but do not have to be assessed every 15 minutes.

3. **Key: C**   **Client Need:** *Physiological Adaptation*

    C. Management of hypovolemic shock includes careful monitoring of fluid balance. A diminished urinary output is characteristic, thus fluid replacement therapy would adequately perfuse the kidneys and increase urine output.

    A. A central venous pressure reading of 10 mm Hg would indicate fluid overload.
    B and D.
    The desired outcome of replacement of fluid volume is increased blood pressure and increased renal perfusion.

4. **Key: A**   **Client Need:** *Pharmacological and Parenteral Therapies*

    A. Curling's ulcer occurs in burn patients and is caused by a generalized stress response. This results in a decreased production of mucus and increased gastric acid secretion. The best treatment for this is prophylactic use of antacids and H2 receptor blockers.
    B, C and D.
    H2 receptors do not enhance gas exchange, facilitate protein absorption or block prostaglandin synthesis.

5.   Key: A   Client Need: *Basic Care and Comfort*

A. The long-term goal is to have the patient return to full function in approximately three months.

B. The purpose of halo traction is immobilization. The patient does not shower; however, the vest can be opened at the sides to allow the patient's torso to be washed.

C and D.
Learning to eat and to ambulate are some of the first activities that a patient will need to master. The patient should eat a balanced diet. There are no dietary restrictions.

6.   Key: B   Client Need: *Reduction of Risk Potential*

B. The nurse should ensure that the head of the bed is elevated correctly (usually on four to six inch blocks), and that the patient does not lie down for two to three hours after eating.

A. Antacids should be taken one to three hours after meals and at bedtime.
C. The diet should be high in protein and low in fat, with small frequent meals to prevent gastric distention.
D. The patient should not lie down for two to three hours after eating.

7.   Key: A   Client Need: *Physiological Adaptation*

A. A concussion is a transient and reversible neuronal dysfunction with instantaneous loss of awareness and responsiveness caused by trauma to the head. The loss of awareness can persist for minutes to hours. The child with a concussion can be cared for and observed at home. The parents are advised to check the child every two hours and to monitor responsiveness or changes in the level of consciousness. Vomiting may be a symptom of increasing intracranial pressure and should be reported to the healthcare provider.

B. Headache is usually controlled by acetaminophen. Sedating drugs are withheld so that an accurate neurological assessment can be completed.
C. There are no dietary restrictions for the patient with a concussion.
D. Activity restriction is not advised; however, if the child's head hurts, the child may wish to rest.

8.   Key: C   Client Need: *Coping and Adaptation*

C. Relationships developed with staff on the psychiatric unit during hospitalization should be terminated when the patient is discharged. The patient, when told about an upcoming discharge, often feels a need to hold onto what has become familiar. The patient's strengths, his/her ability to cope and the fact that the patient will have an outpatient therapist should be emphasized.

A and B.
Maintaining a staff/patient relationship after a patient is discharged contributes to dependency on the part of the patient. The patient/therapist relationship after discharge should be between the patient and the outpatient counselor.
D. With this response the nurse is not setting clear limits for the patient, but rather making excuses for not giving the phone number.

9. **Key: C**   **Client Need:** *Reduction of Risk Potential*

    C. Neuroleptic Malignant Syndrome (NMS) is an emergency state caused by a reaction to antipsychotic medications. Early signs of neuroleptic malignant syndrome are stiffness, fever, sweating and tremors.

    A, B and D.
    Difficulty swallowing, unstable blood pressure and respiratory depression are late manifestations of neuroleptic malignant syndrome.

10. **Key: D**   **Client Need:** *Management of Care*

    D. Nursing diagnoses identified for the patient with inflammatory bowel disease include pain, altered nutrition: less than body requirements, diarrhea, ineffective individual coping and altered health maintenance.

    A. Social isolation is not identified as a nursing diagnosis for the patient with inflammatory bowel disease.
    B. Risk of impaired skin integrity may be a problem for a patient who has had an ileostomy for inflammatory bowel syndrome. However, it is not a priority in the care of a patient with inflammatory bowel disease.
    C. Patients with inflammatory bowel disease have diarrhea, not constipation.

11. **Key: A**   **Client Need:** *Physiological Adaptation*

    A. An ileostomy may be created as a permanent cure for ulcerative colitis or as a temporary measure while the multiple anastamoses of ileoanal reservoir surgery heal.

    B, C and D.
    An ileostomy is not created to prevent the development of colon cancer, limit the spread of the disease or reduce the loss of nutrients from the bowel.

12. **Key: A**   **Client Need:** *Management of Care*

    A. In the case of an incompetent patient, consent must be obtained from the guardian. The nurse should determine if the signature is that of the guardian and if the patient is incompetent. As a client advocate, the nurse monitors treatment planning and delivery of service for possible abuse of patient rights.

    B. If the patient is psychotic, this would not be an appropriate action. The patient may not have insight into why the guardian has signed the consent. The first action should be to verify the signature of the guardian.
    C. The treatment should not be carried out until the signature is verified and the patient is deemed incompetent to sign the consent.
    D. A third party cannot witness a signature after the fact. The signature would have to be witnessed at the time of signing.

13. **Key: C**   **Client Need:** *Physiological Adaptation*

    C. Gargling with salt water can irritate the surgical site and increase the risk of bleeding. The mother should be encouraged to provide the child with fluids at room temperature. Cool fluids are often the fluids of choice.

    A. The parents should be told that throat pain may persist for several days to over a week. The mother's comment indicates such an understanding.

    B. An ice collar may provide some relief from pain.

    D. Liquids (room temperature or cool) and a soft, bland diet are encouraged for the first week. Crisp or hard foods, such as popcorn, potato chips and dry crackers, and acidic foods, such as oranges and tomatoes, should be avoided. Seven to 10 days after surgery children may eat whatever they wish.

14. **Key: A**   **Client Need:** *Management of Care*

    A. Interventions for patients who are socially isolated include encouraging interactions with family, friends and other members of the community.

    B. Food delivery does not encourage social contact.

    C. If the patient is unable to care for himself/herself at home, enrollment in a daycare center would be considered.

    D. Referral to social services may be an option, but it would not be the first course of action.

15. **Key: B**   **Client Need:** *Reduction of Risk Potential*

    B. In this procedure the gall bladder is removed through one of four small incisions in the abdomen.

    A and C.
    In most cases the patient is able to resume normal activities and return to work in two to three days.

    D. In some cases the patient is instructed to restrict fats for four to six weeks. Otherwise, there are no special dietary instructions other than to eat nutritious, well-balanced meals and avoid excessive fat intake.

16. **Key: A**   **Client Need:** *Physiological Adaptation*

    A. In a double-barrel colostomy, the proximal stoma drains feces and the distal stoma drains mucus.

    B, C and D.
    Fecal material drains from the proximal stoma. Black, tarry stool and bright red blood from the rectum are not characteristic of a colostomy.

17. **Key: C**   **Client Need:** *Coping and Adaptation*

    C. If a patient says he/she does not want to talk, the nurse should still spend short, frequent periods of time with the patient. The nurse's response should convey to the patient that it is all right not to talk and that they can just sit quietly together.

    A. This response leaves the patient alone for too long.

    B. This response asks for insight that the patient may not have. A general rule is not to ask "why" of a patient because it may be too confronting.

    D. Patients with moderate and severe depression usually will not seek out the staff to talk.

18. **Key: A**   Client Need: *Reduction of Risk Potential*

    A. Dumping syndrome is a term used for a group of vasomotor and gastrointestinal symptoms that can occur after gastric surgery when patients begin eating. Clinical manifestations of dumping syndrome include weakness, dizziness, diaphoresis, nausea and diarrhea, thought to be caused by rapid gastric emptying. The onset of symptoms is usually three to five minutes after eating and symptoms may last for 20 to 60 minutes.

    B, C and D.
    These manifestations are not indicative of dumping syndrome.

19. **Key: C**   Client Need: *Physiological Adaptation*

    C. Before the patient is discharged from the hospital, the nurse must be certain that the individual can manage the urinary drainage and can detect any deviations from normal. The person should be able to explain the nature of the urinary diversion, the expected appearance of the stoma, the care of the stoma and pouch, and the signs and symptoms to be reported to the physician.

    A. The urinary bladder is removed and a segment of the ileum is connected to a conduit for urinary drainage. Credé's maneuver massages the bladder and would not be indicated for this patient.
    B and D.
    There is no voluntary control over the stoma. Drops of urine flow from the stoma every few seconds. Patients with continent diversions and interval pouches are taught to catheterize and irrigate the pouch.

20. **Key: D**   Client Need: *Pharmacological and Parenteral Therapies*

    D. Cyclophosphamide is a chemical irritant that can cause renal irritation and cystitis. Intake and output ratio and pattern should be monitored.

    A. Tingling in the hands and feet is not a usual side effect of treatment with cyclophosphamide.
    B. Cyclophosphamide should be stored in a tight container at room temperature.
    C. Cyclophosphamide by mouth should be administered on an empty stomach. If nausea and vomiting are severe, it can be taken with food.

21. **Key: D**   Client Need: *Growth and Development*

    D. During the first three days after delivery, vaginal discharge is usually bright red. Abnormal bleeding from lacerations usually spurts, rather than trickles. In the first hour postpartum the bleeding will be bright red or rubra. The amount of bleeding is more significant than the color at this time. The priority treatment is massage of the uterus to increase tone and decrease bleeding.

    A. A pad count is a good intervention, but the priority is to locate the cause of the bleeding.
    B. If the bladder is distended, it may interfere with the ability of the uterus to contract and, therefore, decrease bleeding.
    C. Vital signs are important but the priority must be to massage the uterus to increase muscle tone and decrease bleeding.

22. **Key: D**   **Client Need:** *Management of Care*

   D. Oncovin can cause severe constipation and paralytic ileus. A prophylactic regimen, such as increasing dietary fiber, should be started against these complications at the beginning of treatment.

   A. The patient receiving Oncovin should have adequate rest but environmental stimuli do not have to be reduced.
   B. Gum hyperplasia is seen as a side effect of Dilantin rather than Oncovin.
   C. Oncovin does not cause cardiac dysrhythmias.

23. **Key: C**   **Client Need:** *Reduction of Risk Potential*

   C. Early signs of neuroleptic malignant syndrome are stiffness, fever sweating and tremors.

   A, B and D.
   Difficulty swallowing, unstable blood pressure and respiratory depression are late signs of neuroleptic malignant syndrome.

24. **Key: B**   **Client Need:** *Reduction of Risk Potential*

   B. Because dislocation of a total hip prosthesis is a possible complication of the surgery, the patient's legs are to be kept away from the middle of the body, or abducted. To ensure that abduction is maintained and the prosthesis does not dislocate, the patient is instructed to keep an abduction pillow between the legs.

   A, C and D.
   Only abduction is used to prevent dislocation of the hip. None of the other identified positions are appropriate or should be used when caring for this patient.

25. **Key: A**   **Client Need:** *Reduction of Risk Potential*

   A. CAT scanning is non-invasive and painless, and has a high degree of sensitivity for detecting lesions.

   B. The CAT scan makes use of a narrow beam of x-ray to scan the head in successive layers. The patient is not exposed to a magnetic field.
   C. There is no requirement to lie still for an hour after the study.
   D. Drinking large amounts of water is indicated before abdominal ultrasound studies. It is not required prior to a CAT scan.

26. **Key: A**   **Client Need:** *Pharmacological and Parenteral Therapies*

   A. Gingival hyperplasia is an adverse effect of Dilantin administration.

   B. Nystagmus, diplopia and blurred vision are adverse reactions to Dilantin. Tunnel vision is not a side effect.
   C. Constipation is an adverse reaction to Dilantin. Diarrhea is not identified as a side effect.
   D. Hypotension, not hypertension, is an adverse effect of Dilantin.

27.　**Key: C**　　　　　　　　　　　　　　　　Client Need: *Physiological Adaptation*

　　C. Hodgkin's disease is a malignancy that originates in the lymphoid system. It is characterized by the painless enlargement of lymph nodes and occurs in children 15-19 years of age.

　　A, B and D.
　　All of these assessments should be performed; however, since Hodgkin's disease is suspected, the priority would be assessment of the lymph nodes.

28.　**Key: D**　　　　　　　　　　　　　　　　Client Need: *Management of Care*

　　D. A frequent complication of treatment for childhood cancer is overwhelming infection secondary to neutropenia. The normal white blood cell count for a two-year-old is 6000-17,500 cells/mm3.

　　A, B and C.
　　All of these blood count values are within normal limits for a two-year-old child.

29.　**Key: B**　　　　　　　　　　　　　　　　Client Need: *Growth and Development*

　　B. A full bladder causes the uterus to be displaced above the umbilicus and well to one side of the abdomen. It also prevents the uterus from contracting normally. Nursing interventions focus on helping the woman spontaneously empty her bladder as soon as possible and encouraging her to void.

　　A. The priority nursing action is to determine why the fundus is deviated to the right. This is most commonly associated with a full bladder. After assessment of the bladder, the nurse should check the characteristics of the lochia – amount, color and odor.
　　C. A Foley catheter is not needed unless the patient is unable to void spontaneously.
　　D. Massage is not necessary if the bladder is emptied and the fundus returns to midline.

30.　**Key: C**　　　　　　　　　　　　　　　　Client Need: *Safety and Infection Control*

　　C. Following a craniotomy a patient's fluid intake is restricted to 1500 ml/day, or approximately 63 ml/hr. The nurse should question this order.

　　A, B and D.
　　These are appropriate orders for the patient with a craniotomy. Oxygen is ordered to prevent hypoxia that can lead to cerebral edema. Decadron is used to reduce or prevent cerebral edema and elevation of the head of the bed reduces cerebral edema.

31.　**Key D**　　　　　　　　　　　　　　Client Need: *Pharmacological and Parenteral Therapies*

　　D. Pitressin is an antidiuretic used in the treatment of diabetes insipidus. It is also used to treat transient polyuria due to antidiuretic hormone (ADH) deficiency related to head injury or neurosurgery. A urine output of 45-80 cc/hr would indicate effectiveness of treatment.

　　A and B.
　　Pitressin is not used to decrease intracranial pressure or to increase the level of consciousness.
　　C. The dosage of Pitressin used to stimulate diuresis has little effect on the blood pressure.

32. **Key: D**   **Client Need:** *Physiological Adaptation*

   D. An increase in urine output with low specific gravity may herald the onset of diabetes insipidus. The urine output should be between 45 and 80 ml/hr.

   A and C.
   The expected output should be between 45 and 80 ml/hr. Since the urine output is increased, palpation of the bladder is not indicated.
   B. Fluid intake may be restricted to 1500 to 2000 ml daily.

33. **Key: A**   **Client Need:** *Physiological Adaptation*

   A. Because of the muscle weakness associated with myasthenia gravis, patients have a decreased ability to chew and swallow, which may result in choking and aspiration. Suction should be readily available at home as well as during hospitalization, and the patient and family instructed in its use.

   B and C.
   These apparati are not identified as essential to the home management of the patient with myasthenia gravis.
   D. Due to activity intolerance related to muscle weakness and fatigability, the patient may become more sedentary. If this occurs, the patient may need aids such as an alternating pressure mattress to prevent pressure ulcers. However, a suction apparatus is the priority in every patient with myasthenia gravis.

34. **Key: D**   **Client Need:** *Basic Care and Comfort*

   D. Foods allowed in the diet of a child with phenylketonuria (PKU) are fruits, vegetables, cereals and grains.

   A, B and C.
   Animal proteins, such as meat, fish, eggs and milk, and some vegetable proteins, such as legumes and nuts, contain large amounts of phenylalanine.

35. **Key: D**   **Client Need:** *Physiological Adaptation*

   D. Ménière's disease represents a quadrad, or grouping of four symptoms: fluctuating, progressive sensorineural hearing loss, tinnitus, a feeling of pressure or fullness in the ear and episodic vertigo, which may affect balance.

   A, B and C.
   Distention of the abdomen, swelling of the ankles and shortness of breath are not manifestations of Ménière's disease.

36. **Key: B**   **Client Need:** *Psychosocial Adaptation*

B. **The main elements in the lethality assessment of a suicidal patient include specificity of the plan, lethality of the means or method and the availability of the means. Use of a gun is a highly lethal method of committing suicide. Having ammunition already loaded (availability of the means) makes the risk more immediate.**

A and D.
It is important to follow up with these callers, but the priority is not as high since their comments are less specific in nature.
C. This statement is more specific as far as method, but "if things don't get better," allows time for intervention.

37. **Key: C**   **Client Need:** *Physiological Adaptation*

C. **Hearing impairment is the most common sequela of bacterial meningitis. A six-month follow-up appointment is necessary to assess for hearing loss.**

A. Isolation is required during the acute illness, usually for at least 24 hours of antibiotic therapy. The child is no longer contagious at the time of discharge.
B. There are no dietary recommendations specific to meningitis.
D. After treatment with antibiotics, fever should be resolved.

38. **Key: A**   **Client Need:** *Physiological Adaptation*

A. **Patient education for a patient with multiple sclerosis should focus on building general resistance to illness and includes avoiding fatigue, extremes of heat and cold and exposure to infections. These factors may lead to exacerbation of the illness.**

B and D.
There are no dietary restrictions for the patient with multiple sclerosis. The patient should eat nutritious and well-balanced meals.
C. The patient should achieve a good balance of exercise and rest. Vigorous exercise is not recommended but physical therapy is important to keep the patient as functionally active as possible. The goal of therapy is to relieve spasticity, increase coordination and substitute unaffected muscles for impaired ones.

39. **Key: A**   **Client Need:** *Physiological Adaptation*

A. **Elevating the extremities above heart level counteracts gravitational pull, promotes venous return and prevents venous stasis.**

B. Normal fluid intake is recommended. Dehydration in a patient with venous insufficiency can lead to clot formation.
C. Walking promotes venous return by activating the "muscle pump."
D. Scratching or vigorous rubbing can cause skin abrasions and bacterial invasion. Massaging can dislodge venous thrombi and cause emboli in other parts of the body.

40. **Key: D**   **Client Need:** *Physiological Adaptation*

    D. The patient should be assisted into the prone position every three to four hours for 20 to 30-minute periods. This is necessary to prevent hip flexion contractures.

    A. Crutch-walking is not started until stable balance is achieved. The patient begins ambulating by using the parallel bars.
    B. The patient should be encouraged to turn side to side and to assume a prone position to stretch the flexor muscles and to prevent flexion contracture of the hip. Sitting promotes flexion contractures of the hip.
    C. Elevation of the patient's stump on a pillow is controversial. This practice can promote hip or knee flexion, which leads to difficulties when the patient is ready for an artificial limb.

41. **Key: A**   **Client Need:** *Reduction of Risk Potential*

    A. Pedal pulses should be palpated as part of the full body assessment for all postpartum patients, including a 12-hour postoperative cesarean section patient.

    B. The bowel should be assessed prior to increasing the diet from clear liquids to full liquids.
    C. Patients who have had a cesarean section will not have a perineal incision.
    D. Urine specific gravity is not routinely checked in postpartum patients.

42. **Key: B**   **Client Need:** *Psychosocial Adaptation*

    B. Milieu therapy establishes a consistent, caring environment characterized by safety, structure, support, socialization and self-understanding. It provides opportunities for "corrective experiences" in social interaction and encourages the learning of methods for managing feelings.

    A. Competitive activities may provide too much stimulation for patients and cause them to "act out."
    C. Planning therapy sessions with the psychiatrist may contribute to a positive milieu, but the primary purpose of the therapy is to promote patient interaction and socialization.
    D. Overuse of containment may suppress patient initiative and give the message that the patient is neither expected nor able to control his/her behavior.

43. **Key: B**   **Client Need:** *Reduction of Risk Potential*

    B. Strabismus (cross-eyes) is a malalignment of the eye whereby one eye deviates from the point of fixation. If strabismus persists, eventually the brain suppresses the image produced by the affected eye, which may lead to a type of blindness known as amblyopia. Strabismus should be diagnosed and treated early. Seeing an eye doctor will clarify the diagnosis, determine the etiology and promote early treatment so as to reduce blindness.

    A. Photophobia may occur in children with strabismus. Sunglasses will not correct strabismus or reduce the risk of blindness.
    C. Patching of the eye is a treatment for strabismus, but the patch is applied to the stronger or unaffected eye.
    D. Antibiotics are not used to treat strabismus.

44. **Key: D**   Client Need: *Prevention and Early Detection of Disease*

   D. Adolescents tend to have inadequate diets that are especially lacking in iron and folic acid. This contributes to iron deficiency anemia.

   A. Pregnant adolescents are not at risk for glucose intolerance.
   B. A diet deficient in folic acid has been linked to neural tube defects but not fetal chromosomal abnormalities.
   C. Pregnant adolescents are not at risk for incompetent cervix.

45. **Key: C**   Client Need: *Basic Care and Comfort*

   C. Patients with major burns need a diet high in protein, calories, Vitamin B and Vitamin C for wound healing. This diet has the greatest amount of protein and vitamins.

   A. This diet contains insufficient amounts of protein as well as calories.
   B. There is no source of protein in this diet, except a small amount in the bread.
   D. This diet has less protein and vitamins than the menu in option C.

46. **Key: D**   Client Need: *Physiological Adaptation*

   D. The patient's voice and speech will be altered after surgery. Speech rehabilitation usually consists of writing, using an artificial larynx and esophageal speech.

   A and B.
   Chest percussion and ventilator management are not indicated in the home management of the patient with a laryngectomy.
   C. The patient cannot aspirate following an uncomplicated total laryngectomy because the airway and esophagus are completely separated.

47. **Key: A**   Client Need: *Physiological Adaptation*

   A. Fluctuations of five to 10 centimeters during normal breathing is common. The absence of fluctuations could mean that the tubing is obstructed, that expanded lung tissue has blocked the chest tube or that there is no more air leaking into the pleural space.

   B. The situation would not require dressing reinforcement unless there was drainage on the dressing.
   C. Chest tube drainage is not emptied. This would cause a leak in the closed system.
   D. This situation does not warrant clamping of the tube. The tube is clamped whenever air could enter the chest.

48. **Key: C**   Client Need: *Growth and Development*

   C. In the taking-hold phase of attachment, the mother focuses on the infant and explores body parts, such as fingers, toes, ears and eyes.

   A. The nurse should ascertain why the mother is reluctant to feed the baby. The mother may be anxious but not disinterested.
   B. Having difficulty finding a name does not translate into poor attachment behavior.
   D. Allowing the newborn to cry may be a cultural norm. The nurse should encourage the mother to determine why the infant is crying. In and of itself, this is not a poor attachment behavior but the nurse should observe the mother's response to the infant to determine the reason behind it.

49. Key: B Client Need: *Physiological Adaptation*

B. Any condition that reduces the volume within the vascular compartment by 15% to 25% can result in hypovolemic shock. Central Venous Pressure (CVP) is often used as a guide to overall fluid balance. The normal CVP reading is 3-8 cm of water. A CVP of 4-6 cm is within normal limits and would indicate that the treatment for hypovolemic shock has been successful.

A. A heart rate of 100 to 120 beats/min is a clinical manifestation of unresolved hypovolemic shock.
C. A capillary refill time of eight seconds is indicative of compromised circulation. A capillary refill time greater than three seconds indicates decreased blood flow.
D. A urinary output of 210 ml in eight hours also indicates decreased tissue profusion and unresolved hypovolemic shock. Normal output should be 30 ml per hour for a total of 240 ml per eight hours.

50. Key: C Client Need: *Basic Care and Comfort*

C. During the acute phase and during periods of massive edema, salt is restricted in the form of no added salt at the table and exclusion of foods with very high salt content.

A. An increase in dietary iron is not necessary.
B. Calcium increase is not indicated in the treatment of nephrotic syndrome.
D. There is no evidence that a diet high in protein alters the outcome of the disease. The presence of azotemia and renal failure is a contraindication for a high-protein intake.

51. Key: D Client Need: *Pharmacological and Parenteral Therapies*

D. Since steroids cause immunosuppression, the patient should be taught to report symptoms of infection, such as fever, sore throat or cough.

A. Steroids do not cause hair loss.
B. Steroids cause hyperglycemia. Testing for hyperglycemia should be done by fingerstick at least two times a day. Since patients have different renal thresholds for glucose, urine testing for glucose is not the most appropriate indication of hyperglycemia.
C. Patients may take cathartics, if indicated. However, diarrhea is a frequent side effect of steroids. Patients should be instructed to monitor their bowel patterns.

52. Key: A Client Need: *Pharmacological and Parenteral Therapies*

A. Detoxification and withdrawal are potentially life-threatening and require careful biophysiological monitoring. Drugs whose actions are similar to the drug of dependence are used in progressively decreasing doses to ease the symptoms of withdrawal and to prevent seizure activity. Secobarbital and phenobarbital are both barbiturates.

B. The cause of polyneuritis (Guillain-Barré syndrome) is unknown, but is thought to be a viral agent or an autoimmune reaction. It results in wide-spread inflammation and demyelination of the peripheral nervous system. Phenobarbital is not used to prevent the development of polyneuritis in the patient undergoing detoxification.
C. Phenobarbital is an anti-anxiety agent and may help the patient to accept the withdrawal of Seconal; however, the expected outcome of phenobarbital administration in a patient who is undergoing detoxification is the prevention of seizure activity.
D. Seconal may reduce the patient's anxiety during detoxification, but it will not necessarily assist the patient in becoming optimistic about remaining drug-free.

53. **Key: D**   **Client Need:** *Physiological Adaptation*

    D. Glaucoma is an increase in intraocular pressure. Patients with glaucoma see halos around lights, and experience tunnel vision and deficiencies adjusting to darkness.

    A. Conjunctivitis causes the eyes to water.
    B. Floaters are a symptom of detaching retina.
    C. Hazy vision may be the result of cataract formation.

54. **Key: B**   **Client Need:** *Pharmacological and Parenteral Therapies*

    B. The patient with a platelet count of 50,000 cu ml is prone to bleeding. Using a soft-bristled toothbrush for the child's oral hygiene will prevent irritation to the patient's gums and will decrease the likelihood of a bleeding episode.

    A. The patient on chemotherapy with a decreased platelet count is not required to maintain strict bed rest.
    C. The patient with a decreased platelet count may require a transfusion of platelets, but would not necessarily need a transfusion of red blood cells.
    D. Spicy foods may or may not irritate the gastric mucosa and are not eliminated from the child's diet. Bleeding associated with trauma (such as using a hard-bristled toothbrush for oral hygiene) is likely with a platelet count less than 60,000/cu ml.

55. **Key: A**   **Client Need:** *Physiological Adaptation*

    A. As the child responds to treatment for nephrotic syndrome, fluid retention decreases. Daily weight provides an assessment of fluid retention. Additional methods of monitoring progress include examination of the urine for specific gravity and albumin, measurement of abdominal girth, assessment of edema and monitoring vital signs.

    B. The hematocrit may be elevated but obtaining a hematocrit level every 12 hours is not necessary.
    C. Measurement of abdominal girth may assess edema but measurement every two hours is not required.
    D. Urine dipstick does not provide needed information such as albumin and specific gravity values.

56. **Key: C**   **Client Need:** *Psychosocial Adaptation*

    C. Recognition of the symptoms of mood disorders is essential for the perinatal nurse. Supervision of the mother and the family in the home is a prime concern.

    A. Only after follow-up at home by an RN and/or an early visit to an obstetrician would a psychiatric follow-up be made.
    B. Most postpartum patients do not require antidepressant medications.
    D. Social supports are essential and may help to prevent depression. They should not be discouraged.

57.　Key: A　　　　　　　　　　Client Need: *Pharmacological and Parenteral Therapies*

　　A. Librium is an anti-anxiety agent prescribed to prevent delirium tremens and to relieve the physical and psychological discomfort of withdrawal.

　　B. Ducalox is used to treat constipation and is not the drug of choice for alcohol withdrawal.
　　C. Tylenol is an analgesic and antipyretic and is not the drug of choice for alcohol withdrawal.
　　D. Compazine is widely used to treat nausea and vomiting rather than withdrawal.

58.　Key: C　　　　　　　　　　Client Need: *Physiological Adaptation*

　　C. An atrial septal defect is an abnormal opening between the atria of the heart. It allows blood from the higher-pressure left atrium to flow into the lower-pressure right atrium. Symptoms appear when the child's energy expenditure exceeds the heart's ability to supply oxygenated blood to the tissues. The onset of symptoms may be gradual and the child may curtail activity and experience exercise intolerance. The baby with an atrial septal defect may need to rest while feeding more so than other infants.

　　A. Deliberately attempting to prevent crying should be avoided because it may develop a maladaptive parental pattern of relating to the infant.
　　B. Open repair of an atrial septal defect with cardiopulmonary bypass is usually performed before the child reaches school age. Immediate heart surgery is usually not required.
　　D. Growth and development are usually not affected by an atrial septal defect.

59.　Key: B　　　　　　　　　　Client Need: *Psychosocial Adaptation*

　　B. To increase involvement in group activities, the therapist should be active and supportive. The therapist should create a safe environment, provide direction and model appropriate behavior.

　　A. This response is direct but does not provide support or model behavior.
　　C and D.
　　　Both responses inappropriately include threats to the patient.

60.　Key: B　　　　　　　　　　Client Need: *Reduction of Risk Potential*

　　B. Thrombophlebitis is the formation of a clot with inflammation of a vein. Clinical manifestations are tenderness, redness and warmth. Edema may or may not occur.

　　A. Pallor and edema usually indicate infiltration of an intravenous infusion.
　　C. Mottling and coolness are indicative of poor circulation to a site.
　　D. Leakage of fluid and numbness are manifestations of an infiltrated intravenous infusion. Infiltration causes extravasation and compression.

61.　Key: B　　　　　　　　　　Client Need: *Reduction of Risk Potential*

　　B. Patients in traction should be assessed for nerve and circulatory disturbances. To check for capillary filling times, the patient's nail beds are compressed to produce blanching and assessed for return of color.

　　A. There is no indication that ankle clonus is found in patients with skeletal traction.
　　C. The femoral arteries are proximal to the traction and would not provide information about circulatory disturbances resulting from the traction. Distal pulses should be assessed.
　　D. To check for nerve disturbances, the functioning of the peroneal nerve should be assessed, not the patellar reflex.

62. **Key: B**   Client Need: *Physiological Adaptation*

B. Initial manifestations of a nephrotic reaction in acute glomerulonephritis include periorbital edema, anorexia and dark-colored urine.

A. Common manifestations of acute glomerulonephritis include oliguria, edema, hypertension and circulatory congestion.
C. Fluid loss through diaphoresis does not occur in glomerulonephritis.
D. Jugular vein distention is associated with the later stages of congestive heart failure in adults. It is rarely seen in children.

63. **Key: C**   Client Need: *Physiological Adaptation*

C. The patient with human immunodeficiency virus (HIV) with a nursing diagnosis of altered nutrition: less than body requirements should be monitored daily for signs of improved nutrition. This includes increased weight, muscle strength and energy levels.

A. The patient with altered nutrition: less than body requirements should be provided with high-calorie, high-protein foods six times a day. Raw fruits and vegetables are not considered high-calorie, high-protein foods.
B. The amount of oral fluids for a patient with a nursing diagnosis of altered nutrition: less than body requirements should not be reduced or limited.
D. Increasing the patient's activity level is not appropriate at this time. The patient should be assisted in planning periods of rest and should be instructed to use various assistive devices, such as wheelchairs, as needed.

64. **Key: B**   Client Need: *Growth and Development*

B. Cesarean birth is preferred because it is thought that the virus may be less likely to be transmitted to the infant through this route than through the vaginal route.

A. No antibiotics are needed as a result of the patient's HIV status.
C. External monitoring is preferred to internal monitoring.
D. Epidural anesthesia is not contraindicated for this patient.

65. **Key: C**   Client Need: *Reduction of Risk Potential*

C. Transient ischemic attacks (TIAs) most often precede cerebral thrombosis. At least one-third of the patients who have transient ischemic attacks will have a cerebrovascular accident (CVA) within two to five years.

A. Localized hypoxia can occur as the result of the cerebral artery vessel constriction associated with migraine headaches. However, the patient most at risk for developing a cerebrovascular accident is the patient who has a history of transient ischemic attacks.
B. The patient with myocardial infarction is at risk for developing a cerebrovascular accident because of the possibility of emboli or thrombosis in the heart. However, the patient most at risk for developing a cerebrovascular accident is the patient with the history of transient ischemic attacks.
D. Patients with adult-onset diabetes mellitus develop macrovascular changes from atherosclerosis that can lead to cerebrovascular accidents. However, the person at greatest risk for developing the cerebrovascular accident is the patient with transient ischemic attacks.

66. **Key: D**   Client Need: *Reduction of Risk Potential*

    D. Nausea, vomiting and cravings typical of early pregnancy result in dietary fluctuations, which influence maternal glucose levels and necessitate reduction in insulin dosage.

    A. Urinary frequency is a common complaint for women in early pregnancy. The woman should be alerted to the signs and symptoms of a urinary tract infection because of her diabetes.
    B. Breast enlargement and soreness are common complaints in the first trimester but are not specific to diabetic patients.
    C. The presence of human chorionic gonadotropin in the urine is the basis for urine pregnancy tests. The test is positive for 98% of women seven days after implantation.

67. **Key: C**   Client Need: *Growth and Development*

    C. Fetal lung maturity can be assessed utilizing an amniotic fluid sample. The lecithin/sphingomyelin ratio detects the presence of pulmonary surfactant and thus the ability of the lungs to function after birth.

    A. Fetal muscle mass is not related to the components of amniotic fluid.
    B. Maturity of fetal kidneys can be evaluated by an amniotic fluid sample containing creatinine. If the level of creatinine is 2 mg/dl or greater, the fetal kidneys are thought to be at least 36 weeks of age.
    D. The fetal-placental unit is thought to be functioning well if fetal ultrasounds are within normal limits and the biophysical profile indicates fetal well-being.

68. **Key: A**   Client Need: *Growth and Development*

    A. The patient should be instructed to take short breaths to avoid the urge to push because her cervix is not fully dilated.

    B. Pushing prior to complete dilation may result in a cervical tear and places the mother at risk of hemorrhage.
    C. Pushing is not acceptable without a fully-dilated cervix.
    D. Pressure should not be applied to the patient's back. The patient should be monitored and have a vaginal examination to assess for progress in the first stage of labor.

69. **Key: A**   Client Need: *Growth and Development*

    A. The patient should be instructed to choose an alternative method of contraception until she returns for her six-week, postpartum check-up. At that time her physician will refit her for a new diaphragm.

    B. The diaphragm should be washed with soap and water and dried prior to returning it to its case. It should be stored in a cool place. The woman's understanding is correct.
    C. Spermicidal jellies or creams help prevent sexually transmitted diseases as well as pregnancy. The woman's understanding is correct.
    D. The diaphragm must be left in place for six to eight hours after intercourse. The woman has a correct understanding.

70. **Key: B.**   **Client Need:** *Growth and Development*

    B. The infant's position must be changed every few hours to allow for exposure of the body surface to the phototherapy lights. Eyes and genitalia are protected while under phototherapy.

    A. There is no need to check urine glucose levels in hyperbilirubinemia.
    C. If the infant's position is rotated, there should be no reason for dependent edema to occur.
    D. Emollients should not be used while the infant is under phototherapy because emollients absorb heat and may cause the infant to be burned.

71. **Key: B**   **Client Need:** *Management of Care*

    B. The registered nurse should know the level of skill required to care for a patient so that the nurse can assign appropriate staff who can best meet the patient's needs.

    A. Patient assessment is only one aspect of patient care. The registered nurse assigning staff should have an understanding of the overall capabilities of each staff member so that the nurse can match the staff member's skills to the level of care required for the patient.
    C. The assistant's response to observation should not enter into delegation of care.
    D. While the ability to communicate with other health team members is important in the care of the patient, the level of skill needed for patient care is the most crucial determinant of delegation.

72. **Key: D**   **Client Need:** *Growth and Development*

    D. Crowning occurs when the top of the fetal head can be seen at the vaginal orifice. Since it is the stage of birth immediately before expulsion of the fetus, the woman should be prepared for delivery.

    A. The woman may want to assume a variety of positions.
    B. The nurse should monitor the woman during the bearing down or pushing episodes to make sure that she does not hold her breath for more than five seconds. Prolonged breath-holding may cause a Valsalva maneuver, which causes decreased perfusion across the placenta.
    C. A strong expiratory grunt, which is an involuntary reflex response, may accompany pushing.

73. **Key: A**   **Client Need:** *Growth and Development*

    A. Kegel exercises are performed to strengthen the pelvic-vaginal muscles to control stress incontinence.

    B. Kegel exercises will not promote involution, the return of the reproductive organs to the pre-pregnancy state.
    C. Ligaments will return to pre-pregnant status over the course of the postpartum period.
    D. Kegel exercises will not prevent urinary tract infections.

74. **Key: C**   **Client Need:** *Physiological Adaptation*

    C. Acute glomerulonephritis is the most common of the non-infectious renal diseases in childhood and is the result of a previous streptococcal infection.

    A. Otitis media is often caused by a strain of bacteria not associated with acute glomerulonephritis.
    B. Gastroenteritis typically has a viral etiology.
    D. Viral pneumonia has a viral rather than bacterial etiology.

75. **Key: A**   Client Need: *Physiological Adaptation*

    A. Foods that decrease lower esophageal sphincter pressure, such as chocolate, peppermint, coffee and tea, should be avoided because they cause reflux.

    B. The patient should eat small, frequent meals to prevent over-distention of the stomach.

    C. Milk products should be avoided, especially at bedtime, because milk increases gastric acid secretion.

    D. Antacids are used to relieve heartburn. They should be taken one to three hours after meals and at bedtime.

76. **Key: D**   Client Need: *Physiological Adaptation*

    D. Transient periods of neurological deficit occur in ischemic cerebral attacks. The symptoms vary and may include temporary forgetfulness and weakness.

    A. Throbbing frontal headaches are not identified as a problem in transient ischemic attacks.

    B. Fatigue is a symptom of many different conditions. It may be attributed to lack of oxygen; however, fatigue is not the major manifestation of ischemic cerebral attacks.

    C. Irritability may be a symptom of basic tumors and other cerebral conditions.

77. **Key: C**   Client Need: *Psychosocial Adaptation*

    C. The manic patient who has been monopolizing time will show that setting limits on this behavior has been effective by allowing other patients in the group to have an opportunity to speak. Raising a hand before speaking indicates that the patient is able to control his/her impulses.

    A. Arriving on time for the group does indicate that the manic patient is achieving control of impulses. However, this patient has been monopolizing group time and not constantly speaking shows that the patient has benefited from the limit-setting therapy.

    B. Dressing appropriately also shows improvement in a manic patient's behavior; however, the limit-setting was specifically related to monopolizing group time, thus, raising a hand before speaking would show that the intervention has been effective.

    D. Remaining seated throughout the session also indicates improved impulse control; however, the intervention was geared toward decreasing the amount of time the manic patient spent talking during group therapy. Raising a hand before speaking is the better indicator that the limit setting has been effective.

78. **Key: B**   Client Need: *Physiological Adaptation*

    B. Restlessness is one of the earliest symptoms of hypoxia. Poor concentration and tachycardia also are early clinical manifestations of hypoxia.

    A. Pallor is a manifestation of hypoxia that occurs when PaO2 levels fall below normal.

    C and D.
       Mottling of the extremities, disorientation, stupor, lethargy and depressed reflexes are late signs of hypoxia.

79. Key: A   **Client Need:** *Psychosocial Adaptation*

    A. An expected outcome of teaching is that the patient will set realistic goals. It is easier to cope with being cocaine-free on a daily basis as opposed to never using the drug again.

    B. This is an unrealistic goal for the patient and does not focus on the patient's coping skills.
    C. This is an inappropriate coping strategy that does not encourage the patient to address his/her addiction.
    D. This method of coping substitutes one addiction for another.

80. Key: A   **Client Need:** *Coping and Adaptation*

    A. The goal of systematic desensitization is that the original anxiety-producing stimulus will no longer produce the effect and the patient can engage in the activity. The process includes increasing exposure to elements of the anxiety-producing stimulus in steps, e.g., the patient starts by looking at pictures of airplanes and progresses to visiting an airport, boarding a plane, and sitting in the seat of the plane. This is done until each step of the process does not induce anxiety. The final outcome would be the ability to tolerate a trip in an airplane.

    B. The patient may gain insight during the process of desensitization, but the anticipated outcome is that the patient will be able to tolerate flying.
    C and D.
    These are not favorable responses to systematic desensitization. The goal is that the patient will be able to fly in an airplane without experiencing excessive anxiety.

81. Key: C   **Client Need:** *Reduction of Risk Potential*

    C. Nothing should constrict the arm in which the arteriovenous fistula is located. This includes occlusion by blood pressure cuffs, jewelry or tight-fitting sleeves.

    A, B and D.
    Wearing a sleeveless shirt, keeping a dry dressing on the arm and taking a shower are acceptable actions by the patient.

82. Key: A   **Client Need:** *Reduction of Risk Potential*

    A. Following a hip replacement, the patient's affected hip should be placed in extension, with an abduction wedge between his legs.

    B. The affected hip should be placed in extension.
    C. The pillow should be between the legs to prevent adduction.
    D. A trochanter roll is used to prevent extreme rotation.

83. Key: B   **Client Need:** *Reduction of Risk Potential*

    B. Following a bronchoscopy, the patient should remain NPO until the gag reflex returns.

    A. A fiberoptic scope is inserted through the nose and threaded down the airway to visualize the bronchi.
    C. Once the procedure is completed, the patient should not have any problem with deep breathing.
    D. Dye is not used during the procedure.

84. **Key: D**   **Client Need:** *Pharmacological and Parenteral Therapies*

   D. The normal lithium level is 0.5 –1.5 mEq/L. A level between 1.5 and 2 mEq/L. indicates lithium toxicity. The medication should be withheld, the physician notified, serum levels drawn and the dose re-evaluated.

   A. Lithium should not be given with an antacid because the antacid will block absorption of the lithium. The patient's lithium should be held until the dosage is re-evaluated.
   B. The next dose of lithium should not be given until the dose is re-evaluated.
   C. The patient's lithium blood level indicates toxicity. The dosage should be decreased rather than increased.

85. **Key: C.**   **Client Need:** *Reduction of Risk Potential*

   C. Iodine contrast dye is sometimes used in computed tomography (CT). A rash may indicate an allergy to the dye. Patient preparation prior to a CT scan should include questioning the patient regarding allergies (e.g., iodine and seafood).

   A, B and D.
   Malignant hypothermia, diaphragmatic irritability and generalized edema are not common side effects of computerized tomography with contrast media.

86. **Key: D**   **Client Need:** *Coping and Adaptation*

   D. The nurse should assess the patient to determine the cause and extent of the patient's confusion and behavior before intervening.

   A. Restraining the patient frequently increases confusion and agitation.
   B. Medication may be needed, but an assessment of the patient should be carried out first. Medication should be used as a last resort.
   C. Nursing assessment and intervention to decrease confusion and agitation should be instituted prior to notifying the physician.

87. **Key: D**   **Client Need:** *Reduction of Risk Potential*

   D. Ventricular dysrhythmias are life threatening. The nurse needs to intervene quickly since ventricular dysrhythmias, if left untreated, lead to cardiac arrest.

   A. Moderate levels of anxiety in a patient with a myocardial infarction need to be addressed and treated. Production of epinephrine and norepinephrine make the myocardium more irritable.
   B. Bibasilar rales indicate congestive heart failure. They need to be treated because congestive heart failure puts an added strain on the heart.
   C. Chest pain in a patient who has had a recent myocardial infarction needs to be investigated. It could indicate that the patient's infarction is extending. However, treating ventricular dysrhythmias takes the higher priority since they are life threatening.

88. **Key: D**   **Client Need:** *Physiological Adaptation*

   D. An emergency plan must be made prior to discharge. Utility companies must be notified to ensure priority repair in the event of a power failure.

   A. The homecare company will provide instruction on equipment usage and will be able to provide necessary supplies and service.
   B. The community home care nurse should be available when the child is discharged.
   C. Preparing the family to care for the child with a tracheostomy at home is multi-faceted. The family must be able to demonstrate tracheostomy care before the child is discharged from the hospital.

89. **Key: D**   **Client Need:** *Safety and Infection Control*

    D. Infant car restraints are designed as infant-only models or as convertible infant-toddler seats. Either restraint is a semi-reclined seat that faces the rear of the car. The parents should be instructed to change the placement of the infant before leaving.

    A. The nurse should not allow the family to leave until the infant car seat is placed in the proper position.

    B. Placement should be based on infant safety rather than parent preference.

    C. The nurse should have the parents change the position of the car seat before leaving the hospital.

90. **Key: A**   **Client Need:** *Growth and Development*

    A. Colace will soften stool and decrease the pain associated with movement of hard stool. It also may decrease the mother's fears of passing the first stool after experiencing a lacerated perineum.

    B. Intramuscular pain medications are not routinely given. Narcotics will be constipating.

    C. Enemas may not be necessary. The stool softener is the first choice of therapy.

    D. Prenatal vitamins contain iron, which may be constipating.

91. **Key: A.**   **Client Need:** *Psychosocial Adaptation*

    A. The patient's response to this question will demonstrate her ability to problem-solve, her impulse control and her coping strategies. It would provide the most information on readiness for discharge.

    B. The wording of this question does not encourage the patient to elaborate. It requires only a "yes" or "no" response.

    C. The patient's response will show her level of insight as to the cause of her admission but will not demonstrate her ability to problem solve or handle stress.

    D. The question requires a "yes" or "no" response and does not provide information on readiness for discharge.

92. **Key: B**   **Client Need:** *Psychosocial Adaptation*

    B. The well-being of the woman must be addressed in case of future abuse. Safety issues take precedence in the treatment plan of an abused individual.

    A. The woman should explore the relationship with her own parents and developmental issues that may be related to abuse, but this does not take priority over her safety.

    C. The woman needs to develop awareness that she is not responsible for the abusive episodes.

    D. The woman should learn conflict-resolution skills and new coping behavior. However, addressing personal safety issues is the priority.

93. **Key: D**   **Client Need:** *Psychosocial Adaptation*

   D. A comment such as "I don't deserve to live" may be indicative of suicidal thoughts. It should be addressed directly and take priority.

   A. Listening to the patient is an important aspect of the nurse-patient relationship. However, when a statement by the patient indicates the possibility of suicidal behavior, that statement must be addressed as a priority.
   B. Direct questioning should be used when a patient indicates the possibility of suicidal behavior. The nurse needs to know if the patient intends to harm himself/herself.
   C. "You sound depressed" is an open-ended response by the nurse and a therapeutic communication technique. However, when the potential for suicidal behavior is explored, it must be explored using direct questioning.

94. **Key: D**   **Client Need:** *Psychosocial Adaptation*

   D. Acknowledging the person's fear will indicate acceptance of the patient, but will not feed into the patient's delusional system.

   A. Explaining that the fear is not reasonable is inappropriate since the fear is very real to the patient. This option may encourage the patient to further elaborate on his delusion in an effort to convince the nurse that someone is trying to poison him.
   B. The admission interview should not be delayed until the person is medicated since medication may disguise or diminish admission symptoms.
   C. Helping the patient to identify the alleged poisoner indicates that the nurse believes that someone is trying to poison the patient, and is inappropriate. This type of statement feeds into the patient's delusion.

95. **Key: B.**   **Client Need:** *Physiological Adaptation*

   B. Typically, the first symptom seen at the onset of emphysema is dyspnea on exertion, which progresses to continual dyspnea. Sputum production tends to be scant or absent. The impaired gas exchange leads to decreased oxygen saturation and increasing inability to carry out activities of daily living. Thus, the patient will experience activity intolerance.

   A, C and D.
   Ineffective thermoregulation, chronic pain and non-compliance are not related to impaired gas exchange, dyspnea and a non-productive cough.

96. **Key: B.**   **Client Need:** *Pharmacological and Parenteral Therapies*

   B. There is an increased incidence of seizures in patients taking Clozaril. Clozaril is indicated only in the management of severely ill, schizophrenic patients failing to improve on other drugs.

   A and C.
   Both Prolixin and Clozaril cause extrapyramidal side effects, but the incidence is lower with Clozaril.
   D. Patients taking Clozaril should be monitored weekly for decreases in white blood cells. A major side effect of treatment with Clozaril is agranulocytosis.

97. Key: D.   **Client Need:** *Physiological Adaptation*

    D. The quantitative sweat chloride test is used to make a diagnosis of cystic fibrosis. Normally, sweat chloride content is less than 40 mEq/L. A chloride concentration greater than 60 mEq/L is diagnostic of cystic fibrosis.

    A. Reduced serum calcium is characteristic of advanced renal insufficiency, hypoparathyroidism and inadequate dietary intake of calcium and/or vitamin D.

    B. Reduced hemoglobin is characteristic of anemias and renal failure.

    C. Elevated serum amylase is seen in pancreatitis.

98. Key: A.   **Client Need:** *Pharmacological and Parenteral Therapies*

    A. A side effect of treatment with antipsychotic medications is akathisia, the inability to sit still. The motor restlessness is extremely unpleasant and intolerable for the patient. Re-evaluation of medication type and dosage may need to occur.

    B, C and D.
    If the patient's restlessness is the result of the psychotic disorder, these responses may be true. The behavior first needs to be assessed to determine if it is a symptom of the illness or a side effect of the medication.

99. Key: B   **Client Need:** *Coping and Adaptation*

    C. Having the parent clarify the meaning of the statement allows the parent to elaborate not only on his/her feelings, but also the underlying issues related to the parent feeling at fault.

    A. Reassuring the parent that no one is at fault does not allow for further discussion of the issue.

    B. Referring the parent for genetic counseling may be appropriate, but it is not the best initial action.

    D. Acknowledging the validity of the parent's statement is inappropriate since it allows blame to be placed on the parent.

100. Key: A.   **Client Need:** *Safety and Infection Control*

    A. Houses built before 1960 in the United States were often painted with lead paint.

    B. Ingestion of a daily vitamin that contains iron does not cause lead poisoning.

    C. Well water does not pass through pipes and, therefore, would not be a potential source of lead.

    D. If glue is used in the building of model cars, the child may be exposed to fumes from the glue. However, this does not put the child at risk for developing lead poisoning.

101. Key: B   **Client Need:** *Reduction of Risk Potential*

    B. An early neuromuscular sign of shock is anxiety and restlessness.

    A. A decrease in blood pressure and postural hypotension are early manifestations of shock.

    C. An early manifestation of shock is decreased urinary output, rather than oliguria.

    D. Early manifestations of shock include increased respiratory rate and shallow respirations.

102. Key: A   Client Need: _Reduction of Risk Potential_

    A. Patients with adult respiratory distress syndrome (ARDS) usually require endotracheal intubation, and mechanical ventilation with positive end-expiratory pressure and continuous positive airway pressure.

    B and C.
    Incentive spirometry and chest tube insertion are not indicated in the management of ARDS.
    D. A ventilation-perfusion scan visualizes the distribution of pulmonary blood flow and confirms the diagnoses of pulmonary emboli, pneumonia, tumor and fibrosis.

103. Key: A   Client Need: _Growth and Development_

    A. Severe preeclampsia becomes eclampsia when grand mal seizures or coma occurs. Warning signs of impending eclampsia are amnesia, epigastric pain and hyperreflexia.

    B, C and D.
    A diastolic blood pressure of 90 mm Hg or more, proteinuria of 3+ and a rise in systolic blood pressure of 30 mm Hg or more are characteristic of preeclampsia, rather than eclampsia.

104. Key: D   Client Need: _Physiological Adaptation_

    D. Scoliosis is a complex spinal deformity that includes curvature of the spine. It can be congenital but more commonly develops during the growth spurt of early adolescence. To maintain proper body alignment after surgery, the patient should avoid twisting movements that can cause indwelling instruments to twist the spine. Log-rolling is preferred when moving the child.

    A and B.
    Use of a trapeze and reaching and twisting movements can cause the indwelling instruments to twist the spine.
    C. Trendelenburg position is not recommended and may increase swelling at the surgical site.

105. Key: A   Client Need: _Reduction of Risk Potential_

    A. Following a lumbar laminectomy, the patient should wear anti-embolism stockings or another anti-embolism device to prevent deep vein thrombosis.

    B. Pain and a flat position in bed make urination difficult. Urinary retention, not frequency, usually occurs.
    C. Intermittent claudication occurs in peripheral vascular disease, rather than as a postoperative complication of surgery.
    D. Flank pain is characteristic of renal disease.

106. **Key: B**   Client Need: *Pharmacological and Parenteral Therapies*

B. Adverse reactions to aspirin include tinnitus, hearing loss, dyspepsia, heartburn, anemia and hemolysis. Aspirin has been the primary therapy for both its anti-inflammatory and anti-platelet effect. In the early phase of treatment, there is believed to be an impaired absorption of aspirin. As the course of the disease progresses into the subacute phase, the aspirin dose can be reduced because there is improved absorption, and therefore higher serum levels. Aspirin levels must be monitored to ensure that appropriate therapeutic levels are achieved to accomplish the anti-platelet purpose without producing toxicity.

A. The patient's temperature returns to normal in the subacute phase of Kawasaki disease.
C. In the subacute phase of Kawasaki disease, aspirin is continued for its anti-platelet activity.
D. Desquamation is a symptom of Kawasaki disease and does not indicate the need for modification of drug therapy.

107. **Key: A**   Client Need: *Reduction of Risk Potential*

A. A keto-diastix reagent strip with a positive sugar reaction is indicative of the presence of cerebrospinal fluid (CSF). A negative sugar reaction should occur in the sole presence of nasal mucus.

B, C and D.
Blood, albumin and bicarbonate found in the nasal mucus are not absolute indicators of the presence of CSF.

108. **Key: A**   Client Need: *Physiological Adaptation*

A. Patients with Parkinson's disease experience muscle rigidity and a mask-like facial expression.

B. The patient with Parkinson's disease has tremors that involve the hand, diaphragm, tongue, lips and jaw. They are more prominent at rest and are aggravated by emotional stress.
C and D.
Nystagmus and long-term memory loss are not identified as manifestations of Parkinson's disease.

109. **Key: B**   Client Need: *Management of Care*

B. Nausea is a symptom of impending myocardial infarction (MI) and should be assessed immediately so that treatment can be instituted and further damage to the heart avoided.

A. A patient who is five hours postoperative should be assessed for pain, but this would not take priority over assessing the patient with a possible myocardial infarction.
C. The patient's intravenous (IV) should be assessed and restored, but this action would not be the priority.
D. The patient whose dressing is saturated with serosanguinous drainage should be assessed after the patient with nausea is evaluated by the nurse.

110. **Key: A**   Client Need: *Growth and Development*

A. Rapid uterine growth is associated with a twin gestation.

B. The mother should not experience a low hematocrit due to the twin gestation. The mother's diet may need iron supplements because of the difficulty in getting adequate amounts through dietary intake.
C. Decreased amniotic fluid is not associated with twin gestation.
D. Urinary frequency is a problem for the mother during the first and third trimesters but is not caused by the twin gestation.

CGFNS

Qualifying Exam Practice Exam C

Practice Exam C: Nursing, Part 1

You will have two hours and 30 minutes to complete Nursing, Part 1.

1. A child is to receive 15 ml of an antibiotic solution intravenously during a 20-minute period. The intravenous apparatus delivers 60 drops/ml. To administer the medication within the prescribed time period, the child should receive how many drops per minute?

   A. 15
   B. 30
   C. 45
   D. 60

2. Following a thyroidectomy, the nurse should include which of the following measures in the patient's care plan to detect possible laryngeal nerve damage?

   A. Asking the patient to speak
   B. Stimulating the patient's gag reflex
   C. Determining the patient's ability to swallow
   D. Telling the patient to extend his tongue

3. Following an automobile accident, a young woman is admitted to the hospital with head injuries. To determine if the patient's condition is deteriorating, the nurse should assess her for the

   A. escalation of her discomfort.
   B. quality of her respirations.
   C. narrowing of her pulse pressure.
   D. rapidity of her heart rate.

4. For the first two days following thoracic surgery, a patient received meperidine (Demerol) hydrochloride every three hours. On the third day, three hours after receiving the Demerol, the patient refuses to cough because of pain in the operative area and feeling nervous. The patient's respirations are shallow. Based on the above data, which of the following actions should the nurse take?

   A. Delay giving the medication to prevent the patient from becoming addicted to the narcotic
   B. Delay giving the medication to avoid further depressing the patient's respirations
   C. Administer the medication to facilitate the patient's respiratory exercises
   D. Administer the medication to relieve the patient's tension

5. A nurse gives a patient who has Addison's disease instructions about steroid medication management. Which of the following statements indicates that the patient understands the instructions?

   A. "I will need to have my steroid medication increased if I have surgery."
   B. "I will need to taper my steroid medication when I feel better."
   C. "I will need to take my steroid medication at bedtime."
   D. "I will need to take my steroid medication until my disease is under control."

6. A woman has been given instructions about monitoring her basal body temperature. Which of the following comments, if made by the woman, would indicate that she understood the instructions?

   A. "I will take my temperature every morning before getting out of bed."
   B. "I will use a standard glass thermometer to take my temperature."
   C. "I will be able to predict my ovulation date after taking my temperature for 30 days in a row."
   D. "I will take my temperature with the same thermometer at the same time every day."

7. Which of the following strategies would be most appropriate for a nurse to take when attempting to obtain a blood pressure measurement on an active three-year-old child?

   A. Explain the reason for the procedure using simple diagrams of anatomy and physiology
   B. Have the parent restrain the extremities while the child sits upright in a chair
   C. Allow the child to assist with the procedure by selecting the extremity to be used
   D. Prepare the child several hours in advance by showing the apparatus that will be used

8. A patient with a laryngectomy who is being discharged should be cautioned about using which of the following personal care items?

   A. Deodorant soap
   B. Aftershave lotion
   C. Talcum powder
   D. Mouthwash

9. While a patient is in pelvic traction for low back pain, which of the following assessments should be included in the patient's care plan?

   A. Checking for skin excoriation over the hips because of irritation by the traction belt
   B. Checking for inequality of the femoral pulses due to pressure of the traction apparatus on a common iliac artery
   C. Checking for swelling in the feet and ankles associated with immobility
   D. Checking for foot drop resulting from pressure on the peroneal nerve

10. Eight hours post-lumbar laminectomy, the patient has not voided. The nurse should first determine if

   A. the patient's bladder is distended.
   B. the patient's fluid intake has been sufficient.
   C. there is an order for the patient to get out of bed to urinate.
   D. there is an order to catheterize the patient.

11. A physician tells a 30-year-old man who had an above-the-knee amputation that he will not be able to return to his construction work. Which of the following long-term goals would be an appropriate expectation of the man?

   A. He will develop alternate vocational skills.
   B. He will acknowledge his loss.
   C. He will identify his areas of interest.
   D. He will engage in occupational therapy.

12. The purpose of requiring a patient who is anorexic to remain in a public place for two hours after eating is to enable the nurse to

   A. promote social skills in the patient.
   B. improve the patient's concentration and attention span.
   C. provide positive reinforcement to the patient.
   D. monitor the patient's behavior.

13. A 17-year-old female who has anorexia nervosa is hospitalized for the initial treatment phase. Which of the following statements indicates a correct understanding of the treatment plan?

   A. "I'll write down everything that I eat in my food diary."
   B. "I'll have to be weighed before every meal."
   C. "I'll have to eat foods high in salt with every meal."
   D. "You'll have to watch me eat my meals."

14. A patient who has a long history of cocaine addiction is admitted to the psychiatric unit. When caring for this patient during detoxification, a nurse would expect to observe which of the following behaviors?

   A. Irritability
   B. Seizures
   C. Rhinorrhea
   D. Respiratory depression

15. A 68-year-old woman is admitted to the hospital with congestive heart failure. Which of the following questions would elicit the most significant data about the patient's symptoms?

   A. "When did you last have a chest x-ray?"
   B. "How often do you get up to urinate during the night?"
   C. "How many pillows do you use when sleeping?"
   D. "Have you noticed any weight loss lately?"

16. **Which of the following statements, if made by a patient who has type 1 diabetes, would indicate the patient needs additional instruction?**

    A. "I will check the bottom of my feet in a mirror daily."
    B. " will wear a medical identification bracelet at all times."
    C. "I will incorporate carbohydrates into my diet."
    D. "I will stop monitoring my blood sugar once I am regulated on insulin."

17. **A nurse assesses a patient who may have a flail chest injury. Which of the following findings would support this diagnosis?**

    A. Cough productive of sputum
    B. Pulse oximeter reading of 95%
    C. Respirations of 20/min
    D. Asymmetrical expansion of the thorax

18. **A patient has completed inpatient detoxification for heroin addiction and will be returning home. Which of the following nursing diagnoses would be basic to planning for community living?**

    A. Social isolation related to avoidance of former associates
    B. Ineffective individual coping related to physiological dependence on drugs
    C. Altered thought processes related to a lifestyle of substance abuse
    D. Anxiety related to forced abstinence

19. **A pregnant woman's uterine fundus is palpated at the level of the umbilicus. A nurse would expect the woman to be how many weeks pregnant?**

    A. 12
    B. 16
    C. 20
    D. 24

20. **A nurse has given discharge instructions to the family members of a patient who has undergone a total laryngectomy. Which of the following statements, if made by a family member, indicates a correct understanding of the discharge teaching?**

    A. "I am learning sign language."
    B. "I have bought a home humidifier."
    C. "I feel comfortable doing the wet-to-dry dressings."
    D. "I know that tube feedings will be needed from now on."

21. **When teaching a patient who is taking lithium carbonate (Eskalith), a nurse would stress the importance of**

    A. maintaining a stable fluid intake.
    B. limiting foods containing sodium.
    C. increasing fluids containing potassium.
    D. taking the medication on an empty stomach.

22. **A patient with hypothyroidism is to receive levothyroxine sodium (Synthroid), 75 mcg by IV push. The medication available is labeled 200 mcg/10 ml. Which of the following doses is the correct amount?**

    A. 5.0 ml
    B. 3.75 ml
    C. 4.75 ml
    D. 2.5 ml

23. **Which of the following measures would a nurse advise a patient who has type 1 diabetes to use to prevent lipodystrophy?**

    A. Rotating insulin administration sites
    B. Limiting saturated fats in the diet
    C. Performing daily passive range-of-motion exercises
    D. Monitoring blood glucose levels accurately

24. **A 12-year-old child who has cystic fibrosis plans to play baseball in the summer. A nurse would recommend that the child eat which of the following snack items during games?**

    A. Cheese and crackers
    B. Cookies and milk
    C. Carrots and celery sticks
    D. Apples and melon slices

25. **Which of the following measures would a nurse include in the care plan of a patient who has chronic bronchitis?**

    A. Balancing activity and rest
    B. Eating a low-sodium diet
    C. Restricting fluid intake
    D. Monitoring serum potassium

26. **A pregnant woman asks a nurse, "Why do I need to have an alpha-fetoprotein test performed?" The nurse's response would be based on the understanding that the alpha-fetoprotein test screens for**

    A. maternal Rh sensitization.
    B. fetal alcohol syndrome.
    C. maternal serum albumin levels.
    D. fetal neural tube defects.

27. **A nurse would explain to a patient who has emphysema that home oxygen should be maintained at a low-flow rate for which of the following reasons?**

    A. Low serum oxygen concentrations trigger breathing.
    B. High oxygen flow rates promote combustion.
    C. Oxygen is drying to the respiratory mucosa.
    D. Oxygen tolerance can develop.

28. **A nurse is assessing a patient who has thrombophlebitis. Which of the following findings would indicate to the nurse the potential development of a pulmonary embolism?**

    A. Cheyne-Stokes respirations
    B. Subcutaneous emphysema
    C. Increased somnolence
    D. Severe chest pain

29. **A patient who is undergoing detoxification from heroin addiction complains to the nurse of sever muscle cramps and headache and demands additional Methadone. Which of the following actions should the nurse take first?**

    A. Measure vital signs
    B. Administer prn medication
    C. Provide support and reassurance
    D. Contact the physician

30. **A patient who is taking digoxin (Lanoxin) has a serum potassium level of 2.8 mEq/L. To which of the following nursing interventions would a nurse give priority?**

    A. Hold the medication and notify the physician
    B. Encourage the patient to drink a glass of orange juice
    C. Tell the patient to double the dose of the medication
    D. Administer sodium polystyrene sulfonate (Kayexalate) to the patient

31. **A nurse would instruct a patient who is taking levothyroxine sodium (Synthroid) to immediately report adverse effects, which include**

    A. lethargy.
    B. chest pain.
    C. blurred vision.
    D. urinary retention.

32. **Which of the following findings in a one-year-old child would indicate to a nurse that cardiopulmonary arrest is imminent?**

    A. Respiratory rate of 18 breaths/min
    B. Systolic blood pressure of 72 mm Hg
    C. Apical heart rate of 54 beats/min
    D. Rectal temperature of 97.5°F (35.8°C)

33. **A patient who has anorexia nervosa says to the nurse, "I feel so fat and ugly." Which of the following responses by the nurse would be most therapeutic?**

    A. "Don't be so hard on yourself."
    B. "It sounds as if you're feeling bad about your body."
    C. "You look fine to me."
    D. "I'd love to be your size."

 *Test C / Part 1*

34. A patient who has vascular insufficiency of the lower extremities experiences intermittent claudication. To which of the following nursing diagnoses would a nurse give priority?

   A. Ineffective thermoregulation
   B. Non-compliance with treatment plan
   C. Activity intolerance
   D. Alteration in body image

35. Which of the following measures would a nurse include in the care plan of a patient who has syndrome of inappropriate secretion of antidiuretic hormone (SIADH)?

   A. Straining all urine
   B. Encouraging fluid intake
   C. Monitoring blood glucose
   D. Increasing sodium intake

36. When teaching a patient who has recently tested positive for the human immunodeficiency virus (HIV), a nurse would emphasize the importance of

   A. separating the patient's eating utensils from those of others.
   B. avoiding unprotected sexual encounters.
   C. limiting close contact with children.
   D. minimizing exposure to sunlight.

37. Which of the following nursing diagnoses would be given priority in the care plan of a pregnant woman who is experiencing hyperemesis gravidarum?

   A. Denial
   B. Fluid volume deficit
   C. Self-esteem disturbance
   D. Altered oral mucous membranes

38. A nurse has taught a patient who is newly diagnosed with the human immunodeficiency virus (HIV) about the likelihood for development of acquired immune deficiency syndrome (AIDS). Which of the following statements indicates that the patient has understood the instruction?

   A. "I can expect to develop AIDS in a short time."
   B. "I can expect to remain healthy for a number of years."
   C. " can expect that I will recover fully from this infection."
   D. " can expect that the course of AIDS will be predictable."

39. Which of the following foods is allowed in the diet of a patient with gout?

   A. Cheese
   B. Beef
   C. Sardines
   D. Liver

40. It is suspected that a patient has Lyme disease. Which of the following skin manifestations would a nurse identify as supporting this diagnosis?

   A. Vesicular skin rash
   B. Circular skin rash
   C. Circumscribed mass
   D. Phlebitic streak

41. A patient who has a history of bulimia is brought to the emergency department with a blood pressure of 76/50 mm Hg, a heart rate of 48 beats per minute, lethargy and poor skin turgor. The priority nursing diagnosis for this patient is

   A. fluid volume deficit related to laxative abuse.
   B. self-esteem disturbance related to distorted body image.
   C. alteration in nutrition: less than body requirements, related to binging and purging.
   D. knowledge deficit related to maladaptive coping skills.

42. **Which of the following manifestations in an eight-year-old child who has a mitral valve prolapse would lead the nurse to suspect subacute bacterial endocarditis?**

    A. Throbbing headache and restlessness
    B. Dependent edema and petechiae
    C. Thready peripheral pulses and pallor
    D. Low-grade fever and lethargy

43. **Non-pharmacological pain management measures for toddlers include**

    A. applying protective devices.
    B. limiting visitors.
    C. playing hand-held video games.
    D. blowing soap bubbles.

44. **A patient who has a fractured hip is placed in Buck's traction. A nurse would explain to the patient that the purpose of Buck's traction is to**

    A. prevent contractures.
    B. promote circulation.
    C. conserve body energy.
    D. maintain body alignment.

45. **Which of the following findings, if identified in a newborn who is receiving phototherapy, would indicate that the treatment is effective?**

    A. Urine output improves
    B. Serum bilirubin level decreases
    C. Stool frequency increases
    D. Direct Coombs test becomes negative

46. **The purpose of performing a non-stress test (NST) on a pregnant woman is to**

    A. diagnose fetal asphyxia.
    B. identify fetal cardiac abnormalities.
    C. determine fetal well-being.
    D. evaluate fetal response to contractions.

47. **A nurse observes the development of clots in the continuous bladder irrigation tubing of a patient who had a transurethral resection of the prostate (TURP) four hours ago. Which of the following actions would the nurse take first?**

    A. Offer oral fluids frequently
    B. Discontinue the continuous bladder irrigation
    C. Increase the flow rate of the intravenous solution
    D. Increase the flow rate of the irrigation solution

48. **A patient is scheduled to have coronary artery bypass grafting (CABG). The nurse should focus the preoperative patient teaching on**

    A. informing the patient about a low-fat, low-cholesterol diet.
    B. instructing the patient on how to use an incentive spirometer.
    C. advising the patient to enroll in a cardiac rehabilitation program.
    D. explaining to the patient the benefits of stress reduction measures.

49. **The most appropriate pain scale for a nurse to utilize with a preschool child is a**

    A. numerical analog scale.
    B. FACES Scale.
    C. pain thermometer.
    D. Poker Chip Tool.

50. **The adult child of a patient who has dementia of the Alzheimer type tearfully tells a nurse, "I can't take this another day. Now I'm being accused of stealing my mother's underwear." Which of the following responses by the nurse would be most therapeutic?**

    A. "This must be a difficult time for you and your mother."
    B. "Don't take it personally. Your mother doesn't mean it."
    C. "Have you tried discussing this with your mother."
    D. "Ask your mother where the underwear was last seen."

51. A nurse identifies a 2-mm superficial, intact reddened area that does not blanch over the patient's sacrum. Which of the following instructions would the nurse give to the patient's caregiver?

    A. "Massage the area four times each day."
    B. "Perform range-of-motion exercises with the patient."
    C. "Keep the area covered with a sterile dressing."
    D. "Reposition the patient regularly throughout the day."

52. Which of the following topics would be given priority in the teaching plan for a woman who is attending childbirth education classes at 30 weeks of pregnancy?

    A. Expected signs of labor onset
    B. Management of pregnancy discomforts
    C. Infant feeding patterns
    D. Methods for coping with postpartum blues

53. A nurse should infuse blood products to a pediatric patient within four hours in order to lessen the risk of

    A. bacterial contamination.
    B. thrombus formation.
    C. febrile reaction.
    D. platelet aggregation.

54. A four-year-old child who has multiple trauma is brought to the emergency department in hypovolemic shock. The child's blood type is known to be A-positive. The blood bank sends O-negative blood for replacement therapy. The nurse should administer the O-negative blood because

    A. individuals with any blood type can receive O-negative blood.
    B. severe volume depletion is an indication to administer whichever blood is available in an emergency.
    C. a child this age has not yet developed antibodies against O-negative blood.
    D. any blood type can be given in an emergency if resuscitative drugs are available.

55. A nurse is counseling a woman who has been abused by her spouse. Which of the following comments by the woman indicates that the counseling was effective?

    A. "I love my husband. I know he'll change."
    B. "The next time my husband hits me, I'm going to the battered woman's shelter."
    C. "know what upsets my husband now, so I'll try not to make him angry again."
    D. "I'll get my husband to promise that he won't hurt me again."

56. Which of the following actions would a nurse take prior to changing the dressings of a patient who has sustained a large, partial-thickness burn?

    A. Administering the patient's prescribed analgesic
    B. Obtaining the patient's pulse and blood pressure
    C. Checking the patient's hematocrit and hemoglobin levels
    D. Determining whether the patient has signed a consent for this procedure

57. A patient who is admitted to the intensive care unit after a suicide attempt says to the nurse, "I can't even kill myself correctly." Which of these responses by the nurse would be indicated?

    A. "Do you still want to die?"
    B. "Let's not talk about that now. Just focus on getting better."
    C. "Tell me some things you can do right."
    D. "Have you spoken to your doctor about that?"

58. Which of the following statements, if made by a woman who is 12 weeks pregnant, would be essential for a nurse to further evaluate?

    A. "I thought I wanted to be pregnant, but now I don't know."
    B. "My husband is angry because I got pregnant."
    C. "Being pregnant makes me feel very tired."
    D. "I don't want to get too fat while I'm pregnant."

59. A nurse would encourage a patient who has sustained a serious burn to adhere to which of the following diets during the rehabilitative phase?

   A. Low-sodium, high-potassium
   B. Low-fat, low-carbohydrate
   C. High-protein, high-caloric
   D. High-fiber, low-purine

60. Which of the following interventions would be most appropriate for a patient who is newly admitted for treatment of a major depression?

   A. Short, frequent interactions
   B. Intensive group involvement
   C. Exploring negative feelings
   D. Teaching problem solving

61. A woman who has pregnancy-induced hypertension is receiving magnesium sulfate therapy. Which of the following manifestations would a nurse expect the woman to have if the magnesium sulfate is having the desired effect?

   A. Reduction in patellar reflex response from +4 to +2
   B. Decrease in urine output from 100 ml/hr to 50 ml/hr
   C. Increase in frequency of contractions from every five minutes to every three minutes
   D. Increase in respiratory rate from 12 breaths/min to 18 breaths/min

62. The nurse would instruct the parents of a four-month-old infant who weighs 16 lb (7.3 kg) to place the infant in a car seat in which of the following positions?

   A. Rear-facing in the front passenger seat
   B. Rear-facing in the center back seat
   C. Front-facing in the front passenger seat
   D. Front-facing in the center back seat

63. A mother tells the nurse that she gives her child theophylline (Theo-Dur) sprinkles in all of the following substances. Which of the following foods would the nurse instruct the mother to avoid?

   A. Applesauce
   B. Ice cream
   C. Pudding
   D. Grape juice

64. A patient is to receive heparin sodium, 20,000 units in 1,000 ml of solution intravenously. The fluid is to be regulated to deliver 50 ml of solution each hour. At this rate, the patient should receive how many units of heparin each hour?

   A. 500
   B. 1000
   C. 1500
   D. 2000

65. Which of the following findings, if identified in a child by a school nurse, would be consistent with physical abuse?

   A. Changeable behavior and bruises
   B. Tearfulness and insomnia
   C. Decreased attention span and poor appetite
   D. Nervousness and palpitations

66. Because a woman is receiving oxytocin (Pitocin) for induction of labor, it is essential for the nurse to monitor

   A. fundal height.
   B. patellar reflexes.
   C. cervical changes.
   D. level of consciousness.

67. A female patient reports to the clinic nurse that she tends to have stools that are hard. The woman makes all of these statements about measures that she takes to prevent the problem. Which of these statements should the nurse definitely discuss with her?

   A. "I eat a concentrated, high-fiber cereal almost every morning."
   B. "I drink about eight large glasses of water a day."
   C. "I take one or two tablespoons of mineral oil after breakfast almost every day."
   D. "I drink a four-ounce glass of prune juice at bedtime if I have not had a bowel movement for a day or so."

68. The wife of a patient who is admitted to the hospital with a cerebrovascular accident begins to cry while giving her husband's medical history. The nurse should make which of these comments in response to the wife's behavior?

    A. "You are unable to continue our discussion."
    B. "This discussion is painful for you."
    C. "It is important that we obtain your husband's history."
    D. "I will make a notation that you were too upset to give a complete history."

69. After administering furosemide (Lasix) to a 16-month-old child who has congestive heart failure, a nurse would expect to make which of the following observations?

    A. A decrease in rhonchi breath sounds
    B. A 20-mm Hg decrease in systolic blood pressure
    C. An increase in apical heart rate
    D. A 10-ml/kg increase in urine output

70. A nurse obtains a diet history from a patient who has ulcerative colitis. The nurse should determine that the patient needs teaching if the patient indicated which of these foods as being part of the diet?

    A. Celery
    B. Bananas
    C. White rice
    D. Roast chicken

71. When assessing the knowledge of an adolescent regarding safety, the nurse should consider the leading cause of death in this age group, which is

    A. motor vehicle accidents.
    B. suicide.
    C. poisoning.
    D. drug overdose.

72. A patient is admitted involuntarily to the psychiatric unit. Which of the following patient actions would have indicated the need for involuntary rather than voluntary admission?

    A. The patient stated that voices were telling him to end his life.
    B. The patient tried to harm his wife.
    C. The patient made threatening remarks to his neighbor.
    D. The patient tried to stop traffic outside his home.

73. A woman is receiving oxytocin (Pitocin) for induction of labor. At the peak of successive uterine contractions, the fetal heart rate changes from a baseline of 150 to 110 beats per minute for 30 seconds and then returns to baseline. Which of the following actions would the nurse take first?

    A. Notify the woman's obstetrician
    B. Stop the woman's Pitocin infusion
    C. Position the woman in reverse Trendelenburg
    D. Prepare the woman for an amniotomy

74. Following an adrenalectomy, a patient is to take steroid therapy after discharge from the hospital. Which of these instructions should be given to the patient?

    A. "You should anticipate loss of hair."
    B. "You should test your urine for glucose daily."
    C. "You should avoid taking cathartics."
    D. "You should call the physician if you have a temperature elevation."

75. When assessing a patient who has acquired immune deficiency syndrome (AIDS), which of the following signs and symptoms would be most indicative of AIDS dementia complex?

    A. Headaches
    B. Bronchial infection
    C. Unsteady gait
    D. Diarrhea

76. A nurse is counseling a 16-year-old boy about health promotion. Which of the following statements, if made by the boy, indicates a need for further intervention?

    A. "I drink at least a liter of sports drink whenever I play basketball for more than an hour."
    B. "Since my dad keeps a rifle at home, he has enrolled me in a hunter education course."
    C. "When I go out with my buddies who drink alcohol, I'm always the designated driver."
    D. "I don't use condoms when having sex because my girlfriend is on the pill."

77. After successfully performing the Heimlich maneuver on an 18-month-old child, a nurse would advise the child's parent to perform which of the following measures?

    A. Monitor the child carefully for signs of abdominal bruising
    B. Give the child only liquids to drink for the next 24 hours
    C. Take the child to a healthcare facility for a thorough examination
    D. Check the child's breathing every two hours at night

78. If a patient has acute appendicitis, the report of laboratory tests would most likely show which of these results?

    A. Decreased serum potassium
    B. Elevated leukocyte count
    C. Low hemoglobin determination
    D. Enlarged erythrocytes

79. A patient has a nursing diagnosis of risk for self-harm related to suicidal ideation. Which of the following nursing interventions would be indicated initially?

    A. Promoting self-esteem
    B. Cognitive restructuring
    C. Establishing a "no harm contract"
    D. Involving the patient in milieu therapy

80. The mother of a 15-year-old adolescent who is in active labor is observed reprimanding the girl because she is sucking her thumb. Which of the following comments by a nurse to the adolescent's mother is most appropriate?

    A. "This is not a good time to change your daughter's old habits."
    B. "This behavior helps to keep your daughter's mouth moist."
    C. "Your daughter would be more comfortable if you left the room."
    D. "It is not unusual for your daughter to regress during times of stress."

81. A patient with a diagnosis of gout is on allopurinol (Zyloprim) therapy. Which of the following serum laboratory values should be monitored to determine the effectiveness of treatment?

    A. Glucose
    B. Calcium
    C. Alkaline phosphatase
    D. Uric acid

82. Which of these measures should be included in the care plan of a patient whose left leg is in traction?

    A. Checking the feet for the presence of ankle clonus
    B. Noting the color of the toenails after applying temporary pressure
    C. Assessing the femoral arteries for equality of pulses
    D. Percussing the knee for a patellar reflex

83. Disulfiram (Antabuse) is prescribed for a patient. Which of the following comments, if made by the patient, would indicate a correct understanding of the action of this medication?

    A. "I'll drink fruit juice at social gatherings."
    B. "I'll take my pulse four times each day."
    C. "I'll lie down for half an hour after I take the pill."
    D. "I'll take an antacid before my Antabuse."

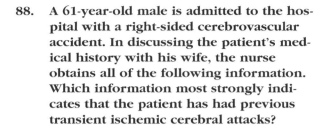

84. Which of the following measures should a nurse include in the care plan of a patient who has a diagnosis of bipolar disorder, manic type?

A. Decrease environmental stimuli
B. Involve the patient in competitive activities
C. Limit the verbalization of feelings
D. Foster independent decision-making

85. The first nursing intervention for a child who has experienced a near-drowning is to

A. call the local emergency number to request assistance.
B. transport the child in an available vehicle to the nearest emergency department.
C. wrap the child in dry blankets to provide warmth.
D. begin cardiopulmonary resuscitation on the child upon removal from the water.

86. Which of the following types of activity would be therapeutic for a patient who is acutely psychotic?

A. Task-oriented
B. Creative
C. Independent
D. Competitive

87. A school nurse thinks that a 17-year-old girl has bulimia. The nurse's diagnosis would be supported if examination of the girl's oropharynx reveals

A. moderate gingival hyperplasia.
B. painful mucosal lesions.
C. extensive tooth decay.
D. a deeply furrowed tongue.

88. A 61-year-old male is admitted to the hospital with a right-sided cerebrovascular accident. In discussing the patient's medical history with his wife, the nurse obtains all of the following information. Which information most strongly indicates that the patient has had previous transient ischemic cerebral attacks?

A. He has throbbing frontal headaches when he becomes emotionally upset.
B. He has often been very fatigued after returning from work.
C. He has recently been irritable and less happy than usual.
D. He has occasionally been forgetful and appeared to be in a daze during their conversations.

89. Which of the following assessment criteria would directly affect the mental health needs of a community?

A. Religious affiliations
B. Recreational facilities
C. The opinions of the residents
D. The demographics of the community

90. A patient who has hypertension attends the clinic. Because of the diagnosis, the nurse should assess the patient for which of these symptoms?

A. Episodes of dizziness
B. Bleeding gums
C. Bradycardia
D. Nearsightedness

91. The nurse teaches the parent of a child with asthma about measures to prevent asthma attacks. Which of the following comments by the parent indicates the need for additional teaching?

A. "I'll buy hypoallergenic bed pillows."
B. "I'll dust and vacuum the house frequently."
C. "I'll have my child sleep with the windows open."
D. "I'll stop disinfecting my child's room with aerosol sprays."

92. Following a hip replacement, the patient should have the affected hip placed in which of these positions?

    A. Extended, with a wedge between the legs
    B. Flexed, with the knee supported on sandbags
    C. Elevated, with pillows under the leg from the knee to the ankle
    D. Rotated externally, with a trochanter roll in place

93. A patient is scheduled for a bronchoscopy. To prepare the patient for the procedure, the nurse should give which of these instructions?

    A. "A small needle will be inserted through the skin into the lung tissue."
    B. "Food and fluids will be withheld for one to two hours following the procedure."
    C. "It will be uncomfortable to breathe deeply following the procedure."
    D. "You will cough up some of the dye during the next few days."

94. A patient who has Parkinson's disease is admitted to the hospital for medication control. In addition to presenting with muscle rigidity, the nurse should expect that the patient will have

    A. a mask-like facial expression.
    B. tremors of the knees when resting.
    C. bilateral nystagmus.
    D. long-term memory loss.

95. When feeding an 18-month-old child two days after he underwent a cleft palate repair, a nurse would offer liquid nutrition using a

    A. plastic cup.
    B. silastic nasogastric tube.
    C. flexible straw.
    D. rubber-coated infant spoon.

96. When a woman is 10 weeks pregnant, which of the following hematology test results would need further investigation?

    A. Hemoglobin level of 9 mg/dL
    B. White blood cell count of 15,000/cu mm
    C. Platelet count of 200,000/cu mm
    D. Red blood cell count of 4,200,000/cu mm

97. Which of the following statements, if made by a patient during a nursing assessment, would be indicative of a risk factor for coronary artery disease?

    A. "I have a cholesterol level of 190 mg/dL."
    B. "I had a parent diagnosed with angina at age 40 years."
    C. "My blood pressure is consistently 100/60 mm Hg."
    D. "I had a recent weight loss of 15 lbs."

98. A nurse should expect a patient diagnosed with angina pectoris to report chest pain during which of the following activities?

    A. Taking a deep breath
    B. Moving the extremities
    C. Climbing a flight of stairs
    D. Sleeping in a supine position

99. Four hours after spontaneous vaginal delivery under local anesthesia, a patient tells the nurse that she has to urinate. Which of the following actions should the nurse take?

    A. Obtain a bedside commode for the patient
    B. Offer the patient a bedpan
    C. Ambulate the patient to the bathroom
    D. Catheterize the patient

100. A patient has a nursing diagnosis of fluid volume excess following a myocardial infarction. Which of the following nursing measures would be most effective in promoting the patient's comfort?

    A. Elevating the head of the patient's bed
    B. Offering the patient a prescribed analgesic
    C. Monitoring the patient's urine output
    D. Encouraging ambulation

101. When analgesia is initiated through an epidural catheter for a woman in labor, it is essential that a nurse monitor the woman's

    A. deep tendon reflexes.
    B. oxygen saturation.
    C. blood pressure.
    D. pupillary reaction.

102. To help a mother anticipate the safety needs of her nine-year-old son who is learning to ride a bicycle, the nurse would teach that

    A. a helmet will reduce his risk of head injury.
    B. the child must never ride without a friend nearby.
    C. a formal course of instruction is recommended.
    D. the child must ride on the sidewalk.

103. Which of the following statements, if made by a patient who has a prescription for warfarin sodium (Coumadin), would indicate the need for further instruction?

    A. "I should avoid using aspirin."
    B. "I should check my radial pulse daily."
    C. "I should limit consumption of green vegetables."
    D. "I should use an electric razor when I shave."

104. Which of these statements, if made by a patient who has a prescription for sublingual nitroglycerin tablets, would indicate a correct understanding of the medication instructions?

    A. "I should take these pills with a full glass of water."
    B. "I should protect these pills from light."
    C. "I should wait 30 minutes before taking the second pill."
    D. "I should chew the pill for a faster effect."

105. Which of the following statements, if made by a patient who is suspected of having congestive heart disease, would support the diagnosis?

    A. "I sleep using two pillows."
    B. "My weight has gone down."
    C. "My ears have a ringing sensation."
    D. "I am not able to tolerate heat."

106. A nurse should expect that a patient who has a diagnosis of increased intracranial pressure would be given mannitol (Osmitrol) to

    A. prevent meningitis.
    B. reduce cerebral edema.
    C. decrease urinary output.
    D. decrease angioedema.

107. When assessing a two-month-old infant suspected of having pyloric stenosis, the nurse would expect which of the following findings?

    A. Absence of bowel sounds
    B. Ribbon-like stools
    C. Decreased appetite
    D. Visible peristalsis

108. During the first hour after delivery of a newborn, it is essential that a nurse assess the mother for

    A. Homans' sign.
    B. perineal discomfort.
    C. uterine atony.
    D. bowel sounds.

109. To determine an appropriate community placement for a patient who has chronic schizophrenia, a nurse should be concerned chiefly with

    A. accessibility of mass transit systems.
    B. employment opportunities.
    C. proximity of grocery stores.
    D. availability of structured daytime activities.

110. It is essential for a nurse to take which of the following actions for a woman in labor who is about to receive epidural analgesia?

    A. Ensure a bolus of intravenous fluid is administered.
    B. Obtain an abdominal ultrasound.
    C. Insert a urinary drainage catheter.
    D. Perform a comprehensive neurological assessment.

111. A patient who has had a spinal cord injury reports an acute pounding headache. A nurse should recognize that this is a symptom of

    A. autonomic dysreflexia.
    B. spinal shock.
    C. grand mal seizures.
    D. decerebration.

112. **Which of the following instructions about urinary management should a nurse give to a patient who is undergoing rehabilitation following a spinal cord injury?**

    A. "Limit your fluid intake during the day."
    B. "Empty your bladder on a timed schedule."
    C. "Drink a glass of cranberry juice every morning."
    D. "Avoid carbonated beverages at all times."

113. **The laboratory informs a nurse that a child's serum potassium level is higher than normal. What additional information is necessary to evaluate this result correctly?**

    A. Type of specimen tube used
    B. Time of the child's last nutritional intake
    C. Method used for specimen collection
    D. Child's serum chloride level

114. **A nurse would recognize that a woman who has had a cesarean delivery with a classical incision may not be allowed to deliver vaginally for subsequent births because of**

    A. the presence of peritoneal adhesions.
    B. loss of abdominal muscle tone.
    C. the risk of uterine rupture.
    D. damage to the pelvic nerve innervation.

115. **All of the following hematology values are obtained from a woman who is 24 hours postpartum. Which of the following values should concern the nurse?**

    A. Hemoglobin level of 9 g/dL
    B. White blood cell count of 15,000/cu mm
    C. Platelet count of 152,000/cu mm
    D. Red blood cell count of 4.2 million/cu mm

116. **Which of the following pieces of equipment should a nurse have available at the bedside of a patient who is experiencing dysphagia following an acute cerebrovascular accident (CVA)?**

    A. Oxygen cannula
    B. Tracheostomy tray
    C. Suction set-up
    D. Padded tongue blade

117. **When a patient who has emphysema reports increased respiratory effort, the nurse should instruct the patient to**

    A. breathe through pursed lips.
    B. increase the humidity in the air.
    C. breathe into a paper bag.
    D. increase the oxygen flow rate.

118. **Which of the following instructions should a nurse give to a patient who has tuberculosis and is receiving rifampin (Rifadin)?**

    A. "Expect your urine to turn reddish-orange."
    B. "Take the medication on an empty stomach."
    C. "Take the medication until your skin test is negative."
    D. "Stay out of the sun while you are taking the medication."

119. **A nurse should expect a patient to demonstrate which of the following findings after receiving electroconvulsive therapy?**

    A. Seizures
    B. Muscle spasms
    C. Personality changes
    D. Short-term memory loss

120. **A patient has been acting out most of the day. To which of the following interventions should a nurse give priority?**

    A. Inform the patient of rules and regulations that must be followed
    B. Tell the patient to control the feelings motivating the behavior
    C. Isolate the patient until the patient gains self-control
    D. Try to elicit the feelings behind the patient's behavior

121. **Because of an outbreak of Escherichia coli-related hemolytic uremic syndrome in the community, a public health nurse should instruct parents about measures to prevent further occurrence, which include**

    A. cooking all chopped meats thoroughly.
    B. drinking bottled mineral water.
    C. sanitizing kitchen surfaces daily.
    D. swimming in chlorine-treated water.

122. A woman who is hospitalized because of abruptio placentae would be carefully monitored for which of the following complications?

    A. Toxic shock syndrome
    B. Pulmonary embolism
    C. Cerebrovascular accident
    D. Disseminated intravascular coagulation

123. Which of the following instructions should a nurse give to a patient in order to reduce the patient's risk for developing osteoporosis?

    A. "Eliminate caffeine from your diet."
    B. "Increase your physical activity."
    C. "Reduce your exposure to sunlight."
    D. "Add iron-rich foods to your diet."

124. Which of the following manifestations should indicate to a nurse that a patient who is receiving ibuprofen (Motrin) requires follow-up before another dose of the medication is given?

    A. Loss of hair
    B. Sensitivity to light
    C. Ringing in the ears
    D. Swelling of the gums

125. Which of the following nursing diagnoses would be specific to planning care for a patient with hypothyroidism?

    A. Altered thought processes
    B. Impaired swallowing
    C. Fluid volume deficit
    D. Activity intolerance

126. Treatment with radioactive iodine (sodium iodide, I131) has been effective for a patient with hyperthyroidism if the patient experiences increased

    A. ability to sleep through the night.
    B. deep tendon reflex reaction.
    C. hearing acuity.
    D. respiratory rate.

127. A patient seems unconcerned about the sudden loss of vision in both eyes. Physical examination fails to reveal a physical cause for this problem. Which of the following terms should the nurse use to describe this phenomenon when charting the behavior?

    A. La belle indifference
    B. Malingering
    C. Hypochondria
    D. Confabulation

128. Which of the following statements made by a patient who is scheduled for a mammogram indicates a need for further teaching?

    A. "I will not use underarm antiperspirant before the procedure."
    B. "A dye will be injected into my vein prior to the procedure."
    C. "I may experience discomfort during the procedure."
    D. "My breasts will be compressed while the x-rays are taken."

129. When assessing an infant born at 42 weeks' gestation, a nurse would expect which of the following findings?

    A. Depressed anterior fontanel
    B. Fine sole creases
    C. Excessive lanugo
    D. Parchment-like skin

130. A child complains of a headache and stomachache only on school days. By midday, the child is bored and the parents allow the child to bake cookies. A nurse should understand that this is an example of

    A. a dysfunctional relationship.
    B. co-dependency.
    C. secondary gain.
    D. confusion.

131. Which of the following statements, if made by the parent of a 10-month-old male infant, would support a nursing diagnosis of knowledge deficit?

    A. "I often place dry corn cereal flakes on my baby's highchair tray so he can feed himself."
    B. "I had to put the mattress in its lowest position so my baby can pull himself up and walk around the crib safely."
    C. "I'm concerned because my baby used to be so friendly, but now he screams when strangers approach."
    D. "I keep the safety restraint seat in the middle of the back seat of the car and secure my baby in it facing forward."

132. A nurse should expect a patient who has been diagnosed with hyperthyroidism to be prescribed propranolol (Inderal) in order to

    A. inhibit the synthesis of thyroid hormone.
    B. increase the effect of calcium on cardiac tissue.
    C. enhance thyroid stimulating hormone TSH secretion from the pituitary gland.
    D. slow the sympathetic nervous system response.

133. An elderly patient reports a diminishing energy level. The nurse should recognize that this symptom is most likely a result of decreased

    A. cardiac output.
    B. bone density.
    C. muscle mass.
    D. joint mobility.

134. A patient says to the nurse, "If you give me a cigarette, I'll go to group therapy." Which of the following responses by the nurse would be therapeutic?

    A. "Here are your cigarettes."
    B. "All patients on this unit are expected to go to group therapy."
    C. "You can have one cigarette, then you must go to group therapy."
    D. "Other patients do not ask me for special treatment. Why are you the only one?"

135. A newborn who is being cared for in an open warming unit has an axillary temperature of 96.2°F (35.7°C). It is essential that the nurse take which of the following actions?

    A. Wrap the newborn in a blanket
    B. Notify the parents of the findings
    C. Increase the heat-control setting on the warming unit
    D. Perform a heel stick to check the capillary blood glucose

136. When planning the care of a patient who has post-traumatic stress disorder, a nurse should include which of the following outcomes?

    A. The patient will be able to use stress management techniques.
    B. The patient will intellectualize about the traumatic experience.
    C. The patient will work through conflicting emotions about the trauma.
    D. The patient will demonstrate a normal range of moods.

137. When teaching the parent of a four-year-old child about expected age-appropriate behaviors during hospitalization, which of the following instructions would a nurse give the parent?

    A. "It would not be unusual if your child starts to wet the bed."
    B. "Most children this age don't cry when their parents go home for the night."
    C. "You can expect your child to stop eating for a few days."
    D. "It is common for children of this age to cooperate for routine procedures."

138. Which of the following nursing measures would be most appropriate for a patient who complains of pain during the immediate postoperative period following surgery for an enlarged prostate gland?

    A. Administering analgesics as ordered
    B. Placing a pillow under the patient's knees
    C. Measuring the patient's abdominal girth
    D. Checking the patency of the indwelling urinary catheter

139. A nurse observes a first-time mother with her newborn. Which of the following actions would prompt the nurse to give the mother further instructions?

    A. Offering the newborn her breast every two hours for feeding
    B. Burping the newborn every 15 minutes during feedings
    C. Offering the newborn a pacifier between feedings
    D. Placing the newborn to sleep prone after feeding

140. The nurse should instruct a patient who has pancreatitis to avoid which of the following types of foods?

    A. Fruits
    B. Vegetables
    C. Meats
    D. Breads

141. The parents of an eight-year-old child are counseled regarding appropriate activities for their hospitalized child. Which of the following activities would a nurse recommend for the child?

    A. Racing toy cars along the corridor
    B. Sorting cards in a trading card collection
    C. Sleeping with a musical stuffed animal
    D. Watching daytime television shows

142. When providing anticipatory guidance to the parents of a toddler, a nurse should give priority to which of the following issues?

    A. Purchasing an appropriate-size potty chair
    B. Enrolling the child in safety swimming classes
    C. Having the child use a plastic training cup for drinking
    D. Having ipecac syrup available for emergency use

143. Which of the following preoperative teaching instructions should a nurse give to a patient who is scheduled for a laparoscopic cholecystectomy?

    A. "You will have an incision down the center of your abdomen."
    B. "You will have a small rubber tube draining bile into a bag."
    C. "Your abdomen will be inflated with gas during surgery"
    D. "Your bowel will be emptied with cleansing enemas."

144. A patient who has an obsessive-compulsive disorder is admitted for major surgery. The patient counts to 95 at each step of a procedure. Which of the following actions by the nurse would demonstrate a correct understanding of the patient's needs?

    A. Explaining the necessity of maintaining the operating room schedule
    B. Assisting the patient with other ways of decreasing anxiety
    C. Making a contract with the patient to eliminate the rituals
    D. Proceeding with preparation for the surgery

145. A nurse makes all of the following observations during a home visit to a six-day-old, healthy, term newborn. Which one would prompt the nurse to give the mother further instructions?

    A. Places the newborn supine in the crib after feeding
    B. Warms expressed breast milk in the microwave oven
    C. Applies isopropyl alcohol to the base of the cord stump after bathing
    D. Washes the newborn's hair after giving the bath

146. **Which of the following strategies would a nurse utilize when administering an oral liquid medication to a toddler?**

    A. Squirt the medication from a syringe slowly into the side of the child's mouth
    B. Dilute the medication in a moderate volume of cold juice and have the child drink it
    C. Mix the medication with a favorite soft food and have the child eat it
    D. Pinch the child's nostrils, then administer the medication from a teaspoon

147. **Which of the following factors is the most decisive in determining the impact of a traumatic event on a client?**

    A. Previous experience with the event
    B. The event's effect on the client's self-perception
    C. The number of other stressors
    D. The size of the support group

148. **Which of the following statements, if made by a patient who has hepatitis B, would support a nursing diagnosis of knowledge deficit related to disease transmission?**

    A. "I am not allowed to donate blood."
    B. "I will need to use protection when I have sexual intercourse."
    C. "I should keep my eating utensils separate from those of others."
    D. "I can become a lifelong carrier of the disease."

149. **A nurse should recognize that an infant would receive which of the following vaccinations during the neonatal period?**

    A. Haemophilus influenza B
    B. Rubella
    C. Hepatitis B
    D. Varicella

150. **When a woman receives a rubella vaccination after delivery, a nurse would give her which of the following instructions?**

    A. "Don't get pregnant for at least three months."
    B. "Refrain from eating eggs and egg products for 48 hours."
    C. "Limit contact with visitors for at least one week."
    D. "Avoid breast-feeding the baby for at least 24 hours."

You have finished the Nursing, Part 1 portion of Practice Test C. Feel free to take a break (a one-hour lunch break will be provided at the Qualifying Exam) before beginning Nursing, Part 2 of Practice Test C. Do not turn the page until you are ready to begin Part 2.

Practice Exam C: Nursing, Part 2

You will have one hour and 50 minutes to complete Nursing, Part 2.

1. Which of the following observations would be most significant when assessing the parents of a child who is suspected of being physically abused?

    A. The parents appear distraught and upset when asked about the injuries.
    B. The parents give a history of the injuries that is not compatible with the actual injuries.
    C. The parents seem eager to take the child home as soon as possible.
    D. The parents cannot recall when the last series of immunizations was given.

2. A nurse witnesses a two-year-old child experiencing a generalized seizure while being evaluated in the emergency department for a high fever. Which of the following actions would a nurse take first?

    A. Protect the child from physical injury
    B. Administer an antipyretic medication rectally
    C. Apply cool compresses to the axilla and groin
    D. Reassure the parents that this is a common occurrence

3. The nurse should teach a patient who has cirrhosis of the liver to avoid which of the following foods in the diet?

    A. Baked chicken
    B. Apple pie
    C. Macaroni
    D. Spinach

4. Which of the following pieces of equipment should a nurse have available when caring for a patient who has bleeding esophageal varices?

    A. Chest tube
    B. Endotracheal tube
    C. Salem sump tube
    D. Sengstaken-Blakemore tube

5. A nurse is assessing a patient for discharge to a residential treatment center. To which of the following factors should a nurse give highest priority?

    A. Family history of mental illness
    B. Developmental history
    C. Individual strengths
    D. Social support systems

6. When the nurse is assessing a patient who has cirrhosis of the liver, which of the following findings would indicate that the patient's condition is worsening?

    A. Positive Babinski reflex
    B. Visual field loss
    C. Flapping hand tremors
    D. Bibasilar lung crackles

7. A patient who is human immunodeficiency virus (HIV) positive has a CD-4 count of 200. To which of the following measures should a nurse give priority in the patient's plan of care?

    A. Implement reverse isolation
    B. Limit the number of venipunctures
    C. Institute regular position changes
    D. Monitor intake and output

8. When assessing the psychiatric patient, a nurse should recognize which of the following strengths as essential to successful living?

    A. Knowledge about medications
    B. Ability to work
    C. Ability to drive
    D. Social skills

9. **Which of the following statements is most appropriate for a nurse to make when initiating a painful procedure on a four-year-old boy?**

   A. "You are a big boy. I know you can handle this."
   B. "You can have your mom hold your hand."
   C. "You are not a baby. I know you won't cry."
   D. "You will get a treat if you are good."

10. **Immediately after a femoral artery cardiac catheterization of a nine-year-old child, all of the following orders are written. Which one should a nurse question?**

    A. Maintain pressure dressing for 24 hours
    B. Assess brachial pulses q 1hr x 4
    C. Maintain recumbent position for eight hours
    D. Assess color of lower extremities q 1hr x 4

11. **A 36-hour-old newborn infant appears slightly jaundiced and has a bilirubin level of 10 mg/dL. A nurse would give the parent which of the following instructions?**

    A. "Feed the baby at least every three hours."
    B. "Give the baby formula instead of breast-feeding for 48 hours."
    C. "Check the baby's temperature every four hours."
    D. "Expose the baby's skin to direct sunlight daily for one hour."

12. **A nurse has given a patient instructions about taking levothyroxine sodium (Synthroid). Which of the following statements, if made by the patient, indicates that the patient has understood the instructions?**

    A. "I can discontinue this medication once my pulse rate is normal."
    B. "I will stop taking this medication if I gain weight."
    C. "I realize that I must take this medication for the rest of my life."
    D. "I need to take this medication whenever I feel tired."

13. **The nurse caring for a patient who is receiving furosemide (Lasix) should monitor the patient's serum level of**

    A. potassium.
    B. glucose.
    C. protein.
    D. creatinine.

14. **When preparing to discharge an infant who is born to a known cocaine abuser, the nurse's teaching plan would include information about the infant's**

    A. need to restrict fluids.
    B. tendency to sleep for long periods.
    C. potential for developing congestive heart failure.
    D. increased risk of sudden infant death syndrome.

15. **The nurse is reviewing the American Dietetic Association (ADA) diet with a 10-year-old child who has diabetes mellitus. The child's selection of which of the following foods in exchange for a serving of meat indicates that the child correctly understands the instructions?**

    A. Cheese omelet
    B. Bacon
    C. Chocolate milk
    D. Baked beans

16. **A nurse caring for a patient who is being treated with lithium carbonate (Eskalith) should be alert for which of the following signs and symptoms?**

    A. Fine motor tremors
    B. Vomiting and diarrhea
    C. Stiff neck and shoulders
    D. Seeing halos around lights

17. **When a newborn is 12-hours-old, the nurse is to give him his first bath. The nurse should initially obtain which of the following assessments?**

    A. Temperature
    B. Weight loss since birth
    C. Size of posterior fontanel
    D. Passage of meconium

18. When caring for a patient who is one hour postpartum, which of the following assessments requires immediate intervention?

    A. Uterine fundus two centimeters below umbilicus
    B. Lower abdominal cramping
    C. Bright red vaginal bleeding
    D. Temperature elevation of 100.6°F (38.1°C)

19. A patient who is scheduled to begin peritoneal dialysis treatments in the home asks a nurse what to expect. Which of these responses by the nurse would be most accurate?

    A. "Fluid will be instilled into your abdominal cavity on a routine basis."
    B. "You will need to be admitted to an acute care center for this treatment."
    C. "You will have a permanent vascular access site created in your arm."
    D. "You will be restricted to bed while this procedure is being carried out."

20. When teaching an obese patient about a diet for weight reduction, which of the following instructions should the nurse include?

    A. "Divide your daily calories into six small meals."
    B. "Decrease your daily intake to 700 calories."
    C. "Select 90 percent of your daily calories from carbohydrates."
    D. "Consume half of your daily caloric allotment at dinner."

21. When caring for an adolescent who is diagnosed with idiopathic scoliosis, a nurse should recognize that the priority concern for the adolescent is related to

    A. body image.
    B. activity limitations.
    C. financial burden.
    D. imposed dependence.

22. Which of the following statements, if made by a patient who has hypertension, would indicate the need for further teaching about antihypertensive medications?

    A. "I should arise slowly from a chair after taking my blood pressure medicine."
    B. "I will not need my blood pressure medicine when my headaches go away."
    C. "The water pills I take will make me go to the bathroom often."
    D. "My water pills are most effective when I take them first thing in the morning."

23. A patient who is admitted to the emergency department reports visual hallucinations and appears disoriented. To determine whether the patient is delirious or demented, a nurse should assess for

    A. memory impairment.
    B. level of consciousness.
    C. auditory hallucinations.
    D. cognitive functioning.

24. The nurse should instruct a patient who has a diagnosis of folic acid deficiency anemia to increase intake of which of the following foods?

    A. Dairy products
    B. Green, leafy vegetables
    C. Citrus juices
    D. Fish and poultry

25. A patient who has a pituitary adenoma is scheduled for a transsphenoidal hypophysectomy. A nurse is teaching the patient about what to expect in the immediate postoperative period. Which of these statements by the nurse would be accurate?

    A. "You will have a pressure dressing on your head."
    B. "You will have to lie flat in bed."
    C. "You will be unable to suck through a straw."
    D. "You will be unable to brush your teeth."

26. A patient who has sustained a fracture of the femur is at risk for which of the following complications in the immediate post-fracture period?

    A. Electrolyte imbalance
    B. Fat embolus
    C. Fluid volume deficit
    D. Disuse syndrome

27. A patient who has a long leg cast says to the nurse, "My thigh is itching under the cast." To provide relief, the nurse should

    A. teach the patient guided imagery techniques.
    B. apply heat to the cast at the site of the itching.
    C. elevate the patient's affected leg on pillows.
    D. encourage the patient to move his/her toes.

28. A nurse is caring for a patient who is receiving lithium carbonate (Eskalith). Prior to administration of the next dose, the nurse finds that the patient's lithium blood level is 1.6 mEq /L. Which of the following actions should the nurse take first?

    A. Call the patient's physician
    B. Withhold the dose
    C. Take the patient's vital signs
    D. Repeat the blood lithium level

29. A nurse should recognize that a patient who has coronary artery disease is receiving acetylsalicylic acid (aspirin) to

    A. relieve pain.
    B. reduce fever.
    C. diminish inflammation.
    D. decrease platelet adhesion.

30. To which of the following nursing diagnoses should a nurse give priority in the care of a patient who has sustained severe burns?

    A. Hyperthermia
    B. Risk of infection
    C. Body image disturbance
    D. Impaired physical mobility

31. A child has morphine sulfate (Roxanol) and acetaminophen (Tylenol) ordered for postoperative pain. The parent asks the nurse, "Why is my child getting two medications for pain at the same time?" The nurse's response would be based on the understanding that

    A. children are more sensitive to the effects of opiates, and non-opiates help to counteract this effect.
    B. non-opiates stimulate the respiratory system, thereby minimizing the depressant effects of opiates.
    C. children often experience nausea from opiates, and non-opiates reduce this effect.
    D. non-opiates affect the peripheral nervous system, and opiates affect the central nervous system.

32. Which of the following snacks is most appropriate for meeting the nutritional needs of a patient with severe burns?

    A. Vanilla milk shake
    B. Carrot sticks
    C. Apple slices
    D. Flavored gelatin

33. A patient has severe burns involving the hands, chest and head. Which of the following nursing actions will prevent contractures in this patient?

    A. Maintaining the patient in a semi-Fowler's position
    B. Applying splints to the patient's hands and wrists
    C. Placing sandbags on either side of the patient's chest
    D. Placing two pillows under the patient's head

34. To which of the following nursing actions would a nurse give priority in the emergency care of a patient who has sustained a compound fracture of the femur?

    A. Splint the leg in its present position
    B. Place the leg in neutral alignment
    C. Irrigate the wound with normal saline
    D. Apply pressure directly over the wound

 *Test C / Part 2*

35. A nurse is caring for a patient who has balanced skeletal traction applied to the femur. Which of the following findings requires immediate nursing intervention?

   A. The foot of the bed is elevated 30 degrees.
   B. The traction weights are resting on the bed frame.
   C. The patient's leg is suspended above the bed.
   D. The overbed trapeze is above the patient's chest.

36. A child is being treated for acute lympho-cytic leukemia and has a platelet count of 50,000 cells/cu mm. Which of the following measures would a nurse include in the care plan?

   A. No rectal temperatures
   B. Respiratory isolation
   C. Bland diet
   D. Strict bed rest

37. A nurse observes a co-worker being verbally abusive to a demented patient. The nurse should report the incident to the

   A. patient's family.
   B. physician.
   C. co-worker's supervisor.
   D. state board of nursing.

38. A nurse makes all of the following observations when assessing a patient who is in cervical traction with a halo apparatus. Which finding would require immediate intervention?

   A. The halo pins have movement.
   B. The halo pin insertion sites are crusted.
   C. The halo vest is snug-fitting.
   D. The straps of the halo vest are loose.

39. Which of the following instructions should a nurse give to a patient who has a prescription for cimetidine (Tagamet) to treat gastroesophageal reflux?

   A. "Take this medication on an empty stomach."
   B. "You will have to take these pills for the rest of your life."
   C. "Inform your healthcare providers before taking any other drug."
   D. "This drug may cause ringing in your ears."

40. Which of the following teaching instructions would a nurse include for a patient who has regional enteritis?

   A. "Limit your dietary protein intake."
   B. "Reduce stress in your lifestyle."
   C. "Decrease your activity level."
   D. "Avoid drinking fruit juices."

41. Which of the following statements, if made by a patient who is administered sulfasalazine (Azulfidine), indicates a correct understanding of the medication?

   A. "I will brush my teeth with a soft toothbrush."
   B. "I will report greenish halos around lights."
   C. "I will need to wear a hat while I am outdoors."
   D. "I will expect a tingling sensation around my mouth."

42. A two-year-old child who has a 48-hour history of loose stools is diagnosed with mild dehydration. As part of the child's treatment plan, which of the following oral re-hydration solutions would a nurse recommend to the child's parent?

   A. Uncarbonated cola
   B. Apple juice
   C. Rice-based oral solution
   D. Mineral water

276

43. Which of the following statements would a nurse include in the preoperative instruction of a patient who is scheduled for an ileostomy?

   A. "You will have one bowel movement per day."
   B. "The stool drainage will be of liquid consistency."
   C. "The pouch will be located on the left side of your abdomen."
   D. "You will be taught how to irrigate your bowel through the stoma."

44. A patient experiences nausea following the removal of a nasogastric tube. Which of the following actions would a nurse take first?

   A. Teach the patient relaxation techniques
   B. Auscultate the patient for bowel sounds
   C. Reinsert the nasogastric tube
   D. Administer the prescribed medication

45. Which of the following statements, if made by a patient who is scheduled for a sigmoid colostomy, would indicate to a nurse that the patient needs further instruction?

   A. "I will have one formed bowel movement daily."
   B. "I will have continuous drainage of liquid stool."
   C. "The pouch will be located on the left side of my abdomen."
   D. "I will be taught how to irrigate my bowel through the stoma."

46. Which of the following statements, if made by a patient who has diverticulosis, would indicate to a nurse that the patient is following the diet plan correctly?

   A. "I eat meat five times a week."
   B. "I do not eat fried foods."
   C. "I drink decaffeinated coffee."
   D. "I eat a green salad every day."

47. Which of the following actions should the nurse take first following a violent episode on a psychiatric unit?

   A. Conduct a staff debriefing
   B. Contact hospital administration
   C. Discuss the incident with the other patients
   D. Call hospital security

48. A patient makes sexually inappropriate comments to the nurse. Which of the following measures would most likely prevent such behavior?

   A. Clarify nurse-patient roles with the patient
   B. Refrain from being alone with the patient
   C. Avoid sexual topics of discussion with the patient
   D. Assign a staff member of the same gender to care for the patient

49. Which of the following orders in a patient's chart immediately following a total gastrectomy would a nurse question?

   A. "Infuse intravenous fluids at the rate of 150 ml/hr."
   B. "Turn, cough and deep breathe every two hours."
   C. "Advance nasogastric tube one inch every four hours."
   D. "Maintain the head of the bed at a 30-degree elevation."

50. When taking a history from the parent of an eight-year-old child who has rheumatic fever, a nurse would expect the child's parent to report a recent episode of

   A. urinary tract infection.
   B. acute gastroenteritis.
   C. contact dermatitis.
   D. acute pharyngitis.

51. A patient has had a total gastrectomy. Which of the following instructions should a nurse give to the patient about how to avoid dumping syndrome?

   A. "Add polyunsaturated fats to your daily meals."
   B. "Eat three balanced meals per day."
   C. "Include complex carbohydrates with your meals."
   D. "Limit fluid intake with your meals."

52. When taking a history from a patient who has a diagnosis of pyelonephritis, a nurse should expect the patient to report which of the following symptoms?

    A. Pain referred to the left shoulder
    B. Low back pain
    C. Flank pain
    D. Right upper quadrant pain

53. A patient who has pyelonephritis is given homecare instructions by a nurse. Which of the following statements indicates that the patient understands the instructions?

    A. "I will need to take antibiotics for at least three months."
    B. "I will have to drink cranberry juice every day."
    C. "I will need to strain my morning urine."
    D. "I will have to weigh myself daily."

54. Which of the following comments, if made by a patient who is administered phenazopyridine hydrochloride (Pyridium), would indicate to a nurse that the medication is effective?

    A. "There is no swelling in my ankles."
    B. "It does not hurt me to urinate."
    C. "I do not have diarrhea."
    D. "My head is not spinning."

55. Which of the following statements, if made by a patient who is administered doxorubicin hydrochloride (Adriamycin), would indicate to a nurse that the patient needs further instruction about the adverse effects of the drug?

    A. "My hair is going to fall out."
    B. "My urine will turn red."
    C. "I can expect to become constipated."
    D. "I may develop an irregular heartbeat."

56. Which of the following strategies would be appropriate for a nurse to include in the rehabilitation teaching plan of a patient who is paraplegic?

    A. Self-catheterization
    B. Assisted coughing
    C. Adaptive feeding techniques
    D. Compensatory swallowing

57. A three-year-old child is brought to the emergency department with a suspected diagnosis of acute epiglottitis. Which of the following actions would be most appropriate for a nurse to take when caring for this child?

    A. Place the child in an upright position in the parent's lap
    B. Inspect the oropharynx with a lighted instrument
    C. Obtain the child's weight on an upright scale
    D. Encourage small amounts of liquid frequently

58. A patient who has a spinal cord injury reports symptoms of autonomic dysreflexia to a nurse. Which of the following assessments should the nurse make immediately?

    A. Pedal pulses
    B. Skin inspection
    C. Breath sounds
    D. Pupillary response

59. A patient is suspected of having a subarachnoid hemorrhage. A nurse should prepare the patient for which of the following diagnostic tests?

    A. Cerebral arteriogram
    B. Intravenous pyelogram (IVP)
    C. Gallium scan
    D. Carotid doppler study

60. A patient who has mental retardation is admitted to a general psychiatric unit. Which of the following actions should the nurse include initially in the patient's plan of care?

    A. Provide reality orientation
    B. Assess the patient's level of functioning
    C. Involve the patient in cognitive restructuring
    D. Encourage participation in the existing program

61. Which of the following statements, if made by a patient who has stress-induced asthma, indicates a need for further teaching?

    A. "The doctor told me that my asthma is all in my head."
    B. "I understand that my attacks are related to my mood."
    C. "I need to use my inhaler before I start exercising."
    D. "The doctor told me that biofeedback might be helpful for my condition."

62. Which of the following actions would a nurse take when caring for a patient who is brought to the emergency department with a potential spinal cord injury?

    A. Taping the patient's eyelids closed
    B. Elevating the head of the patient's bed
    C. Placing the patient in a side-lying position
    D. Maintaining the patient's neck in extension

63. A patient with a head injury is admitted to the hospital with a BP of 130/70, a heart rate of 100 and a respiratory rate of 16. The patient's respirations increase to 24, and the heart rate decreases to 60. Which of the following medication orders should a nurse anticipate?

    A. Phenytoin (Dilantin)
    B. Mannitol (Osmitrol)
    C. Theophylline (Theo-Dur)
    D. Atropine sulfate (Atropisol)

64. A patient says to the nurse, "I'm less of a man since I've been taking my Elavil." Which of the following responses by the nurse would be therapeutic?

    A. "Are you saying that the medication interferes with sexual intimacy?"
    B. "Compliance with your medication regimen is the most important issue here."
    C. "When was the last time you had sex?"
    D. "Are you involved in an intimate relationship now?"

65. A mother asks a nurse why Haemophilus b conjugate vaccine (HibTITER) immunization is required for her two-month-old infant. The nurse should respond that HibTITER will protect the infant against certain diseases, which include

    A. hepatitis.
    B. encephalitis.
    C. epiglottitis.
    D. bronchiolitis.

66. A patient in an ambulatory care center is suspected of having an acoustic neuroma. Which of the following findings, if identified in the patient, would support this diagnosis?

    A. Diplopia
    B. Dysphagia
    C. Tinnitus
    D. Ataxia

67. Which of the following statements, if made by a patient who is scheduled for a lumbar puncture, indicates that the patient understands the procedure?

    A. "The speed of my nerve impulses will be measured."
    B. "Fluid will be removed from my spinal canal."
    C. "Dye will be injected into my arm."
    D. "My brain waves will be studied."

68. To which of the following nursing diagnoses would a nurse give priority in the care plan of a patient who is being treated for Guillain-Barré syndrome?

    A. Ineffective airway clearance
    B. Self-care deficit: feeding
    C. Fluid volume deficit
    D. Risk of injury

69. Which of the following assessment findings should indicate to a nurse that a patient has an active case of tuberculosis?

    A. Reactive tuberculin skin test
    B. Productive cough
    C. Positive chest x-ray
    D. Presence of night sweats

70. **A multiparous woman delivered a 30-weeks' gestation stillborn infant. Which of the following actions would a nurse take initially to foster the mental health of the woman?**

    A. Encourage the woman to seek genetic counseling
    B. Have a picture of the woman's other child brought to the hospital
    C. Offer the woman an opportunity to see and hold the infant
    D. Make arrangements for a member of the clergy to visit with the woman

71. **A patient with myasthenia gravis who is receiving pyridostigmine bromide (Mestinon) makes all of the following statements. Which one should indicate to a nurse that the Mestinon is having a therapeutic effect?**

    A. "My urine has no odor."
    B. "My headaches are gone."
    C. "My vision is less blurry."
    D. "My chewing is stronger."

72. **A nurse has given instructions about making appropriate lifestyle changes to a patient who has venous insufficiency. Which of the following comments, if made by the patient, would indicate compliance with the instructions?**

    A. "I eat fried chicken during the week."
    B. "I put on a girdle in the morning."
    C. "I place a stool under my legs when I sit."
    D. "I drink a beer every night after eating."

73. **A nurse should carefully assess a patient who has partial occlusion of the carotid arteries for development of which of the following conditions?**

    A. Rapid eye movements
    B. Projectile vomiting
    C. Intermittent claudication
    D. Transient ischemic attacks

74. **A 10-year-old child who has cystic fibrosis is receiving pancrelipase (Pancrease) as part of the treatment plan. Which of the following responses in the child indicates that the medication has been effective?**

    A. Increase in appetite
    B. Measurable weight gain
    C. Thinning of respiratory secretions
    D. Improved pulmonary function

75. **When a patient begins clozapine (Clozaril) therapy, a nurse should instruct the patient to return for blood level monitoring**

    A. weekly.
    B. every two weeks.
    C. monthly.
    D. every six months.

76. **Which of the following questions is most important for a nurse to ask when gathering information from a patient who has a history of peripheral vascular disease?**

    A. "Have you had recent lapses of memory?"
    B. "Do you require several pillows to sleep?"
    C. "Have you noticed weakness in your legs?"
    D. "Do you have pain in your calves when you walk?"

77. **A patient who has had a left, above-the-knee amputation asks a nurse why there is a sensation of pain in the left foot. The nurse should know that this sensation is called**

    A. intractable pain.
    B. radiating pain.
    C. phantom pain.
    D. referred pain.

78. **Which of the following observations would help a nurse establish a nursing diagnosis of potential for violence for a patient who has a diagnosis of schizophrenia, paranoid type?**

    A. Avoidance of staff and other patients
    B. Verbal threats to other patients
    C. Refusal to attend group therapy
    D. Continual change of position

79. Which of the following findings in a child with cystic fibrosis would indicate that the pulmonary treatment is achieving the desired therapeutic effect?

    A. Nonproductive cough
    B. Decreased tidal volume
    C. Fewer mucopurulent secretions
    D. Adventitious breath sounds

80. A nurse is planning to teach parents in a parenting education class about ways to reduce the incidence of sudden infant death syndrome (SIDS). Which of the following strategies should the nurse teach?

    A. Position the infant on the back or side when left unattended in the crib
    B. Put a cool mist humidifier in close proximity to the sleeping infant
    C. Avoid placing large stuffed toys in the infant's crib
    D. Place the infant in an infant seat for two hours after feedings

81. After administering an injection of haloperidol decanoate (Haldol) to a patient, the nurse should instruct the patient to

    A. stay recumbent for four hours.
    B. avoid foods containing tyramine.
    C. return for the next injection in four weeks.
    D. decrease salt intake.

82. A patient's blood test results reveal a hematocrit level of 66 mm/dL. To which of the following nursing diagnoses would a nurse give priority?

    A. Ineffective breathing pattern
    B. Activity intolerance
    C. Hyperthermia
    D. Dysreflexia

83. The bowel retraining program for a patient who has had a cerebrovascular accident should include which of these measures?

    A. Checking for impaction daily
    B. Increasing the intake of milk products
    C. Utilizing incontinent pads until control is achieved
    D. Establishing a consistent time for elimination

84. Several patients have reported to the charge nurse that one of the nurses doesn't come when called and is very grouchy and ill-humored. The charge nurse knows that the nurse is having personal problems. The charge nurse's best initial action would be to

    A. ask each of the patients to talk more about the nurse's behavior.
    B. tell the patients that the nurse is going through some difficult times.
    C. report these complaints to the nursing supervisor.
    D. tell the nurse the comments the patients have been making about her.

85. A patient tells the nurse, "The group therapist doesn't like me." Which of the following responses, if made by the nurse, would be the most therapeutic?

    A. "Why do you say that?"
    B. "I wouldn't take it personally."
    C. "Would you like me to talk to the therapist for you?"
    D. "You need to discuss that concern with the therapist."

86. A three-year-old child is to receive pyrvinium pamoate (Povan) as part of the treatment plan for pinworm infestation. A nurse would instruct the child's parent to be aware of adverse effects, including

    A. dry, scaly skin.
    B. bleeding gums.
    C. tea-colored urine.
    D. red-colored stool.

87. A child who has sickle cell anemia has been admitted to the hospital. Which of the following signs and symptoms must be reported to the physician immediately?

    A. Decreased urine output
    B. Vomiting and diarrhea
    C. Chest pain
    D. Nonproductive cough

88. The nurse should assess a patient who has bipolar disorder, manic episode, for which of the following manifestations?

   A. Waxy flexibility
   B. Flat affect
   C. Flight of ideas
   D. Hypersomnia

89. Following an amniocentesis, the nurse should instruct a client to immediately report which of the following signs and symptoms?

   A. Flu-like symptoms
   B. Inability to sleep
   C. A decrease in uterine contractions
   D. An increase in uterine contractions

90. When making a postpartum home visit, the nurse observes that the newborn is sleeping comfortably in a prone position. Parent teaching during this visit will appropriately include

   A. reinforcing this correct positioning of the infant since the baby is comfortable.
   B. teaching the parents that infants should be placed on their backs to sleep.
   C. teaching the parents to alternate the infant's sleeping position from front to back.
   D. teaching the parents that, although the baby appears comfortable, infants sleep best on their backs.

91. A 16-year-old girl who is semiconscious is brought to the emergency department after ingesting an unknown quantity of acetaminophen (Tylenol) and alcohol. To which of the following actions would a nurse give priority?

   A. Inserting a nasogastric tube
   B. Obtaining a urine toxicology sample
   C. Inducing vomiting
   D. Starting an intravenous infusion

92. A child is being treated for lead poisoning (plumbism). Prior to the administration of dimercaprol (BAL in Oil), it is essential that a nurse assess the child for an allergy to

   A. peanuts.
   B. eggs.
   C. erythromycin.
   D. iodine.

93. Which of the following statements by a patient with schizophrenia indicates a correct understanding of the antipsychotic medication therapy?

   A. "I need to follow the dose schedule and tell my nurse if I have any problems."
   B. "When I'm feeling better, I can use smaller doses of my medicine."
   C. "If I don't hear the voices, I don't need the medicine."
   D. "I don't have to worry about many side effects with this medicine."

94. The primary purpose for using the Abnormal Involuntary Movement Scale (AIMS) for a patient who is taking a phenothiazine medication is to identify

   A. tardive dyskinesia.
   B. motor incoordination.
   C. a sluggish pupillary response.
   D. a positive Babinski reflex.

95. Which of the following lunches would be most appropriate for a patient with bipolar disorder, manic episode?

   A. Cheese sandwich, banana and milk shake
   B. Vegetable soup, applesauce and tea
   C. Rice and beans, custard and carbonated water
   D. Beef stew, peas and milk

96. A pregnant woman who has abruptio placentae has an emergency cesarean section under general anesthesia. Which of the following measures should be included in the patient's care in the recovery room?

    A. Maintaining the patient in left lateral Sim's position
    B. Observing the patient for manifestations of infection
    C. Checking the characteristics of the patient's lochia
    D. Assessing the patient for a positive Homans' sign

97. Which of the following behaviors by a patient who has schizophrenia indicates impaired judgment?

    A. Spending money on a new television instead of paying the electric bill
    B. Staying up all night to care for a sick child
    C. Going outside in the rain to help a neighbor change a tire
    D. Leaving personal belongings behind when escaping from a house that has caught on fire

98. During an in-service education session for hospital staff, a nurse provides instruction about methods to prevent the spread of respiratory syncytial virus (RSV) on the pediatric unit. The nurse should stress the importance of which of the following measures as a means of control?

    A. Wearing a face mask when entering an infected patient's room
    B. Washing hands carefully before and after patient contact
    C. Using a negative pressure air-flow system in all patient rooms
    D. Obtaining personal viral titer levels to establish susceptibility

99. Four patients who are in group therapy behave in the following ways. Which behavior would indicate that the patient is benefitting from the therapy?

    A. A depressed patient verbalizes angry feelings to another patient.
    B. A co-dependent patient accepts responsibility for harmony in the group.
    C. A narcissistic patient focuses on recovery.
    D. A borderline personality patient recognizes the faults of others.

100. A seven-year-old child who weighs 60 lb (27.6 kg) is postoperative after an appendectomy and has an order for intravenous hydration. The child is to receive 1640 ml of solution in 24 hours. When using an administration set that delivers 15 drops/ml, how many drops per minute should a nurse administer?

    A. 17
    B. 45
    C. 51
    D. 68

101. Which of the following interventions would be a priority in the teaching care plan for a patient with viral hepatitis?

    A. Limit the daily amount of alcohol
    B. Take acetaminophen (Tylenol) for any discomfort
    C. Rest frequently throughout the day
    D. Use a condom during sexual intercourse

102. A nurse is instructing a patient about adrenal insufficiency (Addison's disease). Which of the following measures should the nurse stress?

    A. Include foods high in potassium in the diet
    B. Limit the intake of high-sodium foods
    C. Restrict exercise
    D. Take the medication with meals or snacks

103. The nurse monitors the therapeutic effectiveness of trihexyphenidyl hydrochloride (Artane) in the treatment of Parkinson's disease by evaluating for a decrease in

    A. bradykinesia.
    B. oculogyric crisis.
    C. tremors.
    D. propulsive gait.

104. A patient with diabetic ketoacidosis is on an intravenous (IV) insulin drip. Which of the following laboratory results requires immediate intervention?

    A. Finger stick glucose level of 70 mg/dL
    B. Serum potassium level of 2.8 mEq/L
    C. Serum osmolality of 280 mOsm/kg
    D. Blood ketones of 0.3 mg/dL

105. Which of the following children is at highest risk for developing anaphylaxis?

    A. A child who has lactose intolerance
    B. A child who had eczema as an infant
    C. A child who has a parent who is allergic to penicillin-containing medications
    D. A child who developed a rash after receiving an antibiotic

106. A patient is receiving intravenous gentamicin (Garamycin) and is ordered to have a peak and trough serum level. At which time should the nurse draw the peak level?

    A. 15-30 minutes after giving the dose
    B. 45-60 minutes before the next dose
    C. 15-30 minutes before the next dose
    D. 45-60 minutes after giving the dose

107. A patient exhibits all of the following symptoms of anorexia nervosa. Which manifestation should be addressed first in her plan of care?

    A. Cold intolerance
    B. Electrolyte imbalance
    C. Amenorrhea
    D. Sleep disturbance

108. A primigravida who delivers is noted to have a vaginal monilial infection. Therefore, it is important for the nurse to monitor the baby for symptoms of

    A. milia.
    B. thrush.
    C. impetigo.
    D. otitis media.

109. A two-year-old child is receiving chelation therapy for acute lead poisoning. In order to monitor for drug toxicity, a nurse would closely evaluate which of the following laboratory values?

    A. Hemoglobin
    B. Blood urea nitrogen
    C. Unconjugated bilirubin
    D. Platelets

110. Following a patient's treatment with pentamidine (Nebupent) treatment, the nurse should observe the patient for

    A. hypokalemia.
    B. hypoglycemia.
    C. stomatitis.
    D. hematuria.

You have finished Nursing, Part 2 of Practice Test C. You may want to take a break or possibly wait another day before taking Practice Test D.

Rationales – Practice Exam C: Nursing, Part 1

1.　**Key: C**　　　　　　　　　　**Client Need:** _Pharmacological and Parenteral Therapies_

　　C. Flow Rate　=　**Volume x Calibration**
　　　　　　　　　　　　Time(minutes)

　　　　Rate　　　=　　$\dfrac{\text{15 ml x 60 gtts/ml}}{\text{20 minutes}}$

　　　　Rate　　　=　　$\dfrac{\text{900 gtts}}{\text{20 min}}$

　　　　Rate　　　=　　**45 gtts/min**

2.　**Key: A**　　　　　　　　　　　**Client Need:** _Reduction of Risk Potential_

　　A. Patients with laryngeal nerve damage have vocal cord paralysis. If the patient's vocal cords were damaged during surgery, he will be unable to speak.

　　B. The gag reflex is tested to see if the patient can take liquids without aspirating.
　　C. The patient who has a swallowing dysfunction is at increased risk for aspiration.
　　D. Extension of the tongue provides information about muscle dysfunction.

3.　**Key: B**　　　　　　　　　　　**Client Need:** _Reduction of Risk Potential_

　　B. Patients with increased intracranial pressure have widening of the pulse pressure, bradycardia and an irregular respiratory pattern.

　　A. Escalation of discomfort is not a sign that a patient with a head injury is deteriorating. A change in level of consciousness to a decreased level is a sensitive and important indicator of the patient's neurologic status.
　　C. There is widening of pulse pressure with increased intracranial pressure. Narrowing of pulse pressure indicates hypovolemic shock.
　　D. Bradycardia is a sign of increasing intracranial pressure.

4.　**Key: C**　　　　　　　　　　　**Client Need:** _Management of Care_

　　C. The best response by the nurse is to administer the medication to facilitate the patient's ability to perform respiratory exercises.

　　A. On the third day following thoracic surgery, the patient still has incisional pain. Administering Demerol as ordered on a short-term basis will not lead to addiction.
　　B. Patients with shallow respirations usually have a rapid respiratory rate.
　　D. Demerol is an analgesic and should not be used to relieve tension. An anti-anxiety agent should be used for tension relief.

5. **Key: A** Client Need: *Pharmacological and Parenteral Therapies*

    A. If surgery is needed for the patient with Addison's disease, careful administration of fluids and corticosteroids is necessary before, during and after surgery to prevent Addisonian crisis.

    B and D.
    There is a need for life-long replacement of adrenal cortex hormones to prevent adrenal insufficiency and acute adrenal crisis with vascular collapse.
    C. There is no indication that steroids should be taken at bedtime identified in the management of hypoadrenalism.

6. **Key: A** Client Need: *Growth and Development*

    A. For best results, the thermometer should be kept by the bedside and the temperature taken upon awakening and before any activity.

    B. The basal body temperature (BBT) recording uses a BBT thermometer, which measures temperature between 96°F and 100°F. It is calibrated by tenths of a degree, thereby facilitating identification of slight temperature changes.
    C. Daily temperature changes should be plotted on a temperature graph. The graph typically shows a biphasic pattern during an ovulatory cycle, whereas the pattern will be monophasic during an anovulatory cycle. Serial BBT charts can be used to indicate if and when the woman is ovulating.
    D. The woman should take her temperature with a basal body temperature thermometer upon awakening. The temperature does not have to be taken at the same time each morning.

7. **Key: C** Client Need: *Growth and Development*

    C. The preschool child is striving for initiative. The nurse should involve the child in care, whenever possible, by having the child hold equipment, remove dressings, select the extremity, etc.

    A. The nurse should use verbal explanations but avoid overestimating the child's comprehension of words. The procedure should be explained in simple terms and in relation to how it affects the child. As with the toddler, the nurse should stress sensory aspects, i.e., what the child will see, hear, taste, smell and feel.
    B. The preschooler may view illness and hospitalization as punishment and there may be fears of bodily harm, intrusion and castration. The nurse should encourage a parental presence and the child should not be restrained.
    D. The preschooler's concept of time and his frustration tolerance are limited. The nurse should instruct the preschooler shortly before the procedure and keep equipment out of sight, except when shown to, or used on, the child.

8. **Key: C** Client Need: *Pharmacological and Parenteral Therapies*

    C. Talcum powder may enter the laryngectomy site and act as a respiratory irritant. A patient with a laryngectomy, or any patient with respiratory disease, should not use it.

    A. Use of deodorant soap is not contraindicated for a patient with a laryngectomy.
    B. Aftershave lotion may be used by the patient who has a laryngectomy.
    D. Mouthwash is not contraindicated for the patient with a laryngectomy.

9. **Key: A**   **Client Need:** *Reduction of Risk Potential*

   A. Pelvic traction can cause irritation and excoriation over the hips because of irritation by the pelvic traction belt.

   B. A pelvic traction belt does not exert pressure on the common iliac artery.
   C. Swelling in the feet and ankles is a result of dependent edema and not the result of immobility in this patient.
   D. Pressure on the peroneal nerve results from leg traction, not pelvic traction.

10. **Key: A**   **Client Need:** *Reduction of Risk Potential*

   A. The first action by the nurse should be to determine if there is bladder distention.

   B. If there is no bladder distention, the nurse should assess the fluid intake of the patient.
   C. Following spinal surgery flat bed rest is usually ordered for one to two days, depending on the extent of the surgery.
   D. If bladder distention is present, the nurse should check for an order to catheterize the patient after all other steps for promoting voiding have been used.

11. **Key: A**   **Client Need:** *Coping and Adaptation*

   A. A long-term goal for a 30-year-old man who is unable to return to construction work would be to develop alternate vocational skills.

   B. Acknowledgement of the patient's loss should be a short-term goal.
   C. Identifying areas of interest is an appropriate short-term goal.
   D. Engaging in occupational therapy is an appropriate short-term goal. The long-term goal should focus on lifestyle change.

12. **Key: D**   **Client Need:** *Psychosocial Adaptation*

   D. Patients with anorexia or bulimia nervosa are usually treated on an outpatient basis. Acute inpatient care provides clients the opportunity to be monitored 24 hours per day and is necessary when physiological symptoms are life threatening. The purpose of requiring the patient on a psychiatric unit to remain in a public place for two hours after eating is to enable the nurse to monitor the patient's behavior. Many patients with eating disorders will attempt to purge immediately following ingestion of food and need to be monitored to prevent this occurrence.

   A. Promoting social skills in patients with anorexia or bulimia is usually done in an outpatient setting in group therapy. Having patients remain in a public place after eating does not insure that social skills will be promoted.
   B. Remaining in a public place for two hours after eating will not necessarily improve the patient's concentration or attention span. Activities that require concentration are generally used to improve attention span.
   C. Remaining in a public place for two hours does not provide positive reinforcement to the patient. Often patient's view this as a negative intervention.

13. **Key: D**   **Client Need: Psychosocial Adaptation**

   D. The initial goal of treatment for a patient with anorexia nervosa is resolution of the life-threatening malnutrition. This is accomplished through strict adherence to dietary requirements, which is monitored by the nurse.

   A. Patients with anorexia nervosa enjoy talking about food and food preparation rather than eating. The initial plan should focus on dietary intake and prevention of electrolyte imbalance.
   B. The patient is weighed daily at the same time and in the same type of clothing.
   C. The diet is planned between the patient and the nutritionist to ensure a 1/4 to 1/2 pound per day weight gain. Salt is not increased in the diet.

14. **Key: A**   **Client Need: *Psychosocial Adaptation***

   A. Symptoms of cocaine withdrawal include anxiety, depression, irritability and fatigue.

   B. Seizures are manifestations of withdrawal from depressants.
   C. Rhinorrhea is a manifestation of opiate withdrawal.
   D. Respiratory depression may be a sign of narcotic use.

15. **Key: C**   **Client Need: *Physiological Adaptation***

   C. Assessing how many pillows the patient sleeps on provides information about orthopnea and the severity of congestive heart failure. Orthopnea is the inability to breathe while lying flat. The patient must sit, stand or use pillows in order to breathe deeply.

   A. A chest x-ray will elicit information about cardiac enlargement, but it is not the best way to obtain information about patient symptoms.
   B. Getting up to urinate at night is indicative of such disorders as diabetes and benign prostatic hypertrophy. The number of times a patient voids is not as important as the amount when assessing the patient with congestive heart failure.
   D. Patients with congestive heart failure retain fluid. There is generally a weight gain rather than a weight loss.

16. **Key: D**   **Client Need: *Physiological Adaptation***

   D. Blood glucose monitoring is recommended two to four times daily (usually before meals and at bedtime) for patients requiring insulin. Monitoring should not be discontinued once insulin regulation is achieved.

   A. Feet must be inspected daily. Use of a mirror is recommended if the patient is visually impaired or unable to see the bottom of the feet.
   B. A goal in the management of Type 1 diabetes is for the patient to state the importance of wearing medical identification.
   C. It is important for the patient to realize that it is not feasible or advisable to remove all sources of sugar from the diet. There are nutritious foods, such as fruits, which should be included in the diet.

17. **Key: D**   Client Need: *Physiological Adaptation*

    D. Flail chest occurs when multiple ribs or the sternum are fractured in more than one place, causing a portion of the chest wall to separate from the chest cage. Since the chest wall no longer provides the support necessary to maintain the bellows function required for normal ventilation, paradoxical breathing or chest movement occurs.

    A. A productive cough is an indication of pneumonia rather than flail chest.
    B. Decreased breath sounds are heard on auscultation and the patient's PaO2 is decreased.
    C. Vital signs show an increase in heart rate and respiratory rate. Successful achievement of patient outcomes includes a respiratory rate of 18/min.

18. **Key: A**   Client Need: *Psychosocial Adaptation*

A. **Substance abusers are often dependent and socially isolated people who use drugs to gain confidence in social situations. The nurse should teach the patient about measures to increase socialization.**

    B, C and D.
    The patient is no longer physically dependent on drugs. These options are not identified as potential nursing diagnoses post-detoxification.

19. **Key: C**   Client Need: *Growth and Development*

    C. At 20 weeks gestation, the fundus is palpable at the umbilicus. Fundal height can be measured with a tape measure and is the height from the symphysis pubis to the fundus in centimeters.

    A. At 12 weeks gestation the fundus is felt about halfway between the symphysis pubis and the top of the pubic bone.
    B. At 16 weeks gestation the fundus is felt about halfway between the top of the pubic bone and the umbilicus.
    D. After the third trimester begins, fundal heights vary due to varying fetal size.

20. **Key: B**   Client Need: *Physiological Adaptation*

    B. Humidification helps to remove crusts and prevent obstruction of the laryngectomy tube.

    A. Unless hearing is impaired, most laryngectomy patients can attempt esophageal speech or use a mechanical device such as an electrolarynges.
    C. No wet-to-dry dressings are indicated. A laryngectomy stoma can be covered with a dry dressing, a handkerchief or a stoma guard.
    D. Usually 10-14 days after surgery the patient with a laryngectomy is ready to begin oral feedings.

21. **Key A:**   Client Need: *Pharmacological and Parenteral Therapies*

    A. Dehydration can cause lithium levels to rise to toxic levels in the blood stream. A fluid intake of 1500-3000 ml/day is recommended to maintain a steady lithium level.

    B. Lithium decreases sodium reabsorption by the renal tubules, which can cause sodium depletion. A normal intake of sodium is recommended while on lithium.
    C. There is no need to increase potassium intake while on lithium.
    D. Lithium causes irritation to the gastric mucosa; therefore, it is recommended that lithium be taken with food or milk.

22. Key: B   **Client Need:** *Pharmacological and Parenteral Therapies*

B. The formula for this calculation is as follows:

$$\frac{\text{Desired amount}}{\text{Available amount}} \quad \text{x} \quad \text{volume} \quad = \quad \text{dose}$$

$$\frac{75 \text{ mcg}}{200 \text{ mcg}} \quad \text{x} \quad 10 \text{ ml} \quad = \quad \text{dose}$$

$$\frac{750}{200} \quad = \quad \text{dose}$$

$$3.75 \text{ ml} \quad = \quad \text{dose}$$

23. Key: A   **Client Need:** *Reduction of Risk Potential*

A. Lipodystrophies such as lipoatrophy (atrophy of subcutaneous tissue) and lipohypertrophy (development of fibrofatty masses at injection sites) are caused by repeated use of an injection site. The patient should be taught to rotate sites.

B and C.
Limiting saturated fats in the diet and performing daily passive range-of-motion exercises will not prevent lipodystrophy.
D. Accurate monitoring of blood glucose levels is necessary for this patient; however, it will not prevent lipodystrophy.

24. Key: A   **Client Need:** *Basic Care and Comfort*

A. Children with cystic fibrosis require a high-protein, high-calorie diet. They usually have chronic weight and nutrition problems because of their increased pulmonary energy demands. A snack of cheese and crackers provides protein and calories.

B. Cookies provide empty calories, have a high carbohydrate content and may contain fat.
C. Carrots and celery sticks are low in calories and provide no protein.
D. Apples and melon slices are also low in calories and provide no protein.

25. Key: A   **Client Need:** *Physiological Adaptation*

A. During an acute exacerbation of bronchitis, patients should limit physical activity to reduce oxygen consumption and decrease ventilatory requirements. Activities are gradually resumed as tolerated and as respiratory function improves.

B and D.
Nutritional alterations are related to anorexia. The nurse should explore ways to maintain dietary intake through the use of small frequent feedings, supplemental foods and high protein drinks. There are no sodium or potassium alterations identified with chronic bronchitis.
C. Adequate fluids are needed to liquefy pulmonary secretions.

26. **Key: D**   **Client Need:** *Growth and Development*

    D. The alpha-fetoprotein (AFP) is found in fetal circulation, amniotic fluid and maternal fluid. Elevated levels reflect open neural tube defects, such as spinal bifida and anencephaly.

    A. Rh sensitization can be detected by type and cross-match.
    B. Fetal alcohol syndrome is not screened for but detected when taking the maternal social history in the prenatal period and the history of other children in the family born with fetal alcohol syndrome.
    C. Maternal albumin levels are not routinely screened for in healthy pregnant women.

27. **Key: A**   **Client Need:** *Reduction of Risk Potential*

    A. The patient with chronic obstructive pulmonary disease (COPD) has had chronic carbon dioxide retention for such a sustained period that oxygen deprivation, rather than a high carbon dioxide level, serves as the primary respiratory stimulus.

    B, C and D.
    These options are not the primary reason for maintaining oxygen at a low flow rate.

28. **Key: D**   **Client Need:** *Reduction of Risk Potential*

    D. More than 80% of all patients with a pulmonary embolism develop sudden and severe chest pain, dyspnea and tachypnea. Other symptoms can include hemoptysis, pleural friction rub, cyanosis, diaphoresis, tachycardia, restlessness, anxiety and a cough.

    A. Cheyne-Stokes respirations (a rhythmic increase and decrease in rate separated by periods of apnea) are not characteristic of pulmonary embolism.
    B. Subcutaneous emphysema may occur after a tracheotomy as a result of leakage of air around the surgical site, or it may occur around the site of a chest tube inserted for a pneumothorax.
    C. Increased somnolence would be characteristic in cerebral embolism, not pulmonary embolism. The patient with a pulmonary embolism usually maintains consciousness.

29. **Key: A**   **Client Need:** *Psychosocial Adaptation*

    A. Initial actions by the nurse caring for a patient who is detoxifying is to provide supportive physical care, monitor vital signs, provide adequate nutrition and hydration and institute seizure precautions.

    B. The prn medication ultimately may be administered but it would not be the first action by the nurse.
    C. Providing support and reassuring the patient is necessary but the nurse first needs to determine if there is a physical cause of the cramps and headache. All physical complaints should be addressed during detoxification even if the nurse suspects that the patient is using the complaint as a means of obtaining medication.
    D. The physician may be contacted, but not until the nurse assesses the patient.

30. **Key: A**   **Client Need:** *Pharmacological and Parenteral Therapies*

    A. Notify the physician prior to giving the dose if the patient is hypokalemic. Hypokalemia may make the patient more susceptible to digoxin toxicity.

    B. Orange juice replaces potassium. However, this is severely depleted potassium requiring medication rather than dietary replacement.
    C. Doubling the dose of digoxin is contraindicated because of the increased risk of toxicity.
    D. Kayexalate is a resin exchange that is used to lower potassium. A serum potassium level of 2.8 mEq/L is already below the normal of 3-5 mEq/L.

31. **Key: B**   **Client Need:** *Pharmacological and Parenteral Therapies*

    B. Advise the patient to notify the physician if headache, nervousness, diarrhea, excessive sweating, heat intolerance, chest pain, palpitations or weight loss occurs. Synthroid is a thyroid preparation, which, if given in too high a dose, can cause symptoms of hyperthyroidism.

    A. Lethargy is not an adverse effect of Synthroid. Since Synthroid is a synthetic form of thyroid hormone, the patient should have an increase in metabolic rate.
    C. Blurred vision is not a side effect of Synthroid.
    D. Urinary retention is not associated with Synthroid use.

32. **Key: C**   **Client Need:** *Reduction of Risk Potential*

    C. Cardiac arrest in the pediatric population is primarily due to prolonged hypoxemia secondary to inadequate circulation. A sign of severe hypoxia and respiratory failure in infants is bradycardia. The normal heart rate for a one-year-old child is 80-150 beats/minute.

    A. The normal respiratory rate for a one-year-old is 30 breaths/minute. While the child's rate is decreased, it is not as significant as the heart rate.
    B. The range of normal systolic blood pressure for one-year-old girls is 72–110 mm Hg and for boys is 71-109 mm Hg.
    D. The normal rectal temperature is 99.7°F. While the child's temperature should be monitored, the most significant sign of impending cardiac arrest is the severely decreased heart rate.

33. **Key: B**   **Client Need:** *Psychosocial Adaptation*

    B. To help patients regain an accurate perception of their body size and nutritional needs, the nurse should first encourage patients to express their feelings about their body size.

    A, C and D.
    These responses negate the patient's concerns and do not encourage discussion of the issues.

34. **Key: C**   **Client Need:** *Management of Care*

    C. Activity intolerance should be addressed as a priority. The pain of intermittent claudication is alleviated by cessation of activity.

    A. Ineffective thermoregulation is not an appropriate nursing diagnosis for the patient with intermittent claudication.
    B. Non-compliance with the treatment plan may occur but the initial priority should be to alleviate the claudication.
    D. Alteration in body image may occur in so much as the patient may feel that his/her body is not functioning as it should or once did. However, this is not the priority nursing diagnosis for this patient.

35. **Key: D**   **Client Need:** *Physiological Adaptation*

    D. A manifestation of syndrome of inappropriate antidiuretic hormone (SIADH) is hyponatremia (decreased serum sodium). The diet should be supplemented with sodium.

    A. Straining of urine is done for patients with probable renal calculi. It is not done for patients with SIADH.
    B. The patient with SIADH experiences fluid overload. Initially fluids may be restricted to100-1000 ml/day.
    C. The blood glucose level does not require monitoring in patients with SIADH. It is not a disorder of glucose metabolism.

36.   Key: B   Client Need: _Physiological Adaptation_

    B. The nurse should instruct the patient to practice safe sex, including the use of a condom, since sexual transmission remains the most common mode of transmission of HIV.

    A. HIV-infected persons can share living quarters with others as long as basic hygiene is practiced. They should not share razors, toothbrushes or other household items that may contain blood or other body fluids. Eating utensils should be cleaned before re-use, but do not have to be stored separately.

    C. The avoidance of crowds and persons with respiratory infections is recommended because the patient's immune system is compromised. Close contact with children who are healthy does not have to be limited.

    D. Exposure to sunlight does not have to be limited.

37.   Key: B   Client Need: _Management of Care_

    B. Fluid volume deficit related to abnormal fluid loss secondary to excessive vomiting and inadequate fluid intake is the priority nursing diagnosis for the patient with hyperemesis gravidarum. Other diagnoses would include altered nutrition: less than body requirements and fear related to effects of hyperemesis on fetal well-being.

    A. Denial is not an appropriate nursing diagnosis for the patient with hyperemesis gravidarum.

    C. Self-esteem disturbance is not a priority nursing diagnosis for this patient.

    D. Oral mucous membranes may become dry if the patient becomes dehydrated. The priority is correcting the fluid deficit.

38.   Key: B   Client Need: _Physiological Adaptation_

    B. The nurse should reinforce that an HIV positive test result means that the patient is infected with the virus, but a positive test does not necessarily mean that the patient has AIDS. AIDS is the last stage of a continuum of HIV infection. The median time between HIV infection and a diagnosis of AIDS is 10 or more years.

    A. HIV infection may exist for many years before it progresses to symptomatic HIV disease, indicated by persistent, unexplained fever, night sweats, diarrhea, weight loss and fatigue, and then to end-stage illness or AIDS.

    C. The median time between HIV infection and a diagnosis of AIDS is 10 or more years. While research on a cure for AIDS continues, the patient should not assume that he/she would recover from HIV infection.

    D. While there are commonalities among patients with AIDS, the course of AIDS is not predictable.

39.   Key: A   Client Need: _Basic Care and Comfort_

    A. The patient with gout ineffectively metabolizes purines. The patient should be instructed to avoid foods high in purine including sardines, organ meats, meats, soups, goose and venison. The patient may eat cheese.

    B, C and D.
    Beef, sardines and liver are high in purine content and should be avoided.

40. Key: B   **Client Need:** *Physiological Adaptation*

B. The most characteristic clinical sign of Lyme disease is a large, round, red lesion that expands. The rash starts four to 20 days after the tick bite and lasts about three weeks. The most common sites are the thighs, buttocks and axilla. Other systemic manifestations of Lyme disease include intermittent fever, headache, fatigue, stiff neck and migratory joint and muscle pain.

A. The rash associated with Lyme disease does not contain vesicles.
C. A circumscribed mass is not associated with Lyme disease. The large, round rash is characteristic of the disease.
D. A phlebitic, or reddish, streak is seen in phlebitis but is not present in Lyme disease.

41. Key: A   **Client Need:** *Psychosocial Adaptation*

A. Fluid volume deficit is a life-threatening situation for the patient with bulimia if it is not addressed immediately.

B, C and D.
Although these nursing diagnoses may be appropriate for a patient with bulimia, they are not the priority nursing diagnosis.

42. Key: D   **Client Need:** *Reduction of Risk Potential*

D. Microorganisms usually grow on a section of the endocardium that has been subjected to abnormal blood streaming and turbulence, such as that which occurs with a mitral valve prolapse. Symptoms of bacterial endocarditis include an insidious onset with unexplained low-grade fever, intermittent fever, anorexia, malaise, myalgias, arthralgias, headache and weight loss. A new murmur, or change in a previously existing one, is frequently found as a result of damage to the myocardium.

A, B and C.
These manifestations are not characteristic of subacute bacterial endocarditis.

43. Key: D   **Client Need:** *Coping and Adaptation*

D. Nonpharmacologic pain management includes having the child blow bubbles to blow the hurt away. This activity is appropriate for a toddler.

A. Protective devices will not reduce pain.
B. Limiting visitors is contraindicated. A young child's ability to tolerate parental absence is limited; therefore, the parents are encouraged to visit frequently. If parents cannot visit, familiar relatives and friends should be encouraged to stay with the child.
C. Hand-held games are not developmentally appropriate for toddlers. Toddlers are too young to physically operate the games.

44. **Key: D** Client Need: _Reduction of Risk Potential_

D. Buck's traction provides a straight pull on the affected extremity and is used to relieve muscle spasm and to immobilize a limb temporarily. Traction also is a mechanism used to maintain correct positioning of bone fragments during healing.

A. Buck's traction does not prevent contractures. It is used to temporarily immobilize a limb.
B and C.
   Traction, in general, is used to reduce and/or immobilize fractures, reduce muscle spams, relieve pressure on nerves and prevent deformities. Buck's traction does not have promotion of circulation or conservation of body energy as its purpose.

45. **Key: B** Client Need: _Growth and Development_

B. The expected outcome of treatment for hyperbilirubinemia is to help the newborn's body reduce serum levels of unconjugated bilirubin. The two principal methods for reducing serum bilirubin levels are phototherapy and exchange blood transfusions.

A. Urinary output is not improved by the use of phototherapy.
C. Phototherapy does not cause an increase in stools.
D. Phototherapy does not convert a direct Coomb's test to negative.

46. **Key: C** Client Need: _Growth and Development_

C. A non-stress test assesses fetal heart rate patterns in relation to fetal movement. This test measures fetal well-being.

A, B and D.
   The non-stress test is indicated in the third trimester for women with diabetes, pregnancy-induced hypertension and other high-risk conditions. It does not measure fetal hypoxia, identify fetal cardiac abnormalities, or evaluate fetal response to contractions. It records fetal heart rate and uterine activity.

47. **Key: D** Client Need: _Basic Care and Comfort_

D. The nurse is responsible for controlling the flow of the irrigation in response to the color and consistency of the urine output and the presence of clots. The flow of the irrigation solution should be increased to flush out the clots and prevent bladder spasms.

A. Oral fluids will not decrease clot formation. The irrigating solution should be increased to flush the clots.
B. The continuous bladder irrigation will be discontinued when the urine is clear.
C. Increasing the flow of the intravenous solution will not decrease clot production.

48. **Key: B** Client Need: _Reduction of Risk Potential_

B. Deep breathing, coughing, use of the incentive spirometer and foot exercises should be explained to, and practiced by, a patient preoperatively.

A, C and D.
   These options will be addressed as part of the overall teaching plan but are less immediate than learning how to use the incentive spirometer.

49. **Key: B**   **Client Need:** *Growth and Development*

   B. Scales using facial expressions of actual children (Oucher) or of cartoon drawings (FACES) are readily accepted by children as young as three years of age.

   A. A numerical scale can be used with children who can count from one to 100.
   C. This tool is not a recognized instrument for evaluating pain levels in children.
   D. Poker chips can be used with children four years of age or older. Each chip represents a different pain intensity.

50. **Key: A**   **Client Need:** *Coping and Adaptation*

   A. Families with members who have dementia are under tremendous stresses. A goal for these individuals is that they will be able to verbalize unacceptable feelings in a supportive environment. This option encourages verbalization.

   B. This response discourages verbalization by the individual.
   C. The patient with dementia does not have the capacity to discuss the issues.
   D. The patient with dementia has a loss of short-term memory and will not recall where the underwear was last seen. This response also does not allow the individual to ventilate.

51. **Key: D**   **Client Need:** *Reduction of Risk Potential*

   D. The nurse should reposition an immobile patient every two hours while in bed and every hour while sitting in a chair in order to prevent pressure ulcers.

   A. Massaging the area will help to increase blood flow but the priority treatment to prevent further breakdown is positioning.
   B. Performing range-of-motion exercises with the patient will help to prevent the complications of immobility, but frequent repositioning, pressure relief devices and skin care can help prevent pressure ulcers.
   C. A dressing can be used to expedite healing if it removes unwanted debris from the ulcer surface, protects exposed viable tissues or provides a barrier between an open ulcer and the environment. However, the main instruction should be to reposition the patient according to schedule.

52. **Key: A**   **Client Need:** *Growth and Development*

   A. During the third trimester the most often asked question by the pregnant woman is, "How will I know when I am in labor?" Educating a woman as to the manifestations of labor is important to decrease the woman's anxiety and allow her to take an active role in her labor and birth.

   B. Childbirth classes at this time will be related to the labor and delivery experience. Previous classes would have focused on the discomforts of pregnancy.
   C. Infant feeding will be addressed briefly and reinforced on the mother-infant unit after delivery.
   D. Postpartum blues will be discussed but are not the primary focus for a patient who is at 30 weeks gestation.

53. **Key: A**   **Client Need:** *Pharmacological and Parenteral Therapies*

   A. Blood should not be allowed to hang at room temperature longer than four to six hours because of the danger of bacteria proliferation and red blood cell hemolysis.

   B and D.
   Thrombus formation and platelet aggregation are not the result of slow or delayed infusion of blood products.
   C. The cause of a febrile reaction is usually a sensitivity to white blood cells in the blood product.

54. **Key: A**   **Client Need:** *Pharmacological and Parenteral Therapies*

    A. The universal donor is blood type O-negative. AB, A, B, and O types, both positive and negative, can receive this blood.

    B and D.
    ABO and Rh incompatibility occurs when blood types do not match. The universal donor type is O-negative. Saline and other intravenous solutions can be used in an emergency until O-negative or the matching blood type is available.

    C. Rh and blood factors are already developed in the fetus so that only the appropriate blood type or the universal donor can be administered.

55. **Key: B**   **Client Need:** *Psychosocial Adaptation*

    B. Since most abused women eventually leave a seriously violent situation, the nurse can be optimistic about the eventual outcome. Interventions may not result in an immediately happy ending, but they can plant the needs of empowerment that facilitate the woman's recovery process. The woman stating that she needs to go to an anonymous shelter, rather than to family or friends, shows understanding that most abusers try to find the woman. Going to a place the abuser expects her to be could be dangerous for all involved.

    A and D.
    Without help to identify the source of his anxiety and change his way of dealing with it, the husband will not make lasting changes.

    C. Abusive spouses change the rules of the marriage without logic or fair warning. What the spouse identified as having made him behave abusively before may not be chosen by him as the cause of abuse at a later time. What made him happy, or never affected him before, may suddenly be blamed for the abuse. The woman cannot always predict which of her behaviors might trigger the abuse. The abuser abuses because he is trying to alleviate anxiety, which may not be caused at all by his relationship with her. This statement would tell the nurse that the woman perceives the problem to be her fault.

56. **Key: A**   **Client Need:** *Physiological Adaptation*

    A. Dressing changes for the burn patient can be very painful. Daily debridement removes the eschar (black, leathery crust that forms over burned tissue) that can harbor microorganisms and cause infection. Narcotics should be administered before dressing changes, debridement and other painful procedures. The nurse should allow enough time for the medication to take effect before beginning the procedure.

    B and C.
    Taking vital signs and obtaining a hemoglobin and hematocrit are not necessary prior to dressing changes.

    D. A signed consent is not required for dressing changes.

57. **Key: A**   **Client Need:** *Psychosocial Adaptation*

    A. Patient safety always takes priority. The nurse should evaluate the level of suicide intent regularly and institute the appropriate level of staff supervision. This can only be done through direct questioning of the patient.

    B. This response minimizes the suicide attempt and encourages the patient to avoid talking about incident.

    C. The patient will probably not be able to focus on his/her strengths at this time.

    D. This response indicates to the patient that the nurse is unwilling to discuss the incident.

58. **Key: B**   Client Need: *Growth and Development*

   B. The most important person to the pregnant woman is generally the father of the child. A major need during a woman's pregnancy is to secure her partner's acceptance of the child and assimilate the child into the family.

   A. Ambivalence is a normal response to pregnancy. Even women who are pleased to be pregnant may experience feelings of hostility toward the pregnancy or unborn child from time to time. If these feelings intensify and persist through the third trimester, this may indicate unresolved conflict with the motherhood role.
   C. Fatigue is common in early pregnancy.
   D. For most women the feeling of liking or not liking their bodies during pregnancy is temporary and does not cause permanent changes in their perceptions of themselves.

59. **Key: C**   Client Need: *Basic Care and Comfort*

   C. Burn patients should eat by mouth as soon as their condition permits. Intake should be adequate to meet the increased protein and calorie requirements for healing. Vitamins would be used to supplement the diet and to aid in tissue repair. Nutritional supplements and snacks to meet high-calorie, high-protein requirements should be encouraged.

   A, B and D.
   None of these diets are indicated as treatment for the burn patient.

60. **Key: A**   Client Need: *Psychosocial Adaptation*

   A. Short, frequent interactions will help to establish a therapeutic relationship while taking into account the patient's poor concentration and attention span, both of which are symptoms of depression.

   B. The depressed patient has difficulty becoming involved in any group activity because of the symptoms of poor attention span and decreased concentration. Placing the patient in an intensive group setting would promote further withdrawal from the environment.
   C and D.
   Until the patient becomes less depressed due to antidepressant therapy and/or the therapeutic milieu, the patient will not have the energy to effectively explore negative feelings or to learn problem-solving skills.

61. **Key: A**   Client Need: *Growth and Development*

   A. One of the most important goals when caring for women with preeclampsia is preventing and controlling seizures. Magnesium sulfate is the drug of choice for controlling seizures during pregnancy. Magnesium sulfate is a central nervous system (CNS) depressant that interferes with the release of acetylcholine at the synapses, decreasing neuromuscular irritability, depressing cardiac conduction and decreasing CNS irritability. A reduction in patellar reflex response would indicate therapeutic effectiveness of the drug.

   B. Acceptable urine output is 30 ml/hr. A decrease from 100 to 50 ml/hr is still acceptable.
   C. It is expected that the fetus will be monitored continuously for changes in fetal heart rate. Contractions will decrease due to a decrease in smooth muscle irritability. Since uterine muscle is smooth muscle tissue, it will relax when magnesium sulfate (MgSO4) is given.
   D. Respiratory rate will decrease, not increase, as a result of the drug, since magnesium sulfate is a CNS depressant.

62. **Key: B**   Client Need: *Safety and Infection Control*

    B. Infants weighing less than 20 pounds (9.08 kg) and/or younger than one year should always be placed in a rear-facing child safety seat in the back of the car. It is the safest place for the child to ride.

    A, C and D.
    These placements are not appropriate for a four-month-old infant.

63. **Key: D**   Client Need: *Basic Care and Comfort*

    D. Grape juice will dissolve sprinkles, which may alter the action and effectiveness of the drug.

    A, B and C.
    Applesauce, ice cream and pudding are all foods on which medication may be sprinkled.

64. **Key: B**   Client Need: *Pharmacological and Parenteral Therapies*

    B. If 20,000 units of heparin are added to 1000 ml of fluid, each ml contains 20 units of heparin. Therefore, 50 ml would contain 1000 units of heparin.

    $$(1) \quad \frac{20000 \text{ units}}{1000 \text{ ml}} \quad = \quad \frac{x \text{ units}}{1 \text{ ml}}$$

    $$1000x \quad = \quad 20000$$

    $$x \quad = \quad 20 \text{ units/ml}$$

    $$(2) \quad 20 \text{ units/ml} \times 50 \text{ ml/hr} \quad = \quad 1000 \text{ units/hr}$$

65. **Key: A**   Client Need: *Psychosocial Adaptation*

    A. Unexplained bruises and behavioral extremes are symptoms of physical abuse.

    B, C and D.
    These signs and symptoms may be the result of physical abuse but they can easily be indicators of other physical or emotional problems. The nurse should further assess the patient.

66. **Key: C**   Client Need: *Pharmacological and Parenteral Therapies*

    C. The goal of induction with Pitocin is to increase cervical dilation. Pitocin stimulates uterine contractions. Once a woman's cervix reaches five to six centimeters and labor is established, the Pitocin should be decreased. The fetal heart rate, uterine resting tone and frequency, and duration and intensity of contractions are monitored continuously.

    A. Fundal height is not part of the nursing assessment of a patient receiving Pitocin.
    B. Patellar reflexes are monitored in patients with pregnancy-induced hypertension or preeclampsia.
    D. The level of consciousness is monitored and is of particular concern for patients receiving magnesium sulfate.

67. **Key: C**   Client Need: *Pharmacological and Parenteral Therapies*

   C. Mineral oil should be administered before breakfast or in the evening for better absorption. Patients should be encouraged not to use laxatives for long-term therapy. Bowel tone will be lost from long-term use.

   A. Eating high-fiber foods assists with constipation.
   B. Drinking large amounts of water assists in the prevention of hard stools.
   D. Prune juice is indicated to assist persons with constipation to have a bowel movement.

68. **Key: B**   Client Need: *Coping and Adaptation*

   B. By acknowledging that the discussion is painful, the nurse provides an opportunity for the wife to express her feelings without the pressure of focusing on the task at hand.

   A, C and D.
   These responses focus on the task to be completed rather than the wife's behavior and need for emotional support.

69. **Key: B**   Client Need: *Pharmacological and Parenteral Therapies*

   B. Congestive heart failure (CHF) is the inability of the heart to pump an adequate amount of blood to the systemic circulation at normal filling pressures to meet the body's metabolic demands. Diuretics, such as furosemide, are given to decrease total body water and increase urine output.

   A. Rhonchi typically occur when mucus narrows the airways. Rales occur when fluid accumulates around the heart and in the airways. This child should not have rhonchi.
   C. The heart rate should decrease as excess fluid is removed.
   D. Typical urine output is 0.5-2 cc/kg/hour. Ten milliliters per kilogram is more than one would actually see.

70. **Key: A**   Client Need: *Basic Care and Comfort*

   A. Celery is high in fiber and may increase diarrhea, which is already a problem in ulcerative colitis.

   B, C and D.
   Bananas, white rice and roast chicken are permitted in the diet of a patient with ulcerative colitis.

71. **Key: A**   Client Need: *Safety and Infection Control*

   A. Injuries kill more U.S. adolescents than any other single cause, with unintentional injury, homicide and suicide accounting for 80% of deaths in teenagers and young adults in 1992. Motor vehicle crashes are the single greatest source of unintentional injury accounting for 78% of all unintentional injuries in young people.

   B, C and D.
   Suicide, poisoning and drug overdosing contribute to adolescent suicide but motor vehicle accidents are the leading cause of death.

72. **Key: B**   Client Need: *Psychosocial Adaptation*

    B. A patient may be admitted involuntarily to a psychiatric unit only when he/she tries to harm self or others.

    A. The patient who hears voices telling him to harm himself would not be admitted involuntarily unless he acted on the command of the voices.
    C. A patient cannot be admitted involuntarily for making threatening remarks. The patient can be committed if he/she acts on those threats.
    D. The patient who tries to stop traffic cannot be admitted involuntarily unless he/she tries to harm self or others.

73. **Key: B**   Client Need: *Growth and Development*

    B. The nurse should discontinue the oxytocin and then notify the physician if the fetal heart rate (FHR) is above 160 beats/min or below 120 beats/min, or if decelerations occur.

    A. Notification of the obstetrician is not the first action to be taken in this situation.
    C. Emergency measures to be taken after discontinuation of pitocin include turning the woman on her side. Reverse Trendelenburg position is not required.
    D. Amniotomy is used to stimulate labor when the condition of the cervix is favorable. It is not listed as an emergency measure for pitocin toxicity.

74. **Key: D**   Client Need: *Pharmacological and Parenteral Therapies*

    D. Steroids cause immunosuppression. The patient should be taught to report symptoms of infection, such as fever, sore throat or cough.

    A. Steroids do not cause hair loss.
    B. While steroids cause hyperglycemia, testing should be done by finger stick for glucose at least two times a day. Patients have different renal thresholds for glucose. Therefore, testing urine for glucose is not the most appropriate indication of hyperglycemia.
    C. Patients may take cathartics, if indicated. However, diarrhea is a frequent side effect of steroids.

75. **Key: C**   Client Need: *Physiological Adaptation*

    C. Symptoms of AIDS dementia include loss of balance, muscle weakness, forgetfulness, confusion and slowed thoughts.

    A, B and D.
    Headaches, bronchial infection and diarrhea are not signs of AIDS dementia.

76.   **Key: D**   **Client Need:** *Prevention and Early Detection of Disease*

   D. All sexually active adolescents should be encouraged to use condoms every time they have intercourse, even if they are using another form of birth control. The condom reduces the risk of sexually transmitted disease (STD). STDs represent one of the major causes of morbidity during adolescence and young adulthood and annually affect approximately 10 million persons under the age of 25 years.

   A. Water depletion may occur with excessive perspiration or increased activity. Thirst is an internal control mechanism to maintain fluid and electrolyte balance. Drinking sports fluids to replace loss from activity is normal.
   B. If parents have guns at home (for hunting, as an example), the guns must never be kept loaded at home and parents must teach their teenagers gun safety and proper handling.
   C. If a teenager has made the choice to drink alcohol, smoke marijuana or snort cocaine, the nurse should present alternatives to driving while intoxicated. Such options include taking public transportation or appointing a designated driver who abstains from substance use.

77.   **Key: C**   **Client Need:** *Growth and Development*

   C. After breathing is restored using the Heimlich maneuver, the child should receive medical attention and be assessed for complications.

   A. To prevent damage to the internal organs, the rescuer's hands should not touch the xiphoid process of the sternum or the lower margins of the ribs.
   B. The child may receive his/her regular diet after medical clearance.
   D. The child experienced choking not apnea; therefore, continued assessment after medical clearance is not necessary.

78.   **Key: B**   **Client Need:** *Basic Care and Comfort*

   B. Because of the inflammatory process, the white blood cell count is elevated in appendicitis.

   A. Hypokalemia is commonly seen with steroid and diuretic therapy.
   C. Low hemoglobin occurs in anemias and hemorrhage.
   D. Erythrocytes do not enlarge in acute appendicitis.

79.   **Key: C**   **Client Need:** *Psychosocial Integrity*

   C. Establishing a "no-harm" contract allows for regular checks with the patient regarding safety and level of suicidal feelings.

   A, B and D.
   Promoting self-esteem, cognitive restructuring and involving the patient in milieu therapy are helpful for the patient to ease suicidal ideation, but they are not the nursing priority that addresses the safety of the patient. Nursing diagnoses that address safety are always the first to be initiated.

80.   **Key: D**   **Client Need:** *Coping and Adaptation*

   D. The mother should be made aware that adolescents often regress when under stress. When the daughter feels that she has more control over what is happening to her and to her body, she should give up thumb sucking.

   A. This response does not provide the mother with an explanation of her daughter's behavior.
   B. This response is not accurate.
   C. There is no need for the mother to leave the room at this time. The mother may provide additional security and support for the daughter.

81. **Key: D** Client Need: *Physiological Adaptation*

    D. Increased uric acid levels are characteristic of gout. Allopurinol inhibits uric acid synthesis and, if effective, will decrease uric acid levels.

    A. Glucose levels would be monitored in patients with diabetes mellitus.
    B. Calcium levels would be monitored in patients with heart disease and osteoporosis.
    C. Alkaline phosphatase would be monitored in patients with liver and bone disease.

82. **Key: B** Client Need: *Reduction of Risk Potential*

    B. Patients in traction should be assessed for nerve and circulatory disturbances. To check for capillary filling times, the patient's nail beds are compressed to produce blanching and assessed for return of color.

    A. There is no indication that ankle clonus is found in patients with skeletal traction.
    C. The femoral arteries are proximal to left leg traction and would not provide any information about circulatory disturbances.
    D. To check for nerve disturbances, the function of the peroneal nerve should be assessed, not the patellar reflex.

83. **Key: A** Client Need: *Pharmacological and Parenteral Therapies*

    A. The patient needs to be aware that ingesting any substances containing alcohol can trigger the alcohol disulfiram reaction. This reaction can include hypotension, severe nausea and vomiting, flushing, throbbing headache and respiratory difficulty.

    B and C.
    Antabuse, by itself, produces transient effects that usually disappear within two weeks such as, drowsiness, fatigue, impotence, headache, acne and a metallic aftertaste. It is not necessary to monitor the pulse rate four times a day or to rest after taking the drug.
    D. Antacids interfere with the absorption of medications and should not be taken with Antabuse.

84. **Key: A** Client Need: *Psychosocial Adaptation*

    A. Manic patients need room to move around and furnishings that do not overstimulate them in order to decrease distractibility. Overstimulation can increase the intensity of symptoms and can lead to aggressive and intrusive behavior.

    B. Competitive games can stimulate aggression and increase psychomotor activity.
    C. Discouraging verbalization of feelings is rarely the correct intervention with a patient.
    D. Manic patients have impaired problem-solving abilities. They exhibit unwarranted optimism and poor judgment due to inaccurate interpretations of the environment.

85. **Key: D** Client Need: *Safety and Infection Control*

    D. With rapid treatment some children can be saved. Resuscitative measures for the near-drowning victim should begin at the scene, and the victim should be transported to the hospital with maximum ventilatory and circulatory support.

    A. Calling the local emergency number should be done after one minute of basic life support.
    B. Attempting to transport a child by automobile wastes valuable time in obtaining help. Transport by the Emergency Medical Service (EMS) is recommended and preferable.
    C. Wrapping warm blankets around the child may promote normothermia, but it is not the first intervention.

86. Key: A   **Client Need:** *Psychosocial Adaptation*

A. The nurse should assign solitary, non-competitive activities that take some concentration. Activities that demand concentration keep the patient's attention on reality and minimize hallucinatory and delusional preoccupation.

B, C and D.
Creative, independent and competitive tasks are not appropriate for the patient who is out of touch with reality. Specific manual tasks within the scope of the patient's abilities can often be useful as distractors from delusional thinking.

87. Key: C   **Client Need:** *Psychosocial Adaptation*

C. Bulimia is an eating disorder characterized by episodes of binge eating alternating with purging behaviors. Physical complications may include potassium depletion with subsequent cardiac arrest, spastic colitis, tetany, tooth discoloration and decay, hypertension and esophageal or gastric perforation. Frequent vomiting and irritation from stomach acid causes erosion of tooth enamel, an increase in dental caries, chronic esophagitis, chronic sore throat, difficulty swallowing, inflammation of the throat and parotitis.

A. Gingival hyperplasia is most frequently seen as a complication of anticonvulsants, such as Dilantin.
B. Painful mucosal lesions are seen in oral herpes or ulcers. While stomach acid can irritate the mucosal lining of the mouth, it generally does not cause painful lesions.
D. A deeply furrowed tongue is not characteristic of bulimia.

88. Key: D   **Client Need:** *Physiological Adaptation*

D. Transient periods of neurological deficit occur in ischemic cerebral attacks. The symptoms vary and may include temporary forgetfulness and weakness.

A. Throbbing frontal headaches are not identified as a problem in transient ischemic attacks.
B. Fatigue is a symptom of many different conditions and may be due to lack of oxygen. However, it is not the major manifestation in ischemic cerebral attacks.
C. Irritability is a symptom of basic tumors and other cerebral conditions.

89. Key: D   **Client Need:** *Prevention and Early Detection of Disease*

D. Studying the demographics of the community will determine what types of treatment modalities are most needed in the community. For example, if there are a large number of elderly living in the area, a geriatric center that offers outpatient, day and inpatient treatment programs might be established.

A. Religious affiliations may have an indirect effect on the mental health needs of the community.
B. The number of recreational facilities may have an indirect effect on the mental health needs of a community.
C. While the opinions of the residents are important, the demographic facts will be a more reliable indicator of the mental health needs of the community.

90. Key: A   **Client Need:** *Physiological Adaptation*

A. A patient with hypertension may experience a variety of symptoms including headache in the occipital region that is worse in the morning on arising, fatigue, dizziness, palpitations, angina, dyspnea, blurring of vision and epistaxis.

B. Bleeding gums are not symptomatic of hypertension.
C. Tachycardia, not bradycardia, occurs in hypertension.
D. Blurring of vision, not nearsightedness, is a symptom of hypertension.

91. **Key: C**   **Client Need:** *Reduction of Risk Potential*

    C. Inhaled allergens are the most common triggers for asthmatic attacks. Sleeping with the windows open allows potential respiratory irritants into the room. This statement by the parent indicates a need for further instruction.

    A. Hypoallergenic pillows may help to decrease respiratory irritants.
    B. Dusting and vacuuming will reduce the amount of respiratory irritants in the home.
    D. Aerosol sprays can be inhaled and frequently trigger asthmatic attacks.

92. **Key: A**   **Client Need:** *Reduction of Risk Potential*

    A. Following a hip replacement, a patient's affected hip should be placed in extension, with an abduction wedge between the legs.

    B. The affected hip should be placed in extension.
    C. The pillow should be between the legs to prevent adduction.
    D. A trochanter roll is used to prevent extreme rotation.

93. **Key: B**   **Client Need:** *Reduction of Risk Potential*

    B. Following a bronchoscopy, the patient should remain NPO until the gag reflex returns.

    A. A fiberoptic scope is inserted through the nose and threaded down the airway to visualize the bronchi.
    C. Once the procedure is completed, the patient should not have any problem with deep breathing.
    D. Dye is not used during the procedure.

94. **Key: A**   **Client Need:** *Physiological Adaptation*

    A. Patients with Parkinson's disease experience muscle rigidity and a mask-like facial expression.

    B. Tremors involve the hand, diaphragm, tongue, lips and jaw. They are more prominent at rest and are aggravated by emotional stress.
    C and D.
    Nystagmus and long-term memory loss are not identified as manifestations of Parkinson's disease.

95. **Key: A**   **Client Need:** *Reduction of Risk Potential*

    A. After cleft palate repair, injury to the newly-closed palate must be prevented. No sharp objects such as spoons or forks are permitted in the child's mouth.

    B. A nasogastric tube is not necessary for this patient.
    C. Liquids are given by mouth but straws are not used since they could irritate the suture line.
    D. Soft foods may be fed from the side of a spoon but allowing the child to use the spoon can result in damage to the operative site.

96. **Key: A**   **Client Need:** *Growth and Development*

    A. An acceptable hemoglobin level in early pregnancy is above 11 mg/dL. This patient should be further assessed for anemia.

    B. An acceptable white blood cell (WBC) count during pregnancy is from 5000 to 15,000/cu mm.
    C. This is a normal blood value that does not generally change during pregnancy.
    D. This is a normal blood value that does not generally change during pregnancy.

97. **Key: B**   Client Need: *Prevention and Early Detection of Disease*

    B. In the Framingham longitudinal study of coronary artery disease (CAD), a family history of heart disease was found to be an independent predictor for coronary artery disease in men.

    A. A patient with a serum cholesterol level greater than 259 mg/dL is three times more likely to develop CAD than is one with a serum level of 200 mg/dL.
    C. Men over 45 years of age with a BP > 140/90 and all adult women with blood pressures > 160/95 have a 50% higher chance of mortality.
    D. Obesity, lack of exercise and stress also increase the risk of CAD.

98. **Key: C**   Client Need: *Physiological Adaptation*

    C. Angina is aggravated by exercise, cold weather, emotional stress and ingestion of meals. Rest or nitroglycerin relieves angina.

    A, B and D.
    Taking a deep breath, moving the extremities or sleeping in a supine position does not aggravate angina.

99. **Key: C**   Client Need: *Growth and Development*

    C. Since the patient delivered under local anesthesia, she should be able to ambulate at this time. The nurse should, however, assist the patient to the bathroom to make sure that she is able to safely ambulate.

    A and B.
    Using a bedpan or using a bedside commode is not necessary for this patient. The patient should be fully mobile four hours after delivery.
    D. Catheterizing a patient post-delivery should only be done when all other measures are not effective.

100. **Key: A**   Client Need: *Physiological Adaptation*

    A. Decreasing venous return to the heart reduces the amount of volume returned to the left ventricle during diastole. This can be accomplished by placing the patient in a high Fowler's position with the feet horizontal in the bed or dangling at the bedside.

    B, C and D.
    Offering analgesia, monitoring urine output and encouraging ambulation are not indicated as comfort measures for this patient.

101. **Key: C**   Client Need: *Pharmacological and Parenteral Therapies*

    C. The chief problem with epidural anesthesia is its tendency to induce hypotension in the laboring woman. The nurse should take the blood pressure every two minutes during the first 20 minutes after each injection of anesthesia.

    A, B and D.
    Assessments of deep tendon reflexes, oxygen saturation and pupillary reaction are not the priority in this situation. The patient's blood pressure should be monitored to assess for hypotension.

102. Key: A   Client Need: _Prevention and Early Detection of Disease_

  A. Correct use of a helmet is essential in preventing head injuries for any cyclist.
  B. Riding with a friend does not insure the child's protection against head injury.
  C. This option does not indicate the content of the formal course of instruction.
  D. Riding on the sidewalks can cause problems for pedestrians as well the cyclist and does not insure protection against head injury. The cyclist can still fall.

103. Key: B   Client Need: _Pharmacological and Parenteral Therapies_

B. Checking the radial pulse is not a required assessment for the patient taking warfarin. Assessments are related to detecting signs of bleeding or thrombosis. The patient needs additional instruction regarding Coumadin therapy.

  A. Aspirin may increase the response to warfarin and increase the risk of bleeding.
  C. Ingestion of large quantities of foods high in vitamin K content may antagonize the anticoagulant effect of warfarin. Vitamin K-rich foods include asparagus, broccoli, brussel sprouts, mustard greens and spinach.
  D. The patient should be instructed to shave with an electric razor during warfarin therapy.

104. Key: B   Client Need: _Pharmacological and Parenteral Therapies_

B. Exposure to air, heat and moisture inactivates nitroglycerin. The patient has a correct understanding of the medication instructions related to storage of the drug.

  A and D.
    The tablet is to be placed under the tongue or in the buccal pouch and allowed to dissolve; it should not be swallowed.
  C. Dosage may be repeated at five-minute intervals for three doses, if necessary.

105. Key: A   Client Need: _Physiological Adaptation_

A. In congestive heart failure (CHF), dyspnea at rest in the recumbent position is known as orthopnea. In performing an assessment of the patient with CHF, the nurse should ask whether the patient uses a number of pillows to sleep, or sleeps in an upright position in a bed or a chair.

  B. The nurse should ask the patient about weight gain. An adult may retain four to seven liters of fluid (10-15 pounds) before pitting edema occurs.
  C. Tinnitus is not a symptom of right or left-sided heart failure.
  D. Intolerance to heat is a symptom of hyperthyroidism. Hyperthyroidism may lead to congestive heart failure.

106. Key: B   Client Need: _Pharmacological and Parenteral Therapies_

B. Mannitol is ordered to promote rapid osmotic diuresis and to reduce intracranial pressure by promoting the movement of excess fluid from the brain tissues into the blood so it can be eliminated.

  A and D.
    Mannitol does not prevent meningitis or decrease angioedema.
  C. Diuretics such as mannitol increase, rather than decrease, urinary output.

107. Key: D   Client Need: *Physiological Adaptation*

 D. **Hypertrophic pyloric stenosis occurs when the circular muscle of the pylorus becomes thickened causing constriction of the pylorus and obstruction of the gastric outlet. The history may vary, but the infant begins to regurgitate small amounts of milk immediately after a feeding. After an infant feeding, peristaltic waves can sometimes be noted moving from left to right toward the pylorus.**

 A. Absence of bowel sounds is usually associated with paralytic ileus.
 B. Ribbon-like stools are seen in Hirschsprung's disease.
 C. The infant is hungry in spite of the vomiting and will usually take milk again after the vomiting.

108. Key: C   Client Need: *Growth and Development*

 C. **Assessments in the immediate postpartum period are focused on early detection of hemorrhage. Atony, or relaxation of the uterine musculature, may occur allowing accumulation of blood. The uterus must be palpated to ascertain that atony is not occurring.**

 A. Assessment for Homans' sign is not necessary in the immediate postpartum period.
 B. Perineal discomfort will be identified by the patient and is not a priority in the first hour postpartum.
 D. Assessment of bowel sounds is not a priority in the early postpartum period.

109. Key: D   Client Need: *Psychosocial Adaptation*

 D. **Most patients with chronic schizophrenia have difficulty structuring their free time, often resist taking medication and need assistance with being responsible for self-care.**

 A, B and C.
   While a patient with chronic schizophrenia may be able to maintain a job, take public transportation and do his/her own shopping, the structure of the community placement program is basic to functioning. Without this basic structure the patient might not be able to perform these more complex tasks.

110. Key: A   Client Need: *Growth and Development*

 A. **Increasing the fluid volume can help decrease the possibility of hypotension, a frequent complication of labor due to peripheral vasodilatation.**

 B. Routine ultrasound is not necessary prior to epidural anesthesia.
 C. If the patient is reminded and able to void every two hours, there is no need for a Foley catheter. The patient will have decreased sensation to void.
 D. Epidural anesthesia does not have significant neurological changes associated with its administration.

111. Key: A   Client Need: *Reduction of Risk Potential*

A. **Autonomic dysreflexia is an acute emergency, which is characterized by severe, pounding headache, hypertension, profuse sweating and bradycardia in patients with cord lesions above the T6 level.**

 B. Spinal shock is characterized by an absence of reflexes, paralyzed and flaccid muscles below the level of the lesion and hypotension.
 C. Grand mal seizures are characterized by intense rigidity of the entire body followed by alterations of muscle relaxation and contraction.
 D. The unconscious patient with severely impaired cerebral function may respond to a stimulus with decerebrate posturing (extremities extended and reflexes exaggerated).

112. **Key: B**   Client Need: _Basic Care and Comfort_

    B. The nurse should emphasize the importance of maintaining an adequate flow of urine by encouraging the drinking of about 2.5 liters of fluid daily; emptying the bladder frequently so that there is minimal residual urine; and giving attention to personal hygiene because infection of the bladder and kidneys almost always occurs by the ascending route.

    A. The nurse should emphasize the importance of drinking about 2.5 liters of fluid daily.
    C. Larger amounts of cranberry juice are required for the prevention of urinary tract infections, which are common in patients with spinal cord injury.
    D. Avoiding carbonated beverages is not identified in the bladder management for a spinal cord injury patient.

113. **Key: C**   Client Need: _Reduction of Risk Potential_

    C. The use of a tourniquet and hemolysis of the specimen can result in high serum potassium levels.

    A. The preservative in the specimen tube may alter the results of a test, but the type of tube should not affect the potassium level.
    B. The hydration status of the patient can cause false positive potassium results, but the time of the nutritional intake should not affect the results.
    D. The nurse should monitor serum chloride, serum magnesium and serum protein test results when hypokalemia is present. Correcting a potassium deficit with potassium only is not effective if chloride, magnesium and protein levels also are low.

114. **Key: C**   Client Need: _Growth and Development_

    C. Due to the risk of uterine rupture, labor and vaginal birth are not recommended in women who have had a previous fundal classical scar.

    A, B and D.
    The risk for uterine rupture is the prime reason for cesarean section in this patient.

115. **Key: A**   Client Need: _Reduction of Risk Potential_

    A. A hemoglobin and hematocrit level is drawn 12 to 24 hours after delivery. If the hemoglobin is below 10 g/dL, supplementary iron is usually prescribed. This may be treated with an oral iron supplement.

    B. The white blood count is within normal range of 5000-9000 cells/cu mm.
    C. The platelet count is within normal range of 150,000-300,000 cells/cu mm.
    D. This is a borderline red blood cell level that should be monitored (normal = 4.4-5.5 million/cu mm), but a hemoglobin of 9 g/dL would be of greater concern.

116. **Key: C**   Client Need: _Reduction of Risk Potential_

    C. The nurse should monitor the patient during feeding and suction the airway as needed to prevent aspiration. Maintain a working suction machine at the patient's bedside.

    A. Oxygen is used for dyspnea as needed. The priority is prevention of aspiration.
    B. A tracheostomy is not indicated unless the upper airway is obstructed or long-term mechanical ventilation is needed.
    D. A padded tongue blade is not used with the patient who experiences difficulty in swallowing.

117. Key: A   Client Need: *Physiological Adaptation*

   A. Pursed-lip breathing prolongs exhalation and increases airway pressure, minimizing the effects of air trapping and assisting the patient with better ventilation.

   B. Humidification may be useful for patients living in a dry climate, or who complain of dry heat in the winter.

   C and D.
   Breathing into a paper bag increases the arterial carbon dioxide level (pCO2). A low arterial oxygen level (Pa02) is the primary drive for breathing in a patient who has emphysema. Oxygen for this patient should be given at 1-3 L/min.

118. Key: A   Client Need: *Pharmacological and Parenteral Therapies*

   A. While taking rifampin (Rifadin), the patient's body fluids (urine, tears and sweat) will be orange in color.

   B. The medication can be taken at bedtime to help prevent nausea.

   C. The medication should be continued for six months or longer as ordered. Once a patient's skin test is positive, chest x-ray is essential to rule out active disease or old, healed lesions.

   D. There is no indication that patients should avoid the sun while taking Rifadin.

119. Key: D   Client Need: *Psychosocial Adaptation*

   D. During a course of electroconvulsive therapy, short-term memory loss is expected.

   A. Although electroconvulsive therapy involves an induced seizure, seizures are not expected after the procedure is completed.

   B. Mild muscle spasms during the procedure are a result of the induced seizure but do not continue after the procedure is completed.

   C. The patient experiences short-term memory loss and confusion during the course of ECT, which can be interpreted as a personality change by significant others of the patient. However, the patient's basic personality remains unchanged.

120. Key: D   Client Need: *Psychosocial Adaptation*

   D. Nursing interventions for a patient who is acting out include patient identification of feelings so that they do not need to be acted out.

   A. The patient may need to be reminded of unit rules if the acting out behavior violates the rules. However, developing an ability to identify the feelings that occur prior to acting out is a priority.

   B. Telling the patient to control the feelings will not be effective if the patient is unaware of why the behavior is occurring.

   C. Isolating the patient is not indicated unless the patient is a danger to himself or others.

121. Key: A   Client Need: *Prevention and Early Detection of Disease*

   A. Escherichia coli (E-coli) grows in meat such as hamburger that is not thoroughly cooked. Parents should be aware of the health hazard of not cooking chopped meats thoroughly.

   B. E-coli bacteria is found in uncooked chopped meats. Drinking bottled mineral water will not prevent an outbreak.

   C. Cleaning kitchen surfaces that come in contact with uncooked meat using soap and hot water after contact is important but surfaces do not need to be sanitized on a daily basis.

   D. Swimming in chorine-treated water does not prevent the spread of E-coli bacteria.

122. **Key: D** Client Need: *Growth and Development*

   D. The primary management of all cases of disseminated intravascular clotting (DIC) involves correction of the underlying cause; e.g., removal of the dead fetus, treatment of existing infection, preeclampsia or eclampsia and removal of placental abruption.

   A. Toxic shock is almost always found in menstruating females who use tampons. The organism is Staphylococcus aureus.
   B. Pulmonary embolism is not associated with disseminated intravascular coagulation or abruptio placentae.
   C. Cerebrovascular accident also is not associated with disseminated intravascular coagulation or abruptio placentae.

123. **Key: B** Client Need: *Reduction of Risk Potential*

   B. Exercise decreases bone resorption and stimulates bone formation. Immobilization produces rapid bone loss.

   A. Excessive caffeine intake can increase calcium loss.
   C. Exposure to sunlight provides vitamin D, which is necessary for the metabolism of calcium.
   D. Assessing the patient's dietary intake of calcium, protein and vitamin D is essential in identifying the risk of osteoporosis.

124. **Key: C** Client Need: *Pharmacological and Parenteral Therapies*

   C. Tinnitus, or ringing in the ears, is a side effect of ibuprofen (Motrin) administration.

   A, B and D.
   Loss of hair, photosensitivity and swelling of the gums are not related to the administration of ibuprofen (Motrin).

125. **Key: A** Client Need: *Physiological Adaptation*

   A. Hypothyroidism is associated with altered thought processes related to diminished cerebral blood flow secondary to decreased cardiac output. It is manifested by forgetfulness, impaired ability to conceptualize and personality changes.

   B. A goiter, or enlarged thyroid gland, may interfere with the functioning of surrounding structures.
   C. Fluid volume deficit can be related to hyperthyroidism due to hypermetabolism and altered nutrition: less than body requirements.
   D. The diagnoses of hypothyroidism and hyperthyroidism can both include activity intolerance in the plan of care for the patient.

126. **Key: A** Client Need: *Physiological Adaptation*

   A. Treatment with I131 decreases the production of thyroid hormone. Its effect would be evidenced by the patient's increased ability to sleep through the night.

   B and D.
   These distractors would indicate a continuance of increased production of thyroid hormone, and ineffective treatment with I131.
   C. Hypothyroidism can cause decreased hearing acuity, resulting from otosclerosis secondary to arteriosclerosis. However, sodium iodide does not affect hearing activity.

127. **Key: A** Client Need: *Psychosocial Adaptation*

   A. An inappropriate lack of concern about difficulties despite their apparent severity is called la belle indifference. This phenomenon is often seen in patients with conversion disorders and is unconscious in nature.

   B. Malingering is a conscious effort to deceive others, often for a personal gain, by pretending physical symptoms.
   C. Hypochondria is an excessive preoccupation with an imaginary illness, even though there are no signs or organic changes. Although there is no organic cause for the blindness, the patient is not excessively preoccupied with the illness.
   D. Confabulation is the detailed fabrication of a story to make up for memory loss. The purpose of confabulation is to maintain self-esteem. It is often seen in dementias.

128. **Key: B** Client Need: *Prevention and Early Detection of Disease*

   B. A contrast mammogram involves injection of a contrast dye into the breast duct. Dye is never injected into a vein prior to a mammogram. The patient's statement indicates the need for further teaching.

   A. Skin creams, antiperspirants, deodorants and powders should be removed prior to the test.
   C and D.
      The patient who is scheduled for a mammogram should be told that the test takes 15-30 minutes, and that compression of the breast may produce a temporary discomfort.

129. **Key: D** Client Need: *Growth and Development*

   D. Characteristics of the postmature infant include the following: dry, cracked skin that is parchment-like at birth, nails of hard consistency extending beyond the fingertips, profuse scalp hair, subcutaneous fat layers that are depleted, loose skin that gives an old-person appearance, long and thin body contour, absent vernix, an alert, wide-eyed appearance and often meconium staining of skin, nails and cord.

   A. On assessment, depression of fontanelles is never within limits. It is associated with dehydration.
   B. Post-term infants will have deep sole creases over the entire sole.
   C. Excessive lanugo is associated with a pre-term infant.

130. **Key: C** Client Need: *Psychosocial Adaptation*

   C. Individuals with somatoform disorders resolve conflicts and reduce anxiety through bodily symptoms. This is the primary gain. They also achieve secondary gains, such as attention and relief from responsibility, from the symptoms.

   A and D.
      The patient's symptoms are not a manifestation of a dysfunctional relationship or confusion.
   B. Co-dependency involves a preoccupation with the thoughts and feelings of another.

131. **Key: C**   **Client Need:** *Growth and Development*

   C. Fear of strangers appears to reach its height during the eighth month, so much so that this phenomenon is often termed "eighth month anxiety" or separation anxiety. An infant at the height of this phase will not go willingly from the parents' arms to a nurse's arms. By 12 months, most children have overcome their fear of strangers and are alert and responsive again when approached. The mother needs to be made aware that the child's behavior is normal.

   A. A major milestone of 10 months is the ability to bring the thumb and first finger together in a pincer grasp. This enables the child to pick up small foods such as cereal from the breakfast tray. The mother's statement does not indicate a knowledge deficit.
   B. If the child sleeps in a crib, the mattress should be at its lowest position so that the height of the side rails increases. The mother's statement does not indicate a knowledge deficit.
   D. Infants are required by law to be placed in car seats when traveling by automobile. The seat can be forward facing once the child struggles to sit up or weighs 21 lbs. The mother's use of the car seat is appropriate.

132. **Key: D**   **Client Need:** *Pharmacological and Parenteral Therapies*

   D. Propranolol (Inderal) is an autonomic nervous system agent that acts as a beta-adrenergic antagonist or sympatholytic blocking agent. It slows the sympathetic nervous system response seen in hyperthyroidism.

   A, B and C.
   Propranolol does not inhibit the synthesis of thyroid hormone, increase the effect of calcium on cardiac tissue or enhance the secretion of thyroid stimulating hormone (TSH).

133. **Key: A**   **Client Need:** *Growth and Development*

   A. Fatigue occurs as a result of a decreased cardiac output in the elderly.

   B. Decreased bone density predisposes the elderly to fractures.
   C. Decreased muscle mass results in decreased strength and agility.
   D. Decreased joint mobility results in decreased overall mobility.

134. **Key: B**   **Client Need:** *Coping and Adaptation*

   B. Consistency in enforcing unit rules is essential to the success of therapy. Patients often test limits but limit setting provides security and tells them what is expected of them while they are on the unit.

   A, C and D.
   Consistent limit setting should be the norm for all patients. The nurse should not make exceptions or become involved in bargaining with the patient.

135. **Key: C**   **Client Need:** *Management of Care*

   C. Increasing the temperature of the warming unit is the action of choice.

   A. An infant in a warming unit should not be wrapped because the blanket will interrupt the thermal environment.
   B. Parents are not routinely informed of the temperature instability of an infant under a radiant warmer.
   D. Glucose is needed for increased energy but a heelstick is not the priority nursing action.

136. **Key: C**   **Client Need:** *Psychosocial Adaptation*

   C. Coping effectively with thoughts and feelings associated with traumatic events is an identified goal for patients with posttraumatic stress disorder.

   A. Stress management techniques may help the patient manage the anxiety associated with working through the conflicting emotions about the trauma. However, working through the conflict is the priority.
   B. Intellectualization is a defense mechanism used to avoid expressing emotion associated with traumatic events.
   D. Working through the conflict must be accomplished before the patient can demonstrate a normal range of mood.

137. **Key: A**   **Client Need:** *Growth and Development*

   A. Children respond to loss of routine and ritualism by demonstrating problems with activities such as feeding, sleeping, dressing, bathing, toileting and social interaction. Although some regression is to be expected in all these areas, sensitivity to the special needs of children can minimize effects.

   B. Most children this age do cry when their parents go home.
   C. Some children at this age do stop eating but it is not an expectation of most children.
   D. If the child has experience with hospitalization, he/she may cooperate. However, the majority of four-year-olds do not willingly participate in routine procedures.

138. **Key: D**   **Client Need:** *Reduction of Risk Potential*

   D. The nurse should maintain the patency of the catheter because clots can obstruct urine flow resulting in painful bladder spasms.

   A. The first intervention is to determine if the catheter is patent. Medication may be given afterward.
   B. Placing a pillow under the patient's knees will not relieve post-prostatectomy pain.
   C. Measuring the patient's abdominal girth is not indicated.

139. **Key: D**   **Client Need:** *Growth and Development*

   D. Due to an increased incidence of sudden infant death syndrome (SIDS) in infants who sleep prone, the American Academy of Pediatrics now advocates against the use of the prone position in the first few months of life.

   A. The breastfeeding newborn will feed every one to three hours during the day.
   B. Most newborns need burping because they swallow air when sucking. If the infant has been crying, he/she should be burped before the feeding and after every ounce of feeding.
   C. Sucking is the infant's chief pleasure that may not be satisfied with feeding. Parents may choose to use a pacifier.

140. **Key: C**   **Client Need:** *Basic Care and Comfort*

   C. The patient should be taught to include more carbohydrates in the diet because they are less stimulating to the pancreas than fatty foods.

   A, B and D.
   The patient with pancreatitis is instructed to increase fruits, vegetables and breads in the diet.

141. Key: B   Client Need: *Coping and Adaptation*

B. According to Erikson, a stage of accomplishment is achieved somewhere between age six and adolescence. The goal of this stage is to achieve a sense of personal and interpersonal competence. The middle childhood years are the time for collections, which constitute another ritual. The younger school-age child's collections are an odd assortment of unrelated objects in messy, disorganized piles. Collections of later years are more orderly and selective, and are organized more neatly in books or boxes.

A. Racing toy cars is an activity of preschoolers.
C. Sleeping with a musical stuffed animal is an activity of toddlers.
D. Watching daytime television shows is an activity of adolescence.

142. Key: D   Client Need: *Safety and Infection Control*

D. Ingestion of toxic agents is common during early childhood. The highest incidence occurs in children under two. Parents should have two doses of ipecac syrup for each child in the home, know its proper use and administration, and have the phone number and location of the nearest poison control center readily available.

A and C.
Purchasing an appropriate potty chair and having the child use a plastic training cup are not the highest priorities when providing anticipatory guidance.
B. Drowning ranks second among boys and third among girls ages one to four years as a cause of accidental death. Supervising children when near any source of water is essential. Teaching swimming to children under age four does not provide drown-proofing and may lead to a false sense of security.

143. Key: C   Client Need: *Reduction of Risk Potential*

C. During a laparoscopic cholecystectomy a one-centimeter puncture is made slightly above the umbilicus, and the abdominal cavity inflated with three to four liters of carbon dioxide to increase visibility.

A. The gall bladder is removed through four small punctures in the abdomen.
B. A patient with an incisional cholecystectomy may have a T-tube for bile drainage if the common bile duct is explored.
D. A cleansing enema is usually not done prior to a laparoscopic cholecystectomy.

144. Key: B   Client Need: *Psychosocial Adaptation*

B. Compulsive behavior is performed for the purpose of decreasing anxiety. Other methods should be encouraged.

A, C and D.
Interfering with the performance of the rituals without substituting a behavior to decrease the anxiety will only make the patient more anxious. The outcome of the surgery may be affected by the patient's anxiety level.

145. Key: B   Client Need: *Growth and Development*

B. Expressed breast milk may be fed to the baby in a bottle, or the milk can be stored and frozen. If breast milk is to be transported, it should be kept cold. To thaw frozen breast milk, it should be placed in lukewarm tap water. A microwave oven should not be used to heat breast milk because it may cause hot spots, which can, in turn, cause thermal burns in an infant's mouth. The mother's statement indicates a need for further instruction.

A, C and D.
These actions by the mother are appropriate and do not require further intervention by the nurse.

146. Key: A   Client Need: *Growth and Development*

A. The dropper or syringe is best placed along the side of the toddler's tongue and the medication administered slowly in small amounts. The nurse should wait for the child to swallow in-between administrations.

B. The medication may be mixed with a small amount of juice. The child may not completely drink a moderate amount of juice and, consequently, may not receive the full dose of medication.
C. It is best not to use a child's favorite food when mixing medication, since the medicine may alter the taste of the food.
D. When medication has an unpleasant taste, the nurse may pinch the child's nose and have the child drink the medicine through a straw. Much of what we taste is associated with smell.

147. Key: B   Client Need: *Coping and Adaptation*

B. How the patient feels about him/herself in relation to the event tells the nurse what impact the traumatic event has had on the patient.

A, C and D.
Previous experience with the event, number of stressors and the size of the patient's support network may influence the impact of the event on the patient. The question asks what is most decisive in determining the impact of the traumatic event on the patient and that is self-perception of the event.

148. Key: C   Client Need: *Physiological Adaptation*

C. Sources of infection for hepatitis B include contaminated needles and syringes, blood products, sexual contact, perinatal transmission and asymptomatic carriers. Eating utensils must be cleaned thoroughly but do not need to be kept separate.

A. Since hepatitis B is transmitted via blood products, the patient is not allowed to donate blood.
B. For patients with hepatitis B, a condom is advised for sexual intercourse, and the partner should be vaccinated.
D. Approximately five to 10 percent of patients with hepatitis B become carriers.

149. **Key: C**   **Client Need:** _Prevention and Early Detection of Disease_

   C. Hepatitis B vaccination is recommended for all infants. The first dose of the vaccine may be given at birth or at one to two months of age in infants born to healthy women. Infants born to an infected mother or a mother who is a chronic carrier should be given the vaccine as well as hepatitis B immunoglobulin within 12 hours of birth. Parental consent should be obtained before administering the vaccine.

   A. Haemophilus influenza B vaccine is given at two months, four months and six months of age.
   B. Rubella vaccine is given at 12 to 15 months of age.
   D. Varicella vaccine is given at 12 to 15 months of age.

150. **Key: A**   **Client Need:** _Prevention and Early Detection of Disease_

   A. Vaccination of pregnant women with the rubella vaccine is contraindicated because it is a live attenuated virus. Women who are vaccinated are advised to refrain from getting pregnant for at least three months after vaccination.

   B. The woman does not have to refrain from eating eggs unless there is a history of anaphylaxis with eggs.
   C. It is not necessary for the woman to avoid contact with others.
   D. It is not necessary to avoid breastfeeding after vaccination.

Rationales-Practice Exam C: Nursing, Part 2

1. **Key: B**   **Client Need:** *Psychosocial Adaptation*

   B. Incompatibility between the history and the injury is probably the most important criterion on which to base the decision to report suspected abuse.

   A, C and D.
   All of these actions by the parents are appropriate and do not necessarily indicate child abuse.

2. **Key: A**   **Client Need:** *Reduction of Risk Potential*

   A. It is impossible to halt a seizure once it has begun and no attempt should be made to do so. The nurse must remain calm, stay with the child and prevent the child from sustaining any harm during the seizure.

   B. Attempts to lower the child's temperature will not prevent or stop the seizure.
   C. Sponging is indicated for elevated temperatures from hyperthermia rather than fever. Ice water and alcohol are inappropriate, potentially dangerous solutions. Sponging or tepid baths are ineffective in treating febrile children, either when used alone or in combination with antipyretics, and cause considerable discomfort.
   D. Parents need to be educated about febrile seizures but this is not an initial priority during a seizure.

3. **Key: A**   **Client Need:** *Basic Care and Comfort*

   A. The diet for cirrhosis includes restricting protein to approximately 35 to 50 grams per day. Carbohydrate intake should be 300 to 400 grams per day. Baked chicken = 27 grams of protein.

   B. Apple pie = 3 grams of protein
   C. Macaroni = 5 grams of protein
   D. Spinach = 5 grams of protein

4. **Key: D**   **Client Need:** *Reduction of Risk Potential*

   D. If bleeding is not controlled by other methods, balloon tamponade of varices may be instituted. The esophagogastric tubes (Sengstaken-Blakemore or Minnesota) are three-lumen or four-lumen tubes with two balloon attachments. One lumen serves as a nasogastric suction tube; the second is used to inflate the esophageal balloon. When the tube is in the stomach, the gastric balloon is inflated and the lumen clamped; the tube is then pulled slowly so that the balloon is held tightly against the cardioesophageal junction. A football helmet-shaped device is used to keep traction on the tube, which keeps it in the proper position. If bleeding continues after the gastric balloon is inflated, the esophageal balloon is inflated to the desired amount of pressure, as determined by the physician, and then clamped. To stop the bleeding, the pressure must be greater than the individual's portal pressure.

   A. Chest tubes allow air and fluid to drain from the pleural space. They also prevent air or fluid from entering the pleural space. Chest tubes are not required for treatment of bleeding esophageal varices.
   B. Endotracheal tubes are artificial airways necessary when normal airway patency and protection cannot be maintained. These tubes are placed in the nose or mouth and passed to just above the tracheal carina. Unless airway patency is an issue, an endotracheal tube is not needed to treat bleeding esophageal varices.
   C. The Salem sump is a double lumen tube used for gastric decompression and can be used as a route for gastric suctioning and sampling. Since the Sengstaken-Blakemore and Minnesota tubes provide for suction, the Salem sump is not required.

5. **Key: C**   Client Need: _Coping and Adaptation_

   C. The individual's strengths are those effective coping mechanisms on which the individual can draw when encountering difficulty. The patient needs a repertoire of effective coping mechanisms in order to function more independently in the residential treatment center.

   A. Although family history of mental illness may influence the style of coping a patient uses, assessment of present coping abilities and strengths is essential to determining the patient's readiness for discharge.
   B. Developmental history may influence the type of program in which the patient is placed. Individual strengths are not necessarily dependent upon one's developmental history.
   D. The patient's social support system is important to success in the residential treatment program. However, a patient's strengths determine how that patient uses and maintains the support system.

6. **Key: C**   Client Need: _Physiological Adaptation_

   C. Clinical manifestations of impending hepatic coma include disorientation and asterixis or flapping hand tremors.

   A, B and D.
   These options are not identified as impending signs of hepatic coma, encephalopathy, ascites or esophageal varices.

7. **Key: A**   Client Need: _Management of Care_

   A. As immune system depletion progresses, CD-4 counts decrease and patients are at higher risk for opportunistic infections, cancers and HIV encephalopathy.

   B, C and D.
   Limiting the number of venipunctures, instituting regular position changes and monitoring intake and output are important in the treatment plan of the patient with a decreased CD-4 count, but protection from infection would be the priority.

8. **Key: D**   Client Need: _Coping and Adaptation_

   D. Social skills consist of simple interactions such as introducing one's self, starting and ending a conversation and asking for help. The patient must be able to effectively interact to get basic needs met.

   A, B and C.
   The ability to work and to drive and knowledge about medications may enhance the patient's success in the community, but these skills are not essential to successful living.

9.   **Key: B**   **Client Need:** *Growth and Development*

   B. When preparing the preschool child for a procedure, it is important to allow choices when possible and encourage parental presence. Other strategies for diverting attention so that the child will be less focused on the procedure include having the child tightly squeeze the hands of a parent or an assistant, count aloud, sing a familiar song such as a nursery rhyme or verbally express discomfort.

   A. Children need to hear from adults that the youngsters did the best they could in the situation no matter how they behaved. It is important for children to know that their worth is not being judged on the basis of their behavior in a stressful situation.
   C. Children should be allowed to express feelings of anger, anxiety, fear, frustration or any other emotion. It is natural for children to strike out in frustration or to try to avoid stress-provoking situations. They need to know it is all right to cry.
   D. Children should be allowed to express feelings. Bargaining with children should not be done.

10.   **Key: B**   **Client Need:** *Safety and Infection Control*

   B. Pulses distal to the catheterization site should be checked for equality and symmetry. The nurse should question checking of the brachial pulse.

   A. The child will have a pressure dressing over the catheterization site.
   C. Depending upon the hospital policy, the child may be kept in bed with the affected extremity in a straight position for four to six hours after venous catheterization and six to eight hours after arterial catheterization to facilitate healing of the cannulated vessel.
   D. The nurse should assess the temperature and color of the affected extremity.

11.   **Key: A**   **Client Need:** *Growth and Development*

   A. The newborn should be fed eight or more times per day. The mother is encouraged to feed her infant around the clock. Early, frequent nursing will enhance meconium excretion and decrease bilirubin levels. Nurseries now initiate early first feedings. Feeding of the newborn soon after birth stimulates the gastrocolic reflex and the passage of meconium. Because bilirubin is excreted in meconium, early feeding may help to prevent jaundice.

   B. Breastfeeding and the need for cessation of breastfeeding to decrease hyperbilirubinemia are not well documented in the nursing research.
   C. There is no need to check the temperature unless the infant is under phototherapy.
   D. Expose to direct sunlight is advice given to parents of an infant with only slightly elevated bilirubin levels but its relative success in decreasing bilirubin levels is not known.

12.   **Key: C**   **Client Need:** *Pharmacological and Parenteral Therapies*

   C. The patient is aware that levothyroxine does not cure hypothyroidism. This therapy is lifelong and must be continued on a daily basis.

   A, B and D.
   The patient should be instructed to take this medication exactly as prescribed and not to discontinue it without consulting the physician.

13.   **Key: A**   **Client Need:** _Pharmacological and Parenteral Therapies_

   A. Electrolyte imbalances may occur with the administration of Lasix. Side effects of Lasix include hypovolemia, dehydration, hyponatremia, hypokalemia, hypochloremia, metabolic alkalosis, hypomagnesemia and hypocalcemia. Nursing measures include monitoring the patient for hypokalemia.

   B. While glucose may also be elevated with the administration of Lasix, potassium values are more critical. Sudden death from cardiac arrest has been reported with the administration of Lasix.
   C and D.
   Protein and creatinine alterations are not identified as adverse effects of Lasix therapy.

14.   **Key: D**   **Client Need:** _Growth and Development_

   D. There may be an increased risk of sudden infant death syndrome (SIDS) in infants whose mothers abused cocaine while pregnant.

   A. In light of diarrhea, fluids may need to be increased to prevent dehydration and electrolyte imbalances.
   B. Infants born to cocaine-abusing mother's sleep for short periods.
   C. Infants born to cocaine-abusing mothers often experience irritability, marked nervousness, rapid changes in mood and hypersensitivity to noise and external stimuli. These neonates exhibit poor feeding, irregular sleep patterns, tachypnea, tachycardia and, often, diarrhea.

15.   **Key: A**   **Client Need:** _Basic Care and Comfort_

   A. The diabetic exchange list for meat includes the choice of cheese and eggs.

   B, C and D.
   Bacon, chocolate milk and baked beans are not included on the meat exchange list as equal substitutes.

16.   **Key: B**   **Client Need:** _Pharmacological and Parenteral Therapies_

   B. Vomiting and diarrhea are early signs of lithium toxicity. Vomiting and diarrhea deplete sodium. Since Lithium is similar in chemical structure to sodium, as the kidneys attempt to compensate for sodium loss by reabsorption of sodium, they also reabsorb lithium, increasing the risk of lithium toxicity.

   A, C and D.
   Fine motor tremors, stiff neck and shoulders and seeing halos around lights are not indicative of lithium toxicity.

17.   **Key: A**   **Client Need:** _Growth and Development_

   A. The infant's temperature must be stable prior to bathing.

   B. Infant's typically lose five to 10 percent of their birth weight prior to discharge. This weight loss is within normal limits.
   C. The posterior fontanel is triangular in shape (0.5 to 1.0 cm). The fontanel should not be depressed or bulging but soft and flat. Its size does not determine the timing of the first bath.
   D. Infants may not pass stool within the first 12 hours of life but should pass meconium within 24 hours. Passage of meconium does not influence the timing of the first bath.

18. **Key: C**   **Client Need:** *Growth and Development*

   C. During the first three days after delivery, vaginal discharge is usually bright red. Abnormal bleeding from lacerations usually spurts, instead of trickling. In the first hour postpartum, the bleeding will be bright red or rubra. The amount of bleeding is more significant than the color at this time.

   A. At the end of the third stage of labor the fundus is approximately two centimeters below the level of the umbilicus. Within 12 hours, the fundus may be one centimeter above the umbilicus.

   B. The intensity of uterine contractions increases immediately after birth.

   D. During the first 24 hours after delivery the woman's temperature may rise to 100.4°F (38°C) due to the dehydrating effects of labor.

19. **Key: A**   **Client Need:** *Reduction of Risk Potential*

   A. Peritoneal dialysis involves repeated cycles of instilling dialysate into the peritoneal cavity, allowing time for substance exchange and then removing the dialysate.

   B. One of the primary advantages of peritoneal dialysis is the relative ease of administration that allows it to be used in community health centers without elaborate and sophisticated equipment. It can be easily managed and often provides the patient with greater independence and mobility than hemodialysis.

   C. Different types of catheters are used in peritoneal dialysis. The catheters are usually tunneled under the skin and inserted into the peritoneum to allow exchange of fluids. Permanent vascular access is used in hemodialysis.

   D. In continuous ambulatory peritoneal dialysis the dialysate is instilled into the abdomen and left in place for four to eight hours. The empty dialysis bag is folded up and carried in a pouch or pocket until it is time to drain the dialysate. The patient's activities are not restricted.

20. **Key: A**   **Client Need:** *Basic Care and Comfort*

   A. Some nutritionists recommend eating several small meals a day because the body's metabolic rate is temporarily increased immediately after eating. When several small meals a day are ingested, more calories are burned due to an increased metabolic rate.

   B. The caloric intake may need to be reduced to 800-1200 calories daily, but the person will need frequent professional monitoring. The nurse should not instruct a patient to reduce his/her intake to this level without medical supervision.

   C. An obese person needs to follow a well-balanced, low-caloric diet.

   D. There is general agreement that consuming most of the daily caloric intake at a large evening meal results in less weight loss than when the calories are more evenly distributed throughout the day.

21. **Key: D**   **Client Need:** *Growth and Development*

   D. It is difficult for a child to be restricted at any phase of development, but the teenager needs continual positive reinforcement, encouragement, and as much independence as can be safely assumed during this time. Adolescents appreciate guidance and assistance regarding participation in social activities. Socialization with peers should be encouraged and every effort made to help the adolescent feel worthwhile.

   A, B and C.

   Body image, activity limitation and financial burdens may be concerns of the adolescent with scoliosis, but the need for independence takes priority at this stage of development.

22.   **Key: B**   Client Need: *Pharmacological and Parenteral Therapies*

   B. It is important to help the patient understand that hypertension is a chronic condition that cannot be cured but can be controlled with drug therapy, diet therapy, an exercise program, periodic evaluation and other lifestyle changes. The patient's statement indicates a need for further instruction.

   A. The patient is aware that to decrease orthostatic hypotension, he/she should arise slowly from the bed and stand slowly.
   C and D.
   The patient is aware that since frequent urination can interrupt sleep, diuretics work best when taken early in the morning rather than at night.

23.   **Key: B**   Client Need: *Psychosocial Adaptation*

   B. Clouding of consciousness and fluctuating level of awareness are symptoms seen in delirium but not dementia.

   A, C and D.
   Memory impairment, auditory hallucinations and cognitive disturbances are manifestations of both dementia and delirium.

24.   **Key: B**   Client Need: *Basic Care and Comfort*

   B. Foods high in folic acid include green and yellow vegetables, liver, citrus fruits, whole grains, yeast and legumes.

   A, C and D.
   Dairy products, citrus juices, and fish and poultry are not high in folic acid.

25.   **Key: D**   Client Need: *Reduction of Risk Potential*

   D. The patient has a suture line at the junction of the gums and upper lip. Toothbrushes with bristles may irritate the suture line and delay healing.

   A. The patient has nasal packing and a gauze dressing under the nose.
   B. The head of the bed should be elevated 30 degrees at all times to reduce cerebral edema.
   C. The patient should avoid sneezing, coughing, bending, vigorous hair brushing, or any activity that will increase intracranial pressure.

26.   **Key: B**   Client Need: *Reduction of Risk Potential*

   B. Complications of fractures include infection, compartment syndrome, venous thrombosis and fat embolism.

   A and C.
   Electrolyte imbalance and fluid volume deficit may occur post-surgery but they are not evident in the immediate post-fracture period.
   D. Disuse syndrome may occur late into the post-fracture period but is not seen immediately.

27. **Key: A**   **Client Need:** *Basic Care and Comfort*

   A. Itching under the cast can be extremely uncomfortable. The patient may be tempted to slip an object under the cast to scratch. This is a dangerous practice because of the possibility of breakage and/or skin irritation. Guided imagery is a way to help patients distract themselves from their pain and may produce a relaxation response.

   B. Heat increases itching due to vasodilatation.
   C. Elevation prevents dependent edema.
   D. Inability to move the toes indicates compression. The cast may be too tight if the patient is unable to move his/her toes.

28. **Key: B**   **Client Need:** *Pharmacological and Parenteral Therapies*

   B. The first step a nurse should take when a blood lithium level is 1.6 mEq/dL or above is to withhold the lithium dose.

   A. The physician should be called to re-evaluate the dose after the nurse has the results of a re-drawn lithium level.
   C. Vital signs may be helpful in assessing if the patient is dehydrated, which can cause an increase in lithium levels. However, this should not be the initial action by the nurse.
   D. The nurse should re-check the lithium level after withholding the dose of lithium.

29. **Key: D**   **Client Need:** *Pharmacological and Parenteral Therapies*

   D. Aspirin prevents platelet aggregation. It is used to prevent the recurrence of transient ischemic attacks (TIAs) and myocardial infarction (MI) and as prophylaxis against myocardial infarction due to fibrin platelet emboli.

   A, B and C.
   While Aspirin can be used to relieve pain, and reduce fever and inflammation, these are not desired outcomes for a patient with coronary artery disease (CAD).

30. **Key: B**   **Client Need:** *Safety and Infection Control*

   B. All burn patients are considered at risk for an often-fatal infection with Clostridium tetani. A routine prophylactic procedure when a patient is admitted to the hospital is the administration of tetanus toxoid intramuscularly. Burn wound infection occurs through either auto-contamination or cross-contamination. The high risk for infection is related to loss of the skin barrier, an impaired immune response, the presence of invasive catheters and invasive procedures. Medical management of the patient during the acute burn phase focuses on infection control, wound care, wound closure, nutritional support, pain management and physical therapy.

   A. Hypothermia is a problem for the burn patient because skin assists in maintaining body temperature.
   C. Body image disturbance is an appropriate nursing diagnosis but does not have higher priority then risk for infection.
   D. Impaired physical mobility is a nursing diagnosis secondary to pain and immobility, but does not have a higher priority than risk for infection.

31. **Key: D**   **Client Need:** *Pharmacological and Parenteral Therapies*

    D. Non-opioids, including acetaminophen, and nonsteroidal anti-inflammatory agents are suitable for mild to moderate pain. Opiates are required for moderate to severe pain. A combination of the two analgesics attacks pain on two levels: non-opioids at the level of the peripheral nervous system and opiates at the central nervous system. This approach provides increased analgesia without increased side effects.

    A, B and C.
    These options do not indicate the purpose for administering a combination of opiates and non-opiates to control pain.

32. **Key: A**   **Client Need:** *Basic Care and Comfort*

    A. The nurse should provide a high-carbohydrate, high-protein diet to meet the increased nutritional needs of the burn patient and to prevent malnutrition. A milk shake contains 11 grams of protein and 60 grams of carbohydrate.

    B. Carrot sticks contain one gram of protein and seven grams of carbohydrate.
    C. Apple slices contain a trace of protein and 17 grams of carbohydrate.
    D. Flavored gelatin contains four grams of protein and 34 grams of carbohydrate.

33. **Key: B**   **Client Need:** *Reduction of Risk Potential*

    B. Contractures and joint deformities are prevented by exercise, positioning and splinting throughout the healing process

    A and D.
    Placing pillows under the head or maintaining semi-Fowler's position contributes to flexion contractures.
    C. Sandbags on either side of the chest will not prevent contractures.

34. **Key: A**   **Client Need:** *Reduction of Risk Potential*

    A. It is important to immobilize the body part before the patient is moved. Adequate splinting is essential to prevent damage to the soft tissue by the bony fragments. No attempt is made to reduce an open fracture, even if bone fragments are protruding through the wound.

    B and D.
    The leg should be splinted in its present position rather than in a neutral position. Pressure should not be applied directly over the wound.
    C. In an open fracture the wound is covered with a clean (sterile) dressing to prevent contamination of deeper tissues.

35. **Key: B**   **Client Need:** *Reduction of Risk Potential*

    B. When skeletal traction is being used, the apparatus is checked to see that the weights hang freely.

    A. Balanced suspension provides countertraction so that the pulling force of the traction is not altered when the bed or patient is moved.
    C. Alignment of the patient's body in traction must be maintained as prescribed to promote an effective line of pull.
    D. The overbed trapeze should be above the patient's chest.

36.   **Key: A**   **Client Need:** *Physiological Adaptation*

   A. Infection increases the tendency toward hemorrhage, and since bleeding sites become more easily infected, special care is taken to avoid performing skin punctures whenever possible. When finger sticks, venipunctures, intramuscular injections and bone marrow tests are performed, aseptic technique must be employed with continued observation for bleeding. Since the rectal area is prone to ulceration from various drugs, hygiene is essential. To prevent additional trauma, rectal temperatures and suppositories are avoided.

   B. Respiratory isolation is not indicated for a decreased platelet count.
   C. Meticulous mouth care, rather than a bland diet, is essential since gingival bleeding with resultant mucositis is a frequent problem.
   D. Most bleeding episodes can be controlled with judicious administration of platelet concentrates or platelet-rich plasma. Severe spontaneous internal hemorrhage usually does not occur until the platelet count is less than 20,000/mm3.

37.   **Key C**   **Client Need:** *Management of Care*

   C. The supervisor is the person next in the chain of command. It is the supervisor's responsibility to call together the interdisciplinary team to decide on the appropriate intervention.

   A and D.
   The interdisciplinary team will decide, based on policy, if and when it is appropriate to notify the family and/or the state board of nursing.
   B. The physician will be notified by the supervisor since the physician is part of the interdisciplinary team.

38.   **Key: A**   **Client Need:** *Management of Care*

   A. The nurse should check the pins and screws for loosening since the halo apparatus is to remain intact without movement. The nurse would notify the physician if there is any sign of loosening in the apparatus and keep a wrench at the bedside.

   B. The halo pin insertion sites should be kept clean and free from crusts. However, crusting would not require immediate intervention.
   C and D.
   Halo traction is usually anchored to a body cast and not contained within a vest.

39.   **Key: C**   **Client Need:** *Pharmacological and Parenteral Therapies*

   C. To prevent drug interactions the patient should be instructed to notify his/her physician prior to taking other medications.

   A. Tagamet does not need to be taken on an empty stomach.
   B. Tagamet does not have to be taken for the rest of the patient's life.
   D. Tagamet does not cause ringing in the ears.

40.   **Key: B**   **Client Need:** *Coping and Adaptation*

   B. The patient with regional enteritis or Crohn's disease must identify stressors and methods to eliminate or reduce them.

   A and D.
   The nurse should assist the patient in selecting high-calorie, high-protein, low-fiber meals. Adequate intake of vitamins and minerals, especially vitamin C found in citrus fruits and juices, should be encouraged. Strained juices are permitted on a low-fiber diet.
   C. Physical activity level is not believed to have an effect on regional enteritis.

41. **Key: C**   Client Need: _Pharmacological and Parenteral Therapies_

    C. Photosensitivity may occur as a side effect of Azulfidine. The patient should be instructed to wear a wide-brimmed hat and long sleeves when out-of-doors.

    A, B and D.
    Bleeding gums, seeing halos around lights and a tingling sensation around the mouth are not associated with administration of Azulfidine.

42. **Key: C**   Client Need: _Basic Care and Comfort_

    C. Rice-based oral rehydration solution (ORS) has been developed as an alternative to the standard glucose oral rehydration solution. These nutrient-based solutions may decrease diarrheal volume loss and shorten the duration of the disease.

    A, B and D.
    Diarrhea is not managed by encouraging intake of clear fluids such as fruit juices, uncarbonated soft drinks and mineral water, since these fluids usually have a high carbohydrate content, a low electrolyte content and high osmolality.

43. **Key: B**   Client Need: _Reduction of Risk Potential_

    B. The nurse should make the patient aware that after surgery, the fecal drainage from the ileostomy is liquid and may be constant.

    A. The drainage from an ileostomy is liquid rather than formed.
    C. The stoma site for an ileostomy is right midline.
    D. Ileostomy stomas should not be irrigated.

44. **Key: B**   Client Need: _Reduction of Risk Potential_

    B. The patient should be assessed for nausea, abdominal discomfort and the presence of bowel sounds.

    A, C and D.
    Before removal of a gastrointestinal tube, GI function is assessed. Bowel sounds are auscultated, the abdomen is observed for distention, the patient is asked whether flatus has been passed and the patient's tolerance of tube clamping and ice chips is noted. Relaxation techniques, reinserting the tube and administering medication may be logical interventions but would not be the first priority.

45. **Key: B**   Client Need: _Reduction of Risk Potential_

    B. The stool from a sigmoid colostomy will be formed rather than liquid. Liquid stool is expected with an ileostomy. The patient should have additional teaching in this regard.

    A, C and D.
    These patient statements indicate a correct understanding of the surgery.

46. **Key: D**   Client Need: _Basic Care and Comfort_

    D. Treatment of diverticulosis involves adherence to a high-fiber diet. Foods high in fiber include bran, whole wheat and fresh vegetables.

    A, B and C.
    Eating meat five times a week, eliminating fat from the diet and drinking decaffeinated beverages are not identified as part of the management of diverticular disease.

47. **Key: A**   Client Need: *Psychosocial Adaptation*

    A. After the crisis (violent episode) is over, it is recommended that the team discuss any concerns they may have had during the crisis, since this type of occurrence can be stressful for staff as well as patients.

    B. The nursing supervisor would be notified of the violent episode. Hospital administration would not be notified unless serious complications arose from the situation.
    C. The incident would be discussed with other patients as a group but would not be done until staff reviewed the situation.
    D. Hospital security may be called during the violent episode but is not usually called afterward.

48. **Key: A**   Client Need: *Psychosocial Adaptation*

    A. Frequently restating the nurse's role throughout the relationship can help the patient to maintain boundaries

    B, C and D.
    Therapeutic nursing responses to sexual advances by a patient include clarifying nurse-patient roles, setting limits on expected behaviors and exploring the meaning of the patient's behavior.

49. **Key: C**   Client Need: *Safety and Infection Control*

    C. To protect the healing suture line, the nurse should not routinely irrigate or reposition the nasogastric tube. The nurse should question this order.

    A. Fluids are given parenterally until the nasogastric tube is removed and the patient is able to drink enough fluids orally. Generally, 1000 ml intravenous solutions are infused at a rate of 125 ml/hr over eight hours.
    B. Turning, deep breathing, incentive spirometry and ambulation are stressed during the period when the pain medication is at its peak effectiveness.
    D. The patient should never lie flat in bed. The accepted position is mid-to-high-Fowler's position.

50. **Key: D**   Client Need: *Physiological Adaptation*

    D. Strong evidence supports a relationship between upper respiratory infection with group A streptococci and subsequent development of rheumatic fever.

    A. Urinary tract infections are mostly caused by E-coli bacteria.
    B. Organisms causing acute gastroenteritis do not cause rheumatic fever.
    C. Contact dermatitis is an inflammatory reaction, not an infectious process.

51. **Key: D**   Client Need: *Reduction of Risk Potential*

    D. Prevention is the most effective means of controlling dumping syndrome. The nurse should instruct the patient to follow a moderate-fat, high-protein diet, with limited carbohydrates. Simple sugars should be avoided, and fluids with meals are discouraged because they increase total volume. The patient should eat small, frequent meals.

    A. A diet with moderate fat is encouraged to delay gastric emptying. Adding polyunsaturated fats to daily meals is not necessary.
    B. Small frequent meals rather than three large meals should be encouraged to decrease total volume.
    C. Complex carbohydrates are limited and simple sugars should be avoided because they leave the stomach more quickly than fats and proteins.

52. **Key: C**   **Client Need:** *Physiological Adaptation*

    C. Clinical manifestations of pyelonephritis include acute flank pain, fever, chills, malaise, leukocytosis and bacteria in the urine.

    A. Pain referred to the left shoulder may be the result of "gas" pains and abdominal distention.
    B. Flank pain, rather than low back pain, is symptomatic of pyelonephritis.
    D. Right upper quadrant pain is indicative of liver or gall bladder disease.

53. **Key: A**   **Client Need:** *Physiological Adaptation*

    A. The course of antibiotic therapy for pyelonephritis may extend over weeks. If the infection becomes chronic, maintenance drug therapy may continue indefinitely.

    B. Cranberry juice in large amounts will acidify the urine and prevent urinary tract infections. It is not used in the treatment of pyelonephritis.
    C. Straining of urine is indicated for patients with renal calculi.
    D. Daily weights would be indicated for patients with urinary retention and/or renal failure.

54. **Key: B**   **Client Need:** *Pharmacological and Parenteral Therapies*

    B. Pyridium is prescribed for symptomatic relief of pain, burning, frequency and urgency arising from irritation of the urinary tract.

    A, C and D.
    Absence of ankle edema, diarrhea and vertigo are not intended effects of Pyridium.

55. **Key: C**   **Client Need:** *Pharmacological and Parenteral Therapies*

    C. Administration of Adriamycin would cause diarrhea rather than constipation. The patient needs additional instruction about the medication.

    A. Administration of Adriamycin will cause complete alopecia that is reversible.
    B. Adriamycin will cause the urine to be reddish in color for one to two days after administration.
    D. Administration of Adriamycin can cause ventricular dysrhythmias and cardiotoxicity.

56. **Key: A**   **Client Need:** *Physiological Adaptation*

    A. Following a spinal cord injury, the bladder becomes atonic and cannot contract reflexively. The patient should be instructed in self-catheterization to avoid over-distention of the bladder.

    B. The paraplegic patient is able to cough, deep breathe and perform chest physiotherapy. There is no indication that assisted coughing is necessary.
    C and D.
    Paraplegia involves dysfunction of the lower extremities, bowel and bladder. There is no indication that adaptive feeding devices or compensatory swallowing techniques are necessary.

57. **Key: A**   **Client Need:** *Physiological Adaptation*

    A. Epiglottitis is frightening for both child and parents. The child is allowed to remain in the position that provides the most comfort and security. The child generally insists on sitting upright, leaning forward. This is easily accomplished by the child sitting in the parent's lap to reduce distress.

    B. Throat inspection should only be attempted when immediate intubation can be performed if needed.
    C. Obtaining the child's weight is not a priority at this time. Epiglottitis is an emergency situation.
    D. The child should be kept NPO.

 *Test C / Part 2 Answers*

58. Key: B   Client Need: *Reduction of Risk Potential*

B. The manifestations of autonomic dysreflexia result from an exaggerated sympathetic response to noxious stimuli. Stimuli are commonly bladder and bowel distention, but can be pressure ulcers, spasms, pain and pressure on the penis or uterine contractions. The nurse should assess for pressure areas on the skin.

A, C and D.
Pedal pulses, breath sounds and pupillary response are not priority assessments for autonomic dysreflexia.

59. Key: A   Client Need: *Reduction of Risk Potential*

A. Cerebral arteriogram or angiogram illuminates the cerebral circulation. This test is used for the diagnosis of vascular aneurysms, malformations, displacements and occluded or leaking blood vessels.

B. An intravenous pyelogram (IVP) provides information about the number, size and location of the kidneys and ureters.
C. A gallium scan is useful in detecting bone problems, and can also be useful in the examination of brain, heart, liver and breast tissue.
D. Carotid doppler studies are used to determine narrowing or occlusion of the carotid arteries.

60. Key: B   Client Need: *Coping and Adaptation*

B. Assessing several areas of functioning such as intellectual functioning, activities of daily living and coping mechanisms helps the nurse to fully develop the plan of care.

A, C and D.
The nurse cannot know the patient's needs or if the patient is capable of participating in these interventions until the level of functioning is determined.

61. Key: A   Client Need: *Coping and Adaptation*

A. Emotional stress is not the only component of asthma. Allergic, immunologic and emotional input can be responsible for asthma attacks. The patient should have further instruction regarding the cause of asthmatic episodes.

B. Mood does play an important role in asthma attacks. The patient's statement indicates an understanding of this and the patient does not require further teaching.
C. With exercise-induced asthma, use of an inhaler prior to exercise decreases the risk of, and the symptoms of, an asthma attack. The patient's statement indicates an understanding of this and the patient does not require further teaching.
D. Biofeedback is helpful in teaching a patient to manage stress before physiological problems occur. The patient's statement indicates an understanding of this and the patient does not require further teaching.

62. Key: D   Client Need: *Physiological Adaptation*

D. The patient must always be maintained in an extended position. No part of the body should be twisted or turned, and the patient cannot be allowed to assume a sitting position. A head immobilizer is used to secure the head and neck in alignment.

A. There is no indication that taping the eyelids shut is necessary in this situation.
B and C.
Use of these positions could cause severance of the spinal cord from bone fragments.

63. **Key: B**   Client Need: *Pharmacological and Parenteral Therapies*

    B. Patient manifestations indicate the decompensation phase of increased intracranial pressure. Osmotic diuretics, such as mannitol, are given to reduce cerebral edema.

    A. Dilantin is an anticonvulsant and is not used to reduce cerebral edema.
    C. Theophylline is a bronchodilator and is not used to reduce cerebral edema.
    D. Atropine sulfate is an autonomic nervous system agent and is not used in the treatment of cerebral edema.

64. **Key: A**   Client Need: *Psychosocial Adaptation*

    A. Some antidepressants interfere with libido. The nurse should clarify the meaning of the patient's statement and convey to the patient a willingness to talk about sexual intimacy concerns with the patient.

    B. This response by the nurse negates the patient's concerns and does not allow for open discussion.
    C. The nurse should clarify the meaning of the patient's comment before asking for additional information.
    D. The nurse should first clarify the patient's original statement.

65. **Key: C**   Client Need: *Growth and Development*

    C. Haemophilus influenzae type B conjugate vaccines are routinely administered to children beginning at two months of age to protect against epiglottitis.

    A, B and D.
    HibTITER does not protect against hepatitis, encephalitis or bronchiolitis.

66. **Key: C**   Client Need: *Physiological Adaptation*

    C. Clinical manifestations of acoustic neuroma begin with tinnitus, or ringing in the ears, and progress to gradual sensorineural hearing loss.

    A. Diplopia is double vision and is not associated with acoustic neuroma.
    B. Dysphagia is difficulty swallowing and is not symptomatic of acoustic neuroma.
    D. Ataxia is lack of coordination in performing a planned, purposeful motion, such as walking. It is not associated with acoustic neuroma.

67. **Key: B**   Client Need: *Reduction of Risk Potential*

    B. A lumbar puncture is carried out by inserting a needle into the subarachnoid space to withdraw cerebrospinal fluid for diagnostic and therapeutic purposes. The patient's statement indicates a correct understanding of the procedure.

    A. Electromyography measures electrical activity associated with innervation of skeletal muscle.
    C. No dyes are used in a lumbar puncture.
    D. Studying brain waves is accomplished through electroencephalography.

68. **Key: A**   **Client Need:** *Management of Care*

A. The patient is at particularly high risk if he/she is unable to cough effectively to clear the airway and has difficulty in swallowing, which may cause aspiration of saliva and precipitate acute respiratory failure.

B. Later in the course of the disease motor paralysis or weakness will affect the patient's ability to self-feed.

C. Muscle paralysis in severe cases may lead to low blood pressure and the need for vasopressant agents and volume expanders. The priority of care is airway maintenance.

D. A total self-care deficit relates to inability to use muscles to protect oneself and places the patient at risk for injury. However, the priority of care is maintenance of a patent airway.

69. **Key: C**   **Client Need:** *Physiological Adaptation*

C. A chest x-ray is essential to rule out clinically active tuberculosis or to detect old, healed lesions.

A. A positive tuberculin test does not mean that active disease is present, but indicates exposure to tuberculosis or the presence of inactive disease.

B. Coughing is a cardinal sign of respiratory disease. A patient with active tuberculosis may have hemoptysis. Definitive diagnosis, however, is by chest x-ray.

D. Night sweats may be a clinical manifestation of tuberculosis, but active disease would need to be evidenced by chest x-ray.

70. **Key: C**   **Client Need:** *Coping and Adaptation*

C. One of the first options to be discussed with the family is whether or not they want to see and hold the baby.

A. There is no indication that genetic counseling is required. If it were, genetic counseling would be part of a long-term plan and not an immediate need.

B. Having a picture of the woman's other child may provide comfort but the immediate need is to deal with the loss of the pregnancy.

D. Having the clergy visit the woman is an appropriate intervention but is not the first action to be taken.

71. **Key: D**   **Client Need:** *Pharmacological and Parenteral Therapies*

D. Anticholinesterase agents, such as pyridostigmine bromide, act by increasing the relative concentration of available acetylcholine at the neuromuscular junction. They increase the response of the muscles to nerve impulses and improve strength. The dosage of pyridostigmine bromide is gradually increased until maximal benefits are achieved (additional strength and less fatigue). The patient is instructed to take the medication 30 minutes before meals for maximal muscle strength.

A, B and C.
Pyridostigmine bromide does not affect the urine, does not relieve headache and does not improve vision.

72. **Key: C**   Client Need: _Physiological Adaptation_

    C. Elevating the legs decreases edema, promotes venous return and provides symptomatic relief. The legs should be elevated frequently throughout the day, preferably for at least 30 minutes every two hours.

    A and D.
     Modifications in diet and alcohol intake will not provide relief to patients with venous insufficiency.
    B. Constricting garments such as girdles or garters should be avoided.

73. **Key: D**   Client Need: _Reduction of Risk Potential_

    D. The cause of transient ischemia attacks (TIAs) is a temporary impairment of blood flow to a specific region of the brain due to a variety of reasons, including atherosclerosis of the vessels supplying the brain, obstruction of the cerebral microcirculation by a small embolus, a decrease in cerebral perfusion pressure or cardiac dysrhythmias. The most common sites of atherosclerosis in the extracranial arteries are at the bifurcation of the common carotid arteries and at the origin of the vertebral arteries.

    A. Rapid eye movements occur in inner ear and neurologic conditions.
    B. Projectile vomiting is present in increased intracranial pressure.
    C. Intermittent claudication is present in peripheral vascular disease.

74. **Key: B**   Client Need: _Pharmacological and Parenteral Therapies_

    B. Digestive management of cystic fibrosis consists of pancreatic enzyme replacement, diet adjustment and, in some cases, fat-soluble vitamin supplementation to promote growth, adequate nutrition and normal bowel movements. Measurable weight gain is an indication of effectiveness of treatment.

    A. Nausea is one of the frequent, undesired, clinical responses to Pancrease.
    C. Pancrease does not thin respiratory secretions.
    D. Pancrease does not affect lung function.

75. **Key: A**   Client Need: _Pharmacological and Parenteral Therapies_

    A. Because of the risk of agranulocytosis, a baseline white blood cell count before initial treatment, a count every week while on the medication and a count for four weeks after discontinuing the drug is recommended.

    B, C and D.
     None of these time frames is indicated for blood level monitoring in the patient taking Clozaril.

76. **Key: D**   Client Need: _Prevention and Early Detection of Disease_

    D. A severe cramp-like pain, intermittent claudication is experienced in the extremities after activity by patients with peripheral arterial insufficiency. When the patient rests, and thereby decreases the metabolic needs of the muscles, the pain subsides. The site of arterial disease can be deduced from the location of the claudication. Calf pain may accompany reduced blood flow through the superficial femoral or popliteal arteries.

    A. Lapse of memory is present in neurological disorders.
    B. Sleeping on several pillows is seen in the patient who has cardiac failure.
    C. Weakness in the legs may be seen in neurological disorders.

77. **Key: C**   Client Need: *Physiological Adaptation*

   C. Phantom pain is used to describe the normal perception of the missing extremity that most amputees feel. When the leg is amputated, the patient will feel the presence of the missing limb for many weeks. This is due to intact peripheral nerves proximal to the amputation site that used to carry messages between the brain and the now amputated part.

   A. Intractable pain is that which is not relieved by the usual medication regimes and comfort measures. It is often experienced by cancer patients.
   B. Radiating pain is that which spreads out from its original source, e.g., pain of cardiac origin spreading to the shoulder, jaw and arm.
   D. Referred pain is that which is felt at a site distal to the original source, e.g., pain in the shoulder caused by abdominal gas pockets pressing on the diaphragm.

78. **Key: B**   Client Need: *Psychosocial Adaptation*

   B. Clues to aggressive behavior include expressing intent to harm others and being threatening to others.

   A and C.
   Avoidance of staff and other patients by a paranoid schizophrenic patient may indicate fear that others will harm the patient, or that the patient may be afraid of harming others, and therefore, chooses to avoid contact. However, by observing just this behavior, one cannot assume that the patient is potentially violent.
   D. Continually changing position may show agitation in the patient, but this behavior alone does not indicate that the patient is potentially violent.

79. **Key: C**   Client Need: *Physiological Adaptation*

   C. Management of pulmonary problems in cystic fibrosis (CF) is directed toward prevention and treatment of pulmonary infection by improving aeration and removing mucopurulent secretions.

   A. Initial pulmonary manifestations of CF are wheezing and a dry, nonproductive cough that eventually becomes loose and productive.
   B. As thick, tenacious mucus accumulates, obstruction occurs and the flow of air is impaired. There is an increase in residual volume and subsequent decrease in vital capacity.
   D. Adventitious sounds are additional respiratory sounds not normally heard.

80. **Key: A**   Client Need: *Growth and Development*

   A. Parents need to be educated that infants should be placed on their sides or supine on a firm sleep surface to help prevent sudden infant death syndrome (SIDS).

   B, C and D.
   The infant's position during sleep is a critical factor in SIDS. Infants who sleep in a prone position are at greater risk of dying from SIDS than infants who are positioned on their backs or sides. The prone position may cause oropharyngeal obstruction; affect thermoregulation, causing overheating of the infant; or affect the arousal state. A cool mist humidifier, avoiding stuffed animals and placing the infant in an infant seat after feeding will not prevent the incidence of SIDS.

81. **Key: C**   **Client Need:** *Pharmacological and Parenteral Therapies*

    C. Haldol (haloperidol decanoate) is released slowly from the muscle into which it was inject-ed; therefore, the effects of the medication last for two to four weeks.

    A. It is not necessary for the patient to stay recumbent for any length of time after an injection of Haldol decanoate. Although rare, some patients experience orthostatic hypotension. All patients receiving Haldol should be taught to rise slowly from a recumbent position and to sit for a few minutes before standing.

    B. Avoidance of tyramine-rich foods is indicated for patients taking monoamine oxidase inhibitors, not haloperidol.

    D. Taking salt supplements is not indicated when being treated with haloperidol.

82. **Key: B**   **Client Need:** *Management of Care*

    B. Hematocrit is an effective indicator of body fluid volume. Increased hematocrit levels can indicate shock due to a large fluid loss and hemoconcentration. Activity intolerance would be the priority nursing diagnosis for this patient.

    A, C and D.
    Ineffective breathing pattern, hyperthermia and dysreflexia are not priority nursing diagnoses for a patient with hemoconcentration or an elevated hematocrit.

83. **Key: D**   **Client Need:** *Basic Care and Comfort*

    D. Bowel retraining is established by providing a consistent time for stool evacuation each day.

    A. Checking for impaction daily is not indicated and can interfere with sphincter control.

    B. Fluids should be increased to at least 3000 ml/day, unless contraindicated by cardiac or renal disease. Dairy products are high in calcium and may be constipating for the patient. High-fiber foods such as oat bran, fruits and vegetables should be encouraged.

    C. Using incontinent pads does not help in bowel retraining and may encourage incontinence.

84. **Key: D**   **Client Need:** *Management of Care*

    D. The charge nurse should discuss patient comments with the nurse and work with the nurse to develop a plan that promotes change in the behavior.

    A. The charge nurse has enough information to begin exploring the situation with the identified nurse. Continuing discussion with the patients is not appropriate unless a piece of information needs to be clarified.

    B. The charge nurse should not discuss the potential reasons for the nurses' behavior with the patients. This violates the nurse's right to confidentiality.

    C. The charge nurse is the first in the chain of command and should address the issues with the nurse.

85. **Key: D** Client Need: *Coping and Adaptation*

   D. The nurse should avoid participating in criticism of another staff person. The concern needs to be resolved between those involved, namely the therapist and the patient. With this statement the nurse conveys confidence in the patient's ability to speak for him/herself.

   A. By asking this question the nurse becomes involved in a situation that does not concern the nurse and does not teach the patient the appropriate process of resolving conflict. Also, the nurse should avoid use of the word "why" because it challenges the person's position and the response is usually to defend one's position rather than address the real issue.
   B. In this example the nurse gives a stereotypical response, which belittles the patient's concern, gives advice and does not direct the patient to deal with the concern appropriately.
   C. By talking to the therapist on behalf of the patient, the nurse accepts responsibility for solving the patient's problem and misses an opportunity to teach the patient how to communicate effectively to resolve conflict.

86. **Key: D** Client Need: *Physiological Integrity*

   D. Povan stains the stool and vomitus bright red.

   A, B and C.
   Dry scaly skin, bleeding gums and tea-colored urine are not side effects of treatment with Povan.

87. **Key: C** Client Need: *Pharmacological and Parenteral Therapies*

   C. Chest pain may indicate an emergency situation (acute chest syndrome) and should be reported to the physician immediately.

   A. While there can be renal involvement in sickle cell anemia, decreased urinary output is not an emergency.
   B. Vomiting and diarrhea can be seen with sickle cell anemia but do not require emergency management, as does chest pain.
   D. A nonproductive cough may be present in sickle cell anemia but it does not require emergency intervention.

88. **Key: C** Client Need: *Psychosocial Adaptation*

   C. Flight of ideas is a manifestation of mania. As the patient's mood state becomes increasingly expansive, speech may become full of irrelevancies. The manic patient jumps quickly from topic to topic, and rapid thinking proceeds to racing and disjointed thinking.

   A. Waxy flexibility, a condition in which the patient remains in any body position in which he/she is placed, is seen in patients with catatonia.
   B. Flat affect, the absence of emotional expression, is seen in depressed or psychotic patients.
   D. Hypersomnia, excessive sleepiness, is seen in depressed patients.

89. **Key: D** Client Need: *Growth and Development*

   D. Following an amniocentesis, the patient is at risk for contractions and preterm labor.

   A. Flu-like symptoms are not associated with amniocentesis.
   B. Inability to sleep is associated with advancing pregnancy. It is not related to amniocentesis.
   C. Contractions should not be present at this time.

90. **Key: B**   Client Need: *Safety and Infection Control*

    B. The nurse should instruct the parents that correct positioning to prevent sudden infant death syndrome (SIDS) is the supine position or the side-lying position.

    A. The prone position is not recommended by the American Academy of Pediatrics.
    C. Sleeping on the back or side only is recommended.
    D. Infants generally sleep in whatever position they are placed. The major reason for placing the infant on its back or side is to prevent SIDS.

91. **Key: D**   Client Need: *Physiological Integrity*

    D. The acronym SIRES is an aid in remembering the essential care in cases of poisoning: Stabilize the patient; Identify the toxic substance; Reverse its effect; Eliminate the substance from the body; and Support the patient and significant others both physically and psychologically. Airway, breathing and circulation must be stabilized. A rapid physical exam is performed. Intravenous lines are inserted and appropriate laboratory studies obtained.

    A and B.
    Neither of these options are a priority for emergency care of a patient who has ingested an unknown quantity of Tylenol and alcohol.
    C. Vomiting should not be induced in a semi-conscious patient because it could result in aspiration.

92. **Key: A**   Client Need: *Physiological Integrity*

    A. Children with allergies to peanuts or penicillin cannot receive dimercaprol (BAL) or D-penicillamine, respectively.

    B, C and D.
    Allergies to eggs, erythromycin or iodine should be noted by the nurse. However, such allergies do not necessarily contradict the use of BAL in Oil.

93. **Key: A**   Client Need: *Psychosocial Integrity*

    A. When teaching clients about schizophrenia, the nurse should include the need to take medication regularly, expected side effects, what to do for the side effects, signs of problems and who to call if problems occur.

    B and C.
    The patient should be taught not to decrease the medication dosage or to stop the medication unless instructed to do so by the physician.
    D. Side effects of antipsychotic medications include extrapyramidal effects such as tardive dyskinesia, akathisia, parkinsonism and dystonia. Anticholinergic side effects include blurred vision, nasal congestion, dry mouth, constipation and urinary hesitancy.

94. **Key: A**   Client Need: *Psychosocial Integrity*

    A. The abnormal involuntary movement scale (AIMS) is used for the assessment of extrapyramidal side effects of antipsychotic medications. Tardive dyskinesia is such a side effect and is characterized by abnormal, involuntary movements that usually begin in the face, neck and jaw, lip smacking and facial grimacing.

    B, C and D.
    Motor incoordination, sluggish pupillary response and a positive Babinski reflex are not measured by the AIMS scale.

95. **Key: A**   **Client Need:** *Psychosocial Integrity*

  A. Manic patients demonstrate hyperactive behavior, as well as poor concentration and attention span, making it difficult for them to sit long enough or focus long enough to eat certain types of foods. Because of these behaviors, such patients are at risk for alteration in nutrition: less than body requirements. Finger foods that are high in nutritious calories and easily portable will decrease the risk of altered nutrition.

  B, C and D.
  While nutritious, these foods are not portable and would not be suitable for a patient with bipolar disorder, manic phase.

96. **Key: C**   **Client Need:** *Psychosocial Integrity*

  C. Lochial flow should be assessed for amount, odor and presence of clots in the early postpartum period.

  A. A fresh postoperative patient should not be placed in the left lateral Sim's position because it puts pressure on the new incision line.
  B. An assessment of signs and symptoms of infection should be completed, but is not part of the initial postpartum assessment in the recovery room.
  D. Homans' sign generally should be assessed in the postpartum period; however, this patient had general anesthesia and will be unable to state whether or not she has calf pain.

97. **Key: A**   **Client Need:** *Psychosocial Integrity*

  A. Not only is the patient demonstrating poor judgment by making a socially irresponsible choice (not paying the electric bill), the patient will not be able to watch the new television if the electricity is turned off due to nonpayment of the bill. The patient shows poor judgment because he/she was not able to reach a logical decision after analyzing the possible consequences of the choice.

  B, C and D.
  These examples show involvement in activities and relationships that are healthy behaviors. The person shows good judgment by making socially-responsible choices.

98. **Key: B**   **Client Need:** *Health Promotion and Maintenance*

  B. The most important infection control procedures to be employed when taking care of a child with respiratory syncytial virus (RSV) is consistent hand-washing and not touching the nasal mucosa or the conjunctiva.

  A. Routine use of gowns and masks has not been shown to be of additional benefit when caring for the patient with RSV.
  C and D.
  Other isolation procedures of potential benefit are those aimed at diminishing the number of hospital personnel, visitors and uninfected patients in contact with the child.

99. **Key: C**   **Client Need:** *Psychosocial Integrity*

   C. **The goal of a therapy group is for each individual to work towards self-understanding and more satisfactory ways of relating to and handling stress.**

   A. Confrontation is used for the purpose of making the second patient change his/her behavior to that desired by the first patient. The first patient is trying to elicit the support of the group to pressure the second patient into the change. The group would benefit the first patient by holding to the group norm that the only behavior a person has the power to change is his/her own.
   B. Taking responsibility for maintaining harmony in the group prevents others from feeling and dealing with the anxiety in the group. This behavior by the codependent patient shows preoccupation with the thoughts and feelings of others as opposed to dealing with his/her own behavior.
   D. Focusing on the problems of others allows this patient to avoid awareness of his/her own problems.

100. **Key: A**   **Client Need:** *Pharmacological and Parenteral Therapies*

   A. **The nurse would first determine the number of milliliters to be administered per hour by dividing the total solution amount by the number of hours of administration.**

$$\frac{1640 \ ml}{24 \ hr} = 68.3 \ ml/hr$$

   To determine the flow rate of the intravenous, multiply the number of milliliters per hour by the number of drops per milliliter and divide by the number of minutes in one hour.

$$\frac{68.3 \ ml/hr \ x \ 15 \ gtts/ml}{60 \ min/hr} = 17.08 \ or \ 17 \ gtts/min$$

101. **Key: C**   **Client Need:** *Physiological Adaptation*

   C. **Manifestations of viral hepatitis include lethargy, irritability, drowsiness and anemia. One of the primary nursing diagnoses for this patient would be activity intolerance related to fatigue. The patient should be instructed to maintain adequate rest to conserve energy.**

   A. The patient with viral hepatitis should be instructed to stop drinking rather than limit the intake of alcohol.
   B. Medications such as chlorpromazine (Thorazine), acetylsalicylic acid (aspirin), acetaminophen (Tylenol) and certain sedatives are given as infrequently as possible to the patient with viral hepatitis because all have the potential to damage the already compromised liver.
   D. Use of a condom during sexual intercourse would be encouraged for all. However, the priority instruction would be to rest frequently throughout the day.

102. Key: D   **Client Need:** *Physiological Adaptation*

D. The patient with primary adrenal insufficiency (Addison's disease) requires glucocorticoid replacement. Oral glucocorticoids irritate the gastric mucosa and should be taken with meals or snacks.

A. In adrenocortical hypofunction the body excretes sodium but retains potassium, causing the potential for arrhythmias and cardiac arrest. The patient should not be instructed to increase the amount of potassium in the diet.

B. Since the patient excretes excess sodium, foods high in sodium do not have to be limited.

C. While the patient with Addison's disease experiences mild fatigue, exercise does not have to be restricted.

103. Key: C   **Client Need:** *Pharmacological and Parenteral Therapies*

C. Artane is used to control the rigidity and tremors associated with Parkinson's disease. It blocks central cholinergic excitatory pathways, returning the dopamine/acetylcholine balance in the brain to normal. This results in decreased salivation and relaxation of smooth muscle with a decrease in tremors.

A. Bradykinesia is defined as sluggishness of physical and mental responses. Artane is not used to control bradykinesia.

B. In occulogyric crisis the eyes fix upward and to one side or downward. Artane is not used as treatment for occulogyric crisis.

D. Artane is not used to control the propulsive gait seen in Parkinson's disease.

104. Key: B   **Client Need:** *Pharmacological and Parenteral Therapies*

B. A serum potassium level of 2.8 mEq/L indicates hypokalemia and should be addressed immediately.

A, C and D.
These laboratory values are within normal limits and would not require immediate intervention by the nurse.

105. Key D   **Client Need:** *Reduction of Risk Potential*

D. Anaphylaxis is the acute clinical syndrome resulting from the interaction of an allergen and a patient who is hypersensitive. Children known to be at risk for anaphylaxis include those who have a history of previous allergic reactions to a specific antigen, a history of allergy, a history of severe reactions in immediate family members and a reaction to a skin test.

A. Lactose intolerance results in diarrhea, abdominal pain, distention and flatus shortly after ingesting milk products.

B. Eczema is an inflammatory disorder of the skin. Infants with eczema often have a family history of eczema, asthma, food allergies or allergic rhinitis.

C. Allergies have a familial tendency. However, the child who already has developed an adverse response to an antibiotic is at greater risk for developing anaphylaxis.

106. Key: A   Client Need: *Pharmacological and Parenteral Therapies*

    A. Serum drug levels are used to aid the physician in determining dosage adjustment for drugs that have a narrow range between therapeutic effect and toxicity. Gentamycin has a relatively short half-life; therefore, peak and trough levels are ordered to ensure adequate therapy. The peak serum level is usually obtained 15-30 minutes after an intravenous dose. The trough level should be drawn 15 minutes before the next scheduled dose.

    B. Peak levels are drawn 15-30 minutes after the IV dose of gentamycin.
    C. Trough levels are drawn approximately 15 minutes before the next scheduled dose of IV gentamycin.
    D. Peak levels are drawn 15-30 minutes after the IV dose of gentamycin.

107. Key: B   Client Need: *Management of Care*

    B. Electrolyte imbalance can lead to cardiac arrhythmias and death. It should be the priority in the plan of care.

    A, C and D.
    Cold intolerance, amenorrhea and sleep disturbance are associated with anorexia nervosa but do not pose the safety risk seen with electrolyte imbalance.

108. Key: B   Client Need: *Reduction of Risk Potential*

    B. Thrush, or oral candidiasis, is characterized by white patches in the oral mucosa. It may be acquired as a result of a vaginal delivery if the mother is infected.

    A. Milia are a normal skin variation. They appear as small white plaques on the infant's nose and chin. They are blocked sebaceous glands.
    C. Impetigo is a staphylococcus infection. It is not commonly seen in newborn infants.
    D. Otitis media or middle ear infection is a childhood infection. It is not seen in newborn infants.

109. Key: B   Client Need: *Pharmacological and Parenteral Therapies*

    B. Chelation should not be performed in the absence of adequate urine flow. Impending renal failure due to drug toxicity is noted by the appearance of protein in the urine, rising blood urine nitrogen and rising serum creatinine levels.

    A, C and D.
    Hemoglobin, unconjugated bilirubin and platelet levels do not require monitoring in the patient receiving chelation therapy.

110. Key: B   Client Need: *Pharmacological and Parenteral Therapies*

    B. Hypoglycemia is a side effect of pentamidine treatment. Therefore, the nurse should assess the patient for manifestations of hypoglycemia.

    A. Hyperkalemia, rather than hypokalemia, is an adverse reaction to pentamidine.
    C. Stomatitis is not a side effect of pentamidine. However, a metallic taste in the mouth can occur with pentamidine administration.
    D. Adverse reactions to pentamidine are acute renal failure, increased serum creatinine and renal toxicity. Hematuria is not reported as an adverse reaction.

CGFNS

Qualifying Exam Practice Exam D

Practice Exam D: Nursing, Part 1

You will have two hours and 30 minutes to complete Nursing, Part 1.

1. **A patient who has type 1 diabetes experiences weakness and tremors. Which of the following actions would a nurse take first?**

   A. Obtaining a urine specimen from the patient
   B. Giving the patient a concentrated source of glucose
   C. Checking the patient's most recent blood glucose level
   D. Administering the patient's prn dose of insulin

2. **A patient who has type 1 diabetes mellitus is taking isophane insulin (NPH insulin) injection. A nurse should advise the patient to be alert for symptoms of hypoglycemia at which of the following times after insulin administration?**

   A. Two hours
   B. Four hours
   C. Eight hours
   D. 20 hours

3. **Which of the following manifestations most likely indicates complications in a patient who has chronic diabetes mellitus?**

   A. Diminished olfactory sensation
   B. Increased deep tendon reflexes
   C. Decreased peripheral sensation
   D. Enhanced calcium excretion

4. **A pregnant woman reports that her last menstrual period was from July 1 to July 5. The nurse would expect her due date to be**

   A. March 24.
   B. March 28.
   C. April 8.
   D. April 12.

5. **A patient is receiving warfarin sodium (Coumadin) therapy. The nurse should be aware that adverse effects associated with Coumadin use include**

   A. blurred vision.
   B. diffuse red rash.
   C. black, tarry stools.
   D. ringing in the ears.

6. **Which of the following serum laboratory results would a nurse expect to identify in a patient who has pancreatitis?**

   A. Decreased cholesterol
   B. Decreased glucose
   C. Elevated amylase
   D. Elevated creatinine

7. **A nurse is preparing a patient for discharge following coronary artery bypass grafting (CABG). Which of the following statements, if made by the patient, would indicate the need for further teaching about the immediate postoperative period?**

   A. "Chicken and fish will be good diet choices for me."
   B. "I will wear elastic stockings when I go home."
   C. "I can perform my normal activities with frequent rest periods."
   D. "Meditation may be effective in helping me to relax."

8. **A patient who has asthma is given instructions about the use of inhalant medications. Which of the following statements, if made by the patient, indicates that the patient understands the instructions?**

   A. "I will use the steroid inhaler one hour before I use the bronchodilator."
   B. "I will use the bronchodilator before I use the steroid inhaler."
   C. "I need to take these medications one hour after each meal."
   D. "I need to alternate the sequence of inhaler administrations."

9. **A nurse assesses a patient who has schizophrenia of the paranoid type. Which of the following behaviors should the nurse expect to observe?**

   A. Elated affect and hyperactivity
   B. Obsessive thoughts and rituals
   C. Hallucinations and delusions
   D. Manipulation and narcissism

10. Which of the following statements, if made by an elderly patient, indicates the patient understands the most effective method for preventing influenza?

    A. "I will stay indoors in bad weather."
    B. "I will have an annual flu vaccine."
    C. "I will wear a mask when my grandchildren visit."
    D. "I will take a daily multivitamin supplement."

11. To help a woman recognize the best time for conceiving, a nurse would instruct the woman to monitor for which of the following manifestations of ovulation?

    A. Drop in body temperature lasting several days
    B. Increase in amount of cervical mucus that is clear and stretches
    C. Abdominal bloating that occurs suddenly
    D. Breast tenderness accompanied by slight nipple discharge

12. A patient who has schizophrenia of the paranoid type says to a nurse, "The FBI is out to get me and you're one of them." Which of the following responses by the nurse would be most therapeutic?

    A. "You seem scared."
    B. "What makes you think the FBI is here?"
    C. "You should go to your room to rest."
    D. "How could an FBI agent get in here?"

13. A nurse is assessing a patient who had a tuberculin (purified protein derivative, PPD) skin test 48 hours ago. Which of the following findings, if identified at the patient's injection site, indicates the patient needs further observation?

    A. Maculopapular rash of 5 mm
    B. Reddened circle of 10 mm
    C. Ecchymotic area of 15 mm
    D. Skin induration of 18 mm

14. A nurse teaches pursed-lip breathing to a patient who has chronic obstructive pulmonary disease (COPD). Which of the following statements indicates the patient understands the instructions?

    A. "I will maintain a supine position during the exercises."
    B. "I will alternate positions during the exercises."
    C. "I will exhale for twice as long as I inhale."
    D. "I will inhale and exhale through my nose."

15. A patient who visits a wellness clinic has a blood pressure of 158/100 mm Hg. Which of the following nursing actions is most appropriate?

    A. Send the patient to the emergency department
    B. Refer the patient for an electrocardiogram as soon as possible
    C. Advise the patient to have the blood pressure re-checked in one week
    D. Encourage the patient to keep a food diary for one month

16. Which of the following manifestations in a six-week-old infant who was born prematurely would lead a nurse to suspect that the infant may have apnea?

    A. Intermittent episodes of acrocyanosis for periods of 10 minutes
    B. Random episodes of breath holding during periods of stress
    C. Transient episodes of mottling with environmental temperature changes
    D. A lapse of spontaneous breathing for 20 or more seconds

17. When a patient has an episode of epistaxis, which of the following actions would a nurse take first?

    A. Applying ice to the back of the patient's neck
    B. Tipping the patient backward and encouraging swallowing
    C. Determining if the patient has a history of hypertension
    D. Having the patient lean forward and pinch the nose

18. A patient who has schizophrenia of the paranoid type says to a nurse, "That guy over there is staring at me and putting a spell on me." Which of the following nursing diagnoses should be given priority for this patient?

    A. High risk of violence related to delusional thinking
    B. Alteration in thought processes related to mistrust
    C. Anxiety related to misinterpretation of external stimuli
    D. Defensive coping related to fear of other patients

19. A 10-year-old boy is admitted to the hospital with a history of fever and right, lower quadrant abdominal pain. Which of the following comfort measures would be taken until a diagnosis is made?

    A. Maintain the child in a recumbent position
    B. Apply warm compresses to the affected area
    C. Obtain an order for an age-appropriate analgesic
    D. Distract the child with an age-appropriate video

20. Which of the following statements, if made by a patient who is administered propranolol hydrochloride (Inderal), indicates that the patient has a correct understanding of the medication?

    A. "I will take the Inderal when I feel dizzy."
    B. "I will take the Inderal with orange juice."
    C. "I will check my pulse before taking the Inderal."
    D. "I will stop using the Inderal when I feel better."

21. A nurse would advise a patient to take a diuretic

    A. in the early morning.
    B. after lunch.
    C. with the evening meal.
    D. at bedtime.

22. Which of the following laboratory results would a nurse check before administering digoxin (Lanoxin) to a patient?

    A. Urinalysis
    B. Urine ketones
    C. Blood glucose
    D. Serum potassium

23. When a 12-year-old child has a diagnosis of appendicitis, which of the following manifestations would be most important for the nurse to follow-up?

    A. Tympanic temperature of 101.2°F (38.4°C)
    B. Absence of stool for 24 hours
    C. Nausea when exposed to food odors
    D. Cessation of abdominal pain

24. Which of the following statements, if made by a patient diagnosed with schizophrenia, indicates to a nurse that the patient needs additional instruction regarding haloperidol (Haldol)?

    A. "I can stop my medicine when I don't hear the voices any more."
    B. "I'll take my Cogentin if my neck feels stiff."
    C. "I'm going to eat bran cereal every morning."
    D. "I have to wear a hat when I go to the beach."

25. When performing a physical assessment of a woman who is 20 weeks pregnant, a nurse would expect to palpate the uterine fundus

    A. at the symphysis pubis.
    B. midway between the symphysis pubis and the umbilicus.
    C. at the umbilicus.
    D. midway between the umbilicus and the xiphoid process.

26. A patient has a diagnosis of syndrome of inappropriate secretion of antidiuretic hormone (SIADH). For which of the following manifestations would a nurse monitor this patient?

    A. Hyperglycemia
    B. Hyponatremia
    C. Polyuria
    D. Dysphagia

27. Which of the following blood chemistry laboratory results in a patient who is in the postoperative period of a renal transplant indicates the transplant was successful?

    A. Bilirubin, 0.7 mg/dL
    B. Creatinine, 1.0 mg/dL
    C. Glucose, 85 mg/dL
    D. Calcium, 6.5 mg/dL

28. Which of the following criteria would be a reliable indicator of improvement in a patient who has a diagnosis of anorexia nervosa?

    A. Electrolyte balance
    B. Energy level
    C. Fluid intake
    D. Desire to eat

29. A two-month-old infant is brought to the emergency department because of projectile vomiting. The emesis contains formula and is bile-stained. The nurse should assess the infant for signs of

    A. viral gastroenteritis.
    B. gastroesophageal reflux.
    C. pyloric stenosis.
    D. Meckel's diverticulum.

30. A parent tells a nurse, "My three-month-old infant recently passed several stools that resembled clumpy red jelly." Based on this information, the nurse should suspect that the infant has developed

    A. celiac disease.
    B. biliary atresia.
    C. intussusception.
    D. ulcerative colitis.

31. A patient who had an acute myocardial infarction complains of severe substernal pain. Which of the following nursing interventions would be most appropriate?

    A. Administering the prescribed morphine
    B. Obtaining an electrocardiogram
    C. Encouraging slow, deep breathing
    D. Eliminating environmental stressors

32. A nurse has given a patient instructions about taking warfarin sodium (Coumadin). Which of the following statements, if made by the patient, indicates that the patient understands the instructions?

    A. "I can expect to gain weight while taking this medication."
    B. "I will take my pulse prior to each dose."
    C. "I can take aspirin when I have a headache."
    D. "I will take the medication at the same time every day."

33. Which of the following manifestations would a nurse expect to identify when assessing the lower extremities of a patient who has chronic arterial insufficiency?

    A. Foot tenderness
    B. Peripheral edema
    C. Rubor with dependency
    D. Increased capillary refill

34. When addressing the concerns of a primipara who is eight weeks pregnant, a nurse would provide the woman with which of the following information?

    A. Dysuria is a normal finding in pregnancy.
    B. Vaginal spotting is common throughout pregnancy.
    C. A 10 lb (4.5 kg) weight gain is anticipated during the first trimester of pregnancy.
    D. Quickening can be expected to occur between 16 and 20 weeks of pregnancy.

35. A six-month-old infant has recently begun cereal feedings. Which of the following manifestations would support a nursing diagnosis of ineffective infant feeding pattern?

    A. Frequent loose stools
    B. Increased abdominal girth
    C. Persistent tongue thrusting
    D. Lengthened time between meals

36. A patient is brought to the emergency department after ingesting cocaine. During the patient assessment, the nurse would expect to observe which of the following signs?

    A. Constricted pupils and lethargy
    B. Tachycardia and chest pain
    C. Nystagmus and paresthesia
    D. Ataxia and bradycardia

37. Which of the following statements, if made by a patient who has gastroesophageal reflux disease (GERD), would support a nursing diagnosis of knowledge deficit?

    A. "I will lie down for 30 minutes after meals."
    B. "I will restrict spicy foods in my diet."
    C. "I should sleep with the head of the bed elevated."
    D. "I should decrease my intake of caffeine."

38. The caregiver of a patient who has Alzheimer's disease says to a nurse, "I just can't take it anymore. My mother is out of control." The nurse's best response would be to

    A. remind the caregiver of the family's responsibilities.
    B. explore alternative care settings for the patient.
    C. refer the caregiver for psychological counseling.
    D. discuss medication options for the patient.

39. Which of the following techniques would a nurse use when interviewing a 94-year-old patient?

    A. Using a low-pitched voice
    B. Enunciating each word slowly
    C. Varying voice intonations
    D. Reinforcing the words with pictures

40. To reduce the risk of fetal neural tube defects, a nurse would evaluate the child-bearing woman's need for which of the following nutrient supplements?

    A. Ferrous sulfate (Feosol)
    B. Calcium carbonate (Tums)
    C. Folic acid (Folvite)
    D. Ascorbic acid (Vitamin C)

41. Which of the following statements, if made by a patient who is addicted to alcohol, would indicate an adequate understanding of disulfiram (Antabuse)?

    A. "I will read the labels on mouthwash before using it."
    B. "I need to take this medication on an empty stomach."
    C. "This medication will decrease my desire for alcohol."
    D. "I need to take precautions in the sun."

42. Which of the following goals would be given priority in the care plan of a two-year-old child who has acute gastroenteritis?

    A. Promote hydration
    B. Reduce lethargy
    C. Preserve skin integrity
    D. Maintain comfort

43. A woman complains of morning sickness during the first trimester of pregnancy. A nurse would suggest that she take which of the following measures to help alleviate the symptoms?

    A. Consume a clear liquid diet
    B. Take prenatal vitamins with milk
    C. Eat foods that are low in protein
    D. Avoid exposure to noxious odors

44. A nurse would expect a patient who has a cataract to report which of the following symptoms?

    A. Decreased color perception
    B. Loss of peripheral vision
    C. Halos around lights
    D. Headaches

45. A patient who has undergone a thyroidectomy would be predisposed to the development of

    A. hypocalcemia.
    B. hyponatremia.
    C. hyperkalemia.
    D. hypermagnesemia.

46. Which of the following laboratory values would a nurse closely monitor in a four-year-old child who has acute gastroenteritis?

    A. Serum amylase
    B. Serum potassium
    C. Total bilirubin
    D. Hemoglobin level

47. When teaching a patient who has a diagnosis of schizophrenia about successful independent living in the community, a nurse should encourage the patient to

    A. establish a structured daily routine.
    B. spend time alone.
    C. plan a program of self-fulfillment.
    D. discontinue medication when symptoms disappear.

48. Which of the following actions by the nurse would be appropriate when caring for a patient who has syndrome of inappropriate secretion of antidiuretic hormone (SIADH)?

    A. Straining the patient's urine
    B. Increasing the patient's fluid intake
    C. Monitoring the patient's blood glucose level
    D. Increasing the patient's sodium intake

49. A patient who is taking lithium carbonate (Eskalith) for the treatment of bipolar disorder, manic type, comes to the outpatient clinic reporting insomnia, hyperactivity and pressured speech. Which of the following questions should a nurse ask the patient first?

    A. "Have you been taking your medication?"
    B. "How much caffeine have you had today?"
    C. "How much sleep did you have last night?"
    D. "Is there something that has been upsetting you?"

50. A 45-year-old nullipara is at risk for having an infant with Trisomy 21. Information regarding which of the following diagnostic studies would be included in the care plan?

    A. Non-stress test
    B. Amniocentesis
    C. Percutaneous umbilical blood sampling
    D. Serum estriol levels

51. Which of the following findings in a 13-year-old girl who has Crohn's disease would indicate that corticosteroid therapy has been effective?

    A. Expansion of muscle mass
    B. Increase in the bulk of the stool
    C. Moon-like appearance of the face
    D. Decreased complaints of abdominal pain

52. When considering the nutritional needs of a patient on the psychiatric unit who has a diagnosis of bipolar disorder, manic type, a nurse should plan to

    A. offer finger foods.
    B. serve food in sealed containers.
    C. engage the patient in food preparation.
    D. seat the patient with other lively patients in the dining room.

53. When preparing a teaching plan for a patient who has recently tested positive for the human immunodeficiency virus (HIV), a nurse would include which of the following statements?

    A. "You should encourage your current and past sexual partners to be tested."
    B. "You will not need to take special precautions at this time."
    C. "You do not have to reveal your condition to anyone."
    D. "You should refrain from physical contact with everyone."

54. Which of the following nursing diagnoses is a priority for a patient with gout?

    A. Pain
    B. Fatigue
    C. Risk of infection
    D. Risk of peripheral neurovascular dysfunction

55. A nurse has taught a family about the prevention of Lyme disease. Which of the following actions, if taken by the family members, indicates the family understands the instructions?

   A. Applying an insect repellant to pets
   B. Wearing clothing that exposes the maximum amount of skin
   C. Checking for the presence of ticks after outdoor activities
   D. Leaving a tick attached to the skin until examined by a healthcare provider

56. Following an amniocentesis, a nurse would instruct the patient to report which of the following adverse effects?

   A. Dependent edema of the lower extremities
   B. Odorless, white vaginal discharge
   C. Intermittent abdominal pain
   D. Frequent urination

57. Which of the following observations of a patient would be most significant in documenting that surgical repair of an abdominal aortic aneurysm has been effective?

   A. Urine output of 30 ml/hr
   B. Presence of pre-tibial edema
   C. Clear sclera
   D. Presence of a carotid bruit

58. The teaching plan for a child who is taking long-term corticosteroid therapy would include which of the following instructions?

   A. Dental check-ups every three months to assess for gingival hyperplasia
   B. Regular physical therapy sessions to prevent muscular hypertrophy
   C. Eye examinations yearly to assess for cataract formation
   D. Regular appointments with a registered dietician to prevent malnutrition

59. Which of the following patients is at greatest risk for the development of a fracture?

   A. An adolescent who is entering puberty
   B. An elderly man who has vertigo
   C. A toddler who is learning to walk
   D. A woman who is postmenopausal

60. A six-year-old child has a short arm cast placed on the right extremity. While assessing the fingers during the immediate period after casting, a nurse would report which of the following findings?

   A. Mild edema
   B. Pain on movement
   C. Slight coolness of the cast when touched
   D. Capillary refill greater than three seconds

61. A nurse is teaching a community group about the prevention of osteoporosis. Which of the following actions would the nurse emphasize?

   A. Lap swimming
   B. Eliminating smoking
   C. Restricting sodium intake
   D. Minimizing sun exposure

62. Which of the following actions should a nurse include in the care plan of a patient who has bulimia?

   A. Stay with the patient for one hour after meals
   B. Decrease environmental stimuli
   C. Weigh the patient twice a day
   D. Discourage verbalization about out-of-control eating

63. Which of the following conditions would a nurse expect to assess in a patient who has Ménière's disease?

   A. Vertigo
   B. Diplopia
   C. Presbycusis
   D. Nystagmus

64. Disclosure of confidential information by the nurse about a patient's condition is legal when the information is

    A. given to law enforcement personnel.
    B. shared with other psychosocial team members.
    C. discussed in private with a family member.
    D. provided to insurance company representatives assigned to the patient's case.

65. Which of the following measures would a nurse include in the care plan of a patient who had a transurethral resection of the prostrate (TURP) two hours ago?

    A. Administering oxygen by nasal cannula
    B. Changing the dressing every two hours
    C. Regulating the flow rate of the irrigation solution
    D. Assessing for the return of the gag reflex

66. Which of the following responses would a nurse expect to find in a reactive non-stress test?

    A. Acceleration of the fetal heart rate with fetal movement
    B. Deceleration of the fetal heart rate without fetal movement
    C. No change in fetal heart rate with fetal movement
    D. No change in fetal heart rate without fetal movement

67. Which of the following patient outcomes would indicate that the manic phase of a bipolar disorder is subsiding?

    A. The patient participates in group activity without disruption.
    B. The patient has an increased ability to verbalize.
    C. The patient assumes leadership in social activities.
    D. The patient initiates multiple projects in art therapy.

68. A nurse would encourage a woman to increase which of the following nutrients in her diet throughout pregnancy?

    A. Protein
    B. Simple carbohydrates
    C. Potassium
    D. Vitamin A

69. A nurse evaluates a three-month-old infant who is developmentally delayed for cerebral palsy. Which of the following findings would a nurse report?

    A. Exaggerated arching of the back
    B. Absence of the extrusion reflex when fed from a spoon
    C. Head circumference measurement less than the 50th percentile
    D. Slight head lag when pulled to a sitting position

70. Which of the following conditions would a nurse expect when assessing a patient who has right-sided heart failure?

    A. Shortness of breath
    B. Peripheral edema
    C. Decreased urinary output
    D. Paroxysmal nocturnal dyspnea

71. A patient is administered diltiazem hydrochloride (Cardizem). Which of the following responses would a nurse expect from a patient if the medication is effective?

    A. Increased bone density
    B. Decreased seizure activity
    C. Blood pressure within normal limits
    D. Serum cholesterol level within normal limits

72. A patient who has pneumonia is admitted to the hospital with a productive cough. Which of the following actions should a nurse carry out first?

    A. Obtain a sputum specimen
    B. Obtain a portable chest x-ray
    C. Administer cefoxitin sodium (Mefoxin), 500 mg every 8h intravenously
    D. Administer guaifenesin with codeine (Robitussin) 30 ml, po, q 4h prn

73. A patient has a chest tube to underwater drainage that is connected to suction. A nurse observes that there is continuous bubbling in the suction control chamber. This finding most likely indicates that

    A. there is a leak in the tubing.
    B. the system is functioning properly.
    C. the tube needs to be repositioned.
    D. additional suction should be applied to the system.

74. A 10-year-old boy who is in the terminal stages of Duchenne muscular dystrophy is being cared for at home. When evaluating for major complications of this disease, a nurse would give priority to assessing which of the following body systems?

    A. Integumentary
    B. Neurological
    C. Respiratory
    D. Gastrointestinal

75. Which of the following topics would be given priority in the teaching plan for a woman who is attending childbirth education classes at 10 weeks of pregnancy?

    A. Breastfeeding techniques
    B. Relaxation methods for labor
    C. Management of pregnancy discomforts
    D. Routine infant care measures

76. A patient who has first-stage dementia of the Alzheimer type is admitted to the hospital. Which of the following symptoms should a nurse expect to observe?

    A. Fluctuating level of consciousness
    B. Forgetfulness
    C. Disorientation
    D. Long-term memory loss

77. Which of the following statements, if made by a patient who has undergone abdominal surgery, would indicate to a nurse that the patient-controlled analgesia (PCA) pump used for management is effective?

    A. "I am able to cough and deep breathe without help."
    B. "I only use the pump when I really need it."
    C. "I am very sleepy most of the time."
    D. "I feel pain only when I move."

78. The nurse is preparing a patient who is to have an intravenous pyelogram (IVP). The patient should be made aware that when the dye is injected during the test, he/she may experience

    A. a feeling of warmth.
    B. a metallic taste in the mouth.
    C. slight chest pain.
    D. shortness of breath.

79. A woman who is 12 weeks pregnant comes to the prenatal clinic for her second visit and tells a nurse, "I thought I wanted to be pregnant, but now I'm not sure." The nurse's response would be based on the understanding that the woman is

    A. considering pregnancy termination.
    B. in need of a social service referral.
    C. experiencing a normal reaction to pregnancy.
    D. exhibiting predictors of child maltreatment syndrome.

80. A patient who is receiving total parenteral nutrition has an elevated blood glucose level and is to be administered intravenous insulin. Which of the following types of insulin should a nurse have available?

    A. Isophane insulin (NPH)
    B. Regular insulin (Humulin R)
    C. Insulin zinc suspension (Lente)
    D. Semi-lente insulin (Semitard)

81. A nurse identifies a 2-mm superficial open blister over a patient's sacrum. The nurse would document this as being which of the following stages of pressure ulcers?

    A. I
    B. II
    C. III
    D. IV

82. A patient who is administered isoniazid (INH) and pyridoxine hydrochloride (Vitamin B6) for treatment of tuberculosis asks a nurse why the Vitamin B6 is necessary. The nurse would respond that

    A. "Vitamin B6 is necessary for the absorption of INH."
    B. "Vitamin B6 activates the metabolism of INH."
    C. "INH leads to Vitamin B6 depletion, which causes neurotoxic effects."
    D. "INH can cause anorexia, which leads to Vitamin B6 deficiency."

83. A nurse is instructing a group at the wellness center about first aid treatment for burns. Which of the following instructions would the nurse give to the group?

   A. "Cover the burned area with butter."
   B. "Apply an antibacterial ointment to the burned area."
   C. "Wrap the burned area with the patient's clothes."
   D. "Submerge the burned area in cool water."

84. A patient who is admitted to a medical unit for treatment of congestive heart disease is tearful, forgetful and anxious. Which of the following symptoms would indicate that the patient is developing dementia?

   A. Sundown phenomenon
   B. Altered level of consciousness
   C. Sleep disturbance
   D. Decreased appetite

85. A nurse should expect a six-month-old infant who has iron deficiency anemia to have which of the following findings?

   A. Weight for length at the 25th percentile
   B. Pale, chubby appearance
   C. History of a fractured clavicle at birth
   D. Delayed eruption of primary teeth

86. Which of the following patients should a nurse recognize as being at greatest risk for suicide?

   A. A middle-aged divorced male who recently lost his job
   B. An elderly married male in chronic pain
   C. A young single female who had a miscarriage
   D. An adolescent female who just broke up with her boyfriend

87. When instructing a patient who needs to restrict potassium intake, which of the following foods would a nurse identify as being the lowest in potassium?

   A. Raisins
   B. Grapes
   C. Spinach
   D. Potato

88. A nurse would explain to a patient who is administered prednisone (Deltasone) for the treatment of rheumatoid arthritis that the expected outcome would be to

   A. enhance the immune system.
   B. increase bone density.
   C. decrease inflammation.
   D. reduce peripheral edema.

89. A nurse has given instructions to a patient who is on steroid therapy. Which of the following statements, if made by the patient, indicates that the patient understands the instructions?

   A. "I will limit carbohydrates in my diet."
   B. "I will avoid individuals who have infections."
   C. "I will take the medication on an empty stomach."
   D. "I will stop the medication when my symptoms subside."

90. When assessing a patient who underwent a colostomy several months ago, a nurse would expect the stoma to appear

   A. dry.
   B. red.
   C. edematous.
   D. retracted.

91. A nurse is assessing a patient who has just had an acute myocardial infarction. The patient would most likely have which of the following laboratory values?

   A. White blood cell count of 7000/cu mm
   B. Creatine kinase of 1250 U/L
   C. Blood urea nitrogen of 6 mq/dL
   D. Potassium of 4.0 mEq/dL

92. A nurse is taking a history from a patient who has just been admitted to the hospital with an acute myocardial infarction. Which of the following questions would be most important for the nurse to ask?

   A. "At what time did the pain start?"
   B. "When did you eat your last meal?"
   C. "Have you experienced a pounding headache?"
   D. "Did you feel fluttering in your chest?"

93. Which of the following symptoms would be most significant when assessing a woman who has pregnancy-induced hypertension?

    A. Severe headaches
    B. Urine output of 200 ml in the last four hours
    C. Dependent edema
    D. Patellar reflexes of +2

94. An eight-year-old boy who has hemophilia A falls in the classroom, injuring his ankle, and is brought to the school nurse. Immediate actions for first aid by the nurse should include

    A. applying warm compresses.
    B. dispensing ibuprofen (Pediaprofen).
    C. administering factor VIII.
    D. immobilizing the joint.

95. Which of the following clinical manifestations would support a nursing diagnosis of decreased cardiac output?

    A. Cool, moist skin
    B. Bounding peripheral pulses
    C. Increased urinary output
    D. Diminished breath sounds

96. To meet the safety needs of a patient who has received thrombolytic therapy, the nurse should

    A. institute protective isolation.
    B. maintain complete bed rest.
    C. limit intramuscular injections.
    D. supply a firm-bristled toothbrush.

97. To which of the following measures should a nurse give priority when planning care for a patient who has undergone a cardiac catheterization via a femoral approach?

    A. Encouraging fluid intake
    B. Keeping the affected leg flexed
    C. Assessing the patient's apical pulse
    D. Monitoring the patient's serum glucose level

98. Which of the following snacks would be appropriate for a patient on a low-fat diet?

    A. A slice of baked apple pie
    B. Cheddar cheese and crackers
    C. Vanilla yogurt
    D. Mixed nuts

99. Which of the following measures should a nurse include in the care plan of a patient who has a diagnosis of major depressive episode?

    A. Maintaining a safe milieu
    B. Providing challenging activities
    C. Decreasing environmental stimulation
    D. Increasing time spent alone

100. When planning care for a patient who has a diagnosis of increased intracranial pressure, a nurse should give priority to which of the following measures?

    A. Limiting environmental stimuli
    B. Increasing fluid intake
    C. Suctioning nasotracheally every hour
    D. Keeping the patient in a recumbent position

101. Which of the following statements, if made by a patient who is scheduled for a magnetic resonance imaging (MRI) scan, would indicate the need for follow-up by a nurse?

    A. "There is a pacemaker in my chest."
    B. "My jewelry will be removed before the procedure."
    C. "I have had two miscarriages in the past."
    D. "I wear contact lenses."

102. To which of the following nursing diagnoses should a nurse give priority in the care of a patient who is suspected of having a spinal cord injury at C4?

    A. Altered health maintenance
    B. Impaired skin integrity
    C. Altered sensory perception: tactile
    D. Ineffective breathing pattern

103. A hospitalized patient who has a spinal cord injury reports an acute, pounding headache. Which of the following actions should the nurse take first?

    A. Suction the patient
    B. Raise the head of the bed
    C. Institute seizure precautions
    D. Administer an analgesic as ordered

104. The nurse observes a nurse's aide assisting a patient with Parkinson's disease during mealtime. Which of the following actions by the aide should the nurse recognize as inappropriate?

    A. Allowing the patient to cut the food
    B. Placing the patient in an upright position
    C. Filling the coffee cup half full
    D. Setting limits on the length of mealtime

105. Which of the following instructions should a nurse give to the caregivers of a patient with Alzheimer's disease?

    A. "Avoid any touching of the patient."
    B. "Keep the patient in bed after dark."
    C. "Allow the patient to choose what to eat at mealtime."
    D. "Establish a routine schedule of activities for the patient."

106. Which of the following nursing measures would be appropriate for a patient who has a nursing diagnosis of unilateral neglect following an acute cerebrovascular accident?

    A. Having the patient look in the direction of the paralyzed side
    B. Transferring the patient out of the bed from the affected side
    C. Placing the patient's personal items on the affected side
    D. Feeding the patient from the paralyzed side

107. A six-year-old child who has celiac disease is selecting food items from a hospital menu. Based on an understanding of celiac disease, a nurse would discourage the child from selecting which of the following foods?

    A. Fried sweet potatoes
    B. Corn meal muffin
    C. Puffed rice cereal
    D. While wheat toast

108. A patient with asthma has orders for all of the following medications. Which medication should a nurse expect to prepare when the patient shows signs of status asthmaticus?

    A. Epinephrine (Adrenaline)
    B. Theophylline (Theo-Dur)
    C. Erythromycin (Robimycin)
    D. Cromolyn sodium (Nasalcrom)

109. When taking a history from a 42-year-old woman, a nurse identifies all of these factors in the patient's life. Which one would indicate a risk factor for developing osteoporosis?

    A. Obesity
    B. Cigarette smoking
    C. African-American ethnicity
    D. Childlessness

110. A patient who has been diagnosed with osteoarthritis asks a nurse, "What does osteoarthritis mean?" Which of the following statements by the nurse would be appropriate?

    A. "Many organs in your body are inflamed."
    B. "Your weight-bearing joints are damaged."
    C. "You have inflammation in your joints."
    D. "There is shortening of your long bones."

111. Which of the following statements, if made by a patient who has rheumatoid arthritis, would indicate a correct understanding of the disease process?

    A. "My bones have become brittle."
    B. "Nodules may develop under my skin."
    C. "Overuse of my joints caused this problem."
    D. "This condition is part of normal aging."

112. A woman at 38 weeks' gestation comes to the hospital because she thinks that she is in labor. It is determined that she is in false labor, and she is to return home. When given this information, she starts to cry. Which of the following responses by the nurse would be most appropriate at this time?

  A. "Don't be upset because you thought you were in labor. Coming to the hospital early happens to many women."
  B. "I'll review the signs of labor with you so that you will not have to make another unnecessary trip."
  C. "Tell me why coming to the hospital early is a problem for you."
  D. "Let's talk about how you are feeling."

113. A patient is admitted to the emergency department for treatment of multiple bruises and a fractured right radial bone. The patient's spouse accompanies the patient. The nurse suspects domestic abuse. Which of these measures should the nurse include when interviewing the patient?

  A. Speaking with the patient alone
  B. Avoiding personal questions while the patient is upset
  C. Questioning the spouse about the injuries
  D. Reporting the suspicions to the police

114. A woman is receiving oxytocin (Pitocin) for induction of labor. Which of the following findings would a nurse expect if the Pitocin is having the desired effect?

  A. Fetal station changes from +1 to 0 in a one-hour period.
  B. Fetal heart rate accelerates by 15 beats for 15 seconds twice in a 10-minute period.
  C. Uterine contractions occur every three minutes and last for 60 seconds.
  D. A 4-cm dilated cervix increases to six centimeters in an eight-hour period.

115. To promote optimal function in a patient who has rheumatoid arthritis, which of the following instructions should a nurse include in the patient's rehabilitation plan?

  A. Apply ice to affected joints
  B. Massage joints when inflamed
  C. Perform daily weight-bearing exercises
  D. Immobilize painful joints

116. An infant who weighs 11 lb (5 kg) is to receive 750 mg of an antibiotic in a 24-hour period. The liquid antibiotic comes in a concentration of 125 mg/5 ml. If the antibiotic is to be given three times each day, how many milliliters would the nurse administer with each dose?

  A. 2
  B. 5
  C. 6.25
  D. 10

117. Which of the following manifestations would be indicative of hyperglycemia in a patient who is receiving prednisone (Deltasone)?

  A. Increased appetite
  B. Muscle twitching
  C. Tachypnea
  D. Diaphoresis

118. When assessing a patient who has hypothyroidism, a nurse should expect the patient to report which of the following manifestations?

  A. Intolerance to cold
  B. Increased appetite
  C. Frequent stools
  D. Rapid heart rate

119. A community health nurse is assessing a family. Which of the following findings suggests the highest risk to mental health?

  A. Child with Down syndrome
  B. Multi-generational household
  C. Single head of household
  D. Family history of depression

120. Which of the following safety measures should a nurse teach to a patient who is receiving treatment with sodium iodide I131 (Iodotope)?

    A. Flush the toilet twice after urinating
    B. Wear gloves while preparing food
    C. Limit exposure to direct sunlight
    D. Disinfect eating utensils after use

121. A woman who is at 30 weeks' gestation is experiencing sudden painless bright red vaginal bleeding. A nurse observes a colleague taking all of the following measures with the woman. Which one would the nurse question?

    A. Palpating uterine firmness
    B. Performing Leopold's maneuvers
    C. Repeating a vaginal exam
    D. Preparing for a non-stress test (NST)

122. Which of the following preoperative instructions by the nurse would be most effective in assisting an elderly patient to adjust to the home environment following cataract surgery?

    A. Prepare meals for freezing before surgery
    B. Eliminate stair-climbing after surgery
    C. Keep your bedroom cool and dry
    D. Elevate the head of your bed when sleeping

123. The nurse assessing an elderly patient should recognize which of the following findings as characteristic of the normal aging process?

    A. Decrease in reasoning ability
    B. Elevation in body temperature
    C. Loss of subcutaneous tissue
    D. Increase in bladder tone

124. Which of the following findings, if identified in a patient who is being treated for benign prostatic hypertrophy (BPH), would indicate that the treatment is having the desired effect?

    A. Increased urine concentration
    B. Increased sperm count
    C. Decreased scrotal swelling
    D. Decreased urinary dribbling

125. Which of the following explanations should a nurse give to a patient regarding the primary cause of peptic ulcer disease?

    A. "A spicy diet contributes to ulcer development."
    B. "Seasonal changes are associated with ulcer disease."
    C. "Executive job positions predispose people to ulcer formation."
    D. "Infection with Helicobacter pylori causes ulcers."

126. Which of the following questions would be most important for a nurse to ask when gathering data from a patient who is suspected of having acute pancreatitis?

    A. "Have you had a recent blood work-up?"
    B. "Do you have a history of diabetes?"
    C. "When was your last bowel movement?"
    D. "How much alcohol do you drink in a week?"

127. The nurse should teach a patient who has acute pancreatitis to avoid which of the following foods?

    A. Pasta and tomato sauce
    B. Rice and green beans
    C. Steak and baked potato
    D. Bread and baked apple

128. Which of the following responses by the nurse would be most appropriate when a patient states during the admission interview on the psychiatric unit that she hears voices?

    A. "Try to focus on the questions that I'm asking you, rather than the voices."
    B. "What are the voices telling you?"
    C. "The voices will go away when you begin treatment."
    D. "Hearing voices must be upsetting to you."

129. Which of the following factors, if noted in a patient's history, would indicate a predisposition for developing cholecystitis?

    A. Obesity
    B. Hypertension
    C. Depression
    D. Childlessness

130. A patient who is on a low-fat diet asks a nurse if dairy products can be included in the meal plan. Which of these responses should the nurse make?

    A. "You can have dairy products as long as you do not exceed 50 grams of fat per day."
    B. "You will need to take calcium supplements of 1500 milligrams daily in place of dairy products."
    C. "You do not have to limit the amount of dairy products that you eat."
    D. "You can substitute goat's milk for the cow's milk in dairy products."

131. Which of the following behaviors is considered a causal factor in the transmission of hepatitis A?

    A. Donating blood
    B. Consuming shellfish
    C. Having multiple sex partners
    D. Getting a tattoo recently

132. A community mental health nurse is caring for an elderly homebound patient who has a diagnosis of major depression. Which of the following observations would be typical of a patient who has received amitriptyline hydrochloride (Elavil) for a week?

    A. Elevated mood
    B. Increased social activity
    C. Improved hygiene
    D. Improved sleep pattern

133. Which of the following foods, if chosen by a patient who is taking a monoamine oxidase inhibitor (MAOI), indicates that the patient is following the prescribed diet?

    A. Prunes
    B. Aged cheese
    C. Fresh vegetables
    D. Sausage

134. The nurse should monitor a patient who is receiving lactulose (Cephulac) for which of the following adverse side effects?

    A. Diarrhea
    B. Petechiae
    C. Polyuria
    D. Flushing

135. A nurse should expect a Sengstaken-Blakemore tube to be ordered for a patient who has bleeding esophageal varices in order to

    A. cause vasoconstriction of the splenic artery.
    B. ensure airway patency.
    C. provide for enteral nutrition.
    D. apply direct pressure to the area.

136. When taking a history from an adolescent who is 12 weeks pregnant, it would be most important for a nurse to ask which of the following questions?

    A. "What drugs are you using?"
    B. "How many meals a day do you eat?"
    C. "Are you in contact with the baby's father?"
    D. "Who will be caring for your baby after delivery?"

137. Which of the following nursing measures would be most appropriate for a patient who has ascites?

    A. Withholding fluids
    B. Measuring abdominal girth
    C. Encouraging ambulation
    D. Monitoring for pedal edema

138. Which of the following laboratory values would support a nursing diagnosis of risk of infection?

    A. White blood cell count of 2500/cu mm
    B. Reticulocyte count of 50,000/cu mm
    C. Platelet count of 250,000/cu mm
    D. Red blood cell count of 3.5 million/cu mm

139. Which of the following findings would lead a nurse to suspect that the ventriculoperitoneal shunt of a seven-year-old child is obstructed?

   A. Frequent complaints of tinnitus
   B. Falling asleep daily in school for the past five days
   C. Occasional complaints of abdominal pain
   D. The presence of fever for the past three days

140. Aluminum hydroxide (Amphojel) is prescribed for a patient who has chronic renal failure. A nurse should recognize that the purpose of the medication for this patient is to

   A. lower the serum potassium level.
   B. diminish the concentration of ammonia.
   C. decrease the serum phosphate level.
   D. reduce the pH of gastric secretions.

141. Which of the following laboratory tests should a nurse expect a physician to order for a patient who has renal insufficiency?

   A. Creatinine clearance
   B. Serum ammonia
   C. Alkaline phosphatase
   D. Serum glutamic-oxaloacetic transaminase

142. Which of the following indicators would provide a nurse with the most reliable evidence that a patient's hemodialysis treatment has been effective?

   A. Body weight
   B. Abdominal girth
   C. Breath sounds
   D. Pedal pulses

143. Which of the following measures would a nurse take with the newborn of a mother who is positive for the human immunodeficiency virus (HIV)?

   A. Allow rooming-in with the mother if the newborn is stable
   B. Restrict newborn visitation to minimize the spread of infection
   C. Encourage the newborn to breast-feed in order to boost immunity
   D. Avoid skin-to-skin contact with the mother until after the newborn's initial bath

144. A nurse can validate that a patient understands safe, effective use of lithium carbonate (Eskalith) if the patient makes which of the following statements?

   A. "I should call the doctor if I have diarrhea or vomiting."
   B. "What I eat or drink has no effect on this medication."
   C. "If I forget a pill, I should take two for my next dose."
   D. "I can stop my medication when my symptoms disappear."

145. A patient admitted to the hospital in sickle cell crisis complains of severe leg pain. Which of the following measures should the nurse institute?

   A. Assist the patient to walk
   B. Elevate the foot of the bed
   C. Provide nasal oxygen at 2 L/min
   D. Administer analgesics as ordered

146. A patient who has hypertension makes all of the following comments. Which comment would indicate to the nurse the need for further teaching?

   A. "I felt better before I started taking the blood pressure medicine."
   B. "I will need to exercise on a regular basis."
   C. "I plan to use lemon juice to season my food."
   D. "It will take a while for the medicine to lower my blood pressure."

147. A patient who consumes excessive alcohol has a prescription for folic acid supplements. A nurse should recognize that the desired effect of this medication is to

   A. promote maturation of red blood cells.
   B. stimulate production of the intrinsic factor.
   C. enhance the synthesis of clotting factors.
   D. increase the rate of glucose uptake.

148. A patient says to the nurse, "I want to tell you something, but you mustn't tell anyone else." Which of the following responses by the nurse would be appropriate?

 A. "I'm glad you can trust me."
 B. "I have to reveal anything that would be essential to your treatment."
 C. "The nurse and patient have a special relationship."
 D. "I am bound to keep it secret because of confidentiality."

149. Pernicious anemia in an elderly patient most likely is the result of

 A. atrophy of the stomach lining.
 B. reduced function of the bone marrow.
 C. diminished liver metabolism.
 D. erosion of the intestinal rugae.

150. A two-month-old infant who was born with Down syndrome has been recently diagnosed with a ventricular septal defect. Based on a diagnosis of congenital heart disease, the nurse would instruct the parent to report which of the following manifestations in the infant immediately?

 A. Mottling with environmental temperature changes
 B. Nasal congestion when recumbent
 C. Brow-sweating during feedings
 D. Tongue-thrusting during episodes of crying

You have finished the Nursing, Part 1 portion of Practice Test D. Feel free to take a break (a one-hour lunch break will be provided at the Qualifying Exam) before beginning Nursing, Part 2 of Practice Test D. Do not turn the page until you are ready to begin Part 2.

Practice Exam D: Nursing, Part 2

You will have one hour and 50 minutes to complete Nursing, Part 2.

1. Which of these questions should a nurse ask a patient who is suspected of having acromegaly?

   A. "Do you urinate often?"
   B. "Are you buying larger size shoes?"
   C. "Is your mouth frequently dry?"
   D. "Have you had increased hair loss?"

2. Which of the following assessment findings, if identified in a patient who has a short leg cast, would require immediate follow-up by a nurse?

   A. Bounding pedal pulses
   B. Rapid capillary refill
   C. Nail beds blanch with pressure
   D. Tingling of the toes

3. A nurse is assessing a patient with a fractured femur. The development of a fat embolus in this patient would be indicated by

   A. calf tenderness.
   B. shortness of breath.
   C. abdominal distention.
   D. urinary retention.

4. Which of the following findings in a 12-hour-old infant boy would require the nurse to investigate further?

   A. The newborn has voided one time
   B. The foreskin on the newborn's penis is not retractable
   C. The newborn has lost 12% of his birth weight
   D. The newborn is excreting milky-looking fluid from his breasts

5. A patient has just been hospitalized for treatment of compulsive hand-washing. The nurse should intervene if staff members are seen behaving in which of the following ways?

   A. Talking to one another within the patient's view
   B. Changing the patient's routine
   C. Turning away from the patient
   D. Touching the patient

6. When assessing a patient who has acquired immune deficiency syndrome (AIDS), which of the following signs and symptoms would be most indicative of AIDS dementia complex?

   A. Headaches
   B. Bronchial infection
   C. Unsteady gait
   D. Diarrhea

7. Which of the following statements, if made by a patient who has myasthenia gravis, would indicate correct understanding of necessary adaptations to the disease?

   A. "My activity tolerance will increase during the day."
   B. "My diet should include high-protein foods."
   C. "I will avoid extremes in temperature."
   D. "I should avoid people who have colds."

8. The nurse caring for a patient who has had a subarachnoid hemorrhage should be aware that increasing intracranial pressure is manifested by

   A. a widening pulse pressure.
   B. an increased heart rate.
   C. a decreased blood pressure.
   D. a decreased body temperature.

9. A hyperactive patient who is on the psychiatric unit is changing his clothes in the day room. Which of the following interventions by the nurse would most likely be effective?

   A. Ask him why he is doing this in front of other people
   B. Take him to his room to finish the activity
   C. Encourage the other patients to leave the area
   D. Lock up his clothes except those that he is wearing

10. A five-year-old child displays hyperactive behavior after receiving a dose of diphenhydramine hydrochloride (Benadryl). The nurse would recognize that

    A. allergic reactions to this drug are common.
    B. this behavior is indicative of inadequate dosing of the drug.
    C. this is a typical adverse effect of the drug.
    D. the blood-brain barrier is sensitive to the drug.

11. Which of the following arterial blood gas levels would a nurse expect to observe when monitoring a patient who has metabolic alkalosis?

    A. pH, 7.50; pCO2, 38 mm Hg; HCO3, 30 mEq
    B. pH, 7.30; pCO2, 56 mm Hg; HCO3, 24 mEq
    C. pH, 7.38; pCO2, 42 mm Hg; HCO3, 25 mEq
    D. pH, 7.26; pCO2, 37 mm Hg; HCO3, 18 mEq

12. To which of the following nursing actions would a nurse give priority in the emergency care of a patient who has sustained a compound fracture of the femur?

    A. Splint the leg in its present position
    B. Place the leg in neutral alignment
    C. Irrigate the wound with normal saline
    D. Apply pressure directly over the wound

13. A patient who has Kaposi's sarcoma has all of the following nursing diagnoses. To which one should the nurse give priority?

    A. Altered thought processes related to lesions
    B. Altered health maintenance related to noncompliance
    C. Defensive coping related to loss of boundaries
    D. Hopelessness related to inability to control disease process

14. A nurse is providing care to a patient who has balanced skeletal traction applied to the femur. Which of the following findings requires immediate nursing intervention?

    A. The foot of the bed is elevated 30 degrees.
    B. The traction weights are resting on the bed frame.
    C. The patient's leg is suspended above the bed.
    D. The overbed trapeze is above the patient's chest.

15. A nurse observes a nurse's aide taking all of the following actions when caring for a patient who is in balanced skeletal traction. Which action requires further discussion by the nurse?

    A. Elevating the patient's head when eating
    B. Instructing the patient to use the trapeze when moving
    C. Raising the patient's hips when placing a bedpan
    D. Removing the weights when positioning the patient

16. A woman who has type 1 diabetes asks a nurse, "How will this pregnancy affect my insulin needs?" The nurse's response would be based on the understanding that insulin needs during pregnancy will

    A. decrease prior to the onset of labor.
    B. remain the same throughout gestation.
    C. increase during the first trimester.
    D. increase during the third trimester.

17. A patient who has low back pain says to a nurse, "I feel the pain down to my ankle." Which of the following actions would the nurse take first?

    A. Teach muscle-relaxing exercises
    B. Encourage frequent rest periods
    C. Assess sensation of the lower extremities
    D. Administer the prescribed pain medication

18. **Which of the following statements, if made by a patient who had a total hip replacement, would indicate to a nurse that the discharge teaching has been effective?**

    A. "I will need to buy an exercise bike."
    B. "I can bend to tie my shoelaces."
    C. "I can sit with my legs crossed at the knee."
    D. "I will need to make my toilet seat higher."

19. **Which of the following statements, if made by the parent of an 18-month-old child who has experienced two episodes of febrile seizures, is accurate?**

    A. "My child will have to take anti-seizure medicine."
    B. "I made an appointment to see a genetic counselor."
    C. "My child will probably outgrow these seizures."
    D. "I've made arrangements to have oxygen equipment at home."

20. **Which of the following statements would a nurse include in the preoperative instructions for a patient who is scheduled for an ileostomy?**

    A. "Your urine will be collected in a pouch subsequent to surgery."
    B. "Your bowel will be visualized with a laparoscope during surgery."
    C. "You will have a nasogastric tube in your nose after surgery."
    D. "You can drink liquids within 24 hours following surgery."

21. **Which of the following findings would be the earliest indicator of fluid volume deficit in a nine-month-old infant who is five percent dehydrated?**

    A. Increased heart rate
    B. Increased urine specific gravity
    C. Decreased urinary output
    D. Decreased blood pressure

22. **A laboring woman's husband assists her during the transitional phase of labor. Which of the following behaviors, if exhibited by the husband, would require intervention by a nurse?**

    A. Offers the woman a bedpan when she says she needs to have a bowel movement
    B. Gives ice chips to the woman when she says her mouth is dry
    C. Provides effleurage when the woman complains of intense abdominal pain
    D. Encourages the woman to fix her gaze on him when she experiences a contraction

23. **A young boy, who is receiving chemotherapy, develops alopecia and says to the nurse, "I'm so ugly. I've lost all my hair." Which of the following responses would be appropriate for the nurse to make to the child?**

    A. "Did you know that because your hair fell out, we know that the medicine is working to make you better?"
    B. "Would you like to see some pictures of famous men who are bald?"
    C. "It's hard to look different from the way you used to look."
    D. "You can wear a baseball cap until your hair grows back."

24. **A community health nurse teaches a mother comfort measures for her six-year-old child who has varicella zoster virus. Which of the following actions, if taken by the mother, requires further intervention?**

    A. Applying a cortisone-based cream to the child's lesions
    B. Patting the child's lesions with calamine lotion
    C. Bathing the child in a tepid oatmeal both
    D. Trimming the child's fingernails very short

25. **Which of the following findings would a nurse expect to assess in an elderly patient who has urinary retention?**

    A. Burning on urination
    B. Hesitancy of urination
    C. Blood in the urine
    D. Foul odor of the urine

26. A patient is newly admitted to the psychiatric unit with a diagnosis of bipolar disorder, manic phase. Which of the following activities would be most appropriate for the patient?

    A. Doing crossword puzzles
    B. Reading quietly in his/her room
    C. Playing a game of table tennis
    D. Working with modeling clay

27. Which of the following actions should a nurse include in the care plan for a patient who has water intoxication?

    A. Measure urine specific gravity
    B. Restrict salt in the diet
    C. Chew gum and hard candy
    D. Avoid ingestion of water

28. A patient who has undergone surgery for creation of an ileal conduit is scheduled for discharge. To determine if the patient will be able to manage self-care at home, a nurse would assess the patient's ability to

    A. irrigate the stoma opening.
    B. change the stoma appliance.
    C. catheterize the stoma pouch.
    D. apply pressure dressings over the stoma.

29. A nurse caring for a patient from a different culture notices that the patient did not eat the food on the meal tray. Which of the following comments by the nurse demonstrates an understanding of cultural diversity?

    A. "What foods do you eat at home?"
    B. "You need to eat to keep up your strength."
    C. "You will lose weight if you do not eat."
    D. "Why didn't yo tell me you don't like hospital food?"

30. Which of the following manifestations would be most significant when assessing a woman for evidence of true labor?

    A. Spontaneous rupture of membranes
    B. Progressive cervical dilatation
    C. Intermittent uterine contractions
    D. Passage of the mucous plug

31. Which of the following questions would be most important for a nurse to ask when taking a history from a patient who is suspected of having multiple sclerosis?

    A. "Are you easily distracted?"
    B. "Is your vision blurred?"
    C. "Has your appetite decreased?"
    D. "Do you have ringing in your ears?"

32. Which of the following nursing measures would be included in the care plan of a quadriplegic patient who is receiving bowel training?

    A. Placing the patient on a bedpan after eating
    B. Stroking the skin on the patient's inner thigh
    C. Limiting fluid intake between meals
    D. Performing rectal digital stimulation

33. When providing care to a patient who has returned to the unit following a cerebral arteriogram, a nurse would give priority to which of the following nursing interventions?

    A. Providing a quiet environment
    B. Encouraging early ambulation
    C. Keeping the involved extremity in a flexed position
    D. Maintaining a pressure dressing over the insertion site

34. Which of the following nursing measures would best promote communication between a nurse and a patient who has expressive aphasia?

    A. Using audiotapes
    B. Pointing to a picture board
    C. Speaking slowly and clearly
    D. Writing in large print

35. A nurse is observing a patient who has water intoxication. Which of the following assessments should the nurse make to determine if the patient is following the plan of care?

    A. Daily weights
    B. Intake and output
    C. Skin turgor
    D. Pedal edema

36. A patient who has sustained a closed head injury is admitted to the hospital without apparent neurological deficits. Which of the following findings indicates a deterioration in the patient's condition?

    A. Pupillary diameter of 5 mm
    B. Capillary refill time of 2.0 sec
    C. Respiratory rate of 24/min
    D. Urinary output of 30 ml/hr

37. Which of the following instructions would a nurse include in the teaching plan for a patient who is taking phenytoin sodium (Dilantin)?

    A. Store the medication in the refrigerator
    B. Brush your teeth after eating
    C. Take the drug on an empty stomach
    D. Instill artificial tears on arising

38. A woman who has tuberculosis and is to be treated with rifampin (Rifadin) is given medication instructions. The woman would show that she understood the instructions about Rifadin if she were to make which of the following comments?

    A. "I should avoid milk products while taking this medication."
    B. "I may need a laxative if I develop hard stools."
    C. "I should expect some burning on urination."
    D. "I may develop orange-colored urine."

39. Which of the following measures would a nurse include in the care plan of a patient who has a cerebellar tumor?

    A. Keep the room darkened
    B. Speak slowly and clearly
    C. Provide memory aids
    D. Ambulate with assistance

40. A 14-year-old is admitted to the hospital after being hit by a car while riding her bicycle. She has a closed head injury and was unconscious for several minutes after the accident. While assessing the child, the nurse obtains all of the following data. Which finding definitely requires further investigation?

    A. The child does not remember the accident
    B. The child asks what day it is
    C. The child has clear drainage from the left ear
    D. The child's pupils constrict in response to light

41. Which of the following manifestations, if reported by a patient, should a nurse recognize as supporting a diagnosis of meningitis?

    A. Pain with neck flexion
    B. Tingling of the lips
    C. Drooling of saliva
    D. Weakness of the legs

42. The parent of a 14-year-old girl calls a rape crisis center and says, "My daughter says she has just been raped. What should I do?" Which of the following responses by the nurse counselor is most appropriate?

    A. "Without allowing your daughter to bathe or change her clothes, take her immediately to the nearest emergency department."
    B. "Make an appointment for your daughter to have a physical examination by your family doctor as soon as possible."
    C. "Take your daughter immediately to the nearest police station and file a criminal report."
    D. "Your daughter needs to go to the nearest health department to be tested for pregnancy and sexually transmitted diseases."

43. Which of the following isolation precautions would a nurse take when caring for a hospitalized 16-year-old boy who has hemophilia A?

    A. Wearing eye shields when accessing the patient's central venous access port
    B. Wearing double gloves when performing invasive procedures on the patient
    C. Wearing gloves and a gown when bathing the patient
    D. Wearing a face mask when entering the patient's room

44. The nurse is caring for a patient with a diagnosis of pancreatitis. All of the following medications are ordered for the patient. Which one should the nurse question?

    A. Meperidine hydrochloride (Demerol)
    B. Morphine sulfate
    C. Propantheline bromide (Pro-Banthine)
    D. Cimetidine (Tagamet)

45. Which of the following findings would indicate to a nurse that a woman is in the transition phase of the first stage of labor?

    A. Increase in bloody show
    B. Urge to void every 15 minutes
    C. Spontaneous rupture of membranes
    D. Contractions lasting 30 seconds

46. A young child has experienced a minor superficial burn to the forearm. As an immediate first aid measure, a nurse would advise the parent to apply which of the following substances to the affected area?

    A. Cool water
    B. Antibiotic ointment
    C. Hydrogen peroxide
    D. Iodine solution

47. A patient with deep vein thrombosis is receiving 1200 units of heparin per hour, intravenously by infusion pump. The solution available is heparin 25,000 units/500 ml. Which of the following is the correct pump setting?

    A. 20 ml/hr
    B. 58 ml/hr
    C. 24 ml/hr
    D. 13 ml/hr

48. Which of the following statements, if made by a patient who has iron deficiency anemia, would indicate that the patient understands the medication instructions?

    A. "I will report any clay-colored stools."
    B. "I will keep the tablets in the refrigerator."
    C. "I will take the pills with orange juice."
    D. "I will expect my urine to become red-tinged."

49. Which of the following statements, if made by a patient who is receiving pyridostigmine bromide (Mestinon), should indicate to a nurse that the drug is having the desired effect?

    A. "I can see clearly."
    B. "I can remember my address."
    C. "I can speak loudly."
    D. "I can sleep through the night."

50. A patient, who has been on long-term treatment with psychotropic medications, exhibits lip smacking and torticollis. The nurse should recognize that these findings are indicative of

    A. tardive dyskinesia.
    B. akathisia.
    C. akinesia.
    D. dystonia.

51. Betamethasone (Celestone) is administered to a woman at 34 weeks' gestation who is in pre-term labor. A nurse would expect which of the following outcomes in the newborn if the drug achieves its desired effect?

    A. Enhanced birth weight
    B. Absence of hemolytic disorders
    C. Strengthened immune response
    D. Decreased severity of respiratory distress syndrome

52. Two days after cataract surgery, a patient makes all of the following statements to a nurse in the surgical ambulatory care center. Which statement would indicate that the patient needs further instruction about safety measures following cataract surgery?

    A. "I sleep with two pillows under my head."
    B. "I carry my groceries home from the supermarket."
    C. "I wear sunglasses when I go outside."
    D. "I placed a raised toilet seat over the commode."

53. A nurse would give a teenage girl who is prescribed tretinoin (Retin-A) for the treatment of acne which of these instructions to follow while using this drug?

    A. Use a reliable form of birth control
    B. Avoid exposure to the sun
    C. Supplement the diet with multivitamins
    D. Refrain from eating fried foods

54. Which of the following findings, if present in a patient who has undergone left femoral-popliteal bypass surgery, would indicate to a nurse that the surgery has been effective?

    A. Positive Babinski's reflex
    B. Active knee flexion
    C. Foot warm to touch
    D. Even hair distribution on leg

55. Which of the following actions would a nurse take with a woman in labor who is experiencing slight shoulder dystocia?

    A. Place the woman in knee-chest position
    B. Apply fundal pressure to the suprapubic area
    C. Prepare for a forceps-assisted delivery
    D. Obtain an order for an oxytocin (Pitocin) infusion

56. A nurse has given instructions about modifying lifestyle behaviors to a patient who has Raynaud's disease. Which of the following statements, if made by the patient, would indicate the need for further teaching?

    A. "I eat a diet high in fat."
    B. "I smoke one pack of cigarettes a day."
    C. "I have a glass of wine with dinner."
    D. "I spend time out in the sun."

57. When planning preoperative care for a child suspected of having Wilms tumor, the nurse should recognize that which of the following interventions places the child at risk for complications?

    A. Palpating the child's abdomen every eight hours
    B. Measuring the child's temperature rectally
    C. Monitoring the child's blood pressure every four hours
    D. Monitoring the child's intake and output

58. When a nurse is wrapping a patient's stump after leg amputation, the patient asks, "Why are you doing this?" The most appropriate response is that wrapping the stump is necessary to

    A. stimulate circulation.
    B. improve healing.
    C. decrease swelling.
    D. control pain.

59. A patient is receiving neuroleptic medication. The nurse should assess the patient for symptoms of an acute dystonic reaction, which include

    A. intention tremors.
    B. ataxic gait.
    C. difficulty swallowing.
    D. psychomotor agitation.

60. **A 16-year-old female is prescribed isotretinoin (Accutane) for the treatment of acne. Which of the following statements, if made by the girl, indicates that she understands the precautions to take while on Accutane?**

 A. "I'll scrub my face at least twice each day."
 B. "I'll take my birth control pill at the same time every day."
 C. "I'll take a double dose if I forget to take my pill one day."
 D. "I'll stop eating fried foods every day."

61. **A 70-year-old patient who is admitted to a cardiac intensive care unit following a myocardial infarction says to the nurse, "I wish I had lived a fuller life." Based on this comment, which of the following nursing diagnoses would be appropriate for this client?**

 A. Powerlessness related to perceived need for physical limitations
 B. Self-esteem disturbance related to altered body image
 C. Impaired adjustment related to compromised physical ability
 D. Spiritual distress related to confrontation with death

62. **Which of the following statements, if made by a mother who experiences a fetal demise at 34 weeks' gestation, would best indicate acceptance of the death?**

 A. "It will be a long time before I try getting pregnant again."
 B. "I should have taken better care of myself while I was pregnant."
 C. "It was probably meant for me to lose the baby at this time."
 D. "I will call my minister to help arrange a funeral service next week."

63. **Which of the following mental health problems is commonly associated with severe, chronic medical disorders?**

 A. Anxiety
 B. Depression
 C. Labile affect
 D. Confusion

64. **Which of the following statements, if made by the parent of an eight-year-old child undergoing treatment for impetigo, indicates an accurate understanding of the treatment plan?**

 A. "I have been draining the lesions as they develop."
 B. "I wash the lesions every day using a freshly laundered cloth."
 C. "I keep the lesions covered with a gauze dressing."
 D. "I remind my child several times each day not to touch the lesions."

65. **Which of the following comments, if made by a patient who has major depression, would indicate an increased risk of suicide?**

 A. "I think I'll lie down. I feel like sleeping."
 B. "I won't be a problem much longer."
 C. "I think the doctor should give me more medicine."
 D. "I miss my family, especially my children."

66. **A parent calls the emergency department and tells a nurse, "My two-year-old child ate about half a bottle of chewable vitamins, but seems to be feeling fine." Which of the following questions would the nurse ask the parent first?**

 A. "Were the vitamins in a locked cabinet?"
 B. "Have you notified your family doctor yet?"
 C. "Did you make your child vomit?"
 D. "Are the vitamins fortified with iron?"

67. **During a typical initial newborn assessment, a nurse would expect to identify the presence of**

 A. an apical heart rate of 94 beats per minute.
 B. hands and feet that have a bluish color.
 C. an eye discharge that is yellow and watery.
 D. an umbilical stump that has two veins and one artery.

68. A patient recently diagnosed with end-stage cancer tells a nurse, "If I had one more chance, I'd give up smoking." The nurse should recognize that the patient is in which of the following stages of grief?

    A. Denial
    B. Bargaining
    C. Anger
    D. Depression

69. A three-year-old child has an upper respiratory infection. During a physical examination, a nurse observes bruises to the lower back and buttocks of the child. The nurse would first assess the child for manifestations of

    A. child maltreatment syndrome.
    B. blood dyscrasias.
    C. neuromuscular dysfunction.
    D. acquired immune deficiency syndrome.

70. A patient who has recovered from a myocardial infarction says to a nurse, "Do you think I can still be with my wife?" Which of the following responses by the nurse would be appropriate?

    A. "It sounds as if you need to have a talk with your physician."
    B. "It sounds as if you are worried about sexual activity."
    C. "It is healthy for you to continue your relationship with your wife."
    D. "Let's just focus on your recovery right now."

71. According to Erikson, which of the following behaviors would indicate that a two-year-old patient's growth and development is progressing successfully?

    A. The child tries new powers of speech.
    B. The child imitates the behavior of others.
    C. The child plays collaboratively with other children.
    D. The child seeks validation from the primary caregiver.

72. Which of the following questions would be most important for a nurse to ask when taking a history from a female patient who has a diagnosis of pelvic inflammatory disease?

    A. "Have you had abdominal surgery?"
    B. "Do you have a history of blood transfusions?"
    C. "How many children do you have?"
    D. "Are you sexually active?"

73. The long-term follow-up care plan for a six-month-old infant who is being treated for acute meningitis would include which of the following interventions?

    A. Pneumogram
    B. Cerebro-spinal fluid culture
    C. Audiology testing
    D. Electroencephalography

74. Which of the following patients would benefit most from group therapy?

    A. A patient in the second stage of dementia
    B. A patient in the manic phase of a bipolar disorder
    C. A patient who has positive signs of schizophrenia
    D. A patient in the working phase of major depression

75. Which of the following instructions regarding mouth care should be given to the parent of a four-year-old child who is receiving cancer chemotherapy?

    A. "Brush your child's teeth twice each day using a firm-bristled toothbrush."
    B. "Avoid using alcohol-based mouth washes to rinse your child's mouth."
    C. "Floss your child's teeth daily with a gortex flossing string."
    D. "Have your child refrain from eating foods that have a high sugar content."

76. During group therapy, a patient says, "I can't believe I'm getting a divorce after being married 22 years!" Which of the following responses by the nurse would maintain group involvement?

   A. "I'm sure it's hard to lose someone you've been with so long."
   B. "Has anyone else experienced the same feelings?"
   C. "Can you identify how you've contributed to this situation?"
   D. "It sounds like you feel responsible for the failure of your marriage."

77. It is suspected that a patient who comes to the ambulatory care center reporting a sore throat has mononucleosis. Which of the following additional findings, if noted by the nurse, would support this diagnosis?

   A. White patches on the tongue
   B. Enlarged lymph nodes
   C. Periorbital edema
   D. Productive cough

78. A nurse has given discharge instructions to a patient who has undergone a laryngectomy. Which of the following statements indicates that the teaching is effective?

   A. "I will need to plug my laryngectomy tube for eating."
   B. "I will not be able to produce effective speech again."
   C. "I will have a change in my sense of smell."
   D. "I will be unable to take showers."

79. A three-year-old child is suspected of having Wilms tumor. Which of the following measures should be avoided when caring for this child?

   A. Obtaining blood pressure readings in all four extremities
   B. Checking deep tendon reflexes
   C. Palpating upper and lower abdominal quadrants
   D. Performing a sterile urinary catheterization

80. Which of the following factors, if noted in a patient's history, indicates a predisposition for the development of endocarditis?

   A. Crowded living conditions
   B. Multiple sex partners
   C. Intravenous drug use
   D. Family tendency toward heart disease

81. A patient who has a diagnosis of valvular heart disease receives discharge instructions from a nurse. Which of the following statements, if made by the patient, would indicate a correct understanding of the discharge teaching?

   A. "I will need to wear a Holter monitor to determine how well I am doing."
   B. "I will have to take antibiotics for the rest of my life."
   C. "I will have to avoid going out in crowded places."
   D. "I will have to inform my dentist of my condition before treatment."

82. When caring for a patient who has a chest tube connected to a water-seal drainage system, a nurse observes that the fluid in the chest tube is not fluctuating. Which of the following nursing interventions is most appropriate?

   A. Assessing for breath sounds
   B. Reinforcing the occlusive dressing
   C. Emptying the drainage container
   D. Clamping the chest tube

83. A patient has a diagnosis of borderline personality disorder. Which of the following nursing diagnoses would be basic to planning nursing care for this patient?

   A. Hopelessness related to psychic injury
   B. Powerlessness related to learned helplessness
   C. Impaired social interaction related to splitting
   D. Impaired adjustment related to loss of relationships

84. A parent of a two-month-old is given instructions about the care of diaper dermatitis. Which of the following comments, if made by the parent, would indicate a need for further instructions?

    A. "I only use alcohol-free baby wipes when cleaning my baby during diaper changes."
    B. "I will remove all of the old diaper cream from my baby before applying more."
    C. "I will need to change diapers frequently so my baby's bottom stays dry."
    D. "Giving my baby fewer bottles will help to reduce diaper irritation."

85. When assessing a patient who has experienced a flail chest injury, a nurse identifies all of the following findings. To which finding should the nurse give priority in planning care for the patient?

    A. Arterial CO2 level of 42 mm Hg
    B. Heart rate of 96 beats per minute
    C. Oxygen saturation of 91%
    D. Respiratory rate of 22 breaths per minute

86. A patient who has Cushing's syndrome asks a nurse, "Why has my face become so round?" The nurse's response is based on the knowledge that adrenal hormone

    A. excess causes lymphedema.
    B. excess causes abnormal distribution of fat.
    C. insufficiency results in hypervolemia.
    D. insufficiency results in electrolyte imbalance.

87. Which of the following statements, if made by a parent of a two-year-old child, would prompt a nurse to recommend that the child be evaluated further for dehydration?

    A. "My child last urinated about four hours ago."
    B. "My child's gums have a pale pink color."
    C. "My child cries, but no tears come out."
    D. "My child's skin feels warm and dry."

88. During health visits, a nurse should continue to measure the head circumference of a child up to the age of

    A. 12 months.
    B. 18 months.
    C. three years.
    D. five years.

89. The central venous catheter of a 10-year-old child who is receiving long-term total parenteral nutrition (TPN) occludes. If the infusion is interrupted for several hours, the nurse would closely monitor laboratory values for

    A. glucose.
    B. ketones.
    C. sodium.
    D. potassium.

90. Which of the following responses of a female patient who is codependent and has low self-esteem indicates that nursing interventions have been successful?

    A. The patient encourages her 16-year-old daughter to prepare her own breakfast.
    B. The patient regularly prepares refreshments for her reading club.
    C. The patient refuses help from her child with meal preparation.
    D. The patient seeks other family members' approval prior to preparing meals.

91. Which of the following activities, if performed by the nurse, is an example of primary prevention?

    A. Identification of problematic behavior in children
    B. Screening for depression
    C. Assessment of family growth and development
    D. Promoting independence in the elderly

92. When performing tracheostomy care for a three-year-old child, it is essential for the nurse to take which of the following steps?

    A. Obtain an order for pre-tracheostomy care sedation
    B. Hyperextend the head to make the tracheostomy site more accessible
    C. Cleanse the tracheostomy stoma with full-strength hydrogen peroxide
    D. Apply new tracheostomy ties prior to removing the soiled ones

93. A patient is admitted to the detoxification unit with a diagnosis of alcohol abuse. Which of the following articles should be omitted from the patient's admission package?

    A. Mouthwash
    B. Liquid soap
    C. Toothpaste
    D. Talcum powder

94. It is essential for a nurse to take which of the following actions immediately after artificial rupture of membranes?

    A. Document the amount of fluid released
    B. Test the amniotic fluid pH
    C. Check the woman's temperature
    D. Assess the fetal heart rate

95. A woman is to undergo a scheduled labor induction. Which of the following findings would alert the nurse that the induction procedure should be questioned?

    A. The woman has a history of precipitous delivery.
    B. A vaginal culture is positive for beta streptococcus.
    C. The fetus is in a breech position.
    D. A non-stress test result is reactive.

96. The nurse should teach a patient who is taking thioridazine hydrochloride (Mellaril) to follow which of the following diets?

    A. Bland
    B. Low-residue
    C. Sodium-restricted
    D. High-fiber

97. Which of the following findings, if identified in a four-year-old child who is receiving intravenous ceftriaxone sodium (Rocephin) for the treatment of pneumonia, indicates that the nurse should question using Rocephin?

    A. Urinary frequency
    B. Frontal headache
    C. Back pain
    D. Moderate itching

98. A patient who has a borderline personality disorder praises one nurse and asserts that all other staff members are terrible. The praised nurse should respond by

    A. showing appreciation for the patient's positive evaluation.
    B. providing reassuring information about the patient's psychosocial integrity.
    C. maintaining objectivity regarding the patient's remarks.
    D. conveying acceptance of the patient's need for a false belief system.

99. Which of the following responses would be the earliest indication that a child who has acute glomerulonephritis is responding positively to treatment?

    A. Decrease in appetite
    B. Decrease in blood pressure
    C. Increase in urinary output
    D. Increase in energy level

100. Which of the following assessment techniques should a nurse use to determine the appropriate placement of a nasogastric tube?

    A. Aspirating drainage through the nasogastric tube
    B. Auscultating for bowel sounds
    C. Palpating over the epigastric region
    D. Inserting the open end of the nasogastric tube into water

101. A Certified Nursing Assistant (CNA) who is bathing a patient with end-stage cirrhosis notices that the patient has become disoriented and reports this observation to the nursing supervisor. Recognizing this as a change from baseline, the supervisor would initially

    A. document the change in orientation in the medical record.
    B. notify the physician.
    C. limit the patient's physical activity.
    D. perform a mental status examination.

102. Which of the following measures should the patient be taught in order to minimize the possibility of oral fungal infections when using steroid inhalers?

    A. Wash the mouthpiece no more than once a day
    B. Rinse the mouth after use of the inhaler
    C. Avoid adding salt to food
    D. Limit the amount of spicy foods in the diet

103. A 12-year-old child who is suspected of having coarctation of the aorta is hospitalized. It is essential that a nurse perform which of the following assessments during the initial physical examination?

    A. Palpating the lower margin of the liver
    B. Monitoring the blood pressure in all four extremities
    C. Measuring the abdominal girth
    D. Performing pulmonary function tests

104. A patient who has had surgery on his right eye (occipital dysplasia, O.D.) for glaucoma complains of severe pain and nausea postoperatively. The nurse initially should carry out which of the following measures?

    A. Remove the dressing and assess for bleeding
    B. Administer acetylsalicylic acid (aspirin) for pain
    C. Position the patient on his/her right side
    D. Notify the physician

105. On the intercom, the patient screams, "It all came apart. I'm dying." On assessment, the nurse finds an eight-inch gaping incision with expulsion of abdominal contents. Which of the following actions should the nurse take first?

    A. Re-close the incision using sterile technique and apply pressure
    B. Assess the patient's blood pressure and heart rate
    C. Cover the incision with sterile saline gauze
    D. Administer a sedative for anxiety

106. Cromolyn sodium (Intal) is ordered for a school-aged child who has asthma. A nurse would determine that the child understands when to take this medication if the child makes which of the following statements?

    A. "I will use my inhaler after meals."
    B. "I will use my inhaler prior to exercise."
    C. "I will use my inhaler when I am having an attack."
    D. "I will use my inhaler after being outside in cold weather."

107. A seven-year-old child who was in a house fire is being evaluated in the emergency department. The child has no visible burn injuries but vomits undigested food with black particles. Which of the following goals would be given priority in the child's care plan?

    A. Minimize discomfort
    B. Conserve urinary output
    C. Maintain a patent airway
    D. Preserve gastrointestinal function

108. The nurse would correctly evaluate the effectiveness of megestrol acetate (Megace) in patients with acquired immune deficiency syndrome (AIDS) by documenting

    A. an increase in appetite.
    B. a decrease in diarrhea.
    C. improved coordination.
    D. control of seizures.

109. A pregnant woman who is at term cannot get to the hospital and calls a neighbor, who is a nurse. As soon as the infant's head is delivered, the nurse should take which of the following actions?

    A. Facilitate delivery of the anterior shoulder
    B. Cleanse the infant's face
    C. Stimulate the infant to cry
    D. Check for a nuchal cord

110. An elderly client who lives alone is admitted to the hospital after a syncopal event. Serum levels of albumin are found to be 2.0 g/dL. Which of the following nursing diagnoses is a priority for this patient?

    A. Potential alteration in comfort
    B. Potential alteration in elimination
    C. Potential alteration in skin integrity
    D. Potential alteration in mobility

 You have finished Nursing, Part 2 of Practice Test D.

Rationales-Practice Exam D: Nursing, Part 1

1.   Key: C   Client Need: *Physiological Adaptation*

   C. The nurse should first check the patient's glucose level by the fingerstick method.

   A.   If the patient is hypoglycemic, no sugar will be found in the urine.
   B.   If the patient's glucose is low, a longer-acting carbohydrate, such as skim milk, is recommended. Over-treatment with large quantities of quick-acting carbohydrates should be avoided.
   D.   If the patient is hypoglycemic, as indicated by weakness and tremors, the patient will not require insulin.

2.   Key: C   Client Need: *Pharmacological and Parenteral Therapies*

   C. Hypoglycemia that occurs in the late afternoon is related to the peaking of the morning NPH injection. NPH onset is three to four hours after administration and its peak, eight to 16 hours after administration.

   A and B.
       This is less than peak time after administration of NPH insulin.
   D. This is more than peak time after administration of NPH insulin.

3.   Key: C   Client Need: *Reduction of Risk Potential*

   C. The nurse must carefully assess the patient with chronic diabetes mellitus to determine the presence of pain, paresthesias, numbness, orthostatic changes and gastrointestinal symptoms.

   A, B and D.
       The most frequently occurring complications of diabetes mellitus include retinopathy, neuropathy and nephropathy.

4.   Key: C   Client Need: *Growth and Development*

   C. Naegles Rule: Last Menstrual Period minus three months, plus seven days, plus one year = Estimated Date of Delivery of April 8th.

   A.   The first day of the woman's last menstrual period would have been June 17th.
   B.   The first day of the last menstrual period would have been June 21st.
   D.   The first day of the last menstrual period would have been July 4th.

5.   Key: C   Client Need: *Pharmacological and Parenteral Therapies*

   C. Adverse effects of Coumadin therapy include bleeding, which would be noted by black, tarry stools.

   A and B.
       Blurred vision and diffuse red rash are not identified as side effects of Coumadin.
   D. Ringing in the ears is a side effect of acetylsalicylic acid (Aspirin) therapy.

6. **Key: C**   **Client Need:** *Reduction of Risk Potential*

    C. Serum amylase is the most important aid in diagnosing acute pancreatitis. Peak levels are reached in 24 hours.

    A and D.
     Cholesterol and creatinine levels are not included in the diagnostic evaluation for pancreatitis.
    B. Transient hyperglycemia occurs in some patients with pancreatitis.

7. **Key: C**   **Client Need:** *Reduction of Risk Potential*

    C. The normal recovery of the body takes four to six weeks. Activities begin gradually with walking. Because the sternum remains unstable for several weeks, patients should avoid any lifting. The patient needs further instruction regarding appropriate activities.

    A. The patient should follow a healthy cardiac diet: low cholesterol and low sodium. Chicken and fish are good dietary choices for the patient.
    B. Since the patient will continue to wear antiembolism stockings at home, the nurse should make sure that a significant other also knows how to apply the stockings.
    D. Meditation is a powerful means of relaxation and is appropriate for the cardiac patient.

8. **Key: B**   **Client Need:** *Pharmacological and Parenteral Therapies*

    B. Patients using bronchodilator inhalant medications along with other inhalants should be instructed to use the bronchodilator first, and wait five minutes before administering the other medications. Dilation of the bronchi allows for greater distribution and absorption of the other inhalants.

    A and D.
     The bronchodilator should be used before other medications to promote greater distribution of those medications.
    C. Patients should take inhalant medications as ordered. There is no indication that the medications should be taken one hour after each meal.

9. **Key: C**   **Client Need:** *Psychosocial Adaptation*

    C. Delusions and hallucinations are the dominant symptoms in paranoid schizophrenia.

    A. Elated affect and hyperactivity are behaviors seen in mania.
    B. Obsessive thoughts and rituals are behaviors typical of obsessive-compulsive disorders.
    D. Manipulation and narcissism are behaviors seen in narcissistic personality disorders.

10. **Key: B**   **Client Need:** *Prevention and Early Detection of Disease*

    B. Influenza immunization is the most effective measure for preventing or minimizing influenza symptoms. Annual flu vaccines are recommended by the Public Health Service for adults with chronic cardiovascular and pulmonary disorders.

    A. Staying indoors in bad weather will not prevent influenza.
    C and D.
     Wearing a mask and taking a multivitamin are not recommended as methods for preventing influenza.

11. **Key: B**   **Client Need:** *Growth and Development*

    B. At the time of ovulation the amount of vaginal mucus increases, and appears thin, watery and clear. Basal body temperature increases 0.3 to 0.6°C approximately 24 to 48 hours after ovulation.

    A. Basal body temperature increases rather than decreases at the time of ovulation.
    C. Mettelschmerz and midcycle spotting, rather than sudden abdominal bloating, may occur at ovulation.
    D. Nipple discharge is not a sign of ovulation.

12. **Key: A**   **Client Need:** *Psychosocial Adaptation*

    A. It is not possible to logically discuss illogical ideas. The nurse should focus on the patient's feelings of anxiety.

    B. The nurse needs to avoid becoming incorporated into the signs and symptoms of the delusion.
    C. Paranoid schizophrenic patients are keenly sensitive to rejection. When these patients sense that others are avoiding them, they feel inadequate.
    D. The nurse should not attempt logical explanations of delusions, since the paranoid patient will only defend the delusions more vigorously.

13. **Key: D**   **Client Need:** *Prevention and Early Detection of Disease*

    D. The nurse should read the test 48-72 hours after the injection by palpating the area for the presence of induration. Only the induration, not the erythema, is measured at its widest.

    A. A maculopapular rash is not indicative of a positive tuberculin skin test.
    B. Erythema without induration is not considered significant.
    C. Ecchymosis should not occur as a result of a PPD test.

14. **Key: C**   **Client Need:** *Physiological Adaptation*

    C. Pursed-lip breathing helps the patient with chronic obstructive pulmonary disease (COPD) to prolong expiration time and rid the lungs of some of the air trapped in the alveoli.

    A and B.
       The patient should sit in a comfortable position during exercises.
    D. The patient should be instructed to inhale through the nose and exhale through the mouth.

15. **Key: C**   **Client Need:** *Prevention and Early Detection of Disease*

    C. The blood pressure reading is the sole determinant of hypertension. It should be measured three consecutive times before making a diagnosis of hypertension.

    A. The patient with a B/P of 158/100 does not require treatment in an emergency department. The B/P should be checked again before determining that the patient has hypertension.
    B. Blood pressure screening, rather than electrocardiogram evaluation, determines hypertension.
    D. The patient does not need to keep a food diary at this time.

16. **Key: D**   Client Need: *Growth and Development*

    D. Preterm infants are periodic breathers. Apnea is primarily an extension of this periodic breathing and can be defined as a lapse of spontaneous breathing for 20 or more seconds, which may or may not be followed by bradycardia and color change.

    A. Acrocyanosis is the presence of cyanosis in the hands and feet and is typically found in the newborn.
    B. Apnea is a lapse of spontaneous breathing for 20 or more seconds.
    C. Transient mottling when an infant is exposed to decreased temperature, stress or overstimulation is normally found in the newborn.

17. **Key: D**   Client Need: *Physiological Adaptation*

    D. Immediate intervention for the patient experiencing epistaxis, or nosebleed, includes applying pressure to the nose to stop the bleeding and positioning the patient upright with the head tilted forward.

    A. Ice packs may be applied to the nasal area.
    B. Upright positioning will provide less blood flow to the head than the supine position. Forward tilting of the head will avoid drainage of blood into the nasopharynx.
    C. Immediate intervention for the patient experiencing a nosebleed includes applying pressure to the nose in an attempt to stop the bleeding. Assessing for hypertension would be secondary.

18. **Key: A**   Client Need: *Psychosocial Adaptation*

    A. Risk for violence related to altered perception and cognitive distortions is the priority diagnosis. Hostility is projected onto the environment and then acted upon. Psychiatric healthcare workers are injured most often by patients with paranoid schizophrenia.

    B, C and D.
    Each of these nursing diagnoses is reasonable for the patient with paranoid schizophrenia, but the priority diagnosis is high risk for violence because it deals with the safety of patients and staff.

19. **Key: D**   Client Need: *Basic Care and Comfort*

    D. Appendicitis is inflammation of the vermiform appendix (blind sac at the end of the cecum). The most common symptoms of appendicitis are colicky, abdominal pain and tenderness with guarding of the abdomen. Initially, pain is generalized or periumbilical; however, it usually descends to the lower, right quadrant. There is often a low-grade fever in appendicitis without perforation. A number of nonpharmacologic techniques can be used with children to relieve pain. By definition, any pain intervention that is not a drug falls into this category. Using an age-appropriate video is a good distraction. This will allow the child to focus on the program and not his pain.

    A. The child should maintain a position of comfort. Children may complain of increased pain upon ambulation. For some children, maintaining a side-lying position with knees flexed may provide the most comfort.
    B. Applying warm compresses increases the possibility of rupture of the appendix and should not be done.
    C. Pain medication may mask the symptoms of appendicitis and delay the initial diagnosis.

378

20. **Key: C**   **Client Need:** *Pharmacological and Parenteral Therapies*

   C. The nurse caring for a patient taking propranalol (Inderal) should assess the patient's pulse daily. If the pulse is slower than baseline or irregular, it should be reported.

   A. Dizziness is a side effect of Inderal, not an indication for use. Inderal is not a drug to be used prn It should be taken at the same times each day.
   B. The patient should take Inderal before meals and with eight ounces of water. There is no indication that Inderal should be taken with orange juice.
   D. The patient should take the Inderal daily and never abruptly stop taking the drug.

21. **Key: A**   **Client Need:** *Pharmacological and Parenteral Therapies*

   A. Diuretics should be administered in early morning, if ordered daily, because diuretic administration later in the day may cause nocturia.

   B, C and D.
   The only time diuretics should be taken at a time other than in the early morning is if the patient has a job that requires him/her to sleep during the day.

22. **Key: D**   **Client Need:** *Pharmacological and Parenteral Therapies*

   D. The nurse should monitor the patient's electrolyte status closely, paying particular attention to sodium and potassium levels. Diuretics can deplete serum potassium and enhance the toxic effects of digitalis.

   A, B and C.
   Urinalysis, urine ketones and blood glucose are not significant to digitalis administration.

23. **Key: D**   **Client Need:** *Reduction of Risk Potential*

   D. Signs of peritonitis usually include fever and sudden relief from pain after perforation. There may be a subsequent increase in pain, which is usually diffuse and accompanied by rigid guarding of the abdomen and progressive abdominal distention. Tachycardia, rapid, shallow breathing as the child refrains from using abdominal muscles, pallor, chills, irritability and restlessness also are manifestations of peritonitis.

   A   There is usually a low-grade fever in appendicitis without perforation. A temperature greater than 102.2° F indicates perforation or viral illness.
   B. A child with appendicitis may experience nausea, vomiting and anorexia after the onset of abdominal pain. Diarrhea, as well as other common signs of childhood illness (such as upper respiratory tract congestion, poor feeding, lethargy or irritability), may accompany appendicitis.
   C. Nausea is a symptom of appendicitis, but the possibility of rupture would take priority for follow-up.

24. **Key: A**   **Client Need:** *Pharmacological and Parenteral Therapies*

   A. Studies show that without medication schizophrenics have a relapse rate of 60 percent. The patient should be instructed to not stop the medication.

   B. Antiparkinsonian medication is prescribed for the patient taking Haldol to counteract extrapyramidal side effects. Cogentin relieves the stiff neck that can accompany Haldol administration.
   C. Constipation is a side effect of treatment with Haldol. The patient should increase the amount of bulk in his/her diet.
   D. Photosensitivity is a side effect of Haldol. The patient should use sunscreen and not expose the skin.

25. **Key: C**   **Client Need:** *Growth and Development*

     C. Fundal height at 20 weeks will be at the level of the umbilicus.

     A. Prior to the first trimester, the fundal height is below the symphysis pubis. At 12 weeks, the fundal height is slightly above the symphysis.
     B. Fundal height for 16 weeks is between the symphysis pubis and the umbilicus.
     D. The fundal height is not always accurate after 36 weeks due to variations in fetal size, but it is generally halfway between the umbilicus and the xyphoid process.

26. **Key: B**   **Client Need:** *Physiological Adaptation*

     B. The nurse caring for a patient with syndrome of inappropriate secretion of antidiuretic hormone (SIADH) should be alert for low urinary output with a high specific gravity, a sudden weight gain or a serum sodium decline.

     A and D.
        Hyperglycemia and dysphagia are not manifestations of SIADH.
     C. The patient with SIADH has a low urinary output and may need diuretics to remove excess fluid volume.

27. **Key: B**   **Client Need:** *Reduction of Risk Potential*

     B. Signs of transplant rejection include decreasing creatinine clearance, increasing serum creatinine, elevated blood urea nitrogen (BUN) levels, fever, weight gain, decreased urine output and increased blood pressure. Normal serum creatinine is 0.2-1.0 mg/dl.

     A, C and D.
        Bilirubin, glucose and calcium levels are not indicative of transplant success or rejection.

28. **Key: A**   **Client Need:** *Psychosocial Adaptation*

     A. The most reliable indicator of improvement in the patient with anorexia nervosa is electrolyte balance. As the patient starved herself, the body entered a hypometabolic state. Decreased nutrients and the loss of electrolytes through vomiting and laxative use contribute to electrolyte imbalances. As the patient begins eating and ceases purging, electrolytes begin returning to normal.

     B. The patient's energy level does increase as the patient begins eating but it is not the most reliable indicator of improvement.
     C. An increase in fluid intake does not necessarily indicate improvement since the patient may substitute fluids for food.
     D. Actual intake of food, rather than a desire to eat, would indicate improvement in the patient with anorexia nervosa.

29. **Key: C**   Client Need: *Physiological Adaptation*

    C. Pyloric stenosis is the narrowing of the sphincter leading from the stomach to the small intestine. With pyloric stenosis vomiting usually starts during the second or third week of life, but may not appear until the infant is several months old. The vomiting usually becomes forceful and projectile. The emesis contains milk or formula and is not bile-stained. Initially, the infant may be hungry and irritable; later, the infant becomes lethargic, dehydrated and malnourished.

    A. The child with acute diarrhea (gastroenteritis) has a sudden increase in frequency, and a change in consistency, of stools. It is often caused by an infectious agent in the gastrointestinal tract.
    B. Gastroesophageal reflux is defined as the passive transfer of gastric contents into the esophagus. Regurgitation or emesis, rather than projectile vomiting, is the most common clinical manifestation. Recurrent reflux of gastric contents can lead to esophagitis, which can cause bleeding from the esophageal mucosa.
    D. The most common clinical manifestations of Meckel's diverticulum include painless, rectal bleeding, abdominal pain and signs of intestinal obstruction.

30. **Key: C**   Client Need: *Physiological Adaptation*

    C. Intussusception is an invagination or telescoping of one portion of the intestine onto another. Initially, the infant has an episode of acute, colicky abdominal pain and the abdomen becomes tender and distended. The classic currant jelly-like stool occurs later in the disease of intussusception.

    A. Symptoms of celiac disease most often appear between ages one and five years. Stools often are described as watery, pale diarrhea with an offensive odor. Vomiting, anemia and constipation also can occur.
    B. In biliary atresia stools become progressively more alcoholic or gray, indicating absence of bile pigment.
    D. The manifestations of ulcerative colitis may be mild, moderate or severe based on the extent of mucosal inflammation and systemic symptoms. Most patients exhibit bloody diarrhea or occult fecal blood.

31. **Key: A**   Client Need: *Pharmacological and Parenteral Therapies*

    A. Morphine is administered to promote analgesia, reduce anxiety and decrease the workload of the heart.

    B, C and D.
    Medical management of myocardial infarction is focused on controlling pain and limiting infarct size. Management includes the use of oxygen, nitrates, morphine, beta blockers, ACE inhibitors and rest.

32. **Key: D**   Client Need: *Pharmacological and Parenteral Therapies*

    D. Coumadin should be taken at the same time each day to maintain the prothrombin time within therapeutic levels.

    A. Nausea, rather than weight gain, is often a side effect of Coumadin.
    B. The pulse rate does not have to be monitored while taking Coumadin. Prothrombin levels should be checked regularly.
    C. The patient should not take over-the-counter drugs, particularly those containing Aspirin. Aspirin interferes with platelet aggregation and enhances the effect of Coumadin.

33. Key: C   Client Need: *Physiological Adaptation*

C.   When the feet of a patient with arterial insufficiency are placed in a dependent position, the skin becomes red. This is known as dependent rubor.

A. The pain of arterial insufficiency is described as a cramping, aching pain that develops in the calf or thigh and occasionally the buttocks. It is not described as tenderness of the foot.
B. Peripheral edema is not an indication of arterial insufficiency. Peripheral edema accompanies venous insufficiency.
D. Reduced capillary refill and reduced arterial blood flow are signs of arterial insufficiency.

34. Key: D   Client Need: *Growth and Development*

D. Quickening is the first fetal movements felt by the pregnant woman, usually between 16 and 18 weeks gestation.

A. The bladder's capacity is greatly reduced in the first and second trimesters.
B. Vaginal spotting is not common throughout pregnancy.
C. A weight gain of two to four pounds is expected during the first trimester.

35. Key: C   Client Need: *Growth and Development*

C. Developmentally, infants are not ready for solid food. The extrusion (protrusion) reflex is strong and often causes food to be pushed out of the mouth. Infants instinctively suck when given food. Between four and six months of age the extrusion reflex fades.

A. Acute diarrhea, a sudden increase in frequency and change in consistency of stools, is often cause by an infectious agent in the gastrointestinal tract. The increased frequency and severity of diarrheal disease in infants is related to age-specific alterations in susceptibility to pathogens.
B. Abdominal circumference or girth is measured just above the level of the umbilicus. In the event of abdominal distention, serial measurements are taken to determine changes in the girth. Abdominal distention can be caused by a variety of gastrointestinal disorders.
D. The amount of formula per feeding and the number of feedings per day vary among infants, but a general guideline for a six-month-old is six ounces per feeding. Infants have an average of 4.7 feedings per day. Those on demand feedings usually determine their own feeding schedule. When introducing solid food, the cereal should be offered before the entire milk feeding is given.

36. Key: B   Client Need: *Psychosocial Adaptation*

B. Tachycardia and chest pain are signs of cocaine use.

A. Constricted pupils and lethargy are signs of opiate ingestion.
C. Nystagmus and paresthesias are symptoms of PCP (Angel Dust) use.
D. Tachycardia, rather than bradycardia, is a sign of cocaine use.

37. Key: A   Client Need: *Physiological Adaptation*

A. The patient with gastroesophageal reflux disease should not lie down immediately after eating. This would encourage backflow of gastric contents. The patient needs further instruction.

B and D.
   Dietary restrictions include avoiding spicy, acidic and fatty foods, as well as drinks containing caffeine, such as coffee, tea and colas.
C. Sleeping with the chest elevated six to eight inches, placing a pillow under the chest or elevating the head on two pillows helps to prevent nocturnal reflux.

38. **Key: B**   **Client Need:** *Coping and Adaptation*

    B. An estimated two-thirds of patients with Alzheimer's disease live at home with the family as primary care providers. Research has pointed to the extensive burden this places on the family. In the final stages of Alzheimer's many families are forced to choose nursing home placement because of the burden of care.

    A. Reminding the caregiver of family responsibilities would not encourage the caregiver to discuss his/her feelings and concerns.
    C. Counseling is not indicated at this point in time. The nurse should allow time for the family to express its concerns and provide information on community resources.
    D. Medication options may be discussed but intervention should focus on relief for the caregivers.

39. **Key: A**   **Client Need:** *Growth and Development*

    A. Elderly hearing loss typically involves diminished hearing of high-pitched sounds.

    B. Over-enunciating words does not make lip-reading easier and is demeaning to the patient.
    C. Varying voice intonation includes use of high-pitched tones, which the patient will have difficulty hearing.
    D. The hearing loss seen in older adults does not require reinforcement of sound with pictures. This action also would be demeaning to the patient.

40. **Key: C**   **Client Need:** *Basic Care and Comfort*

    C. Diets deficient in folate have been implicated as a risk factor in the development of neural tube defects in the fetus.

    A, B and D.
    Ferrous sulfate, calcium carbonate and ascorbic acid deficiencies have not been implicated in development of neural tube defects.

41. **Key: A**   **Client Need:** *Psychosocial Adaptation*

    A. Antabuse can cause a severe reaction when alcohol or alcohol-containing substances are taken while on the drug. Alcohol products to avoid while taking Antabuse include cough medicines, mouthwashes and after-shave lotions.

    B. Antabuse does not need to be taken on an empty stomach.
    C. Antabuse produces a severe reaction that includes hypotension, nausea and vomiting when taken by a person drinking alcohol.
    D. Sun precautions are not indicated for the person taking Antabuse since photosensitivity is not a side effect of the drug.

42. **Key: A**   **Client Need:** *Management of Care*

> **A. Therapeutic management of acute diarrheal disease (acute gastroenteritis) is directed at correcting the fluid and electrolyte imbalance and preventing or treating malnutrition. Major goals are assessment of fluid and electrolyte imbalance, re-hydration, maintenance fluid therapy and reintroduction of an adequate diet.**

> B. Lethargy, defined as abnormal drowsiness or stupor, can be caused by high fevers, dehydration and electrolyte imbalances. While the child with acute gastroenteritis may become lethargic, the correction of the fluid and electrolyte imbalance is the priority.

> C. A patient goal should be to promote skin integrity, since frequent stools will cause irritation to the skin. However, this should not be the priority goal.

> D. A patient goal should be to promote comfort and relieve stress; however, the primary goal for this patient is hydration.

43. **Key: D**   **Client Need:** *Growth and Development*

> **D. The nurse should instruct the patient to avoid odorous food if morning sickness occurs.**

> A, B and C.
> Morning sickness is due to fluctuating hormone levels. Dry foods such as crackers before arising seem to alleviate some of the nausea.

44. **Key: A**   **Client Need:** *Physiological Adaptation*

> **A. A person with cataracts has opacity of the ocular lens and may complain of decreased vision, abnormal color perception and glare in bright lights. The pupils develop a milky-white appearance.**

> B. Impaired peripheral vision occurs in glaucoma, a disease characterized by an increase in intraocular pressure and resulting in progressive loss of vision.

> C. Seeing halos around lights is a symptom of glaucoma.

> D. Headaches are associated with neurologic disorders. They are not associated with cataracts.

45. **Key: A**   **Client Need:** *Reduction of Risk Potential*

> **A. The parathyroid glands are located on the posterior surface of the thyroid gland. During thyroid surgery, parathyroid tissue may be removed inadvertently or damaged. The post-operative thyroidectomy patient is at risk for hypocalcemia due to surgical loss or damage since the parathyroids play a role in calcium regulation.**

> B, C and D.
> Hyponatremia (decreased serum sodium), hyperkalemia (excess serum potassium) and hyper-magnesemia (excess serum magnesium) are not complications of thyroid surgery.

46. **Key: B**   Client Need: _Reduction of Risk Potential_

    B. The most serious consequences of acute diarrheal disease are dehydration, electrolyte disturbances and malnutrition. Therapeutic management of acute diarrheal disease (acute gastroenteritis) is directed at correcting the fluid and electrolyte imbalance and preventing or treating malnutrition. Since the child with acute diarrheal disease loses potassium, he/she should be evaluated for hypokalemia.

    A. Measurement of serum amylase activity is an important diagnostic test for acute and chronic pancreatitis.
    C. This test measures the serum level of bilirubin, a degradation product of the pigmented heme portion of hemoglobin. It is used to detect hemolytic disorders and to confirm observed jaundice.
    D. This test measures the amount of hemoglobin (the main intracellular protein of erythrocytes) in the blood. It functions to carry oxygen to, and remove carbon dioxide from, the cells and acts as a buffer in the maintenance of acid-base balance.

47. **Key: A**   Client Need: _Psychosocial Adaptation_

    A. A structured daily routine provides the patient with a sense of independence and control over the environment.

    B. Social withdrawal is a common behavior of patients with schizophrenia. These patients usually need encouragement to interact with others.
    C. Setting unrealistic goals leads to frustration and failure. The nurse should provide feedback regarding how realistic the patient's goals are, so that the patient does not set him/ herself up for failure.
    D. Studies show that without medication schizophrenics have a relapse rate of 60 percent.

48. **Key: D**   Client Need: _Physiological Adaptation_

    D. Manifestations of syndrome of inappropriate secretion of antidiuretic hormone (SIADH) include hyponatremia. The patient's diet should be supplemented with sodium.

    A. Straining of urine is done for patients suspected of having renal calculi, not for patients with SIADH.
    B. The patient with SIADH experiences fluid overload. Initially fluids may be restricted to 100-1000 ml/day.
    C. The blood glucose level does not require monitoring in patients with SIADH, since SIADH is not a disorder of glucose metabolism.

49. **Key: A**   Client Need: _Pharmacological and Parenteral Therapies_

    A. Insomnia, hyperactivity and pressured speech are signs of mania. A recurrence of signs and symptoms is indicative of a decrease in the lithium level, often caused by the discontinuation or erratic taking of medication by the patient.

    B, C and D.
    While the information gathered from these questions might be useful in planning care, asking the patient if he/she has been taking the medication helps to determine the cause of the relapse. Once the cause is determined and successfully treated by the healthcare team, the signs and symptoms of mania will subside.

50. **Key: B**   **Client Need:** *Growth and Development*

   B. Prenatal assessment of genetic disorders, such as amniocentesis, is indicated in women of advanced age. The incidence of Trisomy 21 or Down syndrome, a chromosomal disorder, increases with maternal or paternal age.

   A. A nonstress test assesses fetal heart rate patterns in relation to fetal movement.
   C. Percutaneous umbilical blood sampling, performed in the second or third trimester, is the most widely used method for fetal blood sampling and fetal transfusion. Indications for this test do not include genetic testing.
   D. Serum estriol levels are used to evaluate fetal and placental function.

51. **Key: D**   **Client Need:** *Physiological Adaptation*

   D. The goals of therapy for Crohn's disease are to control the inflammatory process in order to reduce or eliminate the symptoms, to obtain long-term remission, to promote normal growth and development and to allow as normal a lifestyle as possible. Corticosteroids are the most effective drugs for treating moderate to severe Crohn's disease. Decreased abdominal pain indicates a reduction of symptoms.

   A, B and C.
   The major clinical applications of the glucocorticoids stem from the ability of these drugs to suppress immune responses and inflammation. Severe adverse effects can result from long-term use of corticosteroids and include adrenal suppression, myopathy, osteoporosis, increased susceptibility to infection and a Cushingoid syndrome (including moon face). Expansion of muscle mass and an increase in the bulk of the stool do not indicate the effectiveness of steroid therapy.

52. **Key: A**   **Client Need:** *Psychosocial Adaptation*

   A. The manic patient has poor attention span and concentration. This patient would have difficulty sitting through a meal without becoming distracted or frustrated. Finger foods can be easily handled and are portable. They also can be left in places accessible to the patient.

   B. Sealed containers may be frustrating for the manic patient to open since the patient has difficulty focusing on a task.
   C. Expecting a manic patient to focus on a complicated task, such as food preparation, would be unrealistic.
   D. Lively interactions would intensify the manifestations of mania. Manic patients do best in a calm environment where communication is clear and concise.

53. **Key: A**   **Client Need:** *Physiological Adaptation*

   A. Confidential HIV testing should be encouraged for patients with risk factors. Sexual transmission of HIV still remains the most common mode of transmission.

   B. Blood and body fluid precautions must be taken from first contact with the patient. The nurse should evaluate if the patient avoids transmission to others and uses barrier precautions properly.
   C. In some cases significant others also may be infected and should be tested so that they do not transmit the disease. Disclosure to significant others should be encouraged.
   D. Patients with HIV may share living quarters with others as long as basic hygiene is followed.

54. **Key: A**   **Client Need:** *Management of Care*

   A. Gout is an acute inflammatory condition associated with ineffective metabolism of purines. Uric acid deposits accumulate primarily in the joints of the great toe causing pain, edema and inflammation. The nursing diagnosis applicable to a patient with gout should address the pain and limitation of motion.

   B. Fatigue is not symptomatic of gout.
   C. Interventions are aimed at reducing inflammation and pain. Risk for infection is not a nursing diagnosis associated with gout.
   D. Gout is a metabolic, rather than a neurovascular, disorder.

55. **Key: C**   **Client Need:** *Prevention and Early Detection of Disease*

   C. Lyme disease is transmitted by the deer tick and is most prevalent in the summer and early fall. Symptoms involve the skin, nervous system and joints. Families should be instructed to check often for ticks following outdoor activities, and to thoroughly inspect and wash clothes.

   A. Pets should wear tick collars. Pets should be inspected often, and not allowed on beds or furniture.
   B. Families should be instructed to wear light-colored clothing in order to better see ticks if they are on the clothing. They should wear long pants tucked into boots or long socks, shirts tucked into pants, and closed shoes when engaging in outdoor activities.
   D. Attached ticks should be removed. The area should be washed with soap and water and an antiseptic applied.

56. **Key: C**   **Client Need:** *Growth and Development*

   C. After amniocentesis the woman is monitored for uterine contractions and fetal heart rate. There is also a risk of infection of the amniotic fluid following amniocentesis.

   A. Many pregnant women have dependent edema in the lower extremities. It is not associated with amniocentesis.
   B. Odorless, white vaginal discharge is usually not of concern and is not associated with amniocentesis.
   D. Frequent urination is a common complaint for pregnant women and is not associated with amniocentesis.

57. **Key: A**   **Client Need:** *Reduction of Risk Potential*

   A. Manifestations of adequate tissue perfusion following repair of an abdominal aortic aneurysm is evidenced by a normal blood urea nitrogen, a urine output of 25-30 ml/hr, the presence of distal pulses and the absence of abdominal distention or postoperative ileus.

   B. Pre-tibial edema should not be present post-abdominal aortic aneurysm repair.
   C and D.
       Clear sclera and carotid bruit are not evaluative criteria for a patient post-aneurysm repair.

58. **Key: C**   Client Need: *Pharmacological and Parenteral Therapies*

C. Children who require frequent courses of steroid therapy are highly susceptible to the complications of steroids, such as growth retardation, cataracts, obesity, hypertension, gastrointestinal bleeding, bone demineralization, infections and hyperglycemia.

A, B and D.
Gingival hyperplasia, muscle hypertrophy and malnutrition are not side effects caused by long-term corticosteroid use.

59. **Key: B**   Client Need: *Reduction of Risk Potential*

B. A patient with vertigo has a high risk for injury secondary to dizziness that can lead to falls. Elderly patients are identified as especially susceptible to falls.

A. An adolescent who is entering puberty has a low susceptibility to falls.
C. A toddler learning to walk has an increased susceptibility to falls. However, due to increased cartilage and the protection of underlying tissues, the incidence of fractures in toddlers is low.
D. A postmenopausal woman is prone to fractures secondary to osteoporosis, but the elderly are at greatest risk.

60. **Key: D**   Client Need: *Reduction of Risk Potential*

D. Capillary refill greater than two seconds indicates vascular compromise or pressure from the immobilizing device.

A. Edema is usually present after injury or surgery and is most evident in uncasted, dependent areas. Excessive edema may indicate constriction of vessels from the immobilizing device.
B. Some pain is normal after trauma or surgery. The pain should decrease when the bone is immobilized.
C. Plaster casts set rapidly, but take several hours to dry completely and feel cool to the touch. Promoting the circulation of warm, dry air around a damp cast can enhance moisture evaporation and speed the drying process.

61. **Key: B**   Client Need: *Prevention and Early Detection of Disease*

B. Osteoporosis is a disorder that results in reduction in bone mass. The cause has been attributed to estrogen deficiency, immobilization, use of steroids and high intake of caffeine. Contributing factors are cigarette smoking, diets low in calcium, too much protein in the diet and a sedentary life style. Chronic smoking appears to both lower body estrogen levels and block calcium absorption, thereby increasing the risk of osteoporosis.

A. Weight bearing exercises, such as walking, prevent further bone loss. Lap swimming is non-weight bearing.
C. Caffeine, in the form of coffee, tea and colas, should be restricted or eliminated. Sodium does not have to be reduced.
D. Osteoporosis is not related to excessive sun exposure.

62. **Key: A**   **Client Need: *Psychosocial Adaptation***

   A. Treatment protocols for a patient with bulimia include determining the conditions for bathroom privileges and the indications for close observation by staff. The patient should be observed by staff after meals to make sure that purging does not occur.

   B, C and D.
   Decreasing environmental stimuli, weighing the patient twice daily and discouraging verbalization about eating are not identified as treatment protocols for the patient with bulimia.

63. **Key: A**   **Client Need: *Physiological Adaptation***

   A. Ménière's is a chronic disease of the inner ear characterized by recurrent episodes of vertigo, progressive unilateral nerve deafness and tinnitus. The attacks of vertigo, the sense that the outer world is moving around oneself, are sudden and occur without warning.

   B. Diplopia, or double vision, is not characteristic of Ménière's disease.
   C. Presbycusis, progressive, bilaterally symmetrical perceptive hearing loss occurring with age, is not characteristic of Ménière's disease.
   D. Nystagmus, involuntary rhythmic movements of the eyes, is seen in patients with neurologic disorders.

64. **Key: B**   **Client Need: *Management of Care***

   B. The patient has a right to confidentiality. The duty of confidentiality prohibits a professional from disclosing information obtained as a result of the treatment relationship, except to fellow professionals involved in the patient's care.

   A. Law enforcement officers are not usually part of the patient's treatment team. Exceptions may occur in emergency situations or when court ordered.
   C. Confidential patient information should not be shared with family members unless the patient authorizes the disclosure in writing or there is a clear and present danger to family members. Courts also may order disclosure.
   D. Insurance company representatives are not considered professional members of the treatment team. Confidential patient information should not be shared unless court ordered or in an emergency situation.

65. **Key: C.**   **Client Need: *Reduction of Risk Potential***

   C. A transurethral resection of the prostate is a treatment for benign prostatic hypertrophy (BPH). Prostatic tissue is removed via the urethra. After a transurethral resection, the bladder may be continuously irrigated to remove clotted blood and ensure drainage of urine.

   A. The patient who has undergone a transurethral resection does not require the administration of oxygen unless underlying disease warrants its use.
   B. Since prostate tissue is removed via the urethra, no dressing is required.
   D. A short-acting general anesthetic is used during a transurethral resection. Checking the gag reflex is not necessary.

66. **Key: A**   **Client Need:** *Growth and Development*

    A. Acceleration of the fetal heart rate in response to fetal movement is the desired outcome of the nonstress test (NST).

    B. Decelerations are not a reassuring sign for the fetus and the NST would not be considered reactive.

    C. The expectation is fetal movement and acceleration in fetal heart rate with a reactive NST.

    D. The expectations are fetal movements and fetal heart rate increases.

67. **Key: A**   **Client Need:** *Psychosocial Adaptation*

    A. Signs of improved social interaction include non-disruptive participation in activities.

    B. The patient with mania usually has flight of ideas and rapid, pressured speech. Increased ability to verbalize is not necessarily a sign of improvement.

    C. The manic patient often tries to lead group activities. This would not be a sign of improvement.

    D. The ability to stay focused on a single task would indicate improvement in the manic patient.

68. **Key: A**   **Client Need:** *Growth and Development*

    A. Protein intake should increase from 50 to 60 grams during pregnancy for the synthesis of the products of conception.

    B. Most carbohydrates should be complex, rather than simple, carbohydrates. They should come from nutritious foods and not sweets.

    C. Potassium is not needed in extra amounts during pregnancy.

    D. Excess amounts of vitamin A may be harmful to mother and fetus, even having teratogenic effects. Deficiencies in vitamin A are rare in pregnancy.

69. **Key: A**   **Client Need:** *Physiological Adaptation*

    A. Increased or decreased resistance to passive movement is a sign of abnormal muscle tone. The child may exhibit opisthotonic postures (exaggerated arching of the back) and may feel stiff on handling or dressing.

    B. Other significant signs of motor dysfunction are poor sucking and feeding difficulties with persistent tongue thrust.

    C. Head circumference measurement less than the 50th percentile is a normal finding for a three-month-old infant. The National Center for Health Statistics' growth charts use the fifth and 95th percentiles as criteria for determining which children are outside the normal limits for growth.

    D. When pulled to a sitting position, the child with cerebral palsy may extend the entire body, rigid and unbending at the hip and knee joints. This is an early sign of spasticity. Slight head lag is expected in a normal three-month-old infant.

70. **Key: B**   **Client Need:** *Physiological Adaptation*

    B. Congestive heart failure occurs when the heart is no longer able to pump enough blood to meet the demands of the body. In right-sided heart failure, increased volume and pressure in the systemic veins cause peripheral edema. This is related to an inability of the heart to pump blood forward into the lungs.

    A and D.
       Pulmonary congestion occurs with left-sided heart failure when the heart is unable to pump blood out to the system. Increased pressure in the left side of the heart causes back up of fluid into the pulmonary system, resulting in pulmonary congestion. Manifestations of this congestion are shortness of breath and paroxysmal nocturnal dyspnea.
    C. Decreased urinary output is seen in left-sided heart failure. The heart is unable to pump blood forward and cardiac output is decreased. This, in turn, results in decreased kidney perfusion and, ultimately, decreased urinary output.

71. **Key: C**   **Client Need:** *Pharmacological and Parenteral Therapies*

    C. Diltiazem (Cardizem) is a calcium channel blocker that causes vasodilation and a decrease in peripheral vascular resistance, thus reducing arterial blood pressure.

    A, B and D.
       Cardizem is used in the treatment of angina and hypertension. It is not indicated for control of seizures, reduction of cholesterol or the increasing of bone density.

72. **Key: A**   **Client Need:** *Management of Care*

    A. Pneumonia is an inflammatory process of the bronchioles and alveolar spaces in the lung usually caused by an infection. A productive cough is very common. Color and consistency of sputum will vary depending on the type of pneumonia present. The nurse should collect a sputum specimen first so that the underlying pathology can be identified.

    B. Pneumonia appears on chest x-ray as an area of increased density. Since the patient has already been diagnosed with pneumonia, a chest x-ray would not be indicated.
    C. The key to effective treatment of pneumonia with antibiotics is identification of the organism causing the pneumonia. Antibiotics should not be started until sputum cultures are obtained.
    D. Robitussin, an expectorant, is indicated in the treatment of a dry, nonproductive cough. This patient's cough is already productive.

73. **Key: B**   **Client Need:** *Reduction of Risk Potential*

    B. Chest tubes to water-seal drainage are used to promote lung re-expansion through the removal of air and fluid, and to prevent lung collapse from air entering the chest cavity. When suction is added to an underwater drainage system, gentle bubbling in the suction control chamber should be noted.

    A. When vigorous bubbling is noted, an air leak may be present.
    C. Continuous bubbling in the suction control chamber is normal and does not indicate that the tube needs to be repositioned.
    D. Increasing the suction source can cause more bubbling, but does not increase the effectiveness of suctioning because the outside air offsets further air removal.

74. **Key: C**   **Client Need: *Reduction of Risk Potential***

    C. **Muscular dystrophy is characterized by progressive weakness and wasting of symmetric groups of skeletal muscles, with increasing disability and deformity. The major complications of muscular dystrophy include contractures, disuse atrophy, infections, obesity and cardiopulmonary problems. Ultimately, the disease process involves the diaphragm and auxiliary muscles of respiration. Cardiomegaly is common. Relentless progression continues until death from respiratory failure or cardiac failure results.**

    A, B and D.
      These body systems are not involved in the major complications of Duchenne muscular dystrophy. Skin integrity may be impaired due to decreased mobility. The gastrointestinal system is not impaired, although the child is prone to obesity. The central nervous system is not affected.

75. **Key: C**   **Client Need: *Growth and Development***

    C. **During the first trimester the pregnant woman needs information related to her physiologic and psychosocial care. An expected outcome is that the woman will use the knowledge given her regarding nutritional needs, sexual needs, activities of daily living, discomforts of pregnancy and self care.**

    A. Breastfeeding teaching will be done closer to term and reinforced by lactation consultants in the postpartum period.
    B. Relaxation for labor will be taught closer to the woman's delivery date.
    D. Infant care will be discussed closer to delivery and reinforced on the mother-infant unit after delivery.

76. **Key: B**   **Client Need: *Psychosocial Adaptation***

    B. **In the early stage of Alzheimer's dementia the client complains of forgetfulness and has difficulty remembering appointments and addresses.**

    A. Disturbance of consciousness is a symptom of delirium.
    C. Disorientation is a manifestation of the middle stage of Alzheimer's dementia.
    D. Memory problems become more pronounced in the middle to late stages of Alzheimer's dementia.

77. **Key: A**   **Client Need: *Pharmacological and Parenteral Therapies***

    A. **Patient-controlled analgesia (PCA) is delivered intravenously via a pump that has a predetermined amount of analgesic contained within the unit. PCA is used to achieve better pain control. The patient adjusts the dosage on the basis of his or her pain level. PCA permits greater use of muscles when deep breathing and coughing.**

    B. The nurse should assess the patient for under-medication by questioning the patient for nonverbal cues that indicate pain.
    C. The nurse should assess the patient for signs of over-medication, and check the patient's level of consciousness.
    D. The patient who has optimal pain control is better able to cooperate with therapies and exercises. Pain on movement is an indication that the PCA pump is not being used effectively.

78. **Key: A**   **Client Need:** *Reduction of Risk Potential*

    A. The patient should be made aware that as the dye is injected, he/she may experience a feeling of warmth or heat and flushing of the face.

    B. The patient may experience a salty, rather than metallic, taste in the mouth when the dye is injected.
    C and D.
      Chest pain and shortness of breath should not be experience by the patient when the dye is injected.

79. **Key: C**   **Client Need:** *Coping and Adaptation*

    C. The patient is experiencing a normal reaction to pregnancy. Often, new mothers are ambivalent about the pregnancy in the beginning.

    A, B and D.
      These patient statements do not indicate that the woman is considering termination of the pregnancy, is in need of a social service referral or that she is at risk for abusing the child.

80. **Key: B**   **Client Need:** *Pharmacological and Parenteral Therapies*

    B. Total parenteral nutrition (TPN) is the infusion of nutrients through a central venous catheter. The hyperalimentation solution contains 20% glucose or higher (hypertonic), amino acids, water, vitamins and minerals. It is used for patients unable to eat or digest food in the gastrointestinal tract. Insulin injection (Regular) can be administered via the subcutaneous or intravenous route. Regular insulin has a quick onset and is used to treat the hyperglycemia associated with parenteral nutrition. Intravenously it begins acting within 10 minutes.

    A. Isophane insulin (NPH) can be administered via the subcutaneous or intramuscular route. The onset of action is one to two hours. NPH would not be used intravenously.
    C. Insulin zinc suspension (Lente) can be administered via the subcutaneous or intramuscular route. The onset of action is one to two hours. It should not be used intravenously.
    D. Semi-lente insulin can be administered via the subcutaneous or intramuscular route. The onset of action is one to one and a half hours. It would not be used intravenously.

81. **Key: B**   **Client Need:** *Physiological Adaptation*

    B. Stage II pressure ulcers are identified by skin that is not intact. There is partial-thickness loss of the epidermis, as evidenced by a blister or shallow crater.

    A. Stage I pressure ulcers are identified by skin that is intact, with a red area that does not blanche with external pressure.
    C. Stage III pressure ulcers are identified by full-thickness skin loss. Subcutaneous tissues may be damaged, with a crater-like appearance.
    D. Stage IV pressure ulcers are identified by full-thickness skin loss with extensive destruction to tissues, or damage to muscle, bone and supporting structures.

82. **Key: C** Client Need: *Pharmacological and Parenteral Therapies*

    C. Isoniazid is a drug used to treat tuberculosis. It is the only anti-tuberculosis agent used routinely for prophylaxis. Isoniazid can delete Vitamin B6 in the body and cause neurotoxic effects. Vitamin B6 supplementation (10 to 50 mg) usually accompanies Isoniazid use to decrease the incidence of neuropathy.

    A, B and D.
    Pyridoxine is used in combination with Isoniazid to decrease the incidence of peripheral neuropathy. Pyridoxine is not required for the absorption of B6 and does not activate the metabolism of Isoniazid. The action of Isoniazid, rather than anorexia, leads to B6 depletion.

83. **Key: D** Client Need: *Prevention and Early Detection of Disease*

    D. The first step in treating the victim is to stop the burning process and halt the penetration of heat to the deeper tissues. Flush the burns with low pressure, cool water or submerge the burned area in cool water.

    A and B.
    Oils, salves and ointments should never be used on burns because they hamper treatment at the medical facility.
    C. Carefully remove clothing and jewelry. If wounds are to be covered, dressings (preferably sterile) are used.

84. **Key: A** Client Need: *Psychosocial Adaptation*

    A. Sundowning occurs frequently in patients with dementia and is defined as increased agitation and confusion that occurs in late afternoon.

    B. Altered level of consciousness would indicate delirium.
    C. Sleep disturbance is not a symptom of dementia.
    D. Decreased appetite is not a symptom of dementia, although the patient may not be able to prepare his/her own meals.

85. **Key: B** Client Need: *Physiological Adaptation*

    B. Although chubby in size, infants with iron deficiency anemia are pale, usually demonstrate poor muscle development and are prone to infection.

    A. To assess whether the infant's weight is average for his/her height, compare the weight with a standardized graph. Height and weight should follow the same percentiles. The National Center for Health Statistics' growth charts use the 5th and 95th percentiles as criteria for determining which children are outside the normal limits for growth.
    C. A fractured clavicle at birth is the most common birth injury. It often is associated with difficult vertex or breech deliveries of infants of greater-than-average size.
    D. The age of tooth eruption shows considerable variation among children, but the order of their appearance is fairly regular and predictable. The first primary teeth to erupt are the lower central incisors, which appear at approximately six to eight months of age.

86. **Key: A** Client Need: *Psychosocial Adaptation*

    A. Risk factors for suicide include male gender, living alone and recent loss.

    B, C and D.
    These patients are not at as great a risk for suicide as the divorced male who lives alone and recently lost his job.

87. **Key: B**   Client Need: *Basic Care and Comfort*

   B. The potassium content of one serving of grapes is 105 mg. Of the choices given, it is the lowest in potassium.

   A. The potassium content of one serving of raisins is 1089 mg.
   C. The potassium content of one serving of spinach is 307 mg.
   D. The potassium content of one serving of potatoes is 844 mg.

88. **Key: C**   Client Need: *Pharmacological and Parenteral Therapies*

   C. Rheumatoid arthritis (RA) is characterized by a chronic inflammation of the synovial membrane of the diarthroidal joints (synovial joints). Chronic inflammation can lead to joint damage and deformity. Medications used to decrease the inflammatory process in rheumatoid arthritis include systemic steroids.

   A. The nurse should be alert to the possibility of immunosuppression with the use of prednisone.
   B. A side effect of prednisone use is osteoporosis, a reduction in bone density.
   D. A side effect of prednisone therapy is edema.

89. **Key: B**   Client Need: *Pharmacological and Parenteral Therapies*

   B. The patient should avoid individuals with known contagious diseases due to immunosuppression secondary to the use of steroids.

   A. Most patients receiving steroids should be on a high-potassium, low-sodium diet and may need increased protein intake to decrease the effects of protein catabolism.
   C. Steroids irritate the gastric mucosa and should be taken with meals or milk.
   D. The patient should be cautioned that withdrawal of steroids must be carried out slowly and under close supervision to avoid adrenal insufficiency.

90. **Key: B**   Client Need: *Reduction of Risk Potential*

   B. The patient's colostomy stoma should be deep pink to red in color, shiny and moist like the mucous membrane inside the mouth.

   A. The stoma should be moist rather than dry.
   C. The edema present in the immediate postoperative period should disappear gradually over four to six weeks.
   D. Stomal retraction can develop at any time either because of poor surgical technique or significant weight gain. Stomal retraction makes pouching, and hence maintenance, of the peristomal skin difficult, and in some cases surgical revision may be necessary.

91. **Key: B**   Client Need: *Reduction of Risk Potential*

   B. The enzymes most commonly used to detect myocardial infarction (MI) are creatine kinase (CK) and lactic acid dehydrogenase (LDH). CK is an enzyme found in high concentrations in the heart and skeletal muscles. Since CK exists in relatively few organs, this test is used as a specific index of injury to the myocardium. Thus, it is important in the diagnosis of MI. A normal CK range for men older than 19 years of age is 38-174 U/L; for women older than 19 years of age the CK range is 96-140 U/L.

   A. This cell count represents a normal blood value and is not associated with damage to the myocardium. Leukocytosis of 10,000 to 20,000 cells/mm3 appears on the second day after myocardial infarction and disappears in one week.
   C. Normal blood urea nitrogen (BUN) is 5-25 mg/dl in an adult.
   D. This is a normal serum potassium level.

92. **Key: A**   **Client Need:** *Management of Care*

   A. **Myocardial cells do not die instantly. It takes approximately four to six hours for the entire thickness of the muscle to become necrosed in the majority of patients. Treatment of the acute myocardial infarction is geared to quickly dissolving the thrombus in the coronary artery and re-perfusing the myocardium before cellular death occurs. To be of benefit, thrombolytics must be given as soon as possible, preferably within the first six hours after the onset of pain.**

   B, C and D.
   Knowing when the pain started has the greatest significance in determining the prognosis for treatment.

93. **Key: A**   **Client Need:** *Growth and Development*

   A. **Preeclampsia is a pregnancy-specific condition in which hypertension develops after 20 weeks of gestation in a previously normotensive woman. It is the leading cause of morbidity and mortality in the mother and infant. Severe headache is an indication of hypertension.**

   B. Urine output equal to, or greater than, 30 ml/hr is normal adult output. Urine output less than 120 ml in four hours is a sign of oliguria, which is seen in severe preeclampsia.
   C. Dependent edema is a sign of mild preeclampsia.
   D. Normal patellar reflexes are +2.

94. **Key: D**   **Client Need:** *Management of Care*

   D. **The nurse should first control bleeding by immobilizing and elevating the area.**

   A. Applying warm compresses will increase bleeding. Cold compresses promote vasoconstriction.
   B. The first action by the nurse should be to control bleeding.
   C. Factor VIII replacement therapy should be instituted according to established medical protocol.

95. **Key: A**   **Client Need:** *Physiological Adaptation*

   A. **To compensate for decreased cardiac output the sympathetic nervous system is activated, resulting in constriction of peripheral blood vessels. The decreased blood perfusion causes the skin to feel cool and clammy and to appear pale.**

   B and C.
   Bounding pulses and increased urinary output are not manifestations of decreased cardiac output. If the low cardiac output is secondary to poor left ventricular function, there may be a low BP and decreased urine output.
   D. Rapid respirations typically occur during shock (decreased cardiac output) due to decreased tissue perfusion.

96. **Key: C**   Client Need: *Pharmacological and Parenteral Therapies*

   C. The major complication of thrombolytic therapy is bleeding. The patient is receiving an agent that causes clot dissolution, which may cause the patient to go into a lytic state. Minor bleeding is expected in this patient. The nurse must pay particular attention to signs of bleeding such as a drop in blood pressure and oozing of blood from intravenous, injection and catheter sites.

   A. The patient does not have to be on reverse isolation. Reverse isolation is indicated for the patient with an extremely low white blood cell count.
   B. Complete bedrest is not necessary for the patient on thrombolytic therapy.
   D. A soft-bristled toothbrush should be used to prevent irritation and bleeding of the gums.

97. **Key: A**   Client Need: *Management of Care*

   A. The nurse should encourage fluid intake for adequate fluid replacement and renal elimination of the nephrotoxic contrast dye.

   B. The patient should not have the head of the bed elevated more than 30 degrees and should avoid flexing the femoral area to prevent clot formation.
   C. The patient's femoral pulse on the operative side is monitored every 15 minutes for one hour. While vital signs are monitored, the apical rate is not required in post-procedure care.
   D. The patient's serum glucose level does not have to be monitored as part of post-procedure care.

98. **Key: C**   Client Need: *Basic Care and Comfort*

   C. Yogurt containing whole milk has 7 grams of fat. Low-fat yogurt would be an even better choice since patients on a low-fat diet usually may have only 30 grams of fat.

   A. Apple pie contains 18 grams of fat per serving.
   B. A cracker (1) contains 1 gram of fat per serving. Cheese (cheddar), 1 oz contains 9 grams of fat per serving.
   D. Mixed nuts contain 15 grams of fat per serving.

99. **Key: A**   Client Need: *Psychosocial Adaptation*

   A. Patient safety always takes priority. Depressed patients are often suicidal and need to know that the environment is safe for them.

   B. The depressed patient does not have the energy to participate in challenging activities.
   C. Environmental stimuli should not be increased or decreased but should be appropriate to the patient.
   D. The patient should be encouraged to participate in appropriate activities rather than remain socially isolated.

100. **Key: A**   Client Need: *Physiological Adaptation*

   A. The nurse should orient the patient to the surroundings as needed and provide a quiet environment.

   B. Fluid administration for patients with increased intracranial pressure is controversial. Administer fluid exactly as prescribed and never infuse more than the prescribed amount.
   C. The nurse should not suction via the nose because drainage may indicate a cerebrospinal fluid leak. Suctioning every hour will increase intracranial pressure.
   D. It is important to prevent venous obstruction. The head of the bed should be raised 30 degrees.

101. **Key: A**   **Client Need:** *Management of Care*

   A. Patients with pacemakers, neurostimulators or any type of metal implants, prostheses or shrapnel should not have MRI scans because of the strong magnetic fields created.

   B. All jewelry and metal objects are removed before this procedure.
   C. An MRI is not recommended during pregnancy. A history of miscarriages is not a contraindication for MRI scanning.
   D. There is no restriction related to contact lenses.

102. **Key: D**   **Client Need:** *Management of Care*

   D. The nursing diagnosis most applicable to patients with a spinal cord is high risk for ineffective breathing pattern related to impaired function of the diaphragm, secondary to spinal cord edema. This occurs in injuries at levels C1 to T6.

   A. Altered health maintenance is not identified as applicable for the patient with a spinal cord injury.
   B. A patient with a spinal cord injury has impaired skin integrity related to immobility and poor tissue perfusion. However, ineffective breathing pattern takes priority.
   C. A patient with a spinal cord injury has an altered sensory perception: tactile, which results in risk for injury and lack of self-protective abilities. However, ineffective breathing pattern should be given priority.

103. **Key: B**   **Client Need:** *Physiological Adaptation*

   B. Autonomic dysreflexia is an acute emergency that occurs in patients with cord lesions above the T6 level. It is characterized by severe pounding headache, hypertension, profuse sweating and bradycardia. The patient should be placed in a sitting position to lower the blood pressure.

   A. There is no indication for suctioning in this patient.
   C. Spasms from mild twitches to convulsive movements below the level of the lesion may occur. The patient needs to be protected, but it is not the first priority.
   D. The patient may also require an analgesic to help relieve the headache. Stimulation of the pain receptors may cause autonomic dysreflexia. The priority nursing action, however, should be raising the head of the bed.

104. **Key: D**   **Client Need:** *Safety and Infection Control*

   D. An expected outcome for patients with Parkinson's disease is that they will take time while eating. The nurse should not set time limits on this activity.

   A. Every effort should be made to encourage patients to carry out tasks related to coping with their daily needs and to retain independence.
   B. The intervention is appropriate for patients with Parkinson's disease. Patients should sit upright during mealtimes.
   C. Filling a cup half full will avoid spillage and thermal injuries. Patients with Parkinson's disease experience tremors even at rest.

105. **Key: D**   Client Need: *Psychosocial Adaptation*

   D. Maintaining a regular daily schedule provides security for the patient with Alzheimer's disease.

   A. Use of touch is a means of maintaining contact with the patient.
   B. Reducing injuries from nighttime falls may be accomplished by using night-lights. The patient does not have to be kept in bed after dark.
   C. The caregiver should avoid decision-making situations with the patient.

106. **Key: A**   Client Need: *Physiological Adaptation*

   A. The nurse should teach and remind the patient to turn his head in the direction of objects, sounds and people on the affected side.

   B. The nurse should stand in front of the patient to observe, and if necessary, to help him during transfers.
   C. Personal items should be placed on the patient's non-affected side so the patient can reach them.
   D. Food should be placed in the unaffected side of the patient's mouth to prevent choking and aspiration.

107: **Key: D**   Client Need: *Basic Care and Comfort*

   D. Celiac disease, or gluten-sensitive enteropathy, is a disease of the proximal small intestine characterized by abnormal mucosa and permanent intolerance to gluten. The chief source of gluten is in the grains of wheat and rye. Smaller quantities are found in barley and oats. Whole wheat toast would be contraindicated for this child.

   A, B and C.
   Sweet potatoes, corn meal muffins and puffed rice cereal are appropriate food choices for the child with celiac disease.

108. **Key: A**   Client Need: *Pharmacological and Parenteral Therapies*

   A. In status asthmaticus, the patient is initially treated with beta agonists, such as epinephrine and glucocorticoids.

   B. Methylxanthines, such as theophylline, are not used in acute attacks because they are slower in onset than beta agonists.
   C. Erythromycin is not indicated for the management of status asthmaticus.
   D. Chromolyn sodium is most beneficial between attacks or while the asthma is in remission.

109. **Key: B**   Client Need: *Prevention and Early Detection of Disease*

   B. Osteoporosis risk factors to look for in the health history of a patient include cigarette and alcohol use, exposure to sunlight, lack of exercise, insufficient dietary intake of calcium and caffeine consumption.

   A. Thin, lean-built women are more likely to develop osteoporosis. Obese women can store estrogen in their tissues for use as necessary to maintain a normal level of serum calcium.
   C. Caucasian, postmenopausal women are more likely to develop osteoporosis than women of African-American descent.
   D. Childless women do not have a greater risk for developing osteoporosis than women who have borne children.

110. **Key: B**   Client Need: *Physiological Adaptation*

   B. Osteoarthritis is a degenerative joint disease that particularly affects the weight-bearing joints.

   A. Systemic symptoms such as fatigue, fever and other organ system involvement are absent in osteoarthritis.
   C. Osteoarthritis is a degenerative process. Rheumatoid arthritis is an inflammatory joint disease.
   D. The degenerative process of osteoarthritis causes a thinning of cartilage, and bony surfaces are drawn together. This is characterized by joint-space narrowing.

111. **Key: B.**   Client Need: *Physiological Adaptation*

   B. Rheumatoid arthritis is a chronic, systemic disease characterized by recurrent inflamma-tion of the diarthroidal joints and related structures. It is frequently accompanied by rheumatoid nodules, which are probably the most common extra-articular finding. They appear subcutaneously as firm, nontender masses.

   A. Brittle bones are found in osteoporosis.
   C. The clinical manifestations of rheumatoid arthritis include fatigue, anorexia, weight loss and general-ized joint stiffness. The joints become stiff and inflamed. The cause of rheumatoid arthritis is unknown. Preventive education for osteoarthritis includes elimination of excessive strain on joints.
   D. The cause of rheumatoid arthritis is unknown.

112. **Key: D**   Client Need: *Coping and Adaptation*

   D. With this response the nurse explores the patient's feelings and allows the patient to share why she is upset. The nurse also gives the patient her full attention.

   A. The nurse should not minimize the patient's feelings and should explore the reason why the patient is crying.
   B. A review of the signs and symptoms of labor may be appropriate but again the nurse should not make the patient feel that she has done something wrong.
   C. This response will put the patient on the defensive and does not get to the problem of why the patient is upset.

113. **Key: A**   Client Need: *Psychosocial Adaptation*

   A. The nurse should conduct the interview in private to allow the patient to verbalize without the influence of the spouse.

   B. The nurse should be direct, honest and professional while addressing personal issues, such as abuse, with the patient.
   C and D.
   These options are not considered part of the interviewing process with abuse victims.

114. **Key: C**   Client Need: *Pharmacological and Parenteral Therapies*

   C. When administering Pitocin, the desired contraction pattern is contractions of 40 to 90 seconds duration and two to three minutes apart, with an intensity of 40 to 90 mm Hg.

   A. Fetal station should progress from negative stations to 0 to positive stations.
   B. Fetal accelerations are a reassuring sign of fetal well-being and should occur more frequently than noted.
   D. Once the cervix is dilated five to six centimeters and labor is established, the oxytocin can be reduced.

115. **Key: C**   **Client Need:** *Physiological Adaptation*

   C. Individualized exercise to maintain joint motion is an integral part of the rehabilitative plan for a patient with rheumatoid arthritis.

   A. Application of ice may be beneficial during an acute episode.
   B. During an acute inflammatory episode, encourage decreased activity, increased rest and supportive splints for affected joints should be encouraged.
   D. Painful joints should be immobilized during acute episodes.

116. **Key: D**   **Client Need:** *Pharmacological and Parenteral Therapies*

D. **The nurse would first calculate how much antibiotic should be given for the dose:**

$\dfrac{750 \text{ mg}}{24 \text{ hr}}$	=	$\dfrac{x \text{ mg}}{8 \text{ hr}}$
24x	=	6100
x	=	250 mg/dose

Now calculate the number of milliliters needed per dose:

$\dfrac{\text{Dose Desired}}{\text{Dose on Hand}}$	x	vehicle	=	number of ml/dose
$\dfrac{250 \text{ mg}}{125 \text{ mg}}$	x	5 ml	=	number of ml/dose
		$\dfrac{1250 \text{ mg}}{125 \text{ mg}}$	=	10 ml/dose

117. **Key: A**   **Client Need:** *Pharmacological and Parenteral Therapies*

   A. Signs of hyperglycemia include increased urination, increased appetite, weakness, fatigue, blurred vision, headache, nausea, vomiting and abdominal cramps.

   B, C and D.
   Signs of hypoglycemia include increased muscular activity, seizures, tachypnea and hypothermia. Hyperglycemia, not hypoglycemia, is a side effect of prednisone (Deltasone).

118. **Key: A**   **Client Need:** *Physiological Adaptation*

   A. Signs of hypofunction of the thyroid include dry, thick, inelastic, cold skin and intolerance to cold caused by a decreased metabolic rate.

   B. Appetite decreases with the decreased metabolic rate in hypothyroidism.
   C. Gastrointestinal motility is decreased in hypothyroidism. This causes constipation.
   D. Bradycardia and decreased cardiac contractility lead to decreased cardiac output in hypothyroidism.

119. Key: D   Client Need: *Prevention and Early Detection of Disease*

D. First-degree biologic relatives of patients with major depressive disorders are up to three times more likely to develop depression as members of the general population.

A, B and C.
Having a child with Down syndrome, being part of a multi-generational household and being the single head of a household are not identified as risk factors for mental illness.

120. Key: A   Client Need: *Safety and Infection Control*

A. Because body fluids and waste will be slightly radioactive for 24 to 48 hours, the patient is instructed to flush the toilet two or three times after use.

B, C and D.
Other precautions to teach the patient include sleeping alone for two nights and avoiding contact with children. The patient does not have to wear gloves when preparing food, avoid sunlight or disinfect eating utensils.

121. Key: C   Client Need: *Growth and Development*

C. Placenta previa is characterized by painless uterine bleeding especially during the last trimester. The first significant episode usually begins between the 29th and 30th week. Diagnosis is made by transabdominal ultrasound. Only if ultrasound reveals a normally implanted placenta, would a speculum exam be performed. Conservative management includes bedrest.

A and B.
If a woman is admitted for vaginal bleeding, abdominal assessment for tone and tenderness is usually performed. Leopold's maneuvers are a means of palpating the woman's abdomen to determine positioning of the fetus.
D. Fetal well-being is assessed by means of nonstress testing, a biophysical profile and ultrasonography.

122. Key: A   Client Need: *Reduction of Risk Potential*

A. The nurse can suggest ways to modify the environment and promote safety such as removal of scatter rugs, preparing meals for freezing prior to surgery and getting assistance with climbing steps.

B. The nurse should suggest that the patient get assistance with steps, not avoid stair-climbing.
C and D.
Keeping the bedroom cool and dry and elevating the head of the bed when sleeping are not identified as teaching points for an elderly patient undergoing cataract surgery. The patient should avoid sleeping on the operated side for the first few days postoperatively.

123. Key: C   Client Need: *Growth and Development*

C. An expected aging change in the gerontologic patient is a decrease in collagen and subcutaneous fat.

A. For the majority of healthy older adults, there is no noticeable decline in mental abilities.
B. The older adult has a decrease in body temperature due to decreased metabolic rate.
D. There is a decrease in bladder smooth muscle, elastic tissue and sphincter control.

124. Key: D   Client Need: _Physiological Adaptation_

D. An outcome criterion for the patient with benign prostatic hypertrophy (BPH) is the absence, or satisfactory control, of dribbling.

A. The patient is instructed to drink at least one to two liters of fluid per day and to urinate every two to three hours to flush the urinary tract and prevent urine concentration.
B. The surgery does not affect sperm count unless a vasectomy is performed.
C. This option is not identified as a symptom of BPH. Scrotal swelling occurs with a perineal prostatectomy.

125. Key: D   Client Need: _Physiological Adaptation_

D. Heliobacter pylori is thought to be a dominant factor in peptic ulcer formation.

A. The ingestion of hot or spicy foods has been suggested as a causative factor in peptic ulcer disease, but there is no evidence to substantiate this claim.
B. Peptic ulcers are not associated with seasonal trends.
C. Contrary to common belief, gastric ulcers are not more prevalent among those in managerial or executive positions. Persons from the lower socioeconomic classes and manual or unskilled workers are more prone to gastric ulcers.

126. Key: D   Client Need: _Reduction of Risk Potential_

D. The primary etiologic factors of acute pancreatitis include alcoholism and biliary tract disease.

A, B and C.
A recent blood work-up, a history of diabetes and bowel patterns are not identified as etiological factors in the development of acute pancreatitis.

127. Key: C   Client Need: _Basic Care and Comfort_

C. The diet recommended for pancreatitis is high carbohydrate with low fat and high protein because it is less stimulating to the pancreas. Of the foods listed, the steak and potato meal should be avoided. It contains seven to 15 grams of fat.

A. Pasta and tomato sauce contains one gram of fat per serving.
B. Rice and green beans contains one to two grams of fat per serving.
D. Bread and a baked apple contains one to two grams of fat per serving.

128. Key: B   Client Need: _Psychosocial Adaptation_

B. Since this is a newly admitted patient, the nurse should determine what the voices are telling the patient, since voices often tell patients to harm themselves or others. This information is crucial when planning the patient's care.

A. Concentration on other activities often decreases hallucinations and delusions; however, the nurse, at this point in time, needs to know what the voices are telling the patient.
C. The hallucinations may decrease as medication reduces the patient's anxiety, but the nurse cannot be certain of this.
D. This statement is open-ended and does encourage the patient to talk. However, the nurse needs to know if there is a potential for harm to self or others by the patient, and this can only be determined through direct questioning.

129. Key: A   **Client Need:** *Prevention and Early Detection of Disease*

   A. Factors that increase the occurrence of gall bladder disease are a sedentary lifestyle, a familial tendency and obesity.

   B and C.
   Hypertension and depression are not identified as contributing to the incidence of gall bladder disease.
   D. The incidence of cholelithiasis is highest in women who are multiparous, over the age of 40, postmenopausal and on estrogen therapy.

130. Key: A   **Client Need:** *Basic Care and Comfort*

   A. A low-fat diet contains approximately 50 grams of fat. Milk products allowed on this diet are skim milk, buttermilk and yogurt made from skim milk. Milk products excluded are whole, chocolate, buttermilk made from whole milk and whole milk cheeses.

   B. Calcium supplements should not be used in place of dairy products.
   C. Dairy products do not have to be limited so long as the fat grams are within the patient guidelines.
   D. Goat's milk, like cow's milk, is a dairy product that contains fat.

131. Key: B.   **Client Need:** *Prevention and Early Detection of Disease*

   B. Hepatitis A is spread by the fecal-oral route from the ingestion of water, milk or food, especially shellfish.

   A, C and D.
   Hepatitis B, rather than hepatitis A, is spread by the parenteral and sexual contact routes. Receiving a blood transfusion, rather than donating blood, is a causative factor for hepatitis B transmission.

132. Key: D.   **Client Need:** *Pharmacological and Parenteral Therapies*

   D. A side effect of amitriptyline hydrochloride (Elavil) is sedation. Patient sleep patterns should be improved on this medication.

   A, B and C.
   Elevated mood, increased social activity and improved hygiene would not be observed until the patient had been on this medication for about three weeks. That is when the therapeutic blood level of the drug is reached.

133. Key: C   **Client Need:** *Pharmacological and Parenteral Therapies*

   C. Most fresh vegetables are safe to eat while on a monoamine oxidase inhibitor (MAOI) diet.

   A, B and D.
   Foods to avoid while on a monoamine oxidase inhibitor (MAOI) diet include aged cheese, prunes and fermented meats. Eating such foods while taking an MAOI may result in a hypertensive crisis, a sudden, severe increase in blood pressure caused by high levels of tyramine when tyramine-rich foods or medications are ingested by a patient taking a MAO inhibitor. Without immediate measures to control blood pressure, intracranial hemorrhage and death may result.

134. Key: A   Client Need: *Pharmacological and Parenteral Therapies*

    A. Side effects of the initial dose of Cephulac include flatulence, belching, abdominal cramps, pain and distention. Diarrhea, nausea, vomiting, colon accumulation of hydrogen gas and hypernatremia also are side effects of Cephulac therapy.

    B, C and D.
    Petechiae, polyuria and flushing are not side effects of Cephulac therapy.

135. Key: D   Client Need: *Reduction of Risk Potential*

    D. Sengstaken-Blakemore and Minnesota tubes are used for both compression and decompression in persons with bleeding esophageal varices. Once the tube is inserted and in position, the balloons are inflated to apply pressure to bleeding vessels of the esophagus and the cardiac area of the stomach.

    A, B and C.
    The tubes do not cause vasoconstriction of the splenic artery, ensure airway patency or provide for enteral nutrition.

136. Key: A   Client Need: *Growth and Development*

    A. Current studies show significant drug abuse among pregnant adolescents, and indicate that adolescents underestimate their own abuse.

    B. The adequacy of the adolescent's dietary intake is determined using a comprehensive nutritional assessment tool. However, the first priority is determining the extent of drug use.
    C and D.
    Knowing if the teen is in contact with the father of the baby and who is going to take care of the baby after discharge from the hospital are not as essential in the initial assessment as knowing the extent of drug use.

137. Key: B   Client Need: *Physiological Adaptation*

    B. When ascites is present, measurement of abdominal girth assists in determining the gross amount of abdominal swelling due to accumulated fluid.

    A. Fluid restriction is used if hyponatremia is caused by fluid retention. Fluid restriction is monitored closely because it may lead to decreased output and the hepatorenal syndrome. Measuring abdominal girth is more appropriate.
    C. Patients with cirrhosis have varying levels of fatigue. If the patient has severe fluid excess and ascites or signs and symptoms of other complications, bedrest may be required. If bedrest is not required, the patient should be ambulated within the room or hallway, as tolerated.
    D. Peripheral edema may result from cirrhosis. However, it is more appropriate to measure the abdominal girth for ascites.

138. Key: A   Client Need: *Reduction of Risk Potential*

    A. The normal value of white blood cells (leukocytes) is 5000 to 10,000/L. The nursing diagnosis of risk for infection is supported by altered or insufficient leukocytes.

    B, C and D.
    Red blood cells, platelets and reticulocytes do not affect the patient's risk for infection.

139. **Key: B**   **Client Need:** *Reduction of Risk Potential*

    B. The child with a shunt obstruction often presents as an emergency with clinical manifesta-tion of increased intracranial pressure. In older children who are usually admitted to the hospital for elective or emergency shunt revision, the most valuable indicator of increas-ing intracranial pressure is an alteration in the child's level of consciousness and interaction with the environment. Changes are identified by observing and comparing present behavior with customary behavior, sleep patterns, developmental capabilities and habits obtained through a detailed history and a baseline assessment. This baseline infor-mation serves as a guide for postoperative assessment and evaluation of shunt function.

    A. Tinnitus is not related to ventriculoperitoneal shunt obstruction. Tinnitus is a noise in the ears such as ringing, buzzing or roaring, which at times may be heard by others than the patient. Common causes include prolonged exposure to loud environmental noise, and such pathologi-cal conditions as inflammation and infection of the ear, otoscelerosis, Ménière's disease and labyrinthitis.
    C. There is no documentation to support that the complaint of abdominal pain is related to ven-triculoperitoneal shunt obstruction.
    D. Signs of shunt infection, rather than obstruction, include elevated temperature, poor feeding, vomiting, decreased responsiveness and seizure activity.

140. **Key: C**   **Client Need:** *Pharmacological and Parenteral Therapies*

    C. Aluminum hydroxide is a nonsystemic antacid with moderate neutralizing action. It also lowers serum phosphorous by binding to dietary phosphorus to form insoluble aluminum phosphate, which is excreted in the feces. This prevents formation of urinary phosphate calculi by decreasing excretion of phosphates in the urine. The patient in chronic renal failure cannot excrete phosphorous.

    A. The patient with chronic renal failure has elevated potassium levels, but sodium polystyrene sul-fonate (Kayexalate), not Amphogel, is used to lower potassium levels.
    B. Amphogel does not affect serum ammonia levels.
    D. Amphogel reduces acid concentration and pepsin activity by raising the pH of gastric and intra-esophaegeal secretions.

141. **Key: A**   **Client Need:** *Reduction of Risk Potential*

    A. The creatinine clearance test is a specific measurement that determines kidney function, primarily glomerular filtration. It measures the rate at which creatinine is cleared from the blood by the kidney.

    B. Serum ammonia level measurement is used to evaluate metabolism as well as the progress of severe liver disease and response to treatment.
    C. Alkaline phosphatase is an enzyme used as a tumor marker and an index of bone and liver dis-ease, when correlated with other clinical findings.
    D. Serum glutamic-oxaloacetic transaminase (SGOT) levels will be increased in the presence of myocardial infarction, liver disease, trauma to skeletal muscles, pancreatitis, acute renal disease, crushing injuries, pulmonary emboli and progressive muscular dystrophy.

142. **Key: A**   **Client Need:** *Reduction of Risk Potential*

A. An expected outcome of hemodialysis is that the patient will not develop fluid volume excess or deficit, as evidenced by absence of disequilibrium syndrome. Throughout the process, the nurse should carefully monitor the patient's intake and output, weight, pulse and blood pressure. The nurse should assess for hypovolemia and dialysate retention. The physician determines the amount of fluid loss desired.

B, C and D.
A decrease in body weight due to predetermined fluid loss is the best indicator of the effectiveness of hemodialysis.

143. **Key: A**   **Client Need:** *Growth and Development*

A. The newborn can be with the HIV positive mother in the postpartum period.

B. Visitation does not need to be restricted.
C. Breastfeeding of the newborn is usually contraindicated since the virus can be transmitted through breast milk.
D. Skin contact does not have to be restricted. Contact with bodily fluids should be restricted.

144. **Key: A**   **Client Need:** *Pharmacological and Parenteral Therapies*

A. Causes of increased lithium levels include fluid and electrolyte loss due to diarrhea and vomiting. The patient should be instructed to notify the physician if vomiting and diarrhea occur.

B. Normal hydration and sodium intake is essential to maintaining a therapeutic lithium level. Lithium decreases the amount of sodium reabsorbed by the renal tubules. The amount of lithium in the body is indirectly proportional to the amount of sodium reabsorbed by the renal tubules. High concentrations of lithium in the blood can be caused by dehydration and the intake of too much lithium, thus causing sodium depletion.
C. Doubling the dose that has been determined as therapeutic for a particular patient will cause high concentrations of serum lithium.
D. Discontinuation of the medication will cause symptoms to reappear once the blood level of the lithium has become subtherapeutic.

145. **Key: D**   **Client Need:** *Physiological Adaptation*

D. For the diagnosis of pain related to sickle cell disease the nurse should assess for pain every two to four hours and administer analgesics as needed according to orders. The nurse should apply heat to joints as ordered and provide rest periods for the patient. Additional fluids are indicated to prevent dehydration.

A. Assisting the patient to walk would not be indicated. Treatment of sickle cell disease includes rest during the crisis state.
B. There is no evidence that elevation of the foot of the bed will decrease pain.
C. Oxygen is indicated to prevent further sickling and to reverse hypoxia.

146. **Key: A**   Client Need: *Physiological Adaptation*

   A. **A major problem in the long-term management of the patient with hypertension is poor compliance with the treatment regimen. The reasons include inadequate patient instruction, unpleasant side effects of the drugs, relief of symptoms so that the patient feels cured and lack of motivation.**

   B. Management of hypertension includes drug therapy, diet therapy, exercise and lifestyle changes.
   C. Dietary restrictions include sodium modification. Herbs and spices such as lemon may be substituted for salt.
   D. An antihypertensive drug is started at a low dose, and allowed one to three months to achieve desired effects before the drug is changed or another drug is added.

147. **Key: A**   Client Need: *Pharmacological and Parenteral Therapies*

   A. **Folic acid is essential for nucleoprotein synthesis and maintenance of normal erythropoiesis. It stimulates production of red blood cells (RBCs), white blood cells (WBCs) and platelets in patients with megaloblastic anemia. Folate deficiency is associated with alcoholism.**

   B, C and D.
   Folic acid does not stimulate production of the intrinsic factor, enhance the synthesis of clotting factors or increase the rate of glucose uptake.

148. **Key: B**   Client Need: *Psychosocial Adaptation*

   B. **The nurse should explain that members of the treatment team who are directly responsible for the patient's plan of care will be told of anything that would affect the patient's treatment.**

   A and C.
   The nurse-patient therapeutic relationship is based on trust that the nurse will work with the patient to keep the patient safe and to help the patient function at the highest level possible. Not enlisting the help of the treatment team when necessary would negatively affect the nurse-patient relationship.
   D. When a patient's safety is in jeopardy, the nurse is required to enlist the help of the treatment team to keep that patient safe. If this were the case, the nurse could not be held liable for breaking confidentiality.

149. **Key: A**   Client Need: *Physiological Adaptation*

   A. **Pernicious anemia is caused by impaired Vitamin B12 absorption through the small intestine as a result of deficiency of the intrinsic factor. In the elderly this results from gastric fundus atrophy.**

   B, C and D.
   Reduced function of the bone marrow, diminished liver metabolism and erosion of the intestinal rugae have not been implicated in the development of pernicious anemia.

150. **Key: C**   Client Need: *Reduction of Risk Potential*

   C. **Early signs of congestive heart failure are tachycardia (especially during rest and slight exertion), tachypnea, profuse scalp sweating (especially in infants), fatigue and irritability, sudden weight gain and respiratory distress.**

   A. Mottling due to a decrease in environmental temperature or stress is common in the newborn.
   B. Nasal discharge and congestion are commonly associated with respiratory infections in infants.
   D. Upon inspection, the tongue of the infant with Down syndrome is enlarged and may protrude. This is a normal finding.

Rationales-Practice Exam D: Nursing, Part 2

1. **Key: B**   **Client Need:** *Prevention and Early Detection of Disease*

   B. In acromegaly, changes in appearance occur so slowly that the disease often goes unde-tected for years. In retrospect, the individual may remember a progressive increase in ring, shoe, hat and glove sizes.

   A and C.
   Increased urination and dry mouth are not identified as clinical manifestations of acromegaly.
   D. Hirsutism, rather than hair loss, is a clinical manifestation of acromegaly.

2. **Key: D**   **Client Need:** *Management of Care*

   D. The nurse should report swelling, burning, numbness, coldness, discoloration of the skin, decreased sensation and persistent pain or tingling to the physician. All of these manifes-tations can indicate that the cast is too tight.

   A, B and C.
   Bounding pedal pulses, rapid capillary refill and nail bed blanching with pressure would be expected and do not indicate complications of casting.

3. **Key: B**   **Client Need:** *Physiological Adaptation*

   B. Fat emboli typically travel to the brain and lungs. The nurse should monitor for changes in mental status, and symptoms of acute respiratory distress syndrome, such as chest pain, tachypnea, cyanosis, dyspnea, apprehension and tachycardia.

   A, C and D.
   Calf tenderness, abdominal distention and urinary retention are not clinical manifestations of a fat embolus.

4. **Key: C**   **Client Need:** *Reduction of Risk Potential*

   C. Normal weight loss after birth is 10 percent. A loss of 12 percent would require investigation.

   A. The newborn generally voids within 24 hours after birth.
   B. The prepuce, or foreskin, covers the glans penis and is not retractable in the newborn.
   D. Newborn's secrete a milky fluid called Witches milk.

5. **Key: B**   **Client Need:** *Safety and Infection Control*

   B. The compulsive patient uses rituals as a way of controlling anxiety. The nurse should intervene if staff attempt to change the patient's ritual or routine before the patient has adopted other coping mechanisms. Taking away the routine or the ritual before the patient has learned to control the anxiety by other means can cause overwhelming anxi-ety in the patient, who then may attempt to control the anxiety through more inappropriate and harmful measures.

   A, C and D.
   Staff talking with one another in front of the patient, turning away from the patient or touching the patient may all require intervention by the nurse and should be observed. However, the more immediate need is to intervene so that the patient is able to maintain his/her routine.

6.   **Key: C**   **Client Need:** *Psychosocial Adaptation*

    C. Symptoms of AIDS dementia include loss of balance, muscle weakness, forgetfulness, confusion and slowed thoughts.

    A, B and D.
    Headache, bronchial infection and diarrhea are not indicators of AIDS dementia.

7.   **Key: D.**   **Client Need:** *Physiological Adaptation*

    D. An expected outcome for the patient with myasthenia gravis is avoidance of situations that may predispose to colds and infections and exacerbate symptoms.

    A. Activity tolerance is decreased due to fatigue.
    B. Semi-solid foods may be easier to eat than solids or liquids. High-protein foods are not required, but a balanced diet should be encouraged.
    C. Temperature is not identified as a problem for the patient with myasthenia gravis.

8.   **Key: A**   **Client Need:** *Physiological Adaptation*

    A. Symptoms of increasing intracranial pressure include widening pulse pressure, bradycardia and irregular respiratory pattern.

    B and C.
    Systolic blood pressure increases in an effort to perfuse the brain. This results in a corresponding decrease in heart rate.
    D. Patients with increased intracranial pressure usually experience a rise in body temperature as a late manifestation of increased intracranial pressure.

9.   **Key: B**   **Client Need:** *Psychosocial Adaptation*

    B. As long as the patient is not a danger to staff or other patients, he should be allowed to complete the activity. However, the activity may be upsetting to other patients. Taking the patient to the privacy of his own room allows the patient to continue the activity, which helps to control his anxiety and protects him from potential harm from other patients who may try to stop the behavior.

    A. Asking the patient why he is changing his clothes in front of others asks for insight that the patient does not have. The nurse should avoid "Why" types of questions that request insight from patients with psychosocial disorders.
    C. Encouraging other patients to leave the area is not practical and requires a change in their behavior to accommodate the patient. It is better for the nurse to remove the patient from the area.
    D. Locking up the patient's clothes may encourage the patient to use the more readily available clothes of other patients and could lead to potentially harmful situations.

10.   **Key: C**   **Client Need:** *Pharmacological and Parenteral Therapies*

    C. Side effects of Benadryl include drowsiness, fatigue, headache, tremors, euphoria, nervousness, restlessness, insomnia and confusion. Excitement and fever occur typically in children.

    A. Benadryl is commonly used to treat allergy symptoms. It does not usually cause them.
    B. Inadequate dosing would result in either no effect or side effects as listed.
    D. Benadryl is an antihistamine H1 receptor antagonist. The blood-brain barrier is not sensitive to the drug.

11. **Key: A**   Client Need: *Reduction of Risk Potential*

    A. Metabolic alkalosis is a clinical disturbance characterized by a high pH and a high plasma bicarbonate concentration. The normal blood pH is 7.35-7.45; the normal pCO_2 is 38-42 mm Hg; and the normal bicarbonate level is 24-26 mEq/L.

    B. This arterial blood gas indicates respiratory acidosis. The pH is low (acidotic), the CO_2 level is elevated (respiratory acidosis) and the bicarbonate is normal.

    C. This is a normal arterial blood gas.

    D. This arterial blood gas indicates metabolic acidosis. The pH is low (acidosis), the CO_2 level is borderline normal and the bicarbonate is decreased (metabolic acidosis).

12. **Key: A**   Client Need: *Reduction of Risk Potential*

    A. It is important to immobilize the body part before the patient is moved. Adequate splinting is essential to prevent damage to the soft tissue by the bony fragments. No attempt is made to reduce an open fracture, even if bone fragments are protruding through the wound.

    B and D.
    The leg should be splinted in its present position rather than in neutral position. Pressure should not be applied directly over the wound.

    C. In an open fracture the wound is covered with a clean (sterile) dressing to prevent contamination of deeper tissues.

13. **Key: D**   Client Need: *Management of Care*

    D. Hopelessness related to chronic HIV infection is a priority nursing diagnosis for the patient with Kaposi's sarcoma. The nurse should observe the patient carefully since hopelessness has been implicated in suicidal behavior.

    A, B and C.
    If continuing to feel hopeless, the patient will not be motivated to work on these diagnoses. Alleviation of hopelessness should be the priority.

14. **Key: B**   Client Need: *Safe Effective Care Environment*

    B. When skeletal traction is being used, the nurse should check the apparatus to make certain that the weights hang freely. If the weights are resting on the bed frame, an adequate amount of traction is not being applied to the patient's femur.

    A. Balanced suspension provides countertraction so that the pulling force of the traction is not altered when the bed or patient is moved.

    C. Alignment of the patient's body in traction must be maintained as prescribed to promote an effective line of pull.

    D. The overbed trapeze should be above the patient's chest.

15. **Key: D**   Client Need: *Safety and Infection Control*

    D. The nurse should discuss the principles of traction with the aide so that correct interventions with the patient in skeletal traction are implemented. The weights in skeletal traction should not be removed or allowed to rest on the bed frame. If they do so, the required amount of traction is not being applied.

    A, B and C.
    Elevating the patient's head while eating, having the patient use the trapeze while moving in bed and raising the patient's hips when placing him/her on a bedpan are appropriate actions by the nurse's aide.

16. **Key: D**   **Client Need:** *Growth and Development*

    D. Early in pregnancy, a woman may need less insulin because the fetus is taking so much glucose from the mother for rapid cell growth. Later in pregnancy she will need an increased amount because of increased metabolic need.

    A. The patient may need insulin infusions to maintain serum glucose levels. Serum glucose levels should be obtained every one to two hours.
    B. During the second and third trimesters, because of insulin resistance, the dosage may be increased to maintain target glucose levels.
    C. Early in the pregnancy, maternal insulin needs decrease due to rapid fetal cell growth.

17. **Key: C**   **Client Need:** *Physiological Adaptation*

    C. In cases of low back pain, the nurse should assess for sensory changes by asking whether there is paresthesia or numbness in the involved limb. The nurse should test both extremities for sensation by using a pin or paper clip and a cotton ball for comparison of light and deep touch.

    A, B and D.
    Prior to implementing these nursing interventions, the nurse should perform an assessment of the patient to identify his/her needs.

18. **Key: D**   **Client Need:** *Physiological Adaptation*

    D. Extremes of internal rotation, adduction and 90˚ flexion of the hip must be avoided for four to six weeks postoperatively. Elevated toilet seats at home are necessary to prevent hip flexion.

    A, B and C.
    All of these actions are contraindicated for the patient who has had a total hip replacement because of the restriction on hip movement postoperatively.

19. **Key: C**   **Client Need:** *Physiological Adaptation*

    C. Although most children never have febrile seizures after the first occurrence, a younger age at onset and a family history of febrile seizures are associated with recurring episodes. Most children outgrow febrile seizures by five years of age.

    A. Phenobarbital is ineffective in preventing febrile seizures and can cause a drop in intelligence scores
    B. Boys are affected about twice as often as girls and there appears to be an increased susceptibility in families, indicating a possible genetic predisposition. Given the benign nature of the illness, genetic counseling is not necessary.
    D. Most febrile seizures last for a very short period. If seizure activity persists, it is usually treated with rectal or intravenous Valium rather than oxygen.

20. **Key: C**   **Client Need:** *Physiological Integrity*

    C. The nurse should explain the need for, and function of, all tubes and drains: nasogastric, intravenous and wound. Nasogastric suction is maintained for four to five days after surgery, and the patient is given nothing by mouth to prevent distention and pressure on the suture line.

    A. Ileum drainage, rather than urine, is collected in the pouch.
    B. The patient should be aware that the surgery involves an abdominal incision.
    D. The patient will be NPO following surgery.

21. **Key: A**   **Client Need:** *Reduction of Risk Potential*

    A. Mild isotonic dehydration is associated with a five percent weight loss or fluid deficit up to 50 ml/kg. Tachycardia will be present but the blood pressure and respiratory rate should be normal.

    B. Increased urine specific gravity is not an early sign of fluid volume deficit.
    C. Decreased urine output is not the earliest sign of fluid volume deficit.
    D. Blood pressure remains normal in five percent dehydration.

22. **Key: A**   **Client Need:** *Safety and Infection Control*

    A. During transition the laboring woman has an uncontrollable urge to push or bear down with contractions as if she were going to move her bowels. With that action, the perineum begins to bulge for delivery of the baby.

    B. A woman may have a dry mouth or dry lips during labor, but large oral intake is discouraged during this time. Ice chips are generally enough to relieve this discomfort.
    C. Effleurage, or light massage, can decrease the pain sensation during labor.
    D. Focusing intently on an object is another method of keeping sensory input from the cortex of the brain and displacing pain sensation.

23. **Key: C**   **Client Need:** *Coping and Adaptation*

    C. This response encourages the teenager to elaborate about his body image.

    A. Hair loss is a side effect of chemotherapy and not an indicator of the effectiveness of treatment.
    B. This response may help the teenager to identify with someone else who does not have hair, but it should not be the nurse's initial response.
    D. The nurse can offer suggestions for how to handle the hair loss, but the nurse's initial response should be directed toward getting the patient to talk about his feelings.

24. **Key: A**   **Client Need:** *Basic Care and Comfort*

    A. Medications that affect wound healing, such as corticosteroids, impair phagocytosis, inhibit fibroblast proliferation, depress formation of granulation tissue and inhibit wound closure. They should not be used by patients with varicella.

    B. Calamine lotion provides supportive therapy for patients with varicella.
    C. Oatmeal baths are helpful and soothing.
    D. Children are prone to scratching the lesions. Keeping the fingernails short may prevent scarring.

25. **Key: B**   **Client Need:** *Prevention and Early Detection of Disease*

    B. The nurse should assess the pattern of urination: frequency, number of times voiding per night, urgency and acute urinary retention. Symptoms of gradual obstruction include a decrease in the urinary stream with less force on urination and dribbling at the end of urination. Hesitancy or difficulty in starting the stream is seen.

    A. Burning frequently accompanies urinary tract infections.
    C. Blood in the urine may be due to a malignancy, infection or a side effect of medications.
    D. Foul odor of urine is usually indicative of a urinary tract infection.

26. **Key: D**   **Client Need:** *Psychosocial Adaptation*

    D. Working with modeling clay allows for gross motor movements and does not require attention to detail. It would be an appropriate activity for the patient with a diagnosis of mania.

    A. Puzzles require a level of concentration that the patient with mania usually does not have.
    B. Manic patients usually have difficulty sitting still. Reading quietly would not be an appropriate activity.
    C. Competitive games, such as table tennis, may be too stimulating for the patient and may result in loss of control.

27. **Key: A**   **Client Need:** *Physiological Adaptation*

    A. By regularly monitoring the urine specific gravity of the patient at risk for water intoxication, the nurse can determine overhydration in the patient before dangerous consequences occur.

    B. In overhydration the reabsorption of sodium in the renal tubule decreases, thus putting the patient at risk for hyponatremia. In those patients known to be at risk for water intoxication, sodium tablets are sometimes given daily.
    C. Chewing gum or sucking on hard candy may relieve some of the patient's compulsion to drink excess fluids. However, measuring urine specific gravity is the essential nursing intervention.
    D. Adequate ingestion of water is to be encouraged for a patient with water intoxication.

28. **Key: B**   **Client Need:** *Physiological Adaptation*

    B. The patient or caregiver must learn how to manage the assembly, application and emptying of the selected pouch. Before the patient is discharged from the hospital, the nurse must be certain that the individual can manage the urinary drainage and detect any deviations from normal.

    A and C.
      Irrigation and catheterization of the stoma are not done.
    D. Since the drainage is urinary in nature, an appliance to collect the urine is needed over the stoma rather than dressings.

29. **Key: A**   **Client Need:** *Basic Care and Comfort*

    A. Inquiring as to the types of food eaten at home shows the nurse's awareness of the patient's cultural and dietary norms.

    B. This is a patronizing response that does not allow for discussion of the problem.
    C. This response does not provide an opportunity for discussion of eating patterns and food likes and dislikes.
    D. With this response the nurse assumes that the patient dislikes the food when that may not be the reason that he/she is not eating.

30. **Key: B**   **Client Need: _Growth and Development_**

    B. Signs of true labor include regularly occurring uterine contractions, bloody show, rupture of membranes and progressive cervical dilatation. However, progressive cervical dilatation will occur only when a predictable, regular pattern of uterine contractions occurs.

    A. Labor may or may not begin with rupture of the membranes. There is danger of infection if labor does not begin after membranes rupture.

    C. Intermittent uterine contractions are known as Braxton-Hicks contractions and usually occur in the last days or weeks before labor begins.

    D. Passage of the mucous plug occurs after the cervix begins to ripen or soften. This is a preliminary sign of labor.

31. **Key: B**   **Client Need: _Prevention and Early Detection of Disease_**

    B. Change in vision is an early indicator of multiple sclerosis, along with changes in motor skills and sensations.

    A. Cognitive changes are usually seen late in the course of the disease.

    C and D.

    Some patients my report tinnitus or other vague symptoms, but changes in vision, motor skills and sensation are usually the initial signs of multiple sclerosis.

32. **Key: D**   **Client Need: _Physiological Adaptation_**

    D. The objective of a bowel training program is to establish bowel evacuation through reflex conditioning. Rectal stimulation can be performed to trigger the defecation response.

    A. A quadriplegic patient can be placed on a bedpan at the same time every 48 hours, after rectal stimulation has been performed, to elicit a bowel movement.

    B. When establishing a bladder training program, stroking the inner thigh is a useful technique. There is no indication that this technique is helpful in bowel training.

    C. When establishing a bowel training program, a diet with sufficient fluids is essential.

33. **Key: D**   **Client Need: _Management of Care_**

    D. A pressure dressing, sandbag, ice bag or a combination of the three may be maintained over the site for six to 12 hours to prevent bleeding, swelling or hematoma formation.

    A. Providing a quiet environment is not indicated post-arteriogram.

    B. The nurse should restrict the patient to bedrest for six to 24 hours post-angiography.

    C. The extremity into which the contrast medium was injected is kept straight and immobilized for the length of bedrest.

34. **Key: B**   **Client Need: _Coping and Adaptation_**

    B. To develop strategies to enhance communication, the nurse should provide the patient with a communication board.

    A and D.

    Using audiotapes and writing in large print will not be beneficial for a patient with expressive aphasia.

    C. Speaking slowly and clearly can enhance communication in a patient who has receptive aphasia but it is not effective for the patient who understands what is being said and is unable to express him/herself in response.

35. **Key: A**   **Client Need:** *Reduction of Risk Potential*

  A. For patients at risk for water intoxication, preventative measures include urine specific gravity measurement and regular weights to screen for increases in the body's fluid volume.

  B and C.
  Measurement of intake and output and assessment of skin turgor are not as reliable as indicators of effectiveness of treatment as daily weights.
  D. The presence of pedal edema indicates that treatment has not been effective.

36. **Key: C**   **Client Need:** *Reduction of Risk Potential*

  C. As brain compression increases, deterioration of the patient's condition can be evidenced by respirations that become rapid.

  A. Normal pupil diameter is between three and five millimeters.
  B. Normal capillary refill time is within three seconds.
  D. Although monitoring of fluid and electrolyte imbalance is important, changes in vital signs are the best indication of deterioration and impending danger. A urinary output of 30 ml/hr is within normal range.

37. **Key: B**   **Client Need:** *Pharmacological and Parenteral Therapies*

  B. Use of phenytoin sodium (Dilantin) leads to excessive gingival growth. Brushing two to three times per day helps to retard this growth.

  A. Dilantin should be stored at 59-86°F (15-30°C) and protected from light.
  C. Dilantin should be mixed with food or fluid. Administration of the drug should be followed by drinking a full glass of water or milk or by ingestion of food.
  D. There is no indication that dry eye is a side effect of Dilantin.

38. **Key: D**   **Client Need:** *Pharmacological and Parenteral Therapies*

  D. The urine, sweat and tears of a patient treated with rifampin (Rifadin) may turn orange temporarily. The patient's statement indicates a correct understanding of the medication instructions.

  A. Patients taking rifampin are not required to avoid milk products.
  B. Common side effects of rifampin therapy include hepatitis and febrile reactions. Constipation is not indicated as a side effect of treatment with rifampin.
  C. Burning on urination is not a characteristic side effect of rifampin therapy.

39. **Key: D**   **Client Need:** *Physiological Adaptation*

  D. Tumors of the cerebellum cause dizziness, an ataxic or staggering gait with a tendency to fall toward the side of the lesion, marked muscle incoordination and nystagmus.

  A, B and C.
  Keeping the room darkened, speaking slowly and clearly and providing memory aids are not identified as nursing interventions for the patient with a cerebellar tumor.

40. **Key: C**   **Client Need:** *Reduction of Risk Potential*

     C. Clear drainage from the ear or nose that tests positive for glucose suggests leakage of cerebral spinal fluid (CSF) from a skull fracture.

     A. Amnesia from the moment of the injury and for a variable time period before or after the injury commonly occurs with closed head trauma and loss of consciousness.
     B. The child may be experiencing post-trauma amnesia. This should be expected.
     D. Pupils should be equal in size and respond to light by constricting equally. This is a normal response and does not require further investigation.

41. **Key: A**   **Client Need:** *Physiological Adaptation*

     A. Clinical manifestations of meningitis include: headache, fever, changes in the level of consciousness, nuchal or neck rigidity, photophobia and seizures.

     B, C and D.
     Tingling of the lips, drooling and weakness of the legs are not indications of meningitis.

42. **Key: A**   **Client Need:** *Psychosocial Adaptation*

     A. Evidence of rape can be altered if the victim has bathed, urinated, defecated, douched or changed clothing; therefore, these activities are recorded. The physical exam is carried out as soon as possible after the rape, since physical evidence deteriorates rapidly.

     B. Adolescents who have been raped arrive at the emergency room or practitioner's office under a variety of circumstances. They are usually brought in by parents, friends or the police, but some may seek medical help on their own. They should be seen as soon as possible and should not wait for an appointment.
     C. The physical exam and collection of evidence is carried out as soon as possible. Practitioners specially trained for rape examination should be used when possible. Nurses are often members of this group, known as sexual assault nurse examiners (SANE).
     D. Most care providers prescribe prophylactic administration of antibiotics at the initial exam. Pregnancy prophylaxis with high-dose estrogen is offered to the victim who is not already pregnant or not using a contraceptive method.

43. **Key: A**   **Client Need:** *Safety and Infection Control*

     A. Masks and/or eye protection are worn when it is likely that the eyes and/or nose and mouth will be splashed with body substances or when personnel are working directly over large, open skin lesions. Wearing an eye shield when accessing the patient's central venous port (CVP) is essential.

     B. Gloves must be worn when contact with mucous membranes, non-intact skin, or moist body substances is likely to occur. There is no mention of double gloving in Center for Disease Control (CDC) guidelines.
     C. Gowns or plastic aprons are worn when it is likely that body substances will soil the clothing. They are changed between patient contacts.
     D. CDC guidelines recommend masks for protection from airborne infection. Hepatitis A infections are not airborne.

44. **Key: A**   **Client Need:** *Safety and Infection Control*

   A. The nurse should question the use of morphine sulfate in the treatment of pancreatitis since the drug may cause spasm and exacerbate pain in this patient. The nurse should question this order.

   B. Demerol effectively controls the pain associated with pancreatitis.
   C. Pro-Banthine is an antispasmodic that is often given to the patient with pancreatitis in conjunction with pain medication.
   D. Tagamet may be given to the patient with pancreatitis to decrease gastric acidity.

45. **Key: A**   **Client Need:** *Health Promotion and Maintenance*

   A. During transition, the show turns completely bloody, a change from earlier phases of labor when the show is brown or pale pink.

   B. During labor, spontaneous voiding may become difficult.
   C. Membranes can rupture at any time during labor.
   D. Contractions generally last 45 to 60 seconds during transition.

46. **Key: A**   **Client Need:** *Physiological Adaptation*

   A. The aims of immediate treatment of thermal injury are to stop the burning process, begin emergency procedures, cover the wound, transport the child to medical aid and provide reassurance. Spontaneous cooling of burns by immersion in cool water helps relieve the pain. This is medically acceptable for a minor burn if the period of immersion is no longer than 30 seconds at a time.

   B, C and D.
   Emergency treatment of minor burns includes applying cool water to the burn or holding the burned area under cool running water. The burn should be covered with a clean cloth if there is a risk of damage or contamination. None of these substances should be applied to the burned area.

47. **Key: C**   **Client Need:** *Pharmacological and Parenteral Therapies*

   C. The formula used for this calculation is as follows:

Number of milliliters/hour	=	$\dfrac{\text{Desired Amount}}{\text{Available Amount}}$	x	Solution
	=	$\dfrac{1200\ \text{units/hr}}{25000\ \text{units}}$	x	500 ml
	=	$\dfrac{600000}{25000}$		
	=	24 ml/hr		

48. **Key: C**   Client Need: *Pharmacological and Parenteral Therapies*

   C. Vitamin C may increase the absorption of iron. Orange juice is high in Vitamin C.

   A. The patient should be aware that the stools will become dark green or black.
   B. Iron is stored at room temperature.
   D. Iron discolors stool but does not cause the urine to become red-tinged.

49. **Key: C**   Client Need: *Physiological Adaptation*

   C. Anticholinesterase agents, such as pyridostigmine bromide, act by increasing the relative concentration of available acetylcholine at the neuromuscular junction. They increase the response of the muscles to nerve impulses and improve strength. The dosage of pyridostigmine bromide is gradually increased until maximal benefits are achieved (additional strength and less fatigue). The patient is instructed to take the medication 30 minutes before meals for maximal muscle strength.

   A, B and D.
   The expected response to therapy is increased strength of voice. Improvement in vision, memory and sleeping patterns is not the main goal of therapy.

50. **Key: A**   Client Need: *Psychosocial Adaptation*

   A. Tardive dyskinesia is a late-occurring, sometimes irreversible, neurological side effect of antipsychotic medications. It is characterized by tongue protrusion, lip smacking, choreiform (snake-like) movements of the limbs and trunk and shoulder shrugging.

   B. Akathisia is motor restlessness caused by antipsychotic medications.
   C. Akinesia is slowness or lack of associated movements, e.g., diminished arm swinging while walking, caused by antipsychotic medications.
   D. Dystonia is muscle spasm in any muscle of the body caused by use of antipsychotic medications. It is usually frightening and painful for the patient.

51. **Key: D**   Client Need: *Pharmacological and Parenteral Therapies*

   D. The incidence and severity of respiratory distress syndrome due to fetal lung immaturity is reduced if glucocorticoids, such as betamethasone, are administered to the mother at least 24 to 48 hours before the preterm birth.

   A. Birth weight will not be affected by one or two doses of betamethasone.
   B. Hemolytic disorders are not associated with administration of betamethasone.
   C. Increased immune response is not an associated side effect of the drug.

52. **Key: B**   Client Need: *Reduction of Risk Potential*

   B. The patient should avoid lifting anything heavier than 15 pounds for approximately one week post-cataract surgery. This statement by the patient indicates a need for further instruction.

   A. The patient should not sleep on the operative side for approximately one week after surgery.
   C. The patient should wear sunglasses for comfort.
   D. The patient should avoid bending the head below the waist.

53. **Key: B**   **Client Need:** *Pharmacological and Parenteral Therapies*

    B. The patient and family should be taught to avoid sunlight and sunlamps, and to use protective clothing and sunscreen. The avoidance of sun and the need for daily use of a sunscreen with an SPF factor of at least 15 must be emphasized, since sun exposure may easily result in severe sunburn.

    A. Females with mild to moderate acne may respond well to topical treatment and the addition of an oral contraceptive pill. However, using a reliable form of birth control does not control acne.

    C. Improvement of the adolescent's overall health status is part of the general management when treating acne. Adequate rest, moderate exercise, a well-balanced diet, reduction of emotional stress and elimination of any foci of infection are all part of general health promotion. Supplementation of the diet with vitamins is not required.

    D. Exposure to oils in cooking grease can be a precursor to acne in adolescents working over fast-food restaurant hot oils. There is no known link between dietary intake of fat and the development or worsening of acne lesions.

54. **Key: C**   **Client Need:** *Reduction of Risk Potential*

    C. A desired outcome of femoral-popliteal bypass surgery is that the patient will demonstrate increased perfusion as noted by warm, dry skin, strong pulses, absence of edema and absence of cyanosis in the extremities.

    A and B.
      A positive Babinski reflex and active knee flexion are not identified as patient outcomes in obstructive arterial vascular disorders.

    D. The patient with arterial disease does have loss of hair on the legs, feet and toes. However, hair growth would take time to re-establish, and it may not necessarily be even distribution of hair.

55. **Key: B**   **Client Need:** *Growth and Development*

    B. Fundal pressure is used most often when there is slight shoulder dystocia.

    A. Knee-chest position is the position of choice for a patient with a prolapsed cord. It is not indicated in shoulder dystocia.

    C. Forceps delivery may not be necessary but an episiotomy will be needed. A large mediolateral episiotomy and adequate anesthesia are mandatory in preparation for delivery of the baby.

    D. Pitocin infusion would not be needed to facilitate the delivery of this large an infant.

56. **Key: B**   **Client Need:** *Physiological Adaptation*

    B. Nicotine causes vasoconstriction. The patient needs further teaching regarding the effects of smoking on arterial flow and smoking-cessation techniques.

    A, C and D.
      Topics to teach a patient with Raynaud's disease include the effects of smoking on arterial flow, ways to avoid exposure to cold, the importance of decreasing emotional stress and avoiding drugs that cause vasoconstriction.

57. **Key: A**   **Client Need: *Reduction of Risk Potential***

    A. Wilms tumor, or neuroblastoma, is the most frequent intra-abdominal tumor of childhood and the most common type of renal cancer. Preoperatively it is important that the tumor is not palpated unless absolutely necessary, since manipulation of the tumor may cause dissemination of cancer cells to adjacent and distal sites.

    B and D.
    Preoperative care includes temperature monitoring and intake and output measurement.
    C. The child's blood pressure is assessed frequently since hypertension from excess renin production in the kidney is a possibility.

58. **Key: C**   **Client Need: *Reduction of Risk Potential***

    C. Wrapping a stump helps to reduce edema and shapes the residual limb in a firm conical form for the prosthesis.

    A and D.
    There is no documentation to support these options. Wrapping the residual limb helps to prevent excessive edema.
    B. Healing of the stump is achieved by gentle handling, by controlling residual edema and by maintenance of aseptic technique.

59. **Key: C**   **Client Need: *Pharmacological and Parenteral Therapies***

    C. Acute dystonic reactions involve spasms of the major muscle groups of the neck, back and eyes.

    A. Tremors are not symptomatic of dystonia but can be seen in Parkinsonism, a side effect of antipsychotic medications.
    B. Ataxic gait is not a symptom of a dystonic reaction, but is a symptom of lithium toxicity.
    D. Psychomotor agitation is a symptom of akathisia, a side effect of antipsychotic medications.

60. **Key: B**   **Client Need: *Pharmacological and Parenteral Therapies***

    B. The most significant side effects of Accutane are the teratogenic effects. Accutane is absolutely contraindicated in pregnant women. Sexually active young women must be using an effective contraceptive method during treatment and for one month after treatment.

    A, C and D.
    All of these patient statements indicate an incorrect understanding of the precautions to be taken while on Accutane. Gentle cleansing with a mild cleanser once or twice daily is usually sufficient for acne, the patient should not double dose and there is no link between dietary intake of fat and the development or worsening of acne lesions.

61. **Key: D**   **Client Need: *Coping and Adaptation***

    D. Spiritual distress is usually evidenced by guilt, recriminations and self-blame.

    A, B and C.
    Powerlessness, self-esteem disturbance and impaired adjustment may be appropriate nursing diagnoses for this patient. However, the wish to have a fuller life indicates spiritual distress.

62. **Key: D**   **Client Need:** *Coping and Adaptation*

   D. There are four tasks of mourners. For the woman and her family to adapt to the loss of their baby or loved one, these tasks must be accomplished: accepting the reality of the loss, working through the pain or grief, adjusting to the environment and moving on with life. Accepting the reality of loss occurs when the family comes to grips with the reality of the loss. Seeing, holding, touching and memorializing are all ways the bereaved can confirm the loss.

   A. This statement indicates that the woman has not worked through her anger and grief.
   B. This statement indicates that the patient is experiencing guilt and has not been able to adjust to the loss.
   C. This statement indicates rationalization on the part of the woman, rather than acceptance.

63. **Key: B**   **Client Need:** *Coping and Adaptation*

   B. Depression is the most common mental health problem associated with chronic medical illness. Ten percent or more of major depressive conditions are in response to having a general medical illness.

   A. Anxiety is a normal reaction to stress or treatment and can occur at any phase in the health-illness process.
   C. Labile affect is not common in patients with chronic medical illnesses.
   D. Medical illnesses may cause confusion as a result of the physiological process of the illness. It is not the most common mental health problem associated with the chronically medically ill.

64. **Key: D**   **Client Need:** *Physiological Adaptation*

   D. Impetigo contagiosa is easily spread by self-inoculation; therefore, the child must be cautioned against touching the involved area.

   A. Children and parents are often tempted to squeeze follicular lesions. They must be warned that squeezing will not hasten the resolution of the infection and that there is a risk of making the lesion worse or spreading the infection. No attempt should be made to puncture the surface of the pustule with a needle or sharp instrument.
   B. Using a cloth to wash the lesions everyday may be too abrasive and could rupture the lesions, leading to spread of the lesions.
   C. Topical application of bactericidal ointment may be indicated. There is no documentation to support covering the lesions with a gauze dressing. Burow's solution compresses may help to soften crusts and debris.

65. **Key: B**   **Client Need:** *Psychosocial Adaptation*

   B. This statement can mean that the patient is covertly letting the nurse know that he is considering suicide. Though worded in a positive way, this statement has a negative meaning. Negative statements are indicative of poor self-worth and depression.

   A and D.
      Neither of these options indicates suicide intent. Sleeping more frequently may indicate an increase in depression.
   C. While the reason for change of medication or the type of medication requested in its place could raise suspicion of a suicide plan, this statement alone is not negative and is not indicative of suicidal thoughts.

66. **Key: D**   Client Need: *Safety and Infection Control*

D. Iron poisonings occurs in stages. The initial stage occurs within 30 minutes to six hours of ingestion and is characterized by vomiting, hematemesis, diarrhea, bloody stools and gastric pain. The latency stage occurs in two to 12 hours and is characterized by improvement in the patient. The systemic toxicity stage occurs four to 24 hours later and is characterized by metabolic acidosis, fever, hyperglycemia, bleeding, shock and, often, death.

A. The nurse should not admonish the parents for negligence, lack of appropriate supervision or failure to safe-proof the home in the emergency department. If the nurse prematurely attempts to discuss ways of preventing such a poisoning from recurring, the parent's anxiety will block out any suggestions or offered guidance.

B. A poisoning may or may not require emergency intervention, but in every instance medical evaluation is necessary to initiate appropriate action. Parents are advised to call the Poison Control Center before initializing treatment. Expert advice is essential to minimize side effects.

C. In general, the immediate treatment is to remove the ingested poison by inducing vomiting and absorbing the toxin with activated charcoal, performing gastric lavage or increasing bowel mobility. However, the nurse needs to know the content of the ingested substance before initiating treatment.

67. **Key: B.**   Client Need: *Growth and Development*

B. The normal newborn manifests acrocyanosis, a bluish discoloration of the hands and feet.

A. Heart rate averages 140 beats per minute at birth.

C. In the normal newborn there is no discharge from the eyes. If silver nitrate drops were given, there would be slight discharge.

D. The normal umbilical cord contains two arteries and one vein.

68. **Key: B**   Client Need: *Coping and Adaptation*

B. In the bargaining stage individuals promise to make amends for previous wrongs that may have occurred, or they think may have contributed to their impending death.

A. In the stage of denial, individuals cannot believe that they are really terminally ill. They hope that there has been some mistake or that there will be a miraculous recovery.

C. In the anger stage, individuals are angry about their situation and often find fault with the treatment process and those involved in it, as well as family and friends.

D. In the depression stage, patients realize that they are dying and experience a great sense of loss.

69. **Key: A**   Client Need: *Psychosocial Adaptation*

A. The deliberate infliction of physical injury on a child, usually by the child's caregiver, is termed physical abuse. Warning signs of physical abuse include bruises and welts on the lower back, buttocks and thighs. These bruises may be in various stages of healing.

B. A sudden tendency to bruise is a cardinal symptom of cancer in children. Clinical symptoms of idiopathic thrombocytopenia purpura include petechiae, bruising, bleeding from mucous membranes and prolonged bleeding from abrasions. The pattern of bruising is not indicative of a blood dyscrasia. Assessment for abuse should be performed first.

C. Neuromuscular dysfunction generally results in weakness or abnormal performance of muscles rather than in bruising.

D. The most common AIDS-defining illnesses in children include recurrent bacterial infections, parotitis, interstitial pneumonitis, wasting syndrome and progressive neurologic deterioration. Bruising over the buttocks and lower back is not characteristic.

70. Key: B.   Client Need: *Coping and Adaptation*

   B. The nurse uses the therapeutic technique of clarification to determine exactly what the patient means. This statement also conveys to the patient that the nurse is receptive to a discussion regarding a topic that is often taboo.

   A. The physician is part of the team and needs to be consulted as to what behaviors during sexual intimacy are safe for this patient. However, by making this response, the nurse does not allow the patient to express feelings and concerns. The nurse can answer questions regarding sexual intimacy that are within that nurse's level of competence.
   C. This statement does not clarify what is meant by "relationship." It is also erroneous information, as it may not be safe for the patient to continue sexual activity with his wife at this point in time. This statement does not encourage the patient to verbalize his fears and concerns.
   D. This response ignores the patient's need to verbalize about sexual intimacy with his wife. Clarifying sexual issues is part of the patient's recovery. The nurse needs to question his/her own comfort level with discussing this issue.

71. Key: A   Client Need: *Coping and Adaptation*

   A. This behavior is seen in Erikson's stage of autonomy verses shame and doubt. In this stage, the child tries to gain control over the environment, which includes communicating with others through speech.

   B. This behavior is found in the late childhood stage of development in which the central task is initiative verses guilt.
   C. This behavior is typical of the school-age stage of development in which the central task is industry verses inferiority.
   D. This behavior is found in Erikson's first stage of development (infancy) in which the central task is trust versus mistrust.

72. Key: D   Client Need: *Physiological Adaptation*

   D. Sexually active women who have multiple sexual partners may have an increased risk for pelvic inflammatory disease (PID).

   A, B and C.
   There is no documentation that prior abdominal surgery, blood transfusions or parity increases a patient's risk for PID.

73. Key: C   Client Need: *Physiological Adaptation*

   C. In bacterial meningitis, evaluation of cranial nerve VIII is needed for at least a six-month follow-up period to assess for possible hearing loss.

   A. A four-channel pneumogram is a continuous recording of cardiorespiratory patterns, nasal airflow and oxygen saturation. This test is done to evaluate an infant for apnea.
   B. A definitive diagnosis of acute bacterial meningitis is made only by examination of the cerebral spinal fluid (CSF) by means of a lumbar puncture. The fluid pressure is measured, and samples are obtained for culture and various analyses. It is not generally used in long-term follow-up.
   D. An electroencephalogram (EEG) records changes in the electrical potential of the brain. It is used to detect electrical abnormalities and aid in the detection of seizures.

74. Key: D   **Client Need:** *Psychosocial Adaptation*

D. The patient in the working phase of depression is able to discuss the disorder, to identify its causes and to identify more appropriate coping skills. This patient would be a candidate for group therapy.

A, B and C.
Patients in the second stage of dementia, manic patients and patients with signs of schizophrenia are not able to focus on therapy and would be disruptive to the group.

75. Key: B   **Client Need:** *Physiological Adaptation*

B. Oral ulcers greatly compound anorexia and may be a side effect of chemotherapy. Helpful interventions include rinsing the mouth with normal saline or sodium bicarbonate mouthwashes, and using local anesthetics such as Chloraseptic lozenges or nonprescription medications without alcohol.

A and C.
Helpful interventions include brushing the teeth with a soft-sponged brush or cotton-tipped applicator.
D. A soft, bland diet appropriate for the child's age and food preferences should be provided.

76. Key: B   **Client Need:** *Coping and Adaptation*

B. In group therapy, the nurse should focus on related themes and encourage involvement of others through the curative factor of universality. This can be accomplished by asking if any other member had a similar experience.

A, C and D.
These responses by the nurse focus mainly on the individual patient rather than the group.

77. Key: B   **Client Need:** *Physiological Adaptation*

B. Mononucleosis is an acute disease caused by a herpes-like virus, the Epstein-Barr virus. Early clinical manifestations of mononucleosis include fever, lymphadenopathy and pharyngitis.

A. White patches on the tongue are usually indicative of oral thrush.
C. Periorbital edema can be seen in glomerulonephritis, nephrotic syndrome and other disorders in which fluid retention is pronounced.
D. A productive cough is indicative of respiratory disorders such as pneumonia.

78. Key: C   **Client Need:** *Physiological Adaptation*

C. The patient who has a laryngectomy can expect to have a diminished sense of taste and smell for a period of time after surgery.

A. The trachea of a patient who has had a laryngectomy is brought out through the skin in the neck and sutured in place. This airway should remain clear.
B. Most total laryngectomy patients can attempt esophageal speech and use assistive devices.
D. The patient should be instructed to use a shower shield over the laryngectomy stoma to prevent water from entering the airway.

79. **Key: C** Client Need: *Physiological Adaptation*

    C. One of the most important aspects in the care of the patient with Wilms tumor is not pal-pating the abdomen unless absolutely necessary. Manipulation of the mass may cause dissemination of cancer cells to adjacent and distant sites.

    A, B and D.
    Specific tests for Wilms tumor include an intravenous pyelogram, computerized tomography, hematologic studies, biochemical studies and urinalysis. If a large tumor is present, an inferior venacavagram is necessary to demonstrate possible tumor involvement adjacent to the vena cava. A bone marrow aspiration may be electively performed to rule out metastasis.

80. **Key: C** Client Need: *Prevention and Early Detection of Disease*

    C. Predisposing factors in the development of infective endocarditis include intravenous drug abuse, history of valve replacement, mitral valve prolapse and other structural cardiac defects.

    A. Crowded living conditions is a predisposing factor in the development of tuberculosis.
    B. Multiple sex partners is a risk factor in sexually transmitted disease and cervical cancer.
    D. A family tendency toward heart disease increases the risk of cardiac disorders within the family system.

81. **Key: D** Client Need: *Physiological Adaptation*

    D. Patients with valvular heart disease are at risk for developing infective endocarditis. Therefore, the dentist should be informed of any valve disorder. Organisms that promote tooth decay can attack the valves of the heart. A prophylactic course of antibiotics is usual-ly prescribed prior to invasive dental interventions.

    A and C.
    Using a holter monitor and avoiding crowds are not indicated in the care of a patient with a valve disorder.
    B. Prophylactic antibiotics should be taken prior to any invasive procedure and test.

82. **Key: A** Client Need: *Reduction of Risk Potential*

    A. Fluctuations of five to 10 cm during normal breathing is common. The absence of fluctua-tions could mean that the tubing is obstructed, that expanded lung tissue has blocked the chest tube, or that there is no more air leaking into the pleural space.

    B. The situation would not require dressing reinforcement unless there was drainage.
    C. Chest tube drainage is not emptied. This would cause a break in the closed system.
    D. This situation does not warrant clamping of the tube. The tube is clamped when air could enter the chest.

83. **Key: C** Client Need: *Psychosocial Adaptation*

    C. Splitting is a term that describes a primitive defense mechanism of patients with border-line personality disorder. These individuals see themselves and others as all good or all bad. They are unable to integrate the positive and negative qualities of the self and others into a cohesive whole. This way of thinking impairs their ability to relate effectively to others and they often "play" one staff member against another. This behavior causes chaos on the unit if not addressed by the treatment team.

    A, B and D.
    These nursing diagnoses could be applicable to the care of the borderline patient. However, the nursing diagnosis that addresses splitting is essential to the management of this patient.

84. **Key: D**   **Client Need:** *Growth and Development*

   D. Diaper dermatitis is caused by prolonged and repetitive contact with an irritant, principally urine, feces, soaps, detergents, ointments and friction. The obvious irritants are urine and feces. Nursing interventions are directed at altering the three factors that produce dermatitis: wetness, pH and fecal irritants. Changing the diaper as soon as it becomes wet eliminates a large part of the problem. Removing the diaper to expose intact skin to air facilitates drying. The comment of the parent indicates a need for further instruction.

   A. The parent should avoid over-washing the skin, especially with perfumed soaps or commercial wipes that may be irritating. Non-alcohol based wipes should not cause irritation or drying.
   B. The parent should apply ointment such as zinc oxide in a thick layer to protect the skin. When soiled, the layer of ointment should be wiped off and reapplied.
   C. The parent should use superabsorbent diapers to reduce skin wetness and change the diapers as soon as they become soiled.

85. **Key: C**   **Client Need:** *Management of Care*

   C. Flail chest is associated with impaired gas exchange, as well as the inability to cough and clear secretions. An oxygen saturation of greater than 95% is normal.

   A. A normal arterial carbon dioxide level is 38 to 42 mm Hg.
   B. The normal heart rate for an adult is 60 to 100 beats per minute.
   D. A respiratory rate of 15 to 20 breaths per minute is normal in an adult. A slight increase to 22 breaths per minute is not significant.

86. **Key: B**   **Client Need:** *Physiological Adaptation*

   B. Cushing's syndrome, or hypercortisolism, is characterized by physical changes related to the distribution of fat and the retention of fluid. Moon face is characteristic of Cushing's syndrome.

   A. While adrenal hormone excess causes edema, it does not cause lymphedema. Lymphedema is caused by obstruction of lymph drainage.
   C. Adrenal hormone insufficiency results in hypovolemia and fluid volume deficit.
   D. Adrenal hormone insufficiency results in electrolyte imbalance. However, this is not the cause of moon face.

87. **Key: C**   **Client Need:** *Physiological Adaptation*

   C. Clinical manifestations of dehydration include the presence of any two of the following four factors: capillary refill greater than two seconds, absent tears, dry mucous membranes and general ill appearance.

   A. Urinary output decreases with mild dehydration. As dehydration progresses, the child can develop oliguria and azotemia. Oliguria is defined as urinary output of less than one milliliter/kilogram/hour.
   B. In cases of dehydration mucous membranes can be dry or parched. Skin coloring is pale, gray or mottled. Capillary refill time is increased.
   D. In dehydration skin color is usually pale or gray and skin temperature is cool.

88. **Key: C**   **Client Need:** *Growth and Development*

    C. Head circumference is usually measured in children up to 36 months of age and in any child when growth is questionable.

    A and B.
      Measurement should not be discontinued until 36 months of age.
    D. Measurement would not occur at five years of age unless head growth were questionable.

89. **Key: A**   **Client Need:** *Basic Care and Comfort*

    A. Total parenteral nutrition (TPN) involves intravenous infusion of highly concentrated solutions of protein, glucose and other nutrients. To prevent hypoglycemia when TPN is discontinued, the rate of infusion is decreased gradually. If a child stops receiving TPN abruptly, as in the case of occlusion, glucose levels must be monitored.

    B, C and D.
      Additional amounts of potassium and sodium are often required in hyperalimentation; therefore, observation for signs of potassium and sodium deficit or excess is included in nursing care. However, this is rarely a problem except in children with reduced renal function or metabolic defects. It is not necessary to monitor for ketones.

90. **Key: A**   **Client Need:** *Coping and Adaptation*

    A. Co-dependents try to control events and people around them. The fact that the woman is encouraging her daughter to make her own breakfast, rather than making it for her, shows that the interventions have been successful.

    B, C and D.
      All of these responses demonstrate codependency rather than improvement in the patient.

91. **Key: C**   **Client Need:** *Prevention and Early Detection of Disease*

    C. Primary prevention of abuse includes strengthening individuals and families so they can cope more effectively with stress. Assessment of family growth and development would identify potential situations that could lead to abuse and, thereby, decrease the incidence of abuse.

    A and B.
      Secondary prevention seeks to lower the rate of established cases. Screening and early case finding are examples of secondary prevention.
    D. Tertiary prevention seeks to decrease the amount of disability associated with an existing disorder or illness. Social skills training and promoting of independence are examples of tertiary prevention.

92. **Key: D**   **Client Need:** *Reduction of Risk Potential*

    D. Two people are required to change the ties on the tracheostomy. The old ties are slid to the upper edge of the old wings and the new ties threaded through. When the new ties are in place and secured, the old ties can be cut.

    A. Infants and young children may need to be restrained during tracheostomy care. Elbow restraints are preferable to wrist restraints. Sedation is not required.
    B. The child is suctioned before the procedure to minimize secretions, then restrained and positioned with the neck slightly extended.
    C. The stoma is cleansed with half-strength peroxide.

93. **Key: A**   **Client Need:** *Psychosocial Adaptation*

   A. Mouthwash usually contains 10 to 20 percent alcohol and should be omitted in the admission package given to the patient.

   B, C and D.
   Liquid soap, toothpaste and talcum powder may be given to the patient who has a history of alcohol abuse.

94. **Key: D**   **Client Need:** *Growth and Development*

   D. Artificial rupture of the membranes can be used to stimulate labor when the condition of the cervix is favorable. The fetal heart rate is assessed before and after the procedure to detect changes that may indicate the presence of cord compression or prolapse.

   A and B.
   The fluid is checked for color, odor and consistency. The pH is generally not checked.
   C. The patient's temperature should be checked every two to four hours after the procedure to monitor for signs of infection.

95. **Key: C**   **Client Need:** *Growth and Development*

   C. Breech presentation is one of the absolute indications for cesarean birth. Labor should not be induced.

   A. Precipitous delivery is not an indication for cesarean delivery.
   B. If the mother is positive for group B streptococcus by cervical culture, the treatment is intravenous penicillin prior to delivery. If there is no time to treat the mother, the infant should be carefully monitored for signs and symptoms of infection in the first several days of life.
   D. A reactive stress test is a predictor of fetal well-being and thus would make this mother a candidate for induction.

96. **Key: D**   **Client Need:** *Basic Care and Comfort*

   D. The nurse should encourage a diet high in fiber to prevent constipation, which is a side effect of Mellaril therapy.

   A. A bland diet at one time was used for peptic ulcers. It is not required for patients taking Mellaril.
   B. A low-residue diet may be used in the treatment of diverticulosis and diverticulitis. It is not required for the patient taking Mellaril.
   C. A sodium-restricted diet may be used in the treatment of hypertension and cardiac disease.

97. **Key: D**   **Client Need:** *Pharmacological and Parenteral Therapies*

   D. Manifestations of allergic reactions to Rocephin include rash, pruritis, fever and joint pain. The physician should be notified and therapy modified.

   A. Urinary frequency is not an adverse reaction to Rocephin. Decreased urine output might indicate nephrotoxicity, which is a side effect of Rocephin.
   B. Frontal headache requires further investigation but is generally unrelated to Rocephin administration.
   C. Back pain is not a side effect of Rocephin. Abdominal pain may occur.

98. **Key: C**   Client Need: *Psychosocial Adaptation*

   C. Consistency in implementing the established plan of care and maintaining objectivity regarding the patient's use of splitting are hallmarks of the treatment of a patient with a borderline personality disorder.

   A. Showing appreciation for the patient's positive evaluation will encourage polarization and splitting of staff.
   B. Providing reassuring information about the patient's psychosocial integrity does not address the issue of splitting.
   D. A delusion is a fixed, false belief. The patient with a borderline personality disorder generally is not out of touch with reality and does not display delusional thinking.

99. **Key: C**   Client Need: *Physiological Adaptation*

   C. The first sign of improvement in a child who has acute glomerulonephritis is a small increase in urinary output with a corresponding decrease in body weight followed in one to two days by copious diuresis.

   A, B and D.
   Decrease in appetite, decrease in blood pressure and increase in energy level are not the first signs of improvement in a child with acute glomerulonephritis.

100. **Key: A**   Client Need: *Reduction of Risk Potential*

   A. To verify nasogastric tube placement the nurse should either instill air into the tube with a syringe and listen with a stethoscope for the air passing into the stomach or aspirate gastric contents.

   B, C and D.
   These are not identified as measures to verify tube placement.

101. **Key: D**   Client Need: *Management of Care*

   D. Disorientation is an early sign of hepatic encephalopathy. The nurse should conduct a mental status examination to determine the extent of the disorientation, document the findings and then notify the physician.

   A. The change in orientation should be documented but patient assessment would take priority.
   B. The physician should be notified but an assessment of the patient should be conducted first.
   C. Limiting the patient's physical activity may prevent injuries due to disorientation but the priority nursing action is patient assessment.

102. **Key: B**   Client Need: *Pharmacological and Parenteral Therapies*

   B. The patient should be instructed to rinse his/her mouth after use of the inhaler so that steroid medication does not remain on the tongue and alter oral flora.

   A. The patient should wash the mouthpiece after each use.
   C and D.
   The patient does not have to avoid salt or spicy foods while using a steroid inhaler.

103. **Key: B**   **Client Need:** _Physiological Adaptation_

     B. The nurse should monitor the blood pressure in all four extremities since the blood pressure in the upper and lower extremities would be significantly different due to the coarctation or narrowing of the aorta.

     A. Liver margins are palpated when assessing for congestive heart failure.
     C. Increased abdominal girth is seen in congestive heart failure and in liver disease.
     D. Pulmonary function tests provide an objective method of evaluating the presence and degree of lung disease as well as the patient's response to therapy.

104. **Key: D**   **Client Need:** _Management of Care_

     D. Discomfort post-cataract surgery should be minimal to moderate and may be relieved by use of acetaminophen. Severe pain and nausea are not characteristic in the patient who has had cataract surgery. The physician should be notified immediately to prevent damage to the eye.

     A. The nurse should not remove the dressing unless an order is written to do so.
     B. The patient should not be medicated for severe pain until examined by the physician.
     C. Repositioning is not indicated for this patient. The first action that the nurse should take is notification of the physician.

105. **Key: C**   **Client Need:** _Reduction of Risk Potential_

     C. The first action by the nurse when a patient's incision dehisces is to cover the incision with sterile, saline gauze so that the abdominal contents do not become dry.

     A. The nurse should not attempt to reclose the incision or apply pressure to the incision.
     B. After the nurse covers the incision, he/she should assess the patient's vital signs and then notify the physician.
     D. The nurse may administer an antianxiety agent, if ordered, but this would not be a priority.

106. **Key: B**   **Client Need:** _Pharmacological and Parenteral Therapies_

     B. Intal is used exclusively for prevention of asthmatic attacks.

     A. The nurse should instruct the patient to use the inhaler 30 minutes before meals and at bedtime.
     C. Intal is used to prevent, rather than treat, asthmatic attacks.
     D. Intal appears to act to inhibit both early-phase and late-phase allergen-induced airway narrowing from exposure to exercise, cold dry air and sulfur dioxide. Intal should be used prior to going outside in cold air.

107. Key: C   **Client Need:** *Management of Care*

    C. Possible inhalation injury is suspected when there is a history of exposure to flames in a closed space whether or not burns are present. Sooty material around the nose or in the sputum, singed nasal hairs, mucosal burns of the nose, lips, mouth or throat, hoarse voice and cough and stridor indicate that the affected person requires observation for possible pulmonary injury. Therapeutic management of smoke inhalation is symptomatic; however, administering humidified 100% oxygen as soon as possible and monitoring for signs of respiratory distress is a priority.

    A. Respiratory distress is the primary symptom rather than pain.
    B. Fluid requirements are carefully managed to avoid pulmonary edema while maintaining adequate hydration.
    D. If the child experiences vomiting and/or respiratory distress, the child may be NPO to reduce the risk of aspiration. The priority goal, however, is the patient's airway.

108. Key: A   **Client Need:** *Pharmacological and Parenteral Therapies*

    A. Megace is a hormone and antineoplastic agent. In AIDS patients it is used to increase appetite.

    B. Megace has a side effect of diarrhea. It does not decrease diarrhea.
    C. Megace does not affect the neuromuscular system.
    D. Megace is not used as an anti-seizure medication.

109. Key: D   **Client Need:** *Growth and Development*

    D. The nurse should assess the cord for true knots, or a nuchal cord, before delivery of the infant. If the cord is encircling the head of the infant, it can be slipped over the head prior to delivery to prevent anoxia.

    A. The shoulder should not be delivered until the cord has been examined for knots, and internal rotation has occurred.
    B. The face does not need to be cleaned until the infant is dried after delivery. It is not a priority for the nurse but it may clear the mouth and nose of some secretions.
    C. The infant should not be stimulated to cry at this time. The compression of the chest during delivery will stimulate the cry.

110. Key: C   **Client Need:** *Management of Care*

    C. Decreased serum albumin results in a decrease in colloidal osmotic pressure. As a result, fluid moves out of the intravascular compartment, resulting in edema. The priority nursing diagnosis would be potential alteration in skin integrity.

    A, B and D.
    Potential alteration in comfort, elimination and mobility may be associated nursing diagnoses for the patient with decreased serum albumin; however, they would not take priority over alteration in skin integrity.

CGFNS

Appendices

Appendix A

Glossary of Terms

Academic Records
See Transcript.

Accredited Nursing School/Program
Accreditation is a self-regulatory process by which non-governmental, voluntary organizations recognize an educational institution or program of study that meets or exceeds certain stated criteria of educational quality. (See Commission on Collegiate Nursing Education and National League for Nursing Accreditation Commission.)

American Nurses Association (ANA)
The American Nurses Association (ANA) is a full-service, professional organization representing more than two million nurses in the United States through its 53 constituent state nursing associations. ANA seeks to advance the nursing profession by fostering high standards of nursing practice, promoting the economic and general welfare of nurses in the workplace and lobbying the U.S. Congress and regulatory agencies on healthcare issues affecting nurses and the American public.

Approved Nursing School/Program
This term refers to academic programs that have been approved or recognized by the official government of the country in which the program is administered to ensure compliance with minimum standards. As part of its evaluation of an applicant's eligibility to take the CGFNS Qualifying Exam, CGFNS reviews an applicant's academic records to determine if the applicant has graduated from a government-approved, general nursing program of at least two years in length.

Certification
Certification is a process by which an association or agency grants recognition to an individual who has met pre-determined standards or criteria specified by the association or agency for specialty practice. Certification is usually national in scope. Certification may or may not denote advanced or special competency. For example, CGFNS Certification indicates that one is a first-level, general nurse who has a good likelihood of successfully passing the NCLEX-RN examination and becoming licensed to practice as a registered nurse in the United States.

CGFNS Certification Program
The CGFNS Certification Program (CP) is a three-part certification program for first-level, general nurses educated outside the United States who wish to practice as registered nurses in the United States. It includes a credentials review, followed by the CGFNS Qualifying Exam of nursing knowledge and a test of English language proficiency (TOEFL). Meeting the credentials criteria and passing the two examinations entitles applicants to receive a CGFNS Certificate. (See Certification.)

CGFNS Credentials Evaluation Service
The CGFNS Credentials Evaluation Service (CES) is designed for any nurse educated outside the United States who needs to have his/her educational and professional registration credentials evaluated. The service presents the results of this evaluation in the form of a CES Report. The report describes the nurse's credentials in terms of their comparability to U.S. credentials. The report can be used for immigration, licensure, employment or admission to a U.S. nursing education program. The CES can be used by all nurses educated outside the United States, including registered or professional nurses, as well as enrolled or practical nurses and nursing assistants.

CGFNS Credentials Verification Service for New York State
The New York State Education Department requires that internationally educated registered nurses, licensed practical nurses, physical therapists, physical therapist assistants, occupational therapists and occupational therapy assistants obtain independent verification of the authenticity of their credentials from an approved credentials verification service. The CGFNS Credentials Verification Service for New York State (CVS) was custom-designed to meet the New York State Education Department's requirements. The CVS program independently collects and verifies the authenticity of an applicant's educational and licensure/registration credentials. Once verified, the credentials are forwarded to the New York State Education Department to be evaluated as part of the applicant's New York licensure application.

CGFNS Qualifying Exam
See CGFNS Certification Program.

Commission on Collegiate Nursing Education

The Commission on Collegiate Nursing Education (CCNE) was conceived by the American Association of Colleges of Nursing (AACN) in 1996 and officially began accrediting operations in 1998. CCNE is an autonomous accrediting arm of the AACN, contributing to the improvement of the public's health. As a specialized/professional accrediting agency, CCNE is designed to evaluate and make judgments about the quality of nursing education programs that grant baccalaureate and graduate degrees. CCNE accreditation is a non-governmental peer review process that operates in accordance with nationally recognized standards established for the practice of accreditation in the United States. CCNE serves higher education institutions throughout the United States. (See American Association of Colleges of Nursing.)

Commission on Graduates of Foreign Nursing Schools (CGFNS)

The Commission on Graduates of Foreign Nursing Schools (CGFNS) is a private, nonprofit organization founded in 1977. CGFNS was established through a joint effort spearheaded by the Division of Nursing at the then-Department of Health, Education and Welfare and involving federal agencies and professional nursing organizations. The organization assumes a leadership role in international nursing and healthcare and is an active participant in policy discussions concerning international nursing and healthcare education, licensure and practice. CGFNS also provides programs that evaluate the professional licensure/registration and educational credentials of nurses and other healthcare professionals educated outside the United States. Evaluation services include the CGFNS Certification Program, the CGFNS Credentials Evaluation Service, the CGFNS/ICHP VisaScreen™: Visa Credentials Assessment program and the Credentials Verification Service for New York State.

Credentialing

Credentialing is a process through which one's educational background and/or professional preparation are reviewed to see that they meet certain established, minimum standards. These standards may vary from time to time, depending upon the purpose of the credentials review. Credentialing helps to ensure that standards of education and service are maintained, fostered and observed as an incentive for self-improvement. Credentialing of professionals provides a means for individual accountability and self-regulating of professional services. In this way, it is an alternative to regulation by government agencies. Licensure, certification and accreditation are the three major means of credentialing.

English Language Proficiency

As mandated by the federal government, and as part of the requirements for earning a CGFNS/ICHP VisaScreen Certificate, internationally-educated applicants must demonstrate the required English language competency in oral and written English by submitting passing scores on tests approved by the U.S. Departments of Health and Human Services, as well as Education. Demonstration of English language proficiency is also required for the CGFNS Certification Program. The English proficiency exam requirement is waived for graduates of nursing programs in countries in which the primary language is English. These countries include Australia, Canada (except Quebec), Ireland, New Zealand, the United Kingdom and the United States.

Enrolled Nurse

See Second-Level Nurse.

First-Level Nurse

First-level nurse is a historical phrase used by the International Council of Nurses (ICN) to denote a person who has attained the top level of basic general nursing education and practice in his/her country. Generally, such a person will hold a title of a generalist nurse in his/her country. To be eligible to take the CGFNS Qualifying Exam, you must be educated and registered as a first-level nurse as defined historically by the ICN. You must also meet certain minimum criteria for nursing education and be educated as a general nurse. (See also General Nurse and Registered Nurse.)

General Nurse

General nurse is a historical phrase used to describe a nurse who has studied theory and has had clinical practice in a variety of nursing areas. These include nursing care of the adult (includes medical and surgical nursing), nursing care of children, maternal/infant nursing and psychiatric/mental health nursing. To be eligible to take the CGFNS Qualifying Exam, you must be educated and registered as a general nurse. A nurse who has specialized education or registration as a maternity nurse or midwife, children's nurse, psychiatric nurse, or in another area of specialization without being educated and registered as a general nurse is not eligible to take the CGFNS Qualifying Exam. You must also be a first-level nurse. (See also First-Level Nurse.)

Immigrant (permanent) Occupational Preference Visa

A foreign nurse can apply for and be granted an immigrant visa, which enables him/her to remain permanently in the United States in order to work. This requires sponsorship by an employer. The number of such individuals is limited by U.S. immigration law for each country and for various preference categories.

Immigration and Naturalization Service (INS)

The U.S. Immigration and Naturalization Service (INS) of the U.S. Department of Justice is the federal governmental agency that develops the rules and procedures for determining who can enter the United States. INS also has the responsibility for enforcing immigration laws and regulations.

International Commission on Healthcare Professions (ICHP)

The International Commission on Healthcare Professions (ICHP) is a division of CGFNS. Building on CGFNS' years of experience, ICHP analyzes and verifies education, licensure and registration credentials, as well as other preparation for healthcare professionals, other than physicians. In addition to customized certification and screening programs, the division provides models/benchmarks for international standards, and serves as a clearinghouse on education, licensure and practice standards around the world. ICHP administers the VisaScreen™: Visa Credentials Assessment program that meets federal visa requirements for the screening of healthcare professionals who seek entry into the United States.

International Consultants of Delaware, Inc.

The International Consultants of Delaware, Inc. (ICD) is a division of CGFNS. Established in 1977, ICD is recognized nationally as an expert in the field of international education. ICD is a credentialing agency that evaluated foreign educational documents (for both healthcare and non-healthcare fields) and provides their U.S. equivalents in detailed, accurate reports.

International Council of Nurses (ICN)

The International Council of Nurses (ICN) was established in 1899 and is located in Geneva, Switzerland. ICN is a federation of national nurses associations (the American Nurses Association is a member of the ICN). ICN is dedicated to raising nursing standards, giving ethical guidance to the profession and improving nurses' working conditions on a worldwide basis.

Internationally Educated Nurse

This term refers to a nurse who received some portion of his/her education outside the United States. This may include U.S. citizens or citizens of another country who graduated from schools located outside the United States.

Licensure

Licensure is the process by which an agency of government grants permission to an individual to engage in a given profession upon finding that the applicant has attained the essential degree of competency necessary to ensure the public's health, safety and welfare will be reasonably well protected. In the United States, the authority to practice nursing is granted at the state level, not at the federal level. A state board of nursing, therefore, grants state nursing licenses for registered nurses and practical nurses. Two means by which licenses may be granted are by examination and by endorsement.

Licensure by Endorsement

Some states will grant a license in their state to a nurse already licensed in another U.S. state or territory through a process called endorsement. Licensure by endorsement is often based on meeting a number of predetermined criteria, including (at times) proof or verification of licensure in the original state.

Licensure by Examination

Licensure by examination is sometimes called initial licensure and refers to an application for nurse licensure by a nurse who is not already licensed in another U.S. state or territory. Applicants for licensure by examination must often satisfy specific requirements (that may include a credentials review or earning a CGFNS Certificate) and apply to take the appropriate National Council Licensure Examination (NCLEX-RN examination or NCLEX-PN examination).

Mutual Recognition Model of Licensure

The mutual recognition model allows nurses to have one license (obtained in their state of residency) and to practice in other states, as long as they acknowledge that they are subject to each state's practice laws and discipline. Meanwhile, each state would still have complete authority in determining its licensure requirements and disciplinary actions. The mutual recognition model provides that the nurse would be held accountable for the nursing practice laws and regulations of the state in which the patient is located at the time that care is given. In order for mutual recognition to be put into practice, states must enter into an "interstate compact." An interstate compact is an agreement among two or more states to coordinate certain activities associated with nursing licensure. It is designed to reduce redundant, multiple licensure requirements, enhance information sharing and establish a communal system for disciplinary actions associated with interstate nursing practice.

National Council Licensure Examination (NCLEX)

The National Council of State Boards of Nursing (NCSBN) has developed two licensure examinations used by its U.S. state and territorial boards of nursing to test the entry-level nursing competence of candidates for licensure as registered nurses (NCLEX-RN examination) and as licensed practical or vocational nurses (NCLEX-PN® examination). NCSBN member boards of nursing in all 50 U.S. states, as well as the District of Columbia and all U.S. territories, administer the same exam. The NCLEX-RN and NCLEX-PN licensure examinations are multiple-choice tests administered to test-takers who use computers to answer questions. Scoring is done on a pass/fail basis. The exams test an applicant's nursing knowledge. All U.S. state and territorial boards of nursing use the same national exam, but the procedures and regulations regarding licensing are decided independently by each board. The license obtained is not a national license. It allows for practice only in the state in which the examination was taken or in the multi-state compact of which the state is a member.

National Council of State Boards of Nursing (NCSBN)

National Council of State Boards of Nursing (NCSBN) is the organization through which the state boards of nursing (the state and territorial organizations that regulate nursing in the U.S.) act together on matters of common interest. This includes matters of public health, safety and welfare, including the development of licensure examinations for nursing.

National League for Nursing Accreditation Commission

The National League for Nursing Accreditation Commission (NLNAC) is the non-governmental body that accredits practical, diploma, associate, baccalaureate and master's degree nursing programs in the United States. (See Accreditation.)

Non-Immigrant (temporary) Occupational Preference Visa

This visa category allows U.S. employers to sponsor the entry of qualified professional nurses into the United States for temporary periods of employment.

Practical/Vocational Nurse

See Second-Level Nurse.

Registered or Professional Nurse

Registered or professional nurse is a U.S. nursing title that refers to a first-level, general nurse who is licensed to practice in a U.S. state or territory. As part of its evaluation of an applicant's eligibility to take the CGFNS Qualifying Exam, CGFNS reviews an applicant's educational and professional registration credentials to see that the applicant is a first-level, general nurse in his/her home country. (See First-Level Nurse.)

Registration

Registration is a process by which qualified individuals are listed on an official register maintained by a government or non-governmental agency. Similar to licensure, it enables such persons to use a particular title and attest to employing agencies and individuals that minimum qualifications have been met and maintained.

Second-Level Nurse

Historically, the International Council of Nurses has defined a second-level nurse as follows: "(in countries with more than one level of nursing personnel) as the nurse who gives nursing care in cooperation with and under the supervision of a first-level nurse; sometimes referred to as enrolled nurse, practical nurse, technical nurse, nursing assistant, etc." Second-level nurses are licensed separately from registered nurses in the United States and, therefore, are not eligible for the CGFNS Certification Program.

State Board of Nursing

In the United States, the authority to practice nursing is granted to registered nurses and licensed or registered practical nurses at the state level—not the federal level—by a state board of nursing, which grants a state nursing license. These state boards of nursing are members of the National Council of State Boards of Nursing (NCSBN).

State Nurses Associations

State Nurses Associations are the state-level members of the American Nurses Association (ANA). State associations represent the interests of their membership—nursing professionals—at the state level.

Transcript

This term is used to refer to an applicant's educational credentials or academic records and diploma(s) from a senior secondary school and/or post-secondary program of study.

U.S. Department of Labor

In the United States, the U.S. Department of Labor is the federal governmental agency responsible for verifying certain labor conditions to the U.S. Department of State and the U.S. Department of Justice's Immigration and Naturalization Service.

VisaScreen™: Visa Credentials Assessment

The federal government requires that certain non-U.S. healthcare professionals successfully complete a screening program prior to receiving an occupational visa. CGFNS is named in the 1996 immigration law as a qualified provider of such a screening program. VisaScreen is ICHP's visa credentials assessment program that meets federal visa requirements for the screening of healthcare professionals who seek entry into the United States. VisaScreen includes, an assessment of an applicant's education to ensure that it is comparable to that of a U.S. graduate in the same profession, verification that licenses (both past and present) are valid and unencumbered, English language proficiency testing and, in the case of nurses only, verification that the nurse has either earned a CGFNS Certificate or passed the National Council Licensure Examination for Registered Nurses (NCLEX-RN examination).

A

Appendix B

Check List and Answer Sheets for Practice Tests

Test A	Test B	Test C	Test D		
❏	❏	❏	❏	1.	Sit in a comfortable chair at a table with a hard writing surface.
❏	❏	❏	❏	2.	Remove any papers, calculators and books except for this Official Study Guide. During the actual exam, all personal items and study materials will be stored at designated areas.
❏	❏	❏	❏	3.	Have at least two sharpened pencils with good erasers.
❏	❏	❏	❏	4.	Allow enough light to see clearly.
❏	❏	❏	❏	5.	Remove the appropriate answer sheets for the respective practice tests.
❏	❏	❏	❏	6.	Allow two hours and 30 minutes for Nursing, Part 1, followed by one hour and 50 minutes for Nursing, Part 2. During the actual exam, you will have a one hour lunch between the two parts.
❏	❏	❏	❏	7.	Before you begin timing, fill in all of the identifying information for items 1-13 of the answer sheets.
❏	❏	❏	❏	8.	Fill the selected circles in completely on the answer sheets. Make all answers on the answer sheets and not in the book.
❏	❏	❏	❏	9.	If you skip a question during one of the practice tests, circle the question number in the book and return to it later. Be sure to skip the same number on the answer sheet.
❏	❏	❏	❏	10.	Once you are finished both parts of a practice test, compare your answers to the correct answers and rationales that immediately follow each test.

B

CGFNS QUALIFYING EXAMINATION — NURSING

1 NAME — FAMILY NAME/SURNAME — FIRST — MIDDLE

2 TEST CENTER — CITY — COUNTRY

3 CENTER CODE

4 PART 1 2

5 TEST BOOK NUMBER

6 CGFNS IDENTIFICATION NUMBER

7 DATE OF BIRTH — MO. DAY YR.

8 COUNTRY OF NURSING EDUCATION:

COUNTY CODE 9 0 -

11 DATE OF GRAD. — MO. YR.

12 TEST FORM

9 SEX — FEMALE — MALE

10 Is this the first time you are taking this test? NO YES

13 _____ Signature

Use No. 2 pencil only.
Erase any changes completely.
Make no stray marks on answer sheet.

Mark Reflex® by NCS IM-163410-001:654321   Printed in U.S.A.   RIGHT: ●   WRONG: ⊘ ⊖ ⊗   ©1998 by Commission on Graduates of Foreign Nursing Schools

Answer grid, columns A B C D, questions 1–150.

PRACTICE TEST A — NURSING PART 1 (watermark)

CGFNS QUALIFYING EXAMINATION — NURSING

1	NAME	FAMILY NAME/SURNAME	FIRST	MIDDLE

2	TEST CENTER	CITY	COUNTRY	3	CENTER CODE			

4	PART	1 ○ 2 ○	5	TEST BOOK NUMBER						■ ■

6 CGFNS IDENTIFICATION NUMBER

(0)(0)(0)(0)(0)(0)(0)
(1)(1)(1)(1)(1)(1)(1)
(2)(2)(2)(2)(2)(2)(2)
(3)(3)(3)(3)(3)(3)(3)
(4)(4)(4)(4)(4)(4)(4)
(5)(5)(5)(5)(5)(5)(5)
(6)(6)(6)(6)(6)(6)(6)
(7)(7)(7)(7)(7)(7)(7)
(8)(8)(8)(8)(8)(8)(8)
(9)(9)(9)(9)(9)(9)(9)

7 DATE OF BIRTH

MO.	DAY	YR.

(0)(0) (0)(0) (0)(0)
(1)(1) (1)(1) (1)(1)
(2) (2)(2) (2)(2)
(3) (3)(3) (3)(3)
(4) (4)(4) (4)(4)
(5) (5)(5) (5)(5)
(6) (6)(6) (6)(6)
(7) (7)(7) (7)(7)
(8) (8)(8) (8)(8)
(9) (9)(9) (9)(9)

8 COUNTRY OF NURSING EDUCATION:

9 SEX
FEMALE ○
MALE ○

10 Is this the first time you are taking this test?
○ NO ○ YES

13
_____
Signature

Use No. 2 pencil only.
Erase any changes completely.
Make no stray marks on answer sheet.

COUNTY CODE
9 0

(0)(0)(0)
(1)(1)(1)
(2)(2)(2)
(3)(3)(3)
(4)(4)(4)
(5)(5)(5)
(6)(6)(6)
(7)(7)(7)
(8)(8)(8)
(9)(9)(9)

11 DATE OF GRAD.

MO.	YR.

12 TEST FORM

(0)(0) (0)(0)(0)(0)
(1)(1) (1)(1)(1)(1)
(2)(2) (2)(2)(2)(2)
(3)(3) (3)(3)(3)(3)
(4)(4) (4)(4)(4)(4)
(5)(5) (5)(5)(5)(5)
(6)(6) (6)(6)(6)(6)
(7)(7) (7)(7)(7)(7)
(8)(8) (8)(8)(8)(8)
(9)(9) (9)(9)(9)(9)

I.C.—051 013 980

Mark Reflex® by NCS IM-163410-001:654321 Printed in U.S.A. RIGHT: ● WRONG: ⊘ ⊖ ⊗ ©1998 by Commission on Graduates of Foreign Nursing Schools

1 A B C D ○○○○ 21 A B C D ○○○○ 41 A B C D ○○○○ 61 A B C D ○○○○ 81 A B C D ○○○○ 101 A B C D ○○○○
2 A B C D ○○○○ 22 A B C D ○○○○ 42 A B C D ○○○○ 62 A B C D ○○○○ 82 A B C D ○○○○ 102 A B C D ○○○○
3 A B C D ○○○○ 23 A B C D ○○○○ 43 A B C D ○○○○ 63 A B C D ○○○○ 83 A B C D ○○○○ 103 A B C D ○○○○
4 A B C D ○○○○ 24 A B C D ○○○○ 44 A B C D ○○○○ 64 A B C D ○○○○ 84 A B C D ○○○○ 104 A B C D ○○○○
5 A B C D ○○○○ 25 A B C D ○○○○ 45 A B C D ○○○○ 65 A B C D ○○○○ 85 A B C D ○○○○ 105 A B C D ○○○○
6 A B C D ○○○○ 26 A B C D ○○○○ 46 A B C D ○○○○ 66 A B C D ○○○○ 86 A B C D ○○○○ 106 A B C D ○○○○
7 A B C D ○○○○ 27 A B C D ○○○○ 47 A B C D ○○○○ 67 A B C D ○○○○ 87 A B C D ○○○○ 107 A B C D ○○○○
8 A B C D ○○○○ 28 A B C D ○○○○ 48 A B C D ○○○○ 68 A B C D ○○○○ 88 A B C D ○○○○ 108 A B C D ○○○○
9 A B C D ○○○○ 29 A B C D ○○○○ 49 A B C D ○○○○ 69 A B C D ○○○○ 89 A B C D ○○○○ 109 A B C D ○○○○
10 A B C D ○○○○ 30 A B C D ○○○○ 50 A B C D ○○○○ 70 A B C D ○○○○ 90 A B C D ○○○○ 110 A B C D ○○○○
11 A B C D ○○○○ 31 A B C D ○○○○ 51 A B C D ○○○○ 71 A B C D ○○○○ 91 A B C D ○○○○
12 A B C D ○○○○ 32 A B C D ○○○○ 52 A B C D ○○○○ 72 A B C D ○○○○ 92 A B C D ○○○○
13 A B C D ○○○○ 33 A B C D ○○○○ 53 A B C D ○○○○ 73 A B C D ○○○○ 93 A B C D ○○○○
14 A B C D ○○○○ 34 A B C D ○○○○ 54 A B C D ○○○○ 74 A B C D ○○○○ 94 A B C D ○○○○
15 A B C D ○○○○ 35 A B C D ○○○○ 55 A B C D ○○○○ 75 A B C D ○○○○ 95 A B C D ○○○○
16 A B C D ○○○○ 36 A B C D ○○○○ 56 A B C D ○○○○ 76 A B C D ○○○○ 96 A B C D ○○○○
17 A B C D ○○○○ 37 A B C D ○○○○ 57 A B C D ○○○○ 77 A B C D ○○○○ 97 A B C D ○○○○
18 A B C D ○○○○ 38 A B C D ○○○○ 58 A B C D ○○○○ 78 A B C D ○○○○ 98 A B C D ○○○○
19 A B C D ○○○○ 39 A B C D ○○○○ 59 A B C D ○○○○ 79 A B C D ○○○○ 99 A B C D ○○○○
20 A B C D ○○○○ 40 A B C D ○○○○ 60 A B C D ○○○○ 80 A B C D ○○○○ 100 A B C D ○○○○

PRACTICE TEST A
NURSING PART 2

B

CGFNS QUALIFYING EXAMINATION — NURSING

1 NAME — FAMILY NAME/SURNAME — FIRST — MIDDLE

2 TEST CENTER — CITY — COUNTRY

3 CENTER CODE

4 PART — ○ 1 — ○ 2

5 TEST BOOK NUMBER

6 CGFNS IDENTIFICATION NUMBER

7 DATE OF BIRTH — MO. — DAY — YR.

8 COUNTRY OF NURSING EDUCATION:

9 SEX — FEMALE ○ — MALE ○

10 Is this the first time you are taking this test? ○ NO ○ YES

COUNTY CODE 9 0 -

11 DATE OF GRAD. — MO. — YR.

12 TEST FORM

13 _____ Signature

Use No. 2 pencil only.
Erase any changes completely.
Make no stray marks on answer sheet.

Mark Reflex® by NCS IM-163410-001:654321   Printed in U.S.A.   RIGHT: ● — WRONG: ⊘ ◖ ⊗   ©1998 by Commission on Graduates of Foreign Nursing Schools

I.C.—051 013 980

(Answer grid, questions 1–150, columns A B C D)

B

CGFNS QUALIFYING EXAMINATION — NURSING

1 NAME — FAMILY NAME/SURNAME | FIRST | MIDDLE

2 TEST CENTER — CITY | COUNTRY

3 CENTER CODE

4 PART — 1 ○ 2 ○

5 TEST BOOK NUMBER

6 CGFNS IDENTIFICATION NUMBER

7 DATE OF BIRTH — MO. | DAY | YR.

8 COUNTRY OF NURSING EDUCATION:

COUNTY CODE — 9 0

11 DATE OF GRAD. — MO. | YR.

12 TEST FORM

9 SEX — FEMALE ○ MALE ○

10 Is this the first time you are taking this test? ○ NO ○ YES

13 _____ Signature

Use No. 2 pencil only.
Erase any changes completely.
Make no stray marks on answer sheet.

I.C.—051 013 980

Mark Reflex® by NCS IM-163410-001:654321   Printed in U.S.A.   RIGHT: ● | WRONG: ⊘ ⊖ ⊗   ©1998 by Commission on Graduates of Foreign Nursing Schools

PRACTICE TEST B
NURSING PART 2

1–20, 21–40, 41–60, 61–80, 81–100, 101–110 (answer bubbles A B C D for each question)

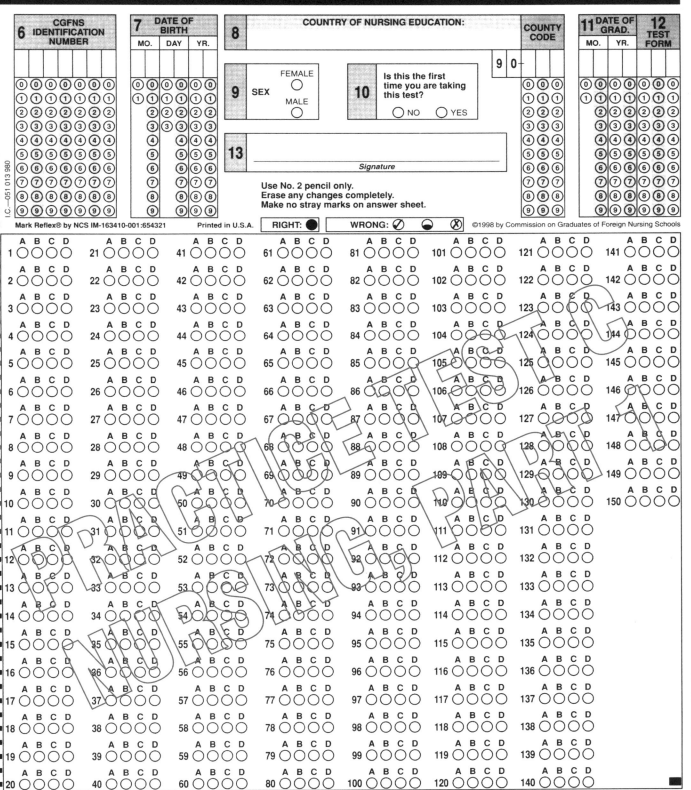

CGFNS QUALIFYING EXAMINATION — NURSING

1 NAME — FAMILY NAME/SURNAME — FIRST — MIDDLE

2 TEST CENTER — CITY — COUNTRY

3 CENTER CODE

4 PART ○1 ○2

5 TEST BOOK NUMBER

6 CGFNS IDENTIFICATION NUMBER

7 DATE OF BIRTH — MO. DAY YR.

8 COUNTRY OF NURSING EDUCATION:

COUNTY CODE 9 0-

11 DATE OF GRAD. — MO. YR.

12 TEST FORM

9 SEX — ○ FEMALE ○ MALE

10 Is this the first time you are taking this test? ○ NO ○ YES

13 _____ *Signature*

Use No. 2 pencil only.
Erase any changes completely.
Make no stray marks on answer sheet.

Mark Reflex® by NCS IM-163410-001:654321   Printed in U.S.A.   RIGHT: ● WRONG: ⊘ ⊖ ⊗   ©1998 by Commission on Graduates of Foreign Nursing Schools

I.C.—051 013 980

PRACTICE TEST C
NURSING PART 1

B

445

CGFNS QUALIFYING EXAMINATION — NURSING

1 NAME	FAMILY NAME/SURNAME	FIRST	MIDDLE

2 TEST CENTER	CITY	COUNTRY	**3** CENTER CODE

4 PART	1 ○ 2 ○	**5** TEST BOOK NUMBER

6 CGFNS IDENTIFICATION NUMBER

7 DATE OF BIRTH — MO. DAY YR.

8 COUNTRY OF NURSING EDUCATION:

COUNTY CODE 9 0 -

11 DATE OF GRAD. — MO. YR.

12 TEST FORM

9 SEX — FEMALE ○ MALE ○

10 Is this the first time you are taking this test? ○ NO ○ YES

13 _____ Signature

Use No. 2 pencil only.
Erase any changes completely.
Make no stray marks on answer sheet.

I.C.—051 013 980

Mark Reflex® by NCS IM-163410-001:654321   Printed in U.S.A.   RIGHT: ●   WRONG: ⊘ ⊖ ⊗   ©1998 by Commission on Graduates of Foreign Nursing Schools

A B C D (answer grid, items 1–110)

CGFNS QUALIFYING EXAMINATION — NURSING

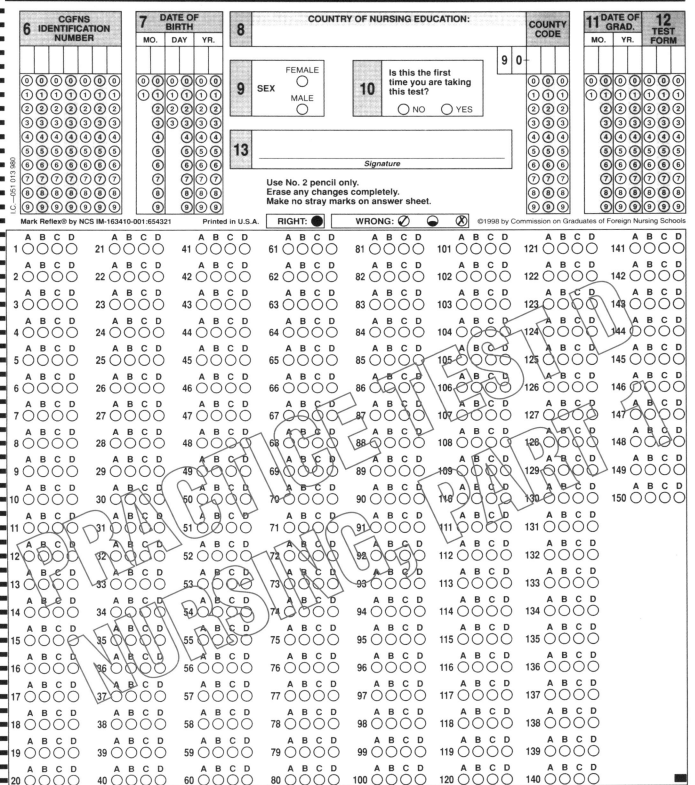

| 1 | NAME | FAMILY NAME/SURNAME | FIRST | MIDDLE |

| 2 | TEST CENTER | CITY | COUNTRY | 3 | CENTER CODE |

| 4 | PART | 1 ○ 2 ○ | 5 | TEST BOOK NUMBER |

6 CGFNS IDENTIFICATION NUMBER

7 DATE OF BIRTH — MO. DAY YR.

8 COUNTRY OF NURSING EDUCATION:

COUNTY CODE — 9 0-

11 DATE OF GRAD. — MO. YR.

12 TEST FORM

9 SEX — FEMALE ○ MALE ○

10 Is this the first time you are taking this test? ○ NO ○ YES

13 _____ Signature

Use No. 2 pencil only.
Erase any changes completely.
Make no stray marks on answer sheet.

Mark Reflex® by NCS IM-163410-001:654321   Printed in U.S.A.   RIGHT: ●   WRONG: ⊘ ⊖ ⊗   ©1998 by Commission on Graduates of Foreign Nursing Schools

I.C.—051 013 980

PRACTICE TEST — NURSING PART 1

B

CGFNS QUALIFYING EXAMINATION — NURSING

1	NAME	FAMILY NAME/SURNAME	FIRST	MIDDLE

2	TEST CENTER	CITY	COUNTRY	3	CENTER CODE

4	PART	1 ○ 2 ○	5	TEST BOOK NUMBER

6 CGFNS IDENTIFICATION NUMBER

0 0 0 0 0 0 0
1 1 1 1 1 1 1
2 2 2 2 2 2 2
3 3 3 3 3 3 3
4 4 4 4 4 4 4
5 5 5 5 5 5 5
6 6 6 6 6 6 6
7 7 7 7 7 7 7
8 8 8 8 8 8 8
9 9 9 9 9 9 9

I.C.—051 013 980

7 DATE OF BIRTH

MO.	DAY	YR.

0 0 0 0 0 0
1 1 1 1 1 1
2 2 2 2 2 2
3 3 3 3 3
4 4 4 4
5 5 5 5
6 6 6 6
7 7 7 7
8 8 8 8
9 9 9

8 COUNTRY OF NURSING EDUCATION:

9 SEX FEMALE ○ MALE ○

10 Is this the first time you are taking this test? ○ NO ○ YES

13 _____ Signature

Use No. 2 pencil only.
Erase any changes completely.
Make no stray marks on answer sheet.

COUNTY CODE

9 0 -

0 0 0
1 1 1
2 2 2
3 3 3
4 4 4
5 5 5
6 6 6
7 7 7
8 8 8
9 9 9

11 DATE OF GRAD.

MO.	YR.

0 0 0 0
1 1 1 1
2 2 2 2
3 3 3 3
4 4 4 4
5 5 5 5
6 6 6 6
7 7 7 7
8 8 8 8
9 9 9 9

12 TEST FORM

0 0 0 0
1 1 1 1
2 2 2 2
3 3 3 3
4 4 4 4
5 5 5 5
6 6 6 6
7 7 7 7
8 8 8 8
9 9 9 9

Mark Reflex® by NCS IM-163410-001:654321   Printed in U.S.A.   RIGHT: ●   WRONG: ⊘ ⊖ ⊗   ©1998 by Commission on Graduates of Foreign Nursing Schools

PRACTICE TEST D
NURSING PART 2

#	A B C D	#	A B C D	#	A B C D	#	A B C D	#	A B C D	#	A B C D
1	○○○○	21	○○○○	41	○○○○	61	○○○○	81	○○○○	101	○○○○
2	○○○○	22	○○○○	42	○○○○	62	○○○○	82	○○○○	102	○○○○
3	○○○○	23	○○○○	43	○○○○	63	○○○○	83	○○○○	103	○○○○
4	○○○○	24	○○○○	44	○○○○	64	○○○○	84	○○○○	104	○○○○
5	○○○○	25	○○○○	45	○○○○	65	○○○○	85	○○○○	105	○○○○
6	○○○○	26	○○○○	46	○○○○	66	○○○○	86	○○○○	106	○○○○
7	○○○○	27	○○○○	47	○○○○	67	○○○○	87	○○○○	107	○○○○
8	○○○○	28	○○○○	48	○○○○	68	○○○○	88	○○○○	108	○○○○
9	○○○○	29	○○○○	49	○○○○	69	○○○○	89	○○○○	109	○○○○
10	○○○○	30	○○○○	50	○○○○	70	○○○○	90	○○○○	110	○○○○
11	○○○○	31	○○○○	51	○○○○	71	○○○○	91	○○○○		
12	○○○○	32	○○○○	52	○○○○	72	○○○○	92	○○○○		
13	○○○○	33	○○○○	53	○○○○	73	○○○○	93	○○○○		
14	○○○○	34	○○○○	54	○○○○	74	○○○○	94	○○○○		
15	○○○○	35	○○○○	55	○○○○	75	○○○○	95	○○○○		
16	○○○○	36	○○○○	56	○○○○	76	○○○○	96	○○○○		
17	○○○○	37	○○○○	57	○○○○	77	○○○○	97	○○○○		
18	○○○○	38	○○○○	58	○○○○	78	○○○○	98	○○○○		
19	○○○○	39	○○○○	59	○○○○	79	○○○○	99	○○○○		
20	○○○○	40	○○○○	60	○○○○	80	○○○○	100	○○○○		

B

CGFNS

Answer Sheets for
Supplemental Practice Exams

B

CGFNS QUALIFYING EXAMINATION — NURSING

1 NAME	FAMILY NAME/SURNAME	FIRST	MIDDLE
2 TEST CENTER	CITY	COUNTRY	3 CENTER CODE

4 PART 1 ○ 2 ○ | 5 TEST BOOK NUMBER

6 CGFNS IDENTIFICATION NUMBER

7 DATE OF BIRTH: MO. DAY YR.

8 COUNTRY OF NURSING EDUCATION: | COUNTY CODE 9 0-

9 SEX: FEMALE ○ MALE ○

10 Is this the first time you are taking this test? ○ NO ○ YES

11 DATE OF GRAD.: MO. YR.

12 TEST FORM

13 Signature

Use No. 2 pencil only.
Erase any changes completely.
Make no stray marks on answer sheet.

I.C.—051 013 980

Mark Reflex® by NCS IM-163410-001:654321 Printed in U.S.A.

RIGHT: ● WRONG: ⊘ ◒ ⊗

1 A B C D	21 A B C D	41 A B C D	61 A B C D	81 A B C D	101 A B C D	121 A B C D	141 A B C D
2 A B C D	22 A B C D	42 A B C D	62 A B C D	82 A B C D	102 A B C D	122 A B C D	142 A B C D
3 A B C D	23 A B C D	43 A B C D	63 A B C D	83 A B C D	103 A B C D	123 A B C D	143 A B C D
4 A B C D	24 A B C D	44 A B C D	64 A B C D	84 A B C D	104 A B C D	124 A B C D	144 A B C D
5 A B C D	25 A B C D	45 A B C D	65 A B C D	85 A B C D	105 A B C D	125 A B C D	145 A B C D
6 A B C D	26 A B C D	46 A B C D	66 A B C D	86 A B C D	106 A B C D	126 A B C D	146 A B C D
7 A B C D	27 A B C D	47 A B C D	67 A B C D	87 A B C D	107 A B C D	127 A B C D	147 A B C D
8 A B C D	28 A B C D	48 A B C D	68 A B C D	88 A B C D	108 A B C D	128 A B C D	148 A B C D
9 A B C D	29 A B C D	49 A B C D	69 A B C D	89 A B C D	109 A B C D	129 A B C D	149 A B C D
10 A B C D	30 A B C D	50 A B C D	70 A B C D	90 A B C D	110 A B C D	130 A B C D	150 A B C D
11 A B C D	31 A B C D	51 A B C D	71 A B C D	91 A B C D	111 A B C D	131 A B C D	
12 A B C D	32 A B C D	52 A B C D	72 A B C D	92 A B C D	112 A B C D	132 A B C D	
13 A B C D	33 A B C D	53 A B C D	73 A B C D	93 A B C D	113 A B C D	133 A B C D	
14 A B C D	34 A B C D	54 A B C D	74 A B C D	94 A B C D	114 A B C D	134 A B C D	
15 A B C D	35 A B C D	55 A B C D	75 A B C D	95 A B C D	115 A B C D	135 A B C D	
16 A B C D	36 A B C D	56 A B C D	76 A B C D	96 A B C D	116 A B C D	136 A B C D	
17 A B C D	37 A B C D	57 A B C D	77 A B C D	97 A B C D	117 A B C D	137 A B C D	
18 A B C D	38 A B C D	58 A B C D	78 A B C D	98 A B C D	118 A B C D	138 A B C D	
19 A B C D	39 A B C D	59 A B C D	79 A B C D	99 A B C D	119 A B C D	139 A B C D	
20 A B C D	40 A B C D	60 A B C D	80 A B C D	100 A B C D	120 A B C D	140 A B C D	

B

CGFNS QUALIFYING EXAMINATION — NURSING

1 NAME — FAMILY NAME/SURNAME — FIRST — MIDDLE

2 TEST CENTER — CITY — COUNTRY — **3 CENTER CODE**

4 PART — 1 ○ 2 ○ — **5 TEST BOOK NUMBER**

6 CGFNS IDENTIFICATION NUMBER

7 DATE OF BIRTH — MO. DAY YR.

8 COUNTRY OF NURSING EDUCATION:

COUNTY CODE 9 0-

11 DATE OF GRAD. — MO. YR.

12 TEST FORM

9 SEX — FEMALE ○ — MALE ○

10 Is this the first time you are taking this test? ○ NO ○ YES

13 _____ Signature

Use No. 2 pencil only.
Erase any changes completely.
Make no stray marks on answer sheet.

Mark Reflex® by NCS IM-163410-001:654321 Printed in U.S.A. **RIGHT:** ● **WRONG:** ⊘ ⊖ ⊗ ©1998 by Commission on Graduates of Foreign Nursing School

I.C.-051 013 980

	A B C D		A B C D		A B C D		A B C D		A B C D
151	○○○○	171	○○○○	191	○○○○	211	○○○○	231	○○○○
152	○○○○	172	○○○○	192	○○○○	212	○○○○	232	○○○○
153	○○○○	173	○○○○	193	○○○○	213	○○○○	233	○○○○
154	○○○○	174	○○○○	194	○○○○	214	○○○○	234	○○○○
155	○○○○	175	○○○○	195	○○○○	215	○○○○	235	○○○○
156	○○○○	176	○○○○	196	○○○○	216	○○○○	236	○○○○
157	○○○○	177	○○○○	197	○○○○	217	○○○○	237	○○○○
158	○○○○	178	○○○○	198	○○○○	218	○○○○	238	○○○○
159	○○○○	179	○○○○	199	○○○○	219	○○○○	239	○○○○
160	○○○○	180	○○○○	200	○○○○	220	○○○○	240	○○○○
161	○○○○	181	○○○○	201	○○○○	221	○○○○	241	○○○○
162	○○○○	182	○○○○	202	○○○○	222	○○○○	242	○○○○
163	○○○○	183	○○○○	203	○○○○	223	○○○○	243	○○○○
164	○○○○	184	○○○○	204	○○○○	224	○○○○	244	○○○○
165	○○○○	185	○○○○	205	○○○○	225	○○○○	245	○○○○
166	○○○○	186	○○○○	206	○○○○	226	○○○○	246	○○○○
167	○○○○	187	○○○○	207	○○○○	227	○○○○	247	○○○○
168	○○○○	188	○○○○	208	○○○○	228	○○○○	248	○○○○
169	○○○○	189	○○○○	209	○○○○	229	○○○○	249	○○○○
170	○○○○	190	○○○○	210	○○○○	230	○○○○	250	○○○○

CD PRACTICE TEST 1

B

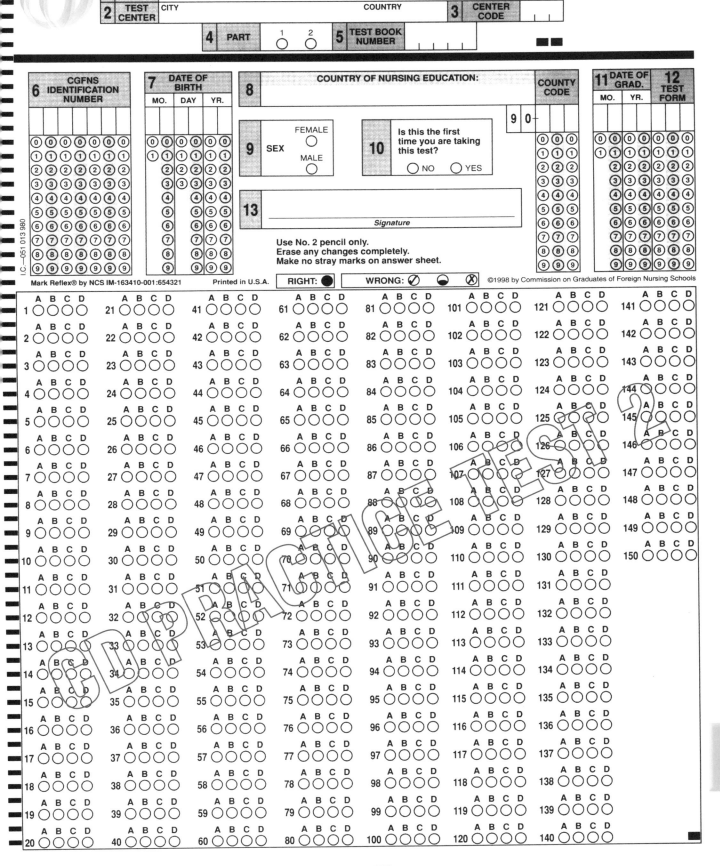

CGFNS QUALIFYING EXAMINATION — NURSING

1	NAME	FAMILY NAME/SURNAME		FIRST		MIDDLE

2	TEST CENTER	CITY	COUNTRY	3	CENTER CODE	

4	PART	1 ○ 2 ○	5	TEST BOOK NUMBER	

6 CGFNS IDENTIFICATION NUMBER

```
0 0 0 0 0 0 0
1 1 1 1 1 1 1
2 2 2 2 2 2 2
3 3 3 3 3 3 3
4 4 4 4 4 4 4
5 5 5 5 5 5 5
6 6 6 6 6 6 6
7 7 7 7 7 7 7
8 8 8 8 8 8 8
9 9 9 9 9 9 9
```

7 DATE OF BIRTH
MO. DAY YR.

```
0 0  0 0  0 0
1 1  1 1  1 1
2    2 2  2 2
3    3 3  3 3
4    4 4  4 4
5    5 5  5 5
6    6 6  6 6
7    7 7  7 7
8    8 8  8 8
9    9 9  9 9
```

8 COUNTRY OF NURSING EDUCATION:

9 SEX FEMALE ○ MALE ○

10 Is this the first time you are taking this test? ○ NO ○ YES

13 _____ Signature

Use No. 2 pencil only.
Erase any changes completely.
Make no stray marks on answer sheet.

COUNTY CODE
9 0 -

11 DATE OF GRAD.
MO. YR.

```
0 0 0
1 1 1
2 2 2
3 3 3
4 4 4
5 5 5
6 6 6
7 7 7
8 8 8
9 9 9
```

12 TEST FORM

```
0 0 0 0 0 0
1 1 1 1 1 1
2 2 2 2 2 2
3 3 3 3 3 3
4 4 4 4 4 4
5 5 5 5 5 5
6 6 6 6 6 6
7 7 7 7 7 7
8 8 8 8 8 8
9 9 9 9 9 9
```

I.C.—051 013 980

Mark Reflex® by NCS IM-163410-001:654321   Printed in U.S.A.   RIGHT: ●   WRONG: ⊘ ⊖ ⊗   ©1998 by Commission on Graduates of Foreign Nursing School

CD PRACTICE TEST 2

#	A B C D	#	A B C D	#	A B C D	#	A B C D	#	A B C D
151	○○○○	171	○○○○	191	○○○○	211	○○○○	231	○○○○
152	○○○○	172	○○○○	192	○○○○	212	○○○○	232	○○○○
153	○○○○	173	○○○○	193	○○○○	213	○○○○	233	○○○○
154	○○○○	174	○○○○	194	○○○○	214	○○○○	234	○○○○
155	○○○○	175	○○○○	195	○○○○	215	○○○○	235	○○○○
156	○○○○	176	○○○○	196	○○○○	216	○○○○	236	○○○○
157	○○○○	177	○○○○	197	○○○○	217	○○○○	237	○○○○
158	○○○○	178	○○○○	198	○○○○	218	○○○○	238	○○○○
159	○○○○	179	○○○○	199	○○○○	219	○○○○	239	○○○○
160	○○○○	180	○○○○	200	○○○○	220	○○○○	240	○○○○
161	○○○○	181	○○○○	201	○○○○	221	○○○○	241	○○○○
162	○○○○	182	○○○○	202	○○○○	222	○○○○	242	○○○○
163	○○○○	183	○○○○	203	○○○○	223	○○○○	243	○○○○
164	○○○○	184	○○○○	204	○○○○	224	○○○○	244	○○○○
165	○○○○	185	○○○○	205	○○○○	225	○○○○	245	○○○○
166	○○○○	186	○○○○	206	○○○○	226	○○○○	246	○○○○
167	○○○○	187	○○○○	207	○○○○	227	○○○○	247	○○○○
168	○○○○	188	○○○○	208	○○○○	228	○○○○	248	○○○○
169	○○○○	189	○○○○	209	○○○○	229	○○○○	249	○○○○
170	○○○○	190	○○○○	210	○○○○	230	○○○○	250	○○○○

B

CGFNS QUALIFYING EXAMINATION — NURSING

1	NAME	FAMILY NAME/SURNAME		FIRST		MIDDLE	

2	TEST CENTER	CITY	COUNTRY	3	CENTER CODE	

4	PART	1 ○ 2 ○	5	TEST BOOK NUMBER	

6 CGFNS IDENTIFICATION NUMBER

7 DATE OF BIRTH
MO. DAY YR.

8 COUNTRY OF NURSING EDUCATION:

COUNTY CODE

9 0-

11 DATE OF GRAD.
MO. YR.

12 TEST FORM

9	SEX	FEMALE ○ MALE ○

10	Is this the first time you are taking this test? ○ NO ○ YES

13	_____ Signature

Use No. 2 pencil only.
Erase any changes completely.
Make no stray marks on answer sheet.

I.C. —051 013 980

Mark Reflex® by NCS IM-163410-001:654321   Printed in U.S.A.   RIGHT: ●   WRONG: ⊘ ⊖ ⊗   ©1998 by Commission on Graduates of Foreign Nursing Schools

1 A B C D   21 A B C D   41 A B C D   61 A B C D   81 A B C D   101 A B C D   121 A B C D   141 A B C D
2 A B C D   22 A B C D   42 A B C D   62 A B C D   82 A B C D   102 A B C D   122 A B C D   142 A B C D
3 A B C D   23 A B C D   43 A B C D   63 A B C D   83 A B C D   103 A B C D   123 A B C D   143 A B C D
4 A B C D   24 A B C D   44 A B C D   64 A B C D   84 A B C D   104 A B C D   124 A B C D   144 A B C D
5 A B C D   25 A B C D   45 A B C D   65 A B C D   85 A B C D   105 A B C D   125 A B C D   145 A B C D
6 A B C D   26 A B C D   46 A B C D   66 A B C D   86 A B C D   106 A B C D   126 A B C D   146 A B C D
7 A B C D   27 A B C D   47 A B C D   67 A B C D   87 A B C D   107 A B C D   127 A B C D   147 A B C D
8 A B C D   28 A B C D   48 A B C D   68 A B C D   88 A B C D   108 A B C D   128 A B C D   148 A B C D
9 A B C D   29 A B C D   49 A B C D   69 A B C D   89 A B C D   109 A B C D   129 A B C D   149 A B C D
10 A B C D   30 A B C D   50 A B C D   70 A B C D   90 A B C D   110 A B C D   130 A B C D   150 A B C D
11 A B C D   31 A B C D   51 A B C D   71 A B C D   91 A B C D   111 A B C D   131 A B C D
12 A B C D   32 A B C D   52 A B C D   72 A B C D   92 A B C D   112 A B C D   132 A B C D
13 A B C D   33 A B C D   53 A B C D   73 A B C D   93 A B C D   113 A B C D   133 A B C D
14 A B C D   34 A B C D   54 A B C D   74 A B C D   94 A B C D   114 A B C D   134 A B C D
15 A B C D   35 A B C D   55 A B C D   75 A B C D   95 A B C D   115 A B C D   135 A B C D
16 A B C D   36 A B C D   56 A B C D   76 A B C D   96 A B C D   116 A B C D   136 A B C D
17 A B C D   37 A B C D   57 A B C D   77 A B C D   97 A B C D   117 A B C D   137 A B C D
18 A B C D   38 A B C D   58 A B C D   78 A B C D   98 A B C D   118 A B C D   138 A B C D
19 A B C D   39 A B C D   59 A B C D   79 A B C D   99 A B C D   119 A B C D   139 A B C D
20 A B C D   40 A B C D   60 A B C D   80 A B C D   100 A B C D   120 A B C D   140 A B C D

CD PRACTICE TEST 3

455

CGFNS QUALIFYING EXAMINATION — NURSING

1 NAME FAMILY NAME/SURNAME   FIRST   MIDDLE

2 TEST CENTER CITY   COUNTRY   **3 CENTER CODE**

4 PART ○1 ○2   **5 TEST BOOK NUMBER**

6 CGFNS IDENTIFICATION NUMBER

7 DATE OF BIRTH — MO.   DAY   YR.

8 COUNTRY OF NURSING EDUCATION: **COUNTY CODE**   9 0-

9 SEX FEMALE ○   MALE ○

10 Is this the first time you are taking this test? ○ NO ○ YES

11 DATE OF GRAD. MO.   YR.

12 TEST FORM

13 _____ Signature

Use No. 2 pencil only.
Erase any changes completely.
Make no stray marks on answer sheet.

I.C. —051 013 980

Mark Reflex® by NCS IM-163410-001:654321   Printed in U.S.A.   **RIGHT:** ●   **WRONG:** ⊘ ⊖ ⊗   ©1998 by Commission on Graduates of Foreign Nursing Schools

151 A B C D 171 A B C D 191 A B C D 211 A B C D 231 A B C D
152 A B C D 172 A B C D 192 A B C D 212 A B C D 232 A B C D
153 A B C D 173 A B C D 193 A B C D 213 A B C D 233 A B C D
154 A B C D 174 A B C D 194 A B C D 214 A B C D 234 A B C D
155 A B C D 175 A B C D 195 A B C D 215 A B C D 235 A B C D
156 A B C D 176 A B C D 196 A B C D 216 A B C D 236 A B C D
157 A B C D 177 A B C D 197 A B C D 217 A B C D 237 A B C D
158 A B C D 178 A B C D 198 A B C D 218 A B C D 238 A B C D
159 A B C D 179 A B C D 199 A B C D 219 A B C D 239 A B C D
160 A B C D 180 A B C D 200 A B C D 220 A B C D 240 A B C D
161 A B C D 181 A B C D 201 A B C D 221 A B C D 241 A B C D
162 A B C D 182 A B C D 202 A B C D 222 A B C D 242 A B C D
163 A B C D 183 A B C D 203 A B C D 223 A B C D 243 A B C D
164 A B C D 184 A B C D 204 A B C D 224 A B C D 244 A B C D
165 A B C D 185 A B C D 205 A B C D 225 A B C D 245 A B C D
166 A B C D 186 A B C D 206 A B C D 226 A B C D 246 A B C D
167 A B C D 187 A B C D 207 A B C D 227 A B C D 247 A B C D
168 A B C D 188 A B C D 208 A B C D 228 A B C D 248 A B C D
169 A B C D 189 A B C D 209 A B C D 229 A B C D 249 A B C D
170 A B C D 190 A B C D 210 A B C D 230 A B C D 250 A B C D

CD PRACTICE TEST 3

CGFNS QUALIFYING EXAMINATION — NURSING

1 NAME — FAMILY NAME/SURNAME — FIRST — MIDDLE

2 TEST CENTER — CITY — COUNTRY — **3** CENTER CODE

4 PART ○1 ○2 **5** TEST BOOK NUMBER ▪▪

6 CGFNS IDENTIFICATION NUMBER

7 DATE OF BIRTH — MO. DAY YR.

8 COUNTRY OF NURSING EDUCATION:

COUNTY CODE 9 0-

11 DATE OF GRAD. — MO. YR. **12** TEST FORM

9 SEX — FEMALE ○ — MALE ○

10 Is this the first time you are taking this test? ○ NO ○ YES

13 _____ Signature

Use No. 2 pencil only.
Erase any changes completely.
Make no stray marks on answer sheet.

Mark Reflex® by NCS IM-163410-001:654321   Printed in U.S.A.   RIGHT: ● WRONG: ⊘ ⊖ ⊗   ©1998 by Commission on Graduates of Foreign Nursing Schools

	A B C D		A B C D		A B C D		A B C D		A B C D		A B C D		A B C D		A B C D
1	○○○○	21	○○○○	41	○○○○	61	○○○○	81	○○○○	101	○○○○	121	○○○○	141	○○○○
2	○○○○	22	○○○○	42	○○○○	62	○○○○	82	○○○○	102	○○○○	122	○○○○	142	○○○○
3	○○○○	23	○○○○	43	○○○○	63	○○○○	83	○○○○	103	○○○○	123	○○○○	143	○○○○
4	○○○○	24	○○○○	44	○○○○	64	○○○○	84	○○○○	104	○○○○	124	○○○○	144	○○○○
5	○○○○	25	○○○○	45	○○○○	65	○○○○	85	○○○○	105	○○○○	125	○○○○	145	○○○○
6	○○○○	26	○○○○	46	○○○○	66	○○○○	86	○○○○	106	○○○○	126	○○○○	146	○○○○
7	○○○○	27	○○○○	47	○○○○	67	○○○○	87	○○○○	107	○○○○	127	○○○○	147	○○○○
8	○○○○	28	○○○○	48	○○○○	68	○○○○	88	○○○○	108	○○○○	128	○○○○	148	○○○○
9	○○○○	29	○○○○	49	○○○○	69	○○○○	89	○○○○	109	○○○○	129	○○○○	149	○○○○
10	○○○○	30	○○○○	50	○○○○	70	○○○○	90	○○○○	110	○○○○	130	○○○○	150	○○○○
11	○○○○	31	○○○○	51	○○○○	71	○○○○	91	○○○○	111	○○○○	131	○○○○		
12	○○○○	32	○○○○	52	○○○○	72	○○○○	92	○○○○	112	○○○○	132	○○○○		
13	○○○○	33	○○○○	53	○○○○	73	○○○○	93	○○○○	113	○○○○	133	○○○○		
14	○○○○	34	○○○○	54	○○○○	74	○○○○	94	○○○○	114	○○○○	134	○○○○		
15	○○○○	35	○○○○	55	○○○○	75	○○○○	95	○○○○	115	○○○○	135	○○○○		
16	○○○○	36	○○○○	56	○○○○	76	○○○○	96	○○○○	116	○○○○	136	○○○○		
17	○○○○	37	○○○○	57	○○○○	77	○○○○	97	○○○○	117	○○○○	137	○○○○		
18	○○○○	38	○○○○	58	○○○○	78	○○○○	98	○○○○	118	○○○○	138	○○○○		
19	○○○○	39	○○○○	59	○○○○	79	○○○○	99	○○○○	119	○○○○	139	○○○○		
20	○○○○	40	○○○○	60	○○○○	80	○○○○	100	○○○○	120	○○○○	140	○○○○		

I.C.—051 013 980

CGFNS QUALIFYING EXAMINATION — NURSING

1	NAME	FAMILY NAME/SURNAME	FIRST	MIDDLE

2	TEST CENTER	CITY	COUNTRY	3	CENTER CODE

4	PART	1 ○ 2 ○	5	TEST BOOK NUMBER

6 CGFNS IDENTIFICATION NUMBER

7 DATE OF BIRTH
MO. | DAY | YR.

8 COUNTRY OF NURSING EDUCATION:

COUNTY CODE

9 0-

11 DATE OF GRAD.
MO. | YR.

12 TEST FORM

(0) through (9) bubble columns

9 SEX — FEMALE ○ / MALE ○

10 Is this the first time you are taking this test? ○ NO ○ YES

13 _____ Signature

Use No. 2 pencil only.
Erase any changes completely.
Make no stray marks on answer sheet.

Mark Reflex® by NCS IM-163410-001:654321   Printed in U.S.A.   RIGHT: ● | WRONG: ⊘ ◒ ⊗   ©1998 by Commission on Graduates of Foreign Nursing Schools

I.C.—051 013 980

A B C D	A B C D	A B C D	A B C D	A B C D	A B C D
1 ○○○○	21 ○○○○	41 ○○○○	61 ○○○○	81 ○○○○	101 ○○○○
2 ○○○○	22 ○○○○	42 ○○○○	62 ○○○○	82 ○○○○	102 ○○○○
3 ○○○○	23 ○○○○	43 ○○○○	63 ○○○○	83 ○○○○	103 ○○○○
4 ○○○○	24 ○○○○	44 ○○○○	64 ○○○○	84 ○○○○	104 ○○○○
5 ○○○○	25 ○○○○	45 ○○○○	65 ○○○○	85 ○○○○	105 ○○○○
6 ○○○○	26 ○○○○	46 ○○○○	66 ○○○○	86 ○○○○	106 ○○○○
7 ○○○○	27 ○○○○	47 ○○○○	67 ○○○○	87 ○○○○	107 ○○○○
8 ○○○○	28 ○○○○	48 ○○○○	68 ○○○○	88 ○○○○	108 ○○○○
9 ○○○○	29 ○○○○	49 ○○○○	69 ○○○○	89 ○○○○	109 ○○○○
10 ○○○○	30 ○○○○	50 ○○○○	70 ○○○○	90 ○○○○	110 ○○○○
11 ○○○○	31 ○○○○	51 ○○○○	71 ○○○○	91 ○○○○	
12 ○○○○	32 ○○○○	52 ○○○○	72 ○○○○	92 ○○○○	
13 ○○○○	33 ○○○○	53 ○○○○	73 ○○○○	93 ○○○○	
14 ○○○○	34 ○○○○	54 ○○○○	74 ○○○○	94 ○○○○	
15 ○○○○	35 ○○○○	55 ○○○○	75 ○○○○	95 ○○○○	
16 ○○○○	36 ○○○○	56 ○○○○	76 ○○○○	96 ○○○○	
17 ○○○○	37 ○○○○	57 ○○○○	77 ○○○○	97 ○○○○	
18 ○○○○	38 ○○○○	58 ○○○○	78 ○○○○	98 ○○○○	
19 ○○○○	39 ○○○○	59 ○○○○	79 ○○○○	99 ○○○○	
20 ○○○○	40 ○○○○	60 ○○○○	80 ○○○○	100 ○○○○	

B